The Changing Nature of Scotland

The Natural Heritage of Scotland Series

Periodically, since it was founded in 1992, Scottish Natural Heritage has organised or jointly organised a conference which has focussed on a particular aspect of Scotland's environment. The papers read at the conferences, after a process of refereeing and editing, have been brought together as a book. The sixteen titles already published in this series are listed below (No. 6 was not based on a conference).

1. *The Islands of Scotland: a Living Marine Heritage*
   Edited by J.M. Baxter and M.B. Usher (1994), 286pp.
2. *Heaths and Moorlands: a Cultural Landscape*
   Edited by D.B.A. Thompson, A.J. Hester and M.B. Usher (1995), 400pp.
3. *Soils, Sustainability and the Natural Heritage*
   Edited by A.G. Taylor, J.E. Gordon and M.B. Usher (1996), 316pp.
4. *Freshwater Quality: Defining the Indefinable?*
   Edited by P.J. Boon and D.L. Howell (1997), 553pp.
5. *Biodiversity in Scotland: Status, Trends and Initiatives*
   Edited by L.V. Fleming, A.C. Newton, J.A. Vickery and M.B. Usher (1997), 309pp.
6. *Land Cover Change: Scotland from the 1940s to the 1980s*
   By E.C. Mackey, M.C. Shrewry and G.J. Tudor (1998), 263pp.
7. *Scotland's Living Coastline*
   Edited by J.M. Baxter, K. Duncan, S.M. Atkins and G. Lees (1999), 209pp.
8. *Landscape Character: Perspectives on Management and Change*
   Edited by M.B. Usher (1999), 213pp.
9. *Earth Science and the Natural Heritage: Interactions and Integrated Management*
   Edited by J.E. Gordon and K.F. Leys (2000), 304pp.
10. *Enjoyment and Understanding of the Natural Heritage*
    Edited by M.B. Usher (2001), 224pp.
11. *The State of Scotland's Environment and Natural Heritage*
    Edited by M.B. Usher, E.C. Mackey and J.C. Curran (2002), 354pp.
12. *Birds of Prey in a Changing Environment*
    Edited by D.B.A. Thompson, S.M. Redpath, A. Fielding, M. Marquiss and C.A. Galbraith (2003), 570pp.
13. *Mountains of Northern Europe: Conservation, Management, People and Nature*
    Edited by D.B.A. Thompson, M.F. Price and C.A. Galbraith (2005), 416pp.
14. *Farming, Forestry and the Natural Heritage: Towards a More Integrated Future*
    Edited by R. Davison and C.A. Galbraith (2006), 333pp.
15. *Energy and the Natural Heritage*
    Edited by C.A. Galbraith and J.M. Baxter (2008), 316pp.
16. *Species Management: Challenges and Solutions for the 21st Century*
    Edited by J.M. Baxter and C.A. Galbraith (2010), 572pp.

This is the seventeenth book in the series.

The Changing Nature of Scotland

Edited by Susan J. Marrs, Simon Foster, Catriona Hendrie, Edward C. Mackey, Des B. A. Thompson

Edinburgh: TSO Scotland

First published in 2011 by The Stationery Office Limited,
26 Rutland Square, Edinburgh, EH1 2BW

British Library Cataloguing in Publication Data
A catalogue record for this book is available from the British Library

ISBN 978 0 11 497359 9

The views expressed in the chapters of this book do not necessarily represent views of the editors or the organisations that supported the conference and this publication.

Captions and copyright credits for front cover images

Top left:	Red Admiral © Woodfall/Photoshot
Top middle:	Red Kite © Lorne Gill/SNH
Top right:	Red Deer © John MacPherson/SNH
Bottom left:	Isle of Noss National Nature Reserve, Shetland © Lorne Gill/SNH
Bottom middle:	Goat Fell and Cir Mhor, Glen Rosa, Isle of Arran © Lorne Gill/SNH
Bottom right:	Caledonian pines by Loch Clair, Beinn Eighe National Nature Reserve © John MacPherson/SNH

Preface

For its size, Scotland has a remarkably rich diversity of landscapes, seascapes and wildlife. Arguably, and disproportionately for its land area and population, it also has one of the finest canons of research and literature on the nature of changes. Some of these studies reach back to the Archaean – more than two and a half billion years ago when the Lewisian gneisses formed – whilst a growing number look ahead to how the land, water and seas, and all that lives in these bodies, are likely to change, and the drivers and consequences of these.

Almost ten years ago, and commenting on the state of Scotland's environment, Usher *et al.* (2002) remarked that 'Scotland demonstrates some very hopeful trends and predictions for the future, but equally there are some aspects of the current state of the environment and natural heritage about which we cannot be so positive.' This prefaced the first comprehensive overview of the state of Scotland's environment, drawing together research and evidence held mainly by Scottish Natural Heritage (SNH), the Scottish Environment Protection Agency, and several other agencies, NGOs and research groups active in Scotland. That book followed the publication of the first major suite of trends reports for Scotland (Mackey *et al.*, 2001).

During 17-18 September 2009, SNH hosted a conference in partnership with other members of Scotland's Environmental and Rural Services (SEARS) in Perth to consider the range of recent changes affecting nature across Scotland. The changing nature of Scotland was described in 25 talks, 42 posters and four displays. We were especially pleased to have the Minister for Environment, Roseanna Cunningham MSP, give the keynote address. The presentations were in one of seven themes: surrounding seas and coast; fresh waters; settlements and built areas; lowlands; woodlands; uplands; and the health and economy. The conference attracted more than 200 delegates, many of them being researchers, employees/members of environmental NGOs, conservation volunteers, government advisers and people with an interest in the natural environment. This book presents the proceedings of that conference, with chapters updated to reflect more recent changes.

Since publication of the *State of Scotland's Environment* report (Usher *et al.*, 2002), at least two major developments have occurred. First, the Millennium Ecosystem Assessment was published in 2005 (UNEP, 2005). This revealed that ecosystems have been altered more rapidly and extensively over the past 50 years than in any comparable time period in human history – with changes to biodiversity substantial and predominantly negative. This critically important report, and work spawned by it, has gone on to detail the value of ecosystems and their 'natural capital' (the ecosystems, biodiversity and natural resources) which underpin economies, societies and individual well-being (TEEB, 2009, 2010). The global ecological footprint (human consumption) has gone from around 50% below the planet's biocapacity (or natural capital) in 1961 to 50% above it in 2007, due principally to a rapidly rising carbon component in the footprint. Half of the global footprint was attributed to just 10 countries; in 2007, Europe's ecological footprint (35 countries including the Russian Federation) was 162% and that of the United Kingdom was 365% (Ewing *et al.*, 2010).

On 2 June 2011 the UK National Ecosystem Assessment was published, with a chapter devoted to Scotland (National Ecosystem Assessment, 2011). This attached financial and functional values to ecosystems and their services. Indeed, outputs from activities which depend on the natural environment have been estimated to amount to around £17.2 billion a year, or 11% of the total Scottish output and supporting 242,000 jobs, or 14% of all full time jobs in Scotland (SNH, 2009). We will see many more such costings being developed as the ecosystem approach is developed to help us frame our understanding of the nature and consequences of environmental change.

The other major development relates to the Convention on Biological Diversity (CBD), which began with the UNECD conference in Rio de Janeiro in 1992. The 10th Conference of the Parties to the CBD (often referred to as COP10) at Nagoya, Japan in October 2010, made 47 Decisions (see Conference of the Parties to the Convention on Biological Diversity, 2010a-c). Among these was Decision X/2 on the preparation of a new Strategic Plan for the period 2011-2020 (COP 2010a). While recognising that the 2010 biodiversity target had inspired action at many levels, the underlying drivers of biodiversity loss were not sufficiently reduced. On the basis that biological diversity underpins ecosystem functioning and the provision of ecosystem services essential for human well-being, the Strategic Plan 2011 – 2020 outlines five ambitous strategic goals. The closing chapter of this book looks ahead to some of the work planned in Scotland.

There is one other comparison with the earlier conference that reveals the harsh nature of major events. Those of us present at the earlier September conference dinner, held on 11 September 2001, will never forget the sense of shock and outrage over the terrorist attacks in the United States earlier that day. This has had far-reaching consequences for travel, the economy and wider environmental services. Ten years on, and some 9,200kms from Scotland, on March 11 2011, a 9.0 magnitude earthquake produced a tsunami 10m high that swept 10km inland along Japan's northeastern coast. The displacement of almost half a million people, tens of thousands of deaths and the threat of nuclear meltdown at the Fukushima I Nuclear Power Plant has caused governments and the public to review attitudes to environmental risk. Catastrophic events such as these, whether natural or human-influenced, can play a pivotal role in defining policy and management responses.

One of the challenges ahead is for us all to think carefully and deliberately about the sorts of changes which may influence the environment, and therefore the many services dependent on it. We have moved a long way in developing our understanding of the nature of change, and the consequences of these. But looking to the future, in the face of climate change and economic difficulties for some regions, we do need to marshal the evidence base more effectively. We need the best research and action to sustain and manage that which matters so deeply to so many of us in Scotland – its natural environment.

References

Conference of the Parties to the Convention on Biological Diversity (COP) (2010a). *Decision X/2: Strategic Plan for Biodiversity 2011 – 2020.* Tenth meeting, Nagoya, Japan, 18-29 October 2010.

COP (2010b). *Decision X/7: Examination of the outcome-oriented goals and targets (and associated indicators) and consideration of their possible adjustment for the period beyond 2010.* Tenth meeting, Nagoya, Japan, 18-29 October 2010.

COP (2010c). *Revised and Updated Strategic Plan: Technical Rationale and Suggested Milestones and Indicators.* UNEP/CBD/COP/10/9 Tenth meeting, Nagoya, Japan, 18-29 October 2010.

Ewing B., Moore, D., Goldfinger, S. *et al.* (2010). *The Ecological Footprint Atlas 2010.* Global Footprint Network, Oakland, California.

Mackey, E.C., Shaw, P., Holbrook, J. *et al.* (2001). *Natural Heritage Trends: Scotland 2001.* Scottish Natural Heritage, Perth.

National Ecosystem Assessment (2011). *The UK National Ecosystem Assessment: Synthesis of the key findings.* UNEP–WCMC, Cambridge.

Scottish Natural Heritage (2009). *Valuing our Environment: The Economic Impact of Scotland's Natural Environment.* SNH, Battleby.

TEEB (2009). *The Economics of Ecosystems and Biodiversity for National and International Policy Makers – Summary: Responding to the Value of Nature 2009.* United Nations Environment Programme, Bonn.

TEEB (2010). *The Economics of Ecosystems and Biodiversity: Mainstreaming the Economics of Nature: A synthesis of the approach, conclusions and recommendations of TEEB.* United Nations Environment Programme, Bonn.

UNEP (United Nations Environment Programme) (2005). *Millennium Ecosystem Assessment: Current Status and Trends.* Island Press, Washington, DC.
Usher, M.B., Mackey, E.C. and Curran, J.C. (eds.) (2002). *The State of Scotland's Environment and Natural Heritage.* TSO, Edinburgh.

Susan J. Marrs, Simon Foster, Catriona Hendrie,
Edward C. Mackey and Des B. A. Thompson
Scottish Natural Heritage
June 2011

Acknowledgements

The production of this book would not have been possible without the help, support and advice of many colleagues, friends and associates. We are especially grateful to the authors of the chapters for their cooperation and commitment. Each chapter has been independently reviewed, and we thank the following referees: Colin Adams, Philip Ashmole, Phil Boon, Jan Breckenridge, Jenny Bryce, Patricia Bruneau, Alan Cameron, Colin Campbell, Jane Clark, Simon Cohen, Andrew Coupar, David Donnan, Andy Douse, Willie Duncan, Robert Duck, Roddy Fairley, Bob Furness, Zoe Kemp, Scott Fergusson, Simon Foster, Rob Garner, Lorne Gill, Jeanette Hall, Sue Haysom, Suzanne Henderson, Catriona Hendrie, Dave Horsfield, Rebecca James, George Logan, Fiona Manson, Ed Mackey, David Marrs, Susan Marrs, Claire McSorley, Clive Mitchell, Ian Napier, Chris Quine, Pete Rawcliffe, Iain Sime, Rob Soutar, Graham Sullivan, Des Thompson, Janet Ullman, Michael Usher, Rene van der Wal, Susan Watt, Jeremy Wilson and several others who preferred to remain anonymous.

The original conference, on which the papers within this publication are based, was organised by Scottish Natural Heritage with input from Scotland's Environmental and Rural Services (SEARS) partners represented by Roy McLachlan, Grant Moir, Gordon Patterson and Chris Spray. We had tremendous support, advice and assistance from Marian Brown, Katie Eardley, Katie Gillham, Colin Galbraith, Rebecca James, Jim Jeffrey, Julie MacDonald, Pam Moncur, Linda Nicholls, Paul Robertson, Janet Ullman and Marion Whitelaw. The conference was held at Perth Concert Hall and thanks are due to Wendy Stenberg and her staff for their efficiency, help and excellent organisation in the lead-in through to the conclusion of the conference. We thank Stewart Stevenson MSP, Minister for Environment and Climate Change, for the Foreword. The conference sessions were ably chaired by Andrew Thin, Mike Neilson, James Curran, Nick Reiter, Eric Baird, Ian Jardine, John Milne and Michelle Francis. And of course we also thank our speakers and those who presented posters; three speakers (Nick Hanley, Jim Mackinnon and Laurence Mee) did not wish to have their talks published, though we have quoted from one of them.

Our Director, Susan Davies, supported the publication of this book. We thank the many photographers, in particular Lorne Gill, for allowing us to use their images, and Eleanor Meikle and Debbie Mackay for providing advice on cover design. Photos are credited, where appropriate, throughout the book. Particular thanks are due to Betty Common for her efficiency, tenacity and invaluable help in researching and sourcing many of the images. We also give particular thanks to Eleanor Charman, Susi Hodgson, Alex Major and Carmen Mayo for producing maps for the various chapters throughout the publication.

Finally, we thank TSO Scotland for tremendous support as our publisher: Shona Hawkes, Nick Bell and Jon Dalrymple have been diligent, patient and helpful in all manner of ways.

Contents

Foreword

Scotland's Environmental and Rural Services (SEARS) organisations are working hard to help individuals and communities throughout Scotland improve their own local environments and adapt to changes. But SEARS is only one link in the chain. Many other organisations, charities, land owners, farmers, volunteers, campaigners and members of the public have vital roles to play. We know we cannot take our natural environment for granted – it's important to our economy and our health and well-being.

Scotland has a fantastic and diverse environment. Climate and geology have helped create the landscapes that visitors and residents appreciate so much. More recently, human activity has had an increasing impact on the appearance and composition of these landscapes from land use patterns of farming and forestry; settlement and transport; and telecommunications, energy and water supply. Beyond the coastline, changes in the marine environment may be less visible but are no less striking.

This book helps us understand what is going on, why it matters – and what we are doing about it. One big question is how can we have a quality, natural environment as well as a prosperous and successful Scotland in the face of anticipated climatic, social and economic changes? Our interaction with the natural environment is constantly changing, and looking back on past changes it is very clear that the environment and the economy are not separate systems – they are interdependent. Long-term economic well-being is dependent on long-term environmental well being. We should also remember that environmental well-being is also dependent on economic health. Economic prosperity creates the resources for mitigating negative impacts and encouraging more environmentally benign behaviour.

In these challenging economic times the Scottish Government is focusing on the creation of a successful Scotland, by building a dynamic and growing economy which will provide prosperity and opportunities whilst ensuring that future generations can enjoy a better quality of life. Our green policies play a big part in helping to position us for economic recovery. Our nation's success depends on a high quality environment.

This book contains the sort of factual evidence base that we strive for in a modern Scotland – and I welcome collaboration among SEARS partners in reporting on the changing nature of Scotland.

Stewart Stevenson MSP
Minister for Environment and Climate Change

May 2011

Contributors

Stewart Angus, Scottish Natural Heritage, Great Glen House, Leachkin Road, Inverness, IV3 8NW. Email: stewart.angus@snh.gov.uk

Philip Ashmole, Kidston Mill, Peebles, EH45 8PH. Email: philip@ashmole.org.uk

Dawn Balmer, British Trust for Ornithology, The Nunnery, Thetford, Norfolk, IP24 2PU. Email: dawn.balmer@bto.org

John Birks, Department of Biology, University of Bergen, Postbox 7800, NO-5020 Bergen, Norway and Environmental Change Research Centre, University College London, Gower Street, WC1E 6BT, UK. Email: john.birks@bio.uib.no

Ralph Blaney, Scottish Natural Heritage, Great Glen House, Leachkin Road, Inverness, IV3 8NW. Email: ralph.blaney@snh.gov.uk

Tom Brereton, Butterfly Conservation, Manor Yard, East Lulworth, Wareham, Dorset, BH20 5QP. Email: tbrereton@butterfly-conservation.org

Rob Brooker, The James Hutton Institute, Craigiebuckler, Aberdeen, AB15 8QH, UK. Email: r.brooker@hutton.ac.uk

Harry Burns, Scottish Government Health Directorate, St Andrew's House, Edinburgh, EH1 3DG. Email: cmo@scotland.gsi.gov.uk

Rob Bushby, John Muir Trust, 41 Commercial Street, Edinburgh, EH6 6JD. Email: rob@johnmuiraward.org

Krystina Campbell, Scottish Natural Heritage, Battleby, Redgorton, Perth, PH1 3EW. Email: krysia.campbell@snh.gov.uk

Mary Christie, Scottish Natural Heritage, Battleby, Redgorton, Perth, PH1 3EW. Email: mary.christie@snh.gov.uk

Mandy Cook, The British Trust for Ornithology Scotland, School of Biological and Environmental Sciences, Cottrell Building, University of Stirling, FK9 4LA. Email: mandy.cook@bto.org

Fiona Crawford, 61 Lochlea Road, Glasgow, G43 2YB.
Email: fiona.crawford@drs.glasgow.gov.uk

Graham Davies, Scottish Environment Protection Agency, 5 Redwood Crescent, Peel Park, East Kilbride, G74 5PP. Email: graham.davies@sepa.org.uk

Judith Dobson, Scottish Environment Protection Agency, Clearwater House, Avenue North, Heriot Watt Research Park, Riccarton, Edinburgh, EH14 4AP. Email: judy.dobson@sepa.org.uk

David Edwards, Centre for Human and Ecological Sciences, Forest Research, Northern Research Station, Roslin, Midlothian, EH25 9SY.
Email: david.edwards@forestry.gsi.gov.uk

Ieuan Evans, The British Trust for Ornithology, The Nunnery, Thetford, Norfolk, IP24 2PU. Email: ieuan.evans@bto.org

James H C Fenton, c/o Scottish Natural Heritage, Great Glen House, Leachkin Road, Inverness, IV3 8NW.

Scott Ferguson, Scottish Natural Heritage, Clydebank, Caspian House, 2 Mariner Court, 8 South Avenue, Clydebank Business Park, Clydebank, G81 2NR.
Email: scott.ferguson@snh.gov.uk

Simon Foster, Scottish Natural Heritage, Great Glen House, Leachkin Road, Inverness, IV3 8NW. Email: simon.foster@snh.gov.uk

Richard Fox, Butterfly Conservation, Manor Yard, East Lulworth, Wareham, Dorset, BH20 5QP. Email: rfox@butterfly-conservation.org

Kenny Freeman, 6, Durno Park, Kirkton of Skene, Westhills, AB32 6GA.
Email: manofcharr@hotmail.com

Colin Galbraith, Scottish Government, Saughton House, Broomhouse, Edinburgh, EH11 3XD. Email: colin.galbraith@scotland.gsi.gov.uk

Richard Gard, 2, Ecclesgreig Road, St Cyrus, Montrose, DD10 0BH.
Email: r.gard@maps4mobiles.co.uk

David Genney, Scottish Natural Heritage, Great Glen House, Leachkin Road, Inverness, IV3 8NW. Email: david.genney@snh.gov.uk

Simon Gillings, British Trust for Ornithology, The Nunnery, Thetford, Norfolk, IP24 2PU. Email: simon.gillings@bto.org

David Gilvear, Centre for River Ecosystem Science, Cottrell Building, School of Biological and Environmental Sciences, Sciences, University of Stirling, Stirling, FK9 4LA. Email: d.j.gilvear@stir.ac.uk

Jayne Glass, Centre for Mountain Studies, Perth College UHI, Crieff Road, Perth, PH1 2NX. Email: jayne.glass@perth.uhi.ac.uk

John-Arvid Grytnes, Department of Biology, University of Bergen, Thormøhlensgate 53A, N-5006 Bergen, Norway. Email: jon.grytnes@bot.uib.no

Jonathan Hall, NFU Scotland, Rural Centre - West Mains, Ingliston, Midlothian, EH28 8LT. Email: jonathan.hall@nfus.org.uk

James Hansom, Department of Geographical and Earth Sciences, University of Glasgow, Glasgow, G12 8QQ. Email: jim.hansom@ges.gla.ac.uk

Catriona Hendrie, c/o Scottish Natural Heritage, Great Glen House, Leachkin Road, Inverness, IV3 8NW.

Julie Hesketh-Laird, Scotch Whisky Association, 20 Atholl Crescent, Edinburgh, EH3 8HF. Email: jhesketh-laird@swa.org.uk

Alison Hester, The James Hutton Institute, Craigiebuckler, Aberdeen, AB15 8QH. Email: a.hester@hutton.ac.uk

Rupert Hough, The James Hutton Institute, Craigiebuckler, Aberdeen, AB15 8QH. Email: r.hough@hutton.ac.uk

Liz Humphreys, BTO Scotland, School of Biological and Environmental Sciences, Cottrell Building, University of Stirling, Stirling, FK9 4LA.
Email: liz.humpreys@bto.org

Gordon Hudson, The James Hutton Institute, Craigiebuckler, Aberdeen, AB15 8QH. Email: g.hudson@hutton.ac.uk

Colin Hunter, Department of Geography and Environment, University of Aberdeen, Elphinstone Road, Aberdeen, AB24 3UF. Email: c.j.hunter@abdn.ac.uk

Eilidh Johnston, Scottish Environmental Protection Agency, Erskine Court, Castle Business Park, Stirling, FK9 4TR. Email: eilidh.johnston@sepa.org.uk

Emma Jordan, Scottish Natural Heritage, Battleby, Redgorton, Perth, PH1 3EW. Email: emma.jordan@snh.gov.uk

Jo Kennedy, 37 Kilmaurs Road, Edinburgh, EH16 5DB.
Email: jokennedy@blueyonder.co.uk

Paul Kirkland, Butterfly Conservation Scotland, Balallan House, 24 Allan Park, Stirling, FK8 2QG. Email: paul.kirkland@btconnect.com

Emily Lambert, Institute of Biological and Environmental Sciences (IBES), University of Aberdeen, Tillydrone Avenue, Aberdeen, AB24 2TZ.
Email: emily.lambert@abdn.ac.uk

Allan Lilly, The James Hutton Institute, Craigiebuckler, Aberdeen, AB15 8QH. Email: a.lilly@hutton.ac.uk

David Long, Royal Botanic Garden Edinburgh, 20A Inverleith Row, Edinburgh, EH3 5LR. Email: d.long@rbge.org.uk

Earl of Lindsay, Scotland's Moorland Forum, c/o The Heather Trust, Newtonrigg, Holywood, Dumfries, DG2 0RA. Email: info@moorlandforum.co.uk

Edward Mackey, Scottish Natural Heritage, Silvan House, 231 Corstorphine Road, Edinburgh, EH12 7AT. Email: ed.mackey@snh.gov.uk

Colin MacLeod, Institute of Biological and Environmental Sciences (IBES), University of Aberdeen, Tillydrone Avenue, Aberdeen, AB24 2TZ. Email: c.d.macleod@abdn.ac.uk

Susan Marrs, Scottish Natural Heritage, Great Glen House, Leachkin Road, Inverness, IV3 8NW. Email: sue.marrs@snh.gov.uk

Davy McCracken, Rural Policy Centre, Scottish Agricultural College, Auchincruive, Ayr, KA6 5HW. Email: davy.mccracken@sac.ac.uk

Bob McIntosh, Forestry Commission, Silvan House, 231 Corstorphine Road, Edinburgh, EH12 7AT. Email: bob.mcintosh@forestry.gsi.gov.uk

Ian McKenzie, Ian McKenzie Consulting Ltd., 72 Durward Avenue, Glasgow, G41 3UE. Email: imck.consulting@btopenworld.com

Alastair McNeill, Scottish Environment Protection Agency, Rivers House, Iron Gray Road, Dumfries, DG2 0JE. Email: alastair.mcneill@homecall.co.uk

Andrew Midgley, Rural Policy Centre, Scottish Agricultural College, West Mains Road, Edinburgh, EH9 3JG. Email: andrew.midgley@sac.ac.uk

Clive Mitchell, Scottish Natural Heritage, Battleby, Redgorton, Perth, PH1 3EW. Email: clive.mitchell@snh.gov.uk

Richard Mitchell, Centre for Population Health Sciences, University of Glasgow, 1 Lilybank Gardens, Glasgow, G12 8RZ. Email: richard.mitchell@glasgow.ac.uk

Peter R. Moore, Scottish Natural Heritage, Great Glen House, Leachkin Road, Inverness, IV3 8NW. Email: pete.moore@snh.gov.uk

Fiona Newcombe, c/o Scottish Natural Heritage, Great Glen House, Leachkin Road, Inverness, IV3 8NW.

Ann Paterson, Scottish Environment Protection Agency, Grasser House, Fodderty Way, Dingwall, IV15 9XB. Email: ann.paterson@sepa.org.uk

James Pearce-Higgins, British Trust for Ornithology, The Nunnery, Thetford, Norfolk, IP24 2PU. Email: james.pearce-higgins@bto.org

Graham Pierce, Institute of Biological and Environmental Sciences (IBES), University of Aberdeen, Tillydrone Avenue, Aberdeen AB24 2TZ and Instituto

Español de Oceanografía, Centro Oceanográfico de Vigo, P.O. Box 1552, 36200, Vigo, España. Email: g.j.pierce@abdn.ac.uk

Martin Price, Centre for Mountain Studies, Perth College UHI, Crieff Road, Perth, PH1 2NX. Email: martin.price@perth.uhi.ac.uk

Julie Procter, Greenspace Scotland, 12 Alpha Centre, Stirling University Innovation Park, Stirling, FK9 4NF. Email: julie.procter@greenspacescotland.org.uk

Chris Quine, Centre for Human and Ecological Sciences, Forest Research, Northern Research Station, Roslin, Midlothian, EH25 9SY.
E-mail: chris.quine@forestry.gsi.gov.uk

Alistair Rennie, Scottish Natural Heritage, Great Glen House, Leachkin Road, Inverness, IV3 8NW. Email: alistair.rennie@snh.gov.uk

Louise Ross, Institute of Biological and Environmental Sciences, University of Aberdeen, Cruickshank Building, St Machar Drive, Aberdeen, AB24 3UU.
Email: louise.ross@abdn.ac.uk

Gordon Rothero, Stronlonag, Glenmassan, Dunoon, Argyll, PA23 8RA.
Email: gprothero@aol.com

Claudia Rowse, Scottish Natural Heritage, Great Glen House, Leachkin Road, Inverness, IV3 8NW. Email: claudia.rowse@snh.gov.uk

David Roy, Centre for Ecology and Hydrology, Maclean Building, Benson Lane, Crowmarsh Gifford, Wallingford, Oxfordshire, OX10 8BB. Email: dbr@ceh.ac.uk

Alister Scott, School of Property, Construction and Planning, Birmingham City University, Perry Barr, Birmingham, B42 2SU. Email: alister.scott@bcu.ac.uk

Beth Scott, Room 412 Zoology, School of Biological Sciences, University of Aberdeen, Tillydrone Avenue, Aberdeen, AB24 2TZ. Email: b.e.scott@abdn.ac.uk

Alastair Simmons, c/o 27 Denmark Street, Lancaster, LA1 5LY.

Chris Spray, IHP-HELP UNESCO Centre for Water Law Policy and Science, University of Dundee, Perth Road, Dundee, DD1 4HN. Email: c.j.spray@dundee.ac.uk

Selina Stead, School of Marine Science and Technology, Ridley Building, Newcastle University, Newcastle upon Tyne, NE1 7RU. Email: selina.stead@newcastle.ac.uk

Stewart Stevenson, The Scottish Parliament, Edinburgh, EH99 1SP. Email: msp@stewartstevenson.net

Paul Sutherland, Scottish Natural Heritage, Holmpark Industrial Estate, New Galloway Road, Newton Stewart, Wigtonshire, DG8 6BF.
Email: paul.sutherland@snh.gov.uk

Bob Swann, British Trust for Ornithology Scotland, School of Biological and Environmental Sciences, Cottrell Building, University of Stirling, Stirling, FK9 4LA. Email: bob.swann@bto.org

Emma Teuten, RSPB Scotland, 2 Lochside View, Edinburgh Park, Edinburgh, EH12 9DH. Email: emma.teuten@rspb.org.uk

Des Thompson, Scottish Natural Heritage, Silvan House, 3rd Floor East, 231 Corstorphine Road, Edinburgh, EH12 7AT. Email: des.thompson@snh.gov.uk

Simon Thorp, Scotland's Moorland Forum, c/o The Heather Trust, Newtonrigg, Holywood, Dumfries, DG2 0RA. Email: simon.thorp@heathertrust.co.uk

Mike Toms, British Trust for Ornithology, The Nunnery, Thetford, Norfolk, IP24 2PU. Email: mike.toms@bto.org

Bill Turrell, Marine Scotland – Science, Marine Laboratory, 375 Victoria Road, Aberdeen, AB11 9DB. Email: bill.turrell@scotland.gsi.gov.uk

Chris Waltho, The Scottish Ornithologists' Club, The Scottish Birdwatching Resource Centre, Waterston House, Aberlady, East Lothian, EH32 0PY.
Email: clydeeider@aol.com

Chris Wernham, British Trust for Ornithology Scotland, School of Biological and Environmental Sciences, Cottrell Building, University of Stirling, Stirling, FK9 4LA. Email: chris.wernham@bto.org

Jeremy Wilson, RSPB Scotland, 2 Lochside View, Edinburgh Park, Edinburgh, EH12 9DH. Email: jeremy.wilson@rspb.org.uk

David Windle, North East Mountain Trust, 30 Hillview Road, Cults, Aberdeen, AB15 9HA. Email: david.windle@Shell.com

Sarah Woodin, Institute of Biological and Environmental Sciences, University of Aberdeen, Cruickshank Building, St Machar Drive, Aberdeen, AB24 3UU.
Email: s.woodin@abdn.ac.uk

The Changing Nature of Scotland

An Overview of the Changing Nature of Scotland

An Overview of the Changing Nature of Scotland

Scotland is a distinctive country. The forces of nature and the imprint of people have given us the land, waterways and seascapes we recognise today. In each region the landscape is the unique product of physical and biological elements and the influences of people – no two areas are the same, and in some places even neighbouring glens, catchments or settlements are very different in character.

This book focuses on the changing nature of Scotland, looking as much at what has happened in the past as to what lies ahead. If one word captures the nature of change it is 'dynamic' – as much because of the complex interactions giving rise to what we see as to the pace and diversity of human, and nature's, handiwork. The ten opening chapters reflect a range of studies undertaken to help us understand the quality, values and changes taking place. In this and other introductory sections we include a loose chronology of some, rather personally selected, key events which have contributed to our work in Scotland; what is striking about these is that decades may pass before we realise their importance or impact.

Some key events for nature in Scotland since 1970

1970	European Conservation Year
1973	UK entered the European Common Market, joining the Common Agricultural Policy (CAP)
1973	Voluntary ban on pesticides aldrin and dieldrin
1975	Sea eagle re-introduction programme for Scotland begins
1975	CITES (Convention on International Trade in Endangered Species of Wild Fauna and Flora) came into force
1976	Ramsar Convention on wetlands ratified in UK, and first Ramsar sites designated
1977	*A Nature Conservation Review* published
1978	National Scenic Areas (NSAs) designated
1979	EC Birds Directive came into force. Bonn Convention on Migratory Species signed by UK Government

Red admiral butterfly. © SNH Images

1981	Wildlife and Countryside Act
1982	First Special Protection Areas (SPAs) classified
1983	NCC began a major programme of SSSI re-notification
1985	An EC Directive obliged developers to undertake EIAs (Environmental Impact Assessments) – these became mandatory in 1990
1985	Amendment of the Wildlife and Countryside Act required a reasonable balance to be struck between forest management for timber production and natural heritage benefits
1987	European Year of the Environment
1989	UK Government announced dismemberment of the NCC and creation of national agencies
1989	First red kite reintroduction programme release in Scotland and England
1990	Countryside Commission for Scotland (CCS) called for National Parks
1991	EC Habitats Directive came into force, with Special Areas of Conservation to be designated for habitats and species (except birds)
1991	JNCC (Joint Nature Conservation Committee) created
1992	SNH created under the Natural Heritage (Scotland) Act 1991, merging the former NCC and CCS; sustainability enshrined in founding legislation
1992	Convention on Biological Diversity (Rio Earth Summit) signed by UK, with the word 'biodiversity' taken from E.O. Wilson's *The Diversity of Life*
1993	Geological Conservation Review *Quaternary of Scotland* and second BTO Breeding Birds Atlas published
1994	*Biodiversity: the UK Action Plan* published by UK Government, giving rise to a plethora of habitat, species and local action plans.
1994	UK-wide Breeding Bird Survey established
1995	European Nature Conservation Year
1995	Publication of *The Natural Heritage of Scotland: an overview*
1996	Deer Act made provisions for control of deer to prevent damage to the natural heritage
1996	UK Government published sustainable development indicators – revised indicators were published in *A Better Quality of Life* in 1999
1997	RSPB reached 1 million members in UK
1998	SNH published proposals for National Parks

1999	First major tranche of SACs proposed to the EC for classification
2000	Scottish Parliament approved the creation of National Parks (Loch Lomond and the Trossachs NP established in 2002, and Cairngorms NP in 2003)
2001	Major outbreak of Foot and Mouth Disease resulted in a suspension of major wildlife surveys and restricted access to the countryside
2003	Land Reform Act paved the way for open access – Scottish Outdoor Access Code was approved by Scottish Parliament in 2004, and came into force in 2005
2004	Scotland's biodiversity strategy published – indicators published in 2007
2007	SNH launched the Species Action Framework – a five year plan aimed at targeting those species in Scotland where it is believed the most difference can be made to Scotland's biodiversity
2009	Beavers reintroduced to Scotland
2009	Countryside Survey 2007 results published – the third UK wide periodic audit of the countryside
2010	International Year of Biodiversity
2010	Deer Commission for Scotland merged with SNH
2011	The UK National Ecosystem Assessment published

In Chapter 1, Colin Galbraith and Ed Mackey place Scotland in a global context. Scotland is importantly positioned and some areas and habitats within Scotland provide refuge and stop-over destinations for many migratory species such as waders and wildfowl. Scotland hosts internationally important populations and assemblages of fungi, plants and animals including seals, freshwater pearl mussel (*Margaritifera margaritifera*), Atlantic salmon (*Salmo salar*) and bryophytes. Key initiatives are driving the need to restore biodiversity across the world. The Millennium Ecosystem Assessment (MEA) details actions needed throughout the world to restore habitats and the species which are dependent upon them (MEA, 2005). Measuring and recording our actions and the response of biodiversity is crucial. Simon Foster, Ed Mackey and Sue Marrs (Chapter 2) highlight the challenges in developing biodiversity indicators for Scotland. In Scotland we have 17 indicators measuring the state of biodiversity. These are used at all levels from policy makers to education to show how Scotland's nature is changing. We can only restore biodiversity if we measure what is happening and raise awareness of the issues. For the indicators to remain current and useful SNH has looked at developing and enhancing them so that they can be of use to a range of users.

Looking to the future Emma Jordan and Mary Christie (Chapter 8) set out SNH's vision for the natural heritage in 2025. Ralph Blaney and Claudia Rowse (Chapter 3) introduce the concept of valuing the environment. This is often seen by many conservationists as flawed (*inter alia* Weaver, 1994; Pearce and Moran, 1994; Nunes and van der Berg, 2001). How, people ask, can we value something that is priceless, and how can we say that one habitat or species is worth more or less than another? Rather than try and put a price on our environment, Blaney and Rowse focus on the benefits that nature brings to Scotland's economy. In Scotland around £17.2 billion of income is generated through the natural environment. The natural environment supports in the region of 242,000 (14%) jobs. This will hopefully widen the eyes of conservationists, economists and businesses to the value that nature brings to Scotland; any loss in the biodiversity is likely to impact on jobs and the economy. Perhaps we cannot and should not value wildlife *per se*, but the benefits in terms of the economy and our health are emerging and are highly important.

Soils are the critical key component to all land-based habitats and species in Scotland, and support a vast array of life. Measuring changes in soil quality and extent at a national level is not straightforward; Allan Lilly, Rupert Hough, Gordon Hudson and the NSIS Sampling Team (Chapter 4) describe the development of the National Soils Inventory for Scotland (NSIS). This is a positive step in improving our understanding of change, not only in terms of soil quality but also extent. Looking ahead we hope to be able to detail trends in soil quality and composition.

Scotland is renowned for its deer and they make an important contribution to Scotland's economy in terms of the income generated from tourism, shooting and food. Fiona Newcombe (Chapter 5) describes how the populations of the four species present (red, roe, sika and fallow) have increased markedly, and how they are now having significant pervasive effects on our habitats in some areas. A fine balancing act is required here as deer provide a valuable input into our economy as well as shaping the habitats upon which they rely.

Butterflies typically respond relatively quickly to environmental change (Thomas *et al.*, 2004); Tom Brereton, Richard Fox, Paul Kirkland, David Roy and Simon Foster (Chapter 6) detail some key trends in Scotland's butterflies, comparing these with work elsewhere. Butterflies are one of the 17 biodiversity state indicators used in Scotland and although abundance has fluctuated, the generalist species (those which are most commonly found in a variety of habitats) have remained stable since the mid 1970s, whilst specialist species declined in the early 1980s but have since remained stable.

Britain has a long and distinguished history of ornithology – the first list of British birds was published in 1666 by Christopher Merrett, an early Fellow of The Royal Society (Bircham, 2007). Since then, more than 400 bird atlases have been published worldwide. In the twentieth century, two atlases were published – in the 1970s and 1990s (Sharrock, 1976; Gibbons *et al.*, 1993) – which mapped breeding bird populations in Britain and Ireland. In Chapter 7, Simon Gillings, Bob Swann, Dawn Balmer and Chris Wernham, all of the British Trust for Ornithology, give a fascinating account of how the most recent project, Bird Atlas 2007-11, is developing. Their work takes advantage of the internet for data capture, which features interactive maps for grid references to improve both the quality and completeness of survey returns. In Scotland the project has harnessed the efforts of more than 3,000 volunteers and is a monument to what can be achieved by channelling the skills and enthusiasm of the volunteering public. When complete, the Atlas will prove an invaluable record of bird distribution and abundance, which should help us understand the nature of change over the last fifty or so years.

The last two chapters of this Section consider how we view the environment. Most of us can enjoy Scotland's scenery, however, we struggle when it comes to defining why we appreciate a specific view. In Chapter 9, James Fenton, Krystina Campbell and Alastair Simmons describe an intriguing project by SNH to define the special qualities of the landscape in National Scenic Areas (NSAs). If we understand what qualities make a NSA special it should be possible to predict the potential impact of any development therein. Visual influence of built development is tracked annually by SNH in one of its Natural Heritage Indicators. The most recent update showed that the extent of Scotland unaffected by any form of visual influence declined from 31% in January 2008 to 28% in December 2009. The indicator uses advanced GIS (Geographic Information System) techniques. Localised changes in the countryside can be recorded through the use of photography – or more specifically rephotography where changes through time can be tracked by taking repeat photographs from precisely the same vantage point. In the closing chapter of this section, Pete Moore (Chapter 10), who is studying for a PhD at Aberdeen University, gives an interesting account of the benefits of rephotography. This work inspires us to see and record Scotland's changing nature through fresh eyes.

References

Bircham, P. (2007). *A History of Ornithology*. The New Naturalists Library, Collins, London.

Gibbons, D.W., Reid, J.B. and Chapman, R.A. (1993). *The New Atlas of Breeding Birds in Britain and Ireland: 1988–1991.* Poyser, London.

Pearce, D. and Moran, D. (1994). *The Economic Value of Biodiversity.* Earthscan Publications Ltd., London.

MEA (2005). *Ecosystems and Human Well-being – Our Human Planet – Summary for Decision Makers*. Millennium Ecosystem Assessment, Island Press, Washington.

Nunes, P.A.L.D. and van den Bergh, J.C.J.M. (2001). Economic valuation of biodiversity: sense or nonsense? *Ecological Economics*, **39**, 203–222.

Sharrock, J.T.R. (1976). *The Atlas of Breeding Birds of Britain and Ireland*. Poyser, Berkhamsted.

Thomas, J.A., Telfer, M.G., Roy, D.B. *et al.* (2004). Comparative losses of British butterflies, birds, and plants and the global extinction crisis. *Science*, **303**, 1879-1881.

Weaver, R.D. (1994). Economic valuation of biodiversity. In *Biodiversity and Landscapes, a Paradox of Humanity*, ed. by K.C. Kim and R.D. Weaver, Cambridge University Press, Cambridge, U.K.

1 The Changing Nature of Scotland: A Global Perspective

Edward C. Mackey and Colin A. Galbraith

Summary

1. The Millennium Ecosystem Assessment provided a new framework for understanding the nature of environmental change across the world. We summarise this as a reference point for taking forward work to sustain nature in Scotland.
2. The results of the recent IUCN assessment of the threat status of the world's species is summarised, which concluded that biodiversity loss is one of the world's most pressing crises on which human life depends.
3. Reviewing the baseline European biodiversity assessment, timed to contribute to the 'International Year of Biodiversity 2010', we find that around 40-85% of habitats and 40-70% of species of European interest had an unfavourable conservation status, with biodiversity diminished to 45% of its natural (pre-industrial) potential by 2000.
4. The UK biodiversity assessment was published in April 2009 and updated in 2010. Using 33 measures, the assessment reported a wide variety of sustained improvements since 2000 (such as plant diversity in arable and horticultural land, and the extent of protected areas) as well as trends showing improvements (e.g. extent of targeted agri-environment schemes, percentage of commercially exploited marine fish stocks harvested sustainably, biological river quality, and time spent in conservation volunteering).
5. In Scotland, 22 biodiversity indicators were first published in 2007, with 17 of these describing wildlife trends and five summarising people's engagement with biodiversity. The broad results arising from work on these are summarised, indicating particular concerns for the marine environment.
6. We reflect on some of the contrasts and differences in trends across Scotland compared with changes across Europe.

Mackey, E.C. and Galbraith, C.A. (2011). The Changing Nature of Scotland: A Global Perspective – *The Changing Nature of Scotland*, eds. S.J. Marrs, S. Foster, C. Hendrie, E.C. Mackey, D.B.A. Thompson. TSO Scotland, Edinburgh, pp 9-22.

1.1 Introduction

Over the past two decades there has been an increase in the need for environmental reporting resulting in the development of trends and indicators covering a range of species and habitats (see for example Foster *et al.*, Chapter 2). In this introductory chapter, we summarise some of the key related activities at the global, European, UK and Scotland-wide levels. As government policies, and indeed legislation, become more evidence-based, it is crucial that we have a systematic means of reporting on what is happening, and understanding the reasons for change.

1.2 Global changes – the Millennium Ecosystem Assessment

Various studies, organisations and agencies have looked at defining the changing state of nature – from the global to regional scales. With the publication of the Millennium Ecosystem Assessment (MEA) in 2005 we had the first comprehensively global stock take on the state of the environment (UNEP, 2005). This provided an audit of the state of biodiversity and looked at some ways in which resource management in the future might be developed. The Assessment's 'conceptual framework' linked human life and livelihoods to the capacities of ecosystems and ecosystem services (provisioning, regulating, cultural and supporting) to sustain the quality of life, security, social relations, freedom of choice and action – all as the basis for human well-being and poverty reduction. Importantly, the Assessment stressed the linkages between habitats, and the connectivity of interactions operating over the short- to long-term, and from the local to global scales (UNEP, 2005).

The MEA concluded that, at the global scale, human well-being had, for the most part, improved appreciably over the latter half of the twentieth century. Ecosystems have so far largely met the rising demand for food, principally through increased agricultural productivity. Fish catches, however, have gone into decline, and a number of targeted stocks throughout the world's oceans have declined or collapsed primarily due to over-fishing. Improvements to human well-being have come about through managed water use – such as flood and pollution control, irrigation and hydro-electricity generation – but at a cost. Trade-offs included increased organic pollution and nitrogen loading from cultivated and urban areas, habitat fragmentation and destruction, and an emergence of human health risks. Increased concentrations of trace gases in the atmosphere have reduced the atmosphere's cleansing capacity, depleted ozone in the troposphere and affected global climate.

In stark contrast the changes to biodiversity were substantial and predominantly negative. Losses were evident at all levels, from ecosystems through to species, populations and genes. The documented rate of species extinction was two orders of magnitude higher than the average rate of species extinction from the fossil record, and could be much higher in the future. Indeed, the changes were accelerating, and ecosystems had altered more rapidly and more extensively over the previous 50 years than recorded in any comparable time in human history – largely to meet rapidly growing demands for food, fresh water, timber, fibre and fuel.

Plate 1.1 Chanterelle - one of many wild foods that can be found in Scotland. © SNH Images

The International Union for Conservation of Nature (IUCN) was first conceived in 1963 and has been evaluating the conservation status of species and subspecies on a global scale – highlighting those threatened with extinction and promoting their conservation (IUCN, 2009). The IUCN Red List of Threatened Species is widely recognised as the basis for the most comprehensive and objective global approach for evaluating the conservation status of plant and animal species (e.g. Lamoreux *et al.*, 2003; Rodrigues *et al.*, 2006). In 2009, 17,291 out of 47,677 species assessed (36%) were classified as threatened with extinction, including 21% of all known mammals, 30% of all known amphibians, 12% of all known birds and 32% of all known seed-bearing plants (IUCN, 2009). The results detail the fact that globally over one third of the species assessed is facing extinction (Table 1.1). This is a cause for considerable concern, and has the potential to disrupt the effective functioning of ecosystems around the world.

Table 1.1 The IUCN Red List Summary (as at 3 November 2009) (From IUCN, 2009).

Red list category	Number assessed	Percentage of total species assessed
Extinct	809	2
Extinct in the wild	66	0.1
Critically endangered	3,325	7
Endangered	4,894	10
Vulnerable	9,075	19
Near threatened	3,650	8
Lower risk/ conservation dependent	281	1
Data deficient	6,557	14
Least concern	19,023	40
Total	47,677	100*

*The numbers do not add up to exactly 100% due to rounding.

Among the world's 5,490 mammals, 79 were Extinct or Extinct in the Wild, with 188 Critically Endangered, 449 Endangered and 505 Vulnerable. Of 1,677 reptiles on the Red List, 469 were threatened with extinction and 22 were already Extinct or Extinct in the Wild. Some 1,895 of the planet's 6,285 amphibians were in danger of extinction, making them the most threatened group of species known. Of these, 39 were already Extinct or Extinct in the Wild, 484 were Critically Endangered, 754 were Endangered and 657 were Vulnerable. Of the 12,151 plants on the Red List, 8,500 were threatened with extinction, with 114 already Extinct or Extinct in the Wild. Among 7,615 invertebrates on the Red List, 2,639 were threatened with extinction; of 1,989 dragonflies and damselflies, 261 were threatened. Some 1,036 of 2,306 molluscs were threatened. Finally, among 3,120 freshwater fishes assessed, 1,147 were threatened with extinction. The 2009 IUCN assessment concluded that biodiversity loss is one of the world's most pressing crises on which human life depends.

For many species and habitat groups there are international or national initiatives to develop our understanding of causes of change, and to identify the actions needed to tackle these. Box 1.1 provides an example of work relating to waterbirds, which arose from a major conference in Scotland, with Box 1.2 summarising a declaration to take action to halt the losses of waterbirds and their wetland habitats.

Box 1.1 Waterbirds around the world: a Scottish contribution

For over a century, pioneering naturalists have determined the way in which waterbird conservation has evolved around the world (Kuijken, 2006). The first European Meeting on Wildfowl Conservation held in St. Andrews, Scotland in 1963, started a process leading to the establishment of the Convention on Wetlands especially as Waterfowl Habitat in Ramsar, Iran, in 1971 (Boere *et al.*, 2006). The Ramsar Convention is considered to be the first of the modern global environment treaties (Kuijken, 2006). In April 2004, a second major international conference was held in Scotland to develop the evidence base and action needed to help sustain the world's waterbirds (Boere *et al.*, 2006). It was attended by more than 450 delegates from 90 countries throughout the world.

Ducks, geese and waders in their seasonal migrations frequently cross many national boundaries, and are truly an international resource; the conservation of wetlands and their flora and fauna calls for far-sighted national policies and coordinated international action (Ramsar Convention, 1971). The Convention's mission is the conservation and wise use of all wetlands through local and national actions and international cooperation, as a contribution towards achieving sustainable development throughout the world (Ramsar Convention website, 2010).

Although wetlands deliver a wealth of ecosystem services that contribute to human well-being, their rate of degradation and loss is more rapid than that of other ecosystems; the status of both freshwater and coastal wetland species is deteriorating faster than those of other ecosystems (Millennium Ecosystem

Assessment, 2005). Climate changes are already affecting waterbirds; the consequences will be multiple, and will greatly exacerbate current negative impacts such as habitat loss and degradation (Boere *et al.*, 2006).

Whilst national and international strategies and legal conservation instruments have scope to help, they need to be much more penetrating in their implementation so as to address root causes of population declines (Stroud *et al.*, 2006).

1.3 Europe: state of nature reporting

The 2005 European state of the environment report, published by the European Environment Agency (EEA), based on 31 country assessments, showed that a third of 37 core environmental indicators were not on target (EEA, 2005). Key concerns included pressure on biodiversity, over-exploitation of marine fisheries, invasive non-native species and the potential impacts of climate change (EEA, 2005). The fourth assessment (EEA, 2007), in which bio-geographical coverage was extended to the 53 countries of the pan-European region (from the Atlantic Ocean in the west, to beyond the central Asian plains in the east, and from the Arctic Ocean in the north to the Mediterranean Sea in the south), identified a number of pressing concerns. The history of production and consumption had depleted and contaminated natural resources; waste generation was growing; and soil degradation and a legacy of contaminated sites were of widespread concern. Atmospheric pollution (particularly fine particles and ozone) were considered to pose a threat to human health and the environment; emissions had increased by more than 10% in Eastern Europe since 2000. Although water quality had improved, some large rivers and many smaller watercourses remained severely polluted; in eastern and southern Europe the quality of water supply and sanitation had deteriorated throughout the previous 15 years. Eutrophication affected all enclosed seas and sheltered marine waters. Over-fishing and destructive fishing practices occurred in all seas; major oil spills had generally decreased but oil discharges remained significant. Impacts of climate change, on society and natural resources, were becoming evident. Biodiversity loss (particularly in farmland, mountain regions, forests and coastal zones) was linked to land use changes, urban and infrastructure development, acidification, eutrophication, desertification, overexploitation and climate change. More than 700 species were found to be under threat while the number of invasive non-native species was increasing. Particularly significant in this report was the scale and geographical breadth of the assessment. The trends reported were not confined to a few countries; instead, there was a picture of widespread and rapid change.

Building on this, the first European biodiversity assessment, based on the 26 pan-European 'Streamlining European 2010 Biodiversity Indicators', was published in 2009 (EEA, 2009). This provided a baseline report for the 'International Year of Biodiversity 2010'. While acknowledging that considerable progress had been made, it was clear that the 2010 target of halting biodiversity loss in Europe would not be achieved. Some 40-85% of habitats and 40-70% of species of European interest had an unfavourable conservation status. It was estimated that biodiversity had fallen to 45% of its natural (pre-industrial) potential by 2000 and that without greater urgency of policy implementation and integration it could fall to a third by 2050.

Box 1.2 Waterbirds around the world: the 'Edinburgh Declaration'

The 'Edinburgh Declaration' is an example of the type of coordinated action required to stop and reverse the loss of biodiversity. Emerging from the 2004 'Waterbirds around the world' conference (Boere *et al.*, 2006; see Box 1.1), the declaration sought to:

- Halt and reverse wetland loss and degradation;
- Complete national and international wetland inventories, and promote the conservation of wetlands of importance to waterbirds in the context of surrounding areas, especially through the participation of local communities;
- Extend and strengthen international networks of key sites for waterbirds along all flyways;
- Establish and extend formal agreements and other co-operation arrangements between countries to conserve species, where possible within the frameworks provided by the Conventions on Migratory Species, Biological Diversity and Wetlands;
- Fund and implement recovery plans for all globally threatened waterbird species;
- Halt and reverse recently revealed declines of long-distance migrant shorebirds through sustainable management by governments and others of human activities at sites of unique importance to them;
- Restore albatross and petrel populations to favourable conservation status through urgent and internationally coordinated conservation actions, especially through the framework provided by the Agreement on the Conservation of Albatrosses and Petrels;
- Substantially reduce pollution in the marine environment and establish sustainable harvesting of marine resources;

- Underpin future conservation decisions with high-quality scientific advice drawn from co-ordinated, and adequately funded, research and monitoring programmes notably the International Waterbird Census, and to this end, urge governments and other partners to work together collaboratively and supportively;
- Develop policy-relevant indicators of the status of the world's wetlands, especially in the context of the 2010 target, using waterbird and other data generated from robust and sustainable monitoring schemes;
- Invest in communication, education and public awareness activities as a key element of waterbird and wetlands conservation; and
- Assess disease risk, and establish monitoring programmes in relation to migratory waterbird movements, the trade of wild birds, and implications for human health.

1.4 United Kingdom: the biodiversity assessment

Across the UK, there are many activities centred on assessing the nature of biodiversity change. The UK biodiversity assessment was published in April 2009 and updated in 2010 (Defra, 2010). The assessment detailed 33 measures which showed the changing state of UK biodiversity. Among the measures, those showing long term and sustained improvement since 2000 were: plant diversity in arable and horticultural land; the extent of protected areas; the extent of targeted agri-environment schemes; the percentage of commercially exploited marine fish stocks harvested sustainably; and biological river quality. Trends that had improved since 2000 included woodland breeding birds and bats (in contrast to their deterioration in the longer-term); the conservation status of UK priority species; the effective population size of native cattle breeds; the condition of protected areas; the proportion of woodland under certified management; the extent of entry-level agri-environment schemes; expenditure on both UK and global biodiversity; and time spent in conservation volunteering.

Long-term deterioration was evident among populations of farmland breeding birds, however, and in populations of specialist butterflies, plant diversity (in woodland, grassland and boundary habitats), invasive non-native species (number of species present in marine, freshwater and terrestrial environments), and marine ecosystem integrity (proportion of large fish). The four short- and long-term trend characteristics, shown by wild birds, are illustrated in Figure 1.1.

Although the population index for all species of wild birds for the UK remained relatively stable since 1970, within the four categories (seabirds, water and wetland

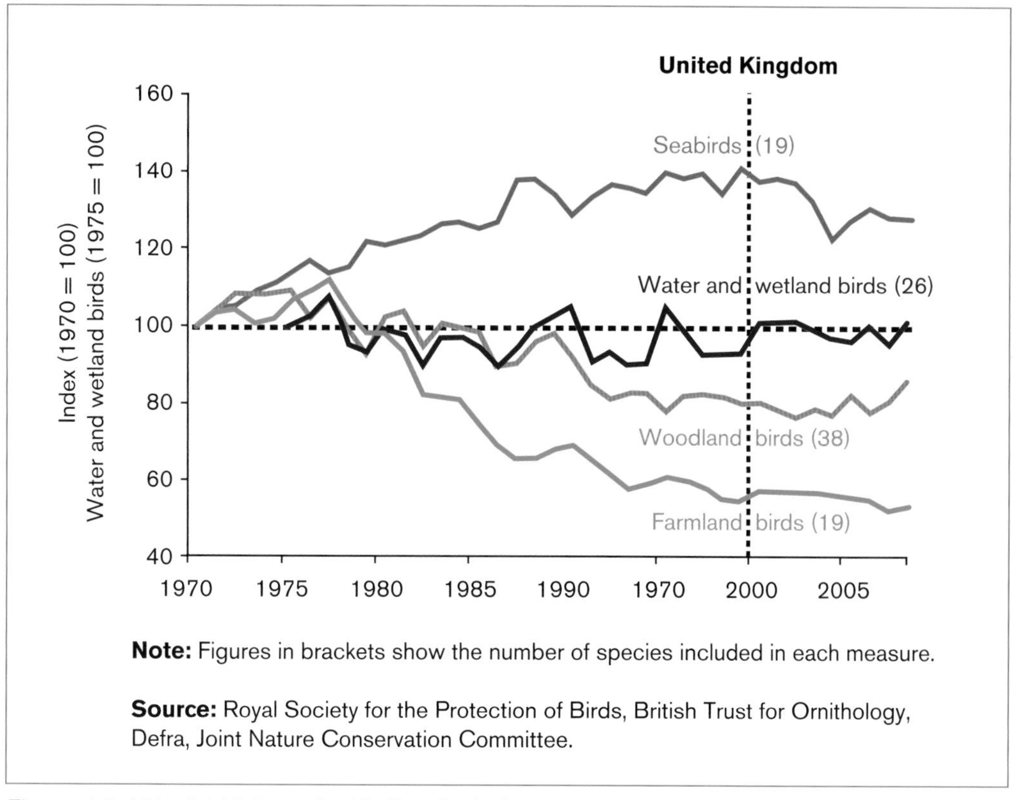

Figure 1.1 UK wild bird trends: biodiversity indicator 2010. Reproduced, with permission, from Biodiversity Indicators in Your Pocket 2010 (Defra 2010).

birds, woodland birds and farmland birds) the picture was varied. Seabirds were 27% above the 1970 baseline value in 2008 but declining. Having fluctuated over the years, water and wetland birds showed no overall change. Woodland birds were 14% below baseline in 2008, though the trend since 2002 has been upwards. Finally, farmland bird populations fell by 47% between 1970 and 2008.

Among seabirds, a 45% decline in kittiwake (*Rissa tridactyla*) numbers has been linked in-part to increased sea surface temperatures and, in some regions, to commercial exploitation of their sandeel prey (notably lesser- *Ammodytes tobianus* and greater- sandeel *Hyperoplus lanceolatus*) (Defra, 2011). The water and wetland birds that tended to increase were birds of slow flowing or standing water, in contrast to declines among birds of wet grassland. Long term declines among woodland and farmland birds were due primarily to declines among specialist species (such as tree pipit (*Anthus trivialis*) or corn bunting (*Emberiza calandra*); see Wilson, Chapter 26), in contrast to more adaptable or generalist species (such as woodpigeon (*Columba palumbus*) or long-tailed tit (*Aegithalos caudatus*)) (Defra, 2011).

1.5 Scotland: assessing its biodiversity

Turning to Scotland, the results of work on 22 biodiversity indicators were first published in 2007 (Scottish Government, 2007). Of these, 17 describe wildlife trends and five describe people's engagement with biodiversity (see Foster *et al.*, Chapter 2; Marrs and Foster, Chapter 11). Positive trends were evident among terrestrial breeding birds (between 1994 and 2008, 50 of 65 bird species in Scotland increased in abundance, by 31% overall). Wintering waterbirds (38 species) were 12% above the 1975/76 baseline value in 2007/08, despite declines since 1995/96; goose numbers had increased the most (to 308% over baseline) but waders had fallen to 90% of baseline in 2007/08, which may be due in part to major changes in migration routes and some poor survey coverage in some of the 'newer' ranges used by these birds in eastern and northern Scotland.

Plate 1.2 Scots pine woodland, Loch Maree National Nature Reserve. Native Scots pine woodlands are managed and protected under the EC Habitats Directive. © SNH Images

Across Scotland's 1,451 protected areas in 2010, 70% of species and 63% of habitat and geological features had been assessed to be in favourable condition (78% collectively when remedial management is taken into account). Environmental improvements had reduced air, land and water pollution, allowing wildlife to re-colonise parts of Scotland that had become degraded by industrialisation and dereliction. Fish diversity was being restored in the catchments and estuaries of the Forth and Clyde; otter (*Lutra lutra*) occupancy (presence at 1,376 survey sites within 574 different 10km-squares in both freshwater and coastal localities across Scotland) rose from 57% in 1979 to 92% in 2004. Among 39 'priority' habitats last assessed in 2008, 43% were stable or increasing. Of the 197 priority species, 37% were stable or increasing (with 'priority' being priority for action due to vulnerability / history of decline).

There were more equivocal trends for butterflies and moths. Although butterfly trends were stable between 1979 and 2009, specialist species, that is those restricted to specific habitats, had decreased to around half of their 1979 abundance, while generalist, those which tend to be more widespread or opportunistic, species had increased. Moth abundance among 185 of the commoner species fluctuated between 1975 and 2004, with emerging evidence pointing to long-term declines among common moth species in Britain. Vascular plant diversity fell by nearly 10% between 1998 and 2007. The majority (84%) of 867 non-native species for which comparative records of geographical distribution were available in 2004 showed no change; only 2% declined, and 14% increased.

Trends in the marine environment were predominantly negative. Among 11 commercial fish stocks assessed annually, six were at full reproductive capacity (not in danger of collapse) in 2007. Among marine plankton, the formerly dominant cold water species *Calanus finmarchicus* had fallen to 48% of its 1958 abundance by 2009, while the warmer water species *C. helgolandicus* had increased three-fold (332%). By 2009 seabird abundance had fallen to 72% of the survey base year in 1986 and breeding productivity had declined to 62%. Box 1.3 develops the evidence base on waterbirds in Scotland.

Box 1.3 Waterbirds around the world: Scotland's marine and freshwater birds

At a scale of 1:25,000, Scotland has a coastal length of 16,518km, with 2,043 mapped rocks and islands. Inshore waters, within 12 nautical miles of the coast, approach 89,000km^2 – somewhat larger than the land area. Scottish offshore waters extend out to 200 nautical miles. Some 70% of the coast is hard coast (rocks and cliffs), 29% soft coast (unconsolidated gravels, sand and silts) and less than 1% artificial structures (harbours and sea walls). The length of cliff in Scotland approaches 2,500km (Mackey and Mudge, 2010).

Open water covers about two per cent of Scotland's land area. On 1:50,000 scale maps, the river length is around 100,000 km and standing water bodies (lochs) number 27,000. The interplay of weather, altitude, geology, soil type, landform and land use has resulted in a diversity of fresh waters and associated assemblages of habitats and species. Of international importance are deep, unpolluted lochs formed as a result of glacial activity and extensive blanket bog and pool ecosystems, which are globally rare, reflecting distinctive climatic, topographic and hydrological conditions (Mackey and Mudge, 2010).

Since the Ramsar Convention was ratified by the UK Government in 1976, 51 Ramsar sites have been designated in Scotland, with a total area of 3,132 km^2 (SNH web site, 2010).

Scotland's coasts and inland waters hold several internationally important concentrations of waterbirds (Scotland's biodiversity indicators, published on the Scottish Natural Heritage web site www.snh.gov.uk). Trends of 38 species of waders and wildfowl in Scotland have been monitored since 1975. Waders, such as oystercatcher (*Haematopus ostralegus*) and lapwing (*Vanellus vanellus*) are commonly associated with wetland and coastal environments. Many, such as bar-tailed godwit (*Limosa lapponica*) are long distance migrants, breeding in the high Arctic and wintering on Scottish coasts. Wildfowl (geese, ducks, grebes and swans) such as wigeon (*Anas penelope*) and greylag goose (*Anser anser*) occur on inland waters and estuaries.

1.6 Conclusions

It is clear that global and European trends in biodiversity and more widely across the environment are both relevant and recognisable to the situation here in Scotland. While we can point to wildlife trends that put Scotland in a relatively favourable light, equally noteworthy are similarities between assessments at different bio-geographical scales across Europe, with the marine environment a particular concern.

The challenges of conserving biodiversity, and of maintaining the ecosystem services upon which life and livelihoods in Scotland depend, are appreciable but certainly no worse than elsewhere. Looking ahead, we will require careful, and potentially costly, management measures to be in place if we are to maintain the image of Scotland as a relatively wild, clean environment. Nevertheless, Scotland's expansive uplands and mountains, coasts and islands, fresh waters and surrounding seas do evoke an invigorating sense of naturalness. Most striking, in terms of improvement to the overall ecosystem perhaps, is the formerly polluted and degraded urban and post-industrial environments have been in large measure restored and transformed in recent decades – Atlantic salmon (*Salmo salar*) and otter have largely re-colonised their former range. Targeted action to arrest declines among the most vulnerable plants and animals more widely is showing signs of success.

Scotland's natural environment is highly valued: indisputably a key asset for us all. We are progressing through an era of rapid change, with formidable challenges ahead. However, we also have a better understanding of the nature of change and underlying mechanisms than at any other time in our history. Looking to 2020 and beyond, the accounts in this book will undoubtedly help to extend knowledge and inform action. The state of the economy may constrain action, but the revolutionary changes of a low carbon future are already beginning to transform Scotland. Accommodating all the requirements for life – housing, infrastructure, energy generation, food production, woodland restoration – without degrading the environment within which we live, and the ecosystem services upon which we depend, presents a range of challenges. To address them, Scotland can offer leadership, a history of effective conservation management, and a culture of innovation, science and determination.

Acknowledgements

We thank the thousands of volunteers who contribute so much of the international and national survey and monitoring schemes on reports on trends and indicators are based.

References

Boere, G.C., Galbraith, C.A. and Stroud, D.A. (eds.) (2006). *Waterbirds around the world: A global overview of the conservation, management and research of the world's waterbird flyways.* The Stationery Office, Edinburgh, U.K.

Defra (Department for Environment, Food and Rural Affairs) (2010). *UK Biodiversity Indicators in Your Pocket 2010: Measuring progress towards halting biodiversity loss.* Defra, London.

Defra (2011). *Wild Bird Populations in the UK: Statistical Release.* Defra, London. (www.defra.gov.uk/evidence/statistics/environment/wildlife)

EEA (European Environment Agency) (2005). *The European Environment: State and Outlook 2005.* EEA, Copenhagen.

EEA (2007). *Europe's environment – the fourth assessment.* EEA, Copenhagen.

EEA (2009). *Progress towards the European 2010 biodiversity target.* EEA, Copenhagen.

IUCN (2009). *IUCN Red List of Threatened Species.* http://www.iucnredlist.org, accessed 3 November 2009.

Kuijken, E. (2006). A short history of waterbird conservation. In *Waterbirds around the world*, ed. by G.C. Boere, C.A. Galbraith and D.A. Stroud. The Stationery Office, Edinburgh, UK. pp 52-59.

Lamoreux, J., Akçakya, H.R., Bennum, L. *et al.* (2003) Value of the IUCN Red List. *Trends in Ecology and Evolution*, **18**, 214-215.

Mackey, E.C. and Mudge, G.P. (2010). *Scotland's Wildlife: An assessment of biodiversity in 2010.* Scottish Natural Heritage, Inverness.

Millennium Ecosystem Assessment (2005). *Ecosystems and Human well-being: Wetlands and Water Synthesis.* World Resources Institute, Washington, DC.

Ramsar Convention (1971). *Convention on Wetlands of International Importance especially as Waterfowl Habitat.* Ramsar, Iran.

Ramsar Convention website. (2010). www.ramsar.org, accessed 3 November 2009.

Rodrigues, A.S.L, Pilgrim, J.D., Lamoreux, J.F., Hoffmann, M. and Brooks, T.M. (2006). The value of the IUCN Red List for conservation. *Trends in Ecology & Evolution*, **21**,71-76.

Scottish Government (2007). Scotland's Biodiversity Indicators. The Scottish Government, Edinburgh (and updated on the SNH web site www.snh.gov.uk).

Scottish Natural Heritage 2010. www.snh.gov.uk.

Stroud, D.A., Boere, G.C., Galbraith, C.A. and Thompson, D.B.A. (2006). Waterbird conservation in a new millennium – where from and where to? In *Waterbirds around the world*, ed. by G.C. Boere, C.A. Galbraith and D.A. Stroud. The Stationery Office, Edinburgh, UK. pp 29-30.

UNEP (United Nations Environment Programme) (2005). *Millennium Ecosystem Assessment: Current Status and Trends.* Island Press, Washington, DC.

2 The Challenges of Developing Biodiversity Indicators for Scotland

Simon Foster, Edward C. Mackey and Susan J. Marrs

Summary

1. Indicators provide a succinct overview of how different components of our biodiversity are changing. In Scotland, we have developed 22 biodiversity indicators, of which 17 measure the changing state and five measure peoples' engagement with biodiversity.
2. Since their inception Scotland's biodiversity indicators have been developed and improved. Here we describe the development of the indicator suite, using two case studies to illustrate ongoing improvements.
3. The indicator for terrestrial breeding birds, for example, has incorporated improvements in analytical techniques so that we can interpret the significance of changes. Species coverage has been improved through targeted surveys in woodland and the involvement of a greater number of volunteer recorders.
4. Scotland hosts internationally important numbers of seabirds. The seabird indicator describes their abundance, with the addition more recently of breeding productivity. As productivity is more responsive than abundance to environmental change, it provides a more sensitive way of assessing the fortunes of Scotland's seabirds and reasons for declines.
5. Indicators should be relevant at a range of spatial scales, particularly if we want to track progress against global targets such as halting the loss of biodiversity. Looking ahead, we aim to improve the speed and accessibility of indicator reporting, to capitalise on advances in new analytical techniques, and keep abreast of policy developments which may call for the formulation of new indicators.

Foster, S., Mackey, E.C. and Marrs, S.J. (2011). The Challenges of Developing Biodiversity Indicators for Scotland – *The Changing Nature of Scotland*, eds. S.J. Marrs, S. Foster, C. Hendrie, E.C. Mackey, D.B.A. Thompson. TSO Scotland, Edinburgh, pp 23-38.

2.1 Introduction

Indicators provide a succinct overview of how different components of our biodiversity are changing, and thereby help inform policy, advice and management. Singleton *et al.* (2000) describe indicators as 'an integrated value, derived from a reproducible assessment, which reflects the significance of change'. A good indicator allows for early intervention should problems arise, and helps track progress toward a predefined target. They also summarise complex information in a consistent way in order to track change through time and can be used to determine, for example, the effectiveness of a policy, the state of the economy or the state of our natural environment. Perhaps some of the more recognisable indicators are those that tell us how the economy is changing for example the Financial Times Stock Exchange (FTSE) 100. The FTSE 100 summarises complex economic information, including the price of shares, into a format which enables changes in the economy to be tracked. Similarly there are indicators which measure the health of people, such as the Scottish Government's National Indicator measuring the number of people dying as a result of coronary heart disease (Scottish Government, 2009). These indicators although quite different in subject have some commonality. They are easily recognised and meaningful, simplify complex underlying data into a format which can be used by policy makers, are easily understood by the public, and can, perhaps most importantly, be readily updated. The development of a single indicator to track biodiversity has been likened to the search for the holy grail, and at present best practice recommends a suite of relevant biodiversity indicators (*inter alia* Dale and Beyeler, 2001; Bispo *et al.*, 2009; Feld *et al.*, 2010).

Measuring change in our natural environment is important for a number of reasons, notably to determine: whether ecosystems and their services are being conserved; the effectiveness of land management policies and the benefits of reducing pollution; and whether development is sustainable. Since the early 1980s a range of indicators have been proposed and developed around key policies (Rowell, 1994). Schneider (1992) identified seven criteria which indicators should meet:

- Easy to measure;
- Inexpensive to measure;
- Provide early warning of ecosystem damage;
- They are more sensitive to ecological change (than other measures);
- Imply the state of the ecosystem;
- Useful to policy makers; and
- Provide to the public an index of the health of the environment.

In 2003 this was refined by Gregory *et al.* (2003) who stated that 'they [indicators] must be; quantitative, simplifying, user driven, policy relevant, scientifically credible, responsive to changes, easily understood, realistic to collect and susceptible to analysis'. In this paper we look at the development of biodiversity indicators in Scotland, selected to track progress with Scotland's Biodiversity Strategy and describe some of the improvements that have been made to two of the indicators since their inception in 2004.

2.1.1. Indicator development in Scotland

In 1996, a group of 14 environmental organisations ranging from central and local government, government agencies, research and non-government organisations met to define a set of environmental indicators for Scotland (Singleton *et al.*, 2000). The purpose was to establish a shared view of how key aspects of the natural and built environment could be quantified and tracked through time. The outcome was a candidate list of 138 '*potential*' indicators. These covered 16 public policy sectors and six environmental themes: climate change; species and habitats; air quality; soil-water interaction; development; and toxic substances. The indicators were embedded within a DPSIR audit framework (Driving forces, Pressure, State, Impact, Response), 81 were characterised as 'state', 33 as 'pressure' and 24 as 'response' indicators.

While this helped to inform, and was informed by, the subsequent publication of 147 sustainable development indicators for the UK, (DETR, 1999), the Scottish initiative did not secure the level of government endorsement necessary to take it forward (Dunion *et al.*, 2002). Some of the proposed indicators were aspirational, where the required data were poor or unavailable, and some opportunistic. Nevertheless, important parts of the candidate list have been developed. Since 2001, Key Scottish Environment Statistics have been published annually and made available on-line. The tenth edition, in 2010, reported 41 trends across 10 environmental themes: background; public attitudes; global atmosphere; air quality; water; marine; radioactivity; waste; land; and biodiversity (Scottish Government, 2010).

The value of indicators to measure the changing state of biodiversity is widely acknowledged (de Heer *et al.*, 2005). The Convention on Biological Diversity (CBD), adopted at the United Nations 'Earth Summit' in Rio de Janeiro, Brazil in June 1992, refers to monitoring key components of biodiversity (Article 7) and reporting on delivery (Article 26). Between 2001 and 2003, the Subsidiary Body on Scientific, Technical and Technological Advice to the CBD Conference of Parties (COP) undertook a global review of biodiversity indicators from which it established general principles for developing national-level indicators. It advocated four basic functions of indicators: simplification, quantification, standardisation and communication. Importantly, it also recommended pragmatism, a willingness to learn by experience and to make improvements through time. Based on its recommendations, the seventh COP established a framework of 17 indicators for assessing progress towards the 2010 biodiversity target. By use of best-fit data, the framework could guide indicator development at global, regional, national and local levels (COP 7 Decision VII/30).

The global framework for 2010 reporting fosters consistency along with flexibility to reflect biogeographical, policy and data differences at regional, national and sub-national scales. Scotland is represented within the UK biodiversity indicator suite for CBD reporting, and has a biodiversity strategy in its own right (Scottish Executive, 2004). Indicator development was undertaken at the national (UK) and country (Scotland) scales, with close correspondence between the Scotland and UK suites. The relationships between Scotland's biodiversity indicators and those at national, European and global scales are illustrated in Table 2.1. Some indicators (such as genetic diversity of farm breeds) work best at the UK scale. Conversely, some indicators for Scotland are additional to the UK suite, e.g. otter range (which shows the re-establishment of otter populations in areas where they had been absent for a number of years) marine plankton and estuarine fish, together with greenspace and aspects of public awareness and involvement.

Scotland's Biodiversity Strategy, '*It's In Your Hands*' (2004), sets out a 25-year vision and framework for action. The aim of the strategy was 'to conserve biodiversity for the health, enjoyment and well-being of the people of Scotland now and in the future' (Scottish Executive, 2004). The Strategy provided a foundation for Scotland's contribution to the UK's obligations under the CBD, Scotland's commitment to sustainable development, and the statutory duty on public bodies to conserve biodiversity under the Nature Conservation (Scotland) Act 2004.

In developing a strategy for the protection and enhancement of Scotland's biodiversity (Scottish Executive Environment Group, 2003), the Scottish Biodiversity Forum stated that it would need indicators to enable measurement of progress and proper reporting. Although the availability of biodiversity trend data was reasonably well known (Mackey *et al.*, 2001; Saunders, 2004), an appreciable amount of development was required to create the indicator suite. Candidate biodiversity indicators were put forward by the Scottish Biodiversity Forum Action Plan and Science Group. These were chosen on the basis that they would fulfil established criteria, that data were available or deliverable for reporting within the required timescale, and they reflected the wider state of the ecosystems of which they are part. Following a review and public consultation in May 2004, the Indicators

Table 2.1 How Scotland's indicators link in to national and global assessments. For clarity the table shows the main relationships, however several of the indicators at a Scotland level will feed into different broader scale indicators.

Scotland Biodiversity	UK Biodiversity	European Biodiversity	Global Biodiversity
BAP priority habitats	UK BAP priority species	Extent of selected biomes, ecosystems, habitats	Trends in extent of selected biomes, ecosystems, and habitats
Notified habitats in favourable condition	Protected areas	Coverage of protected areas	
BAP priority species	UK BAP priority species	Status of protected / threatened species	Change in status of threatened species
Notified species in favourable condition	Protected areas	Coverage of protected areas	
Terrestrial breeding birds Wintering waterbirds Breeding seabirds	Selected species - wild birds	Abundance & distribution of selected species	Trends in abundance and distribution of selected species
Terrestrial insects - butterflies	Selected species - butterflies		
Terrestrial insects - moths			
Vascular plant diversity	Plant diversity		
Woodland structure		Extent of selected biomes, ecosystems, habitats	Area of forest, agricultural and aquaculture ecosystems under sustainable management
	Sustainable woodland management	Sectors under sustainable management	
	Area of agri-environment land		

Table 2.1 continued

Scotland Biodiversity	UK Biodiversity	European Biodiversity	Global Biodiversity
	Habitat connectivity	Connectivity/fragmentation of ecosystems	Connectivity/fragmentation of ecosystems
Otters Freshwater macro-invertebrates	River quality	Water quality in aquatic ecosystems	Water quality of freshwater ecosystems
Estuarine fish Marine fish stocks	Sustainable fisheries Marine ecosystem integrity	European commercial fish stocks	Trends in abundance and distribution of selected species
Marine plankton		Marine trophic index	Marine trophic index
Non-native species	Impacts of invasive species	Number & costs of invasive alien species	Trends in invasive alien species
	Genetic diversity	Genetic diversity of livestock, fish & cultivated plants Genetic resource patent applications	Genetic diversity of livestock, fish & cultivated plants
	Ecological impacts of air pollution	Nitrogen deposition	Nitrogen deposition
	Spring index	Impact of climate change on biodiversity	Ecological footprint and related concepts

Working Group of the Scottish Biodiversity Forum proposed a suite of 22 biodiversity indicators for Scotland's Biodiversity Strategy. First published by the Scottish Government in November 2007 (Scottish Government, 2007), they are now maintained and updated by SNH. These are split into two groups – 17 state indicators (measuring the state of Scotland's biodiversity) and five engagement indicators (measuring Scotland's peoples' involvement with biodiversity; see Marrs and Foster, Chapter 11) (Table 2.1).

The indicators are updated as frequently as survey time frames permit. Following analysis and quality assurance they are published online. They are used routinely as evidence for policy development and in reporting. Three of Scotland's biodiversity indicators have been adapted for use within Scotland's National Performance Framework (terrestrial breeding birds, site condition, visits to the outdoors) and Rural Development Programme (farmland birds).

2.2 Developing biodiversity indicators

Once indicators have been agreed there comes the need to update, refine and adapt them in light of new knowledge, better data and improving analytical techniques. It has to be recognised that no indicator of biodiversity will be perfect, and the development phase is likely to be iterative. As surveys continue over time, data are added and we may see improvements in the sample sizes and areas covered, as well as improvements in the analytical techniques employed.

The 2010 Biodiversity Indicators Partnership (2010 BIP) brings together a host of international organisations working to support the regular delivery of the 2010 biodiversity target indicators at the global and national levels. In 2010 the Partnership developed a Biodiversity Indicator Development Framework. This work was achieved using the experiences that have been gained from a number of countries including Scotland. Figure 2.1 illustrates the framework used for the development of indicators.

2.2.1 Indicator development case studies

In order to demonstrate how Scotland's biodiversity indicators have been developed we focus here on two case studies – Terrestrial Breeding Birds, and Abundance of Breeding Seabirds. These indicators each have an overarching indicator that gives a headline summary of the state of the environment, and sub-indicators (by habitat or feeding preference) that give more detailed information on which policy may be based.

The two examples demonstrate how we started from an initial indicator as part of a research project, and then refined and adapted them in response to improvements in analytical techniques, data availability and the needs of users. This

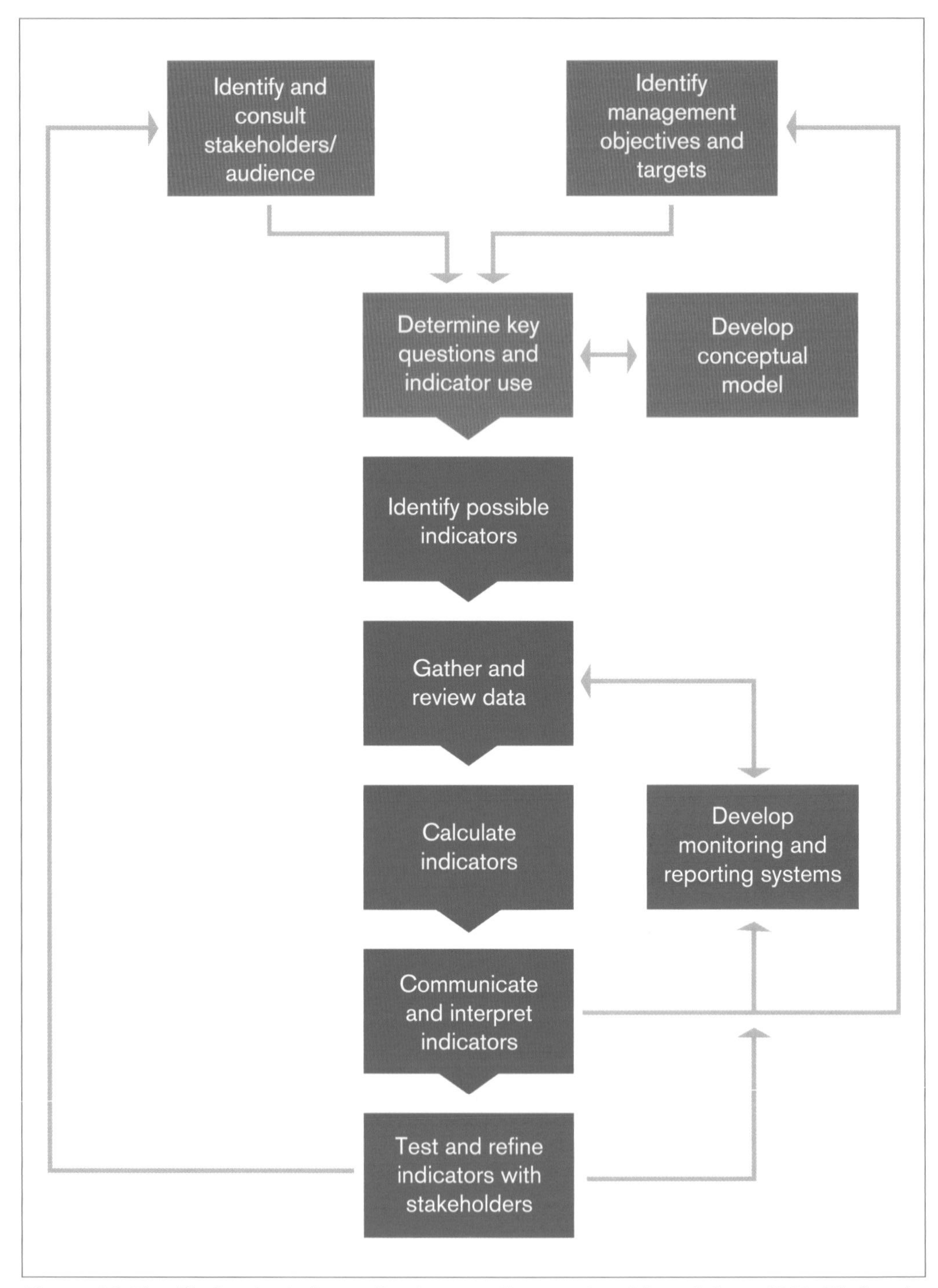

Figure 2.1 The Biodiversity Indicator Development Framework. Adapted from 2010 Biodiversity Indicators Partnership (2010). The colour coded boxes relate to the three stages for development namely: Purpose (red) – actions needed for selecting successful indicators. Production (blue) – essential to generate indicators. Permanence (green) – mechanisms for ensuring indicator continuity and sustainability.

paper does not cover the full indicator set, of which others have also been refined and updated including butterflies (see Brereton, Chapter 6), marine plankton, wintering waterbirds and Biodiversity Action Plan habitats and species.

2.2.2 *Terrestrial breeding birds*

The Terrestrial Breeding Bird Indicator (Figure 2.2) describes the changing state of around 60 species of breeding bird in Scotland (SNH, 2010). The majority of the data are from the volunteer-led British Trust for Ornithology (BTO) Breeding Bird Survey (BBS) which surveys around 300 sites in Scotland every year (Risely *et al.*, 2010). This indicator has seen the most development from the suite of 17, partly as a result of its prominence as one of the Scottish Government's National Performance Indicators.

The indicator is divided into four categories with an overarching headline indicator comprising all species, and three sub-indicators for farmland birds, woodland birds and upland birds. Species were grouped based on the habitats that they preferred using Jacob's Preference Index. This index is a measure of habitat use in relation to the frequency of that habitat among the sample surveyed (Jacobs, 1974). Data that can be used to produce a robust indicator for terrestrial

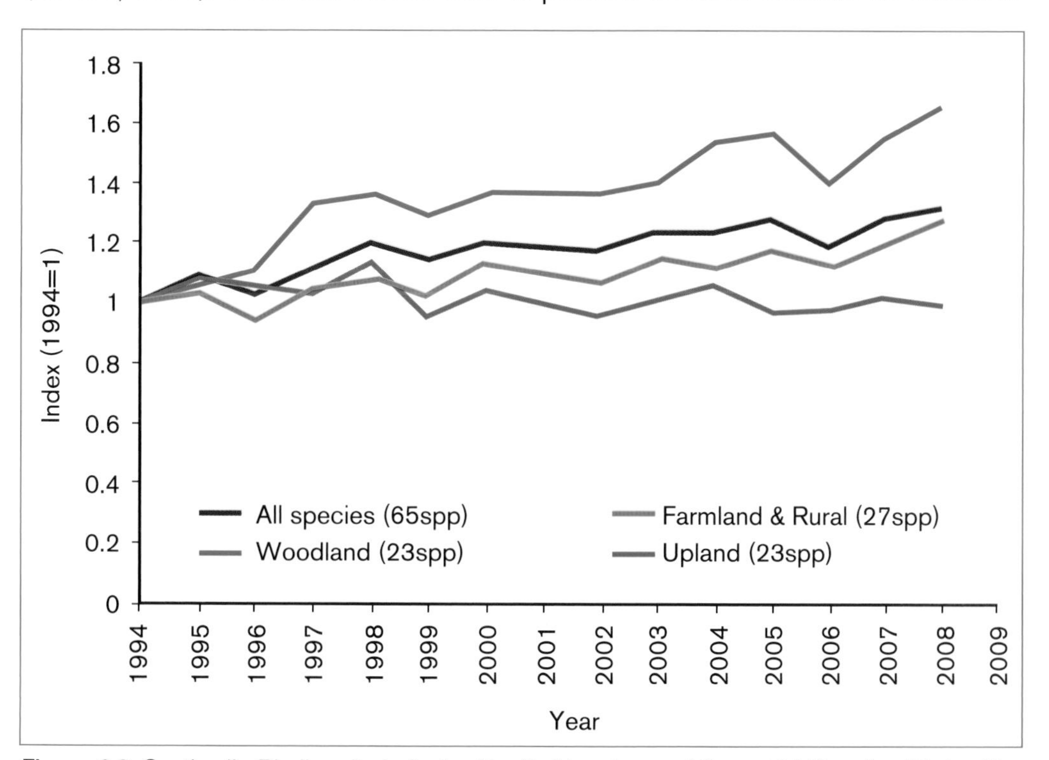

Figure 2.2 Scotland's Biodiversity Indicator No. 3: Abundance of Terrestrial Breeding Birds. The index tracks the abundance of 65 bird species in relation to a reference point in 1994.

breeding birds in Scotland only date back to 1994. Therefore, to account for historical declines that may have occurred, Noble *et al.* (2007) looked at the historical range changes as a proxy for declining populations. They showed that the declines in Scotland were apparent, although not as severe as elsewhere. This context of historical decline is important to bear in mind when the indicators are showing improvement (de Heer *et al.*, 2005). One of the groupings (farmland birds) has historically shown significant declines throughout much of their UK range before the start of the time series (Wilson, Chapter 26).

Improving the accuracy of this indicator has involved enhancing the survey coverage. In Scotland, as in most countries, volunteer led surveys are usually most consistently undertaken close to towns, cities and roads. This can lead to relatively poor estimates of some habitats, particularly uplands and woodlands. To address some of these issues SNH and Forestry Commission funded BTO to augment the BBS in Scotland, specifically targeting woodlands, so that a greater number of species could be included within the indicator. The results of this project showed that it was possible to increase the number of species and improve coverage of woodland areas in Scotland (Eglington and Noble, 2010).

In response to requests from users of the indicator, following an apparent decline in 2006 (see Figure 2.2), BTO undertook work to enable the significance of annual changes to be determined and smoothed the data to show the general trends. The work highlighted that for the duration of the indicator only two years showed significant declines and five significant increases, furthermore smoothing the data allowed the underlying trend (i.e. the trend with the annual fluctuations accounted for) to be shown (Noble and Thaxter, in press).

2.2.3 Abundance of breeding seabirds

Scotland hosts around 6.6 million seabirds, representing approximately 76% of the UK populations (Mitchell *et al.*, 2004). They are an important indicator of the state of the marine environment as their breeding performance often reflects conditions therein (Frederiksen *et al.*, 2007). Seabirds are one of the top predators within the marine environment and changes in lower trophic levels are likely to be manifested in seabird populations. They are also affected by anthropogenic pressures such as changes in fishing effort, fishing practices (e.g. discarding at sea) or pollution (Parsons *et al.*, 2008). In 2006 the first indicator was produced which tracked the abundance of seabirds. The modelling methods used to determine the trend of the composite indicator were at the time novel and more importantly produced a robust way of analysing, presenting and updating trends in seabird populations (Parsons *et al.*, 2006).

Plate 2.1 Black-legged kittiwakes. © Lorne Gill, SNH

Changes in seabird breeding productivity, unlike abundance, operate on a within-year timescale and therefore may provide a more useful indicator of environmental change (Parsons *et al.*, 2008). As such in 2008, an indicator for the breeding productivity was developed. Since 2009 it has been possible to produce updates more quickly so that the indicator from the previous year is now available by the start of the breeding season in the following year. Indicators are of course out of date as soon as they are published, therefore rapid updates mean that the results are more relevant, which is of particular importance in periods of change such as in the declines that have been observed in seabirds throughout Scotland (Figure 2.3).

Parsons *et al.* (2006) also identified a series of other 'alternative' indicators, such as one which tracks the trends in seabirds that feed mostly on sand eels (*Ammodytes spp.*). Future updates or requests to show this aspect of seabird ecology can be produced relatively rapidly.

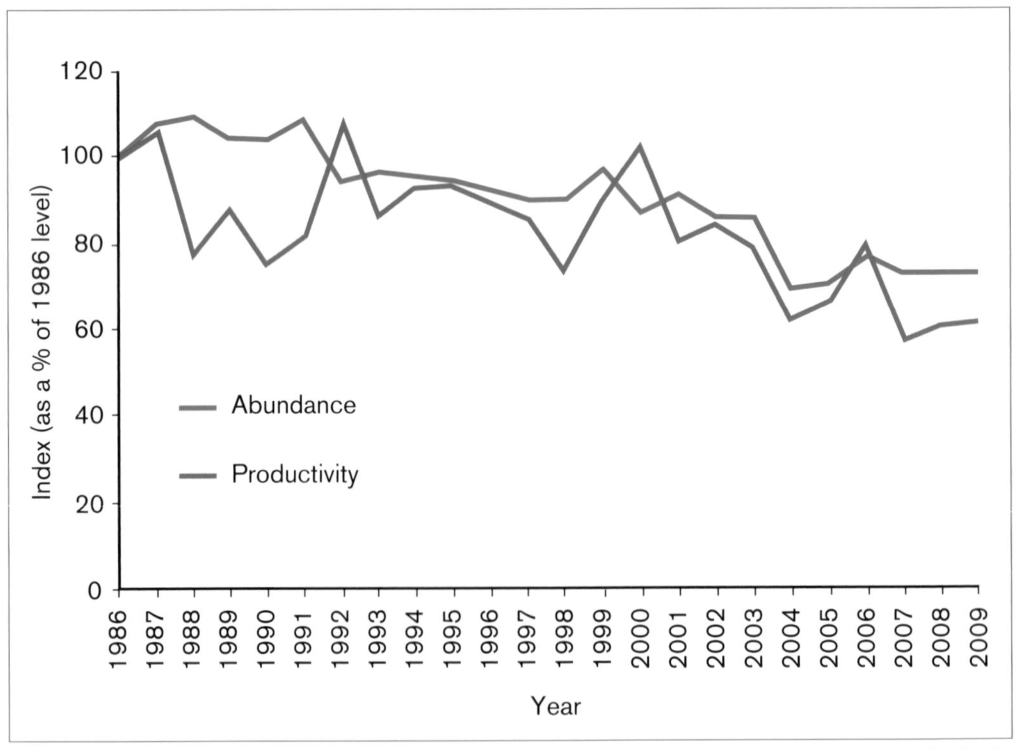

Figure 2.3 Scotland's Biodiversity Indicator No. 5: Abundance and Productivity of Breeding Seabirds in Scotland. The index tracks the abundance and productivity of 12 seabird species.

2.3 The future of indicators in Scotland

The 22 biodiversity indicators have been central to Scotland's assessment of the 2010 target to halt biodiversity loss (Mackey and Mudge, 2010). They are hosted on the SNH website and are among a relatively few national examples cited by the 2010 Biodiversity Indicators Partnership (2010 BIP), a global initiative to further develop and promote indicators for the consistent monitoring and assessment of biodiversity.

Continuing advances in available data and improvements in the techniques for the production of indicators mean that they can be developed at different spatial scales from regional to national, and international to global. Scholes *et al.* (2008) argue that there is a need for national to global scale biodiversity measurements in order to be able to assess whether targets, such as the CBD 'reduce the rate of loss of biodiversity by 2010', are being met. There is read-across between Scotland's biodiversity indicators to the global indicators however comparisons at different scales are not necessarily exact and in some instances there can be no proper match (Table 2.1).

In 2009 the CBD reviewed the extent to which progress had been made in meeting the global biodiversity target and to develop a new, post 2010 strategic plan and associated targets (UNEP-WCMC, 2009). This review highlighted achievements and perhaps more importantly identified areas that required further work, making six recommendations, summarised as follows.

- A small set (10-15) of broad headline indicators should be developed.
- The current framework of global indicators should be modified and simplified into four 'focal areas'.
- Additional measures on threats to biodiversity, status of diversity, ecosystem services and policy responses should be developed.
- National capacity for framework application, indicator development, data collection and information management should be further developed and properly resourced.
- Priority must be given to developing a communication strategy for the post-2010 targets and indicators in order to inform policy discussions and ensure effective communication of messages.
- A flexible and inclusive process/partnership for post-2010 indicator development should be maintained and adequately resourced.

Developing a suite of biodiversity indicators is an important step in an ongoing iterative process. Continuing improvements in spatial coverage and analytical techniques counterbalanced with limited resources means that a pragmatic approach needs to be adopted. Delivery of indicators should be streamlined and rigorous data management standards employed. At the time of writing SNH was in the process of being designated as a provider of Official Statistics – a standard developed by the Office of National Statistics in the UK. In the future, indicators will continue to be developed with maximum utility in mind, focussing on those that can be applied at local scales (e.g. regional) that also feed into the broad headline global assessments. We need to ensure we target the communication of our indicators, making the most of this valuable knowledge base, which should be at the forefront of policy discussions.

Acknowledgements

SNH maintains Scotland's Biodiversity Indicators on their website (http://www.snh.gov.uk/publications-data-and-research/trends) and we gratefully acknowledge the following organisations whose contribution is essential for their delivery and development: British Trust for Ornithology; Butterfly Conservation; Centre for Ecology and Hydrology; Forestry Commission Scotland; Joint Nature Conservation Committee; Marine Scotland – Science; Scottish Environment Protection Agency; Sir Alister Hardy Foundation for Ocean Science, and Vincent Wildlife Trust. Much of the data are generated by thousands of volunteers across Scotland without whom many of these indicators could not be produced and we thank them for their ongoing support and commitment.

References

Bispo, A., Cluzeau, D., Creamer, M. *et al.* (2009). Indicators for monitoring soil biodiversity. *Integrated Environmental Assessment and Management*, **5**, 717-719.

Dale, V.H. and Beyeler, S.C. (2001). Challenges in the development and use of ecological indicators. *Ecological Indicators*, **1**, 3-10.

Department for Environment, Transport and the Regions (DETR) (1999). *Quality of Life Counts. Indicators for a Strategy for Sustainable Development for the United Kingdom: a baseline assessment.* DETR, Rotherham.

de Heer, M., Kapos, V. and ten Brink, B.J.E. (2005). Biodiversity trends in Europe: development and testing of a species trend indicator for evaluating progress towards the 2010 target. *Philsophical Transactions of the Royal Society B*, **360**, 297-308.

Dunion, K., Holbrook, J. and Sargent, B. (2002). The role of indicators in reporting on the state of Scotland and its environment. In *The State of Scotland's*

Environment and Natural Heritage, ed. by M.B. Usher, E.C. Mackey and J.C. Curran. TSO, Edinburgh.

Eglington, S. and Noble, D.G. (2010). Final Report for 2009 on the Scottish Woodland Breeding Bird Surveys. *BTO Research Report* No. 549. BTO, Thetford.

Feld, C.K., Sousa, J.P., da Silva, P.M. and Dawson, T.P. (2010). Indicators for biodiversity and ecosystem services: towards an improved framework for ecosystems assessment. *Biodiversity Conservation*, **19**, 2895-2919.

Frederiksen, M., Mavor, R.A. and Wanless, S. (2007). Seabirds as environmental indicators: the advantages of combining datasets. *Marine Ecology Progress Series*, **352**, 205-211.

Gregory, R.D., Noble, D., Field, R. *et al.* (2003). Using birds as indicators of biodiversity. *Ornis Hungarica*, **12-13**, 11-24.

Jacobs, J. (1974). Quantitative measurement of food selection. *Oecologia*, **14**, 413-417.

Mackey, E.C., Shaw, P., Holbrook, J. *et al.* (2001). *Natural Heritage Trends: Scotland 2001.* Scottish Natural Heritage, Battleby.

Mackey, E.C. and Mudge, G. (2010). *Scotland's Wildlife: An assessment of biodiversity in 2010.* Scottish Natural Heritage, Inverness.

Mitchell, I.P., Newton, S.F., Ratcliffe, N. and Dunn, T.E. (2004). *Seabird Populations of Britain and Ireland.* T. and A. D. Poyser, London.

Noble, D.G., Joys, A.C. and Eaton, M.A. (2007). Natural Heritage Trends: A Scottish Biodiversity Indicator for Terrestrial Breeding Birds. *Scottish Natural Heritage Commissioned Report* No. 245.

Noble, D.G. and Thaxter, C.B. (in press). Assessing the significance of changes in the Scottish terrestrial breeding bird indicator. *Scottish Natural Heritage Commissioned Research Report.*

Parsons, M., Mitchell, I.P., Butler, A. *et al.* (2006). Natural Heritage Trends: Abundance of Breeding Seabirds in Scotland. *Scottish Natural Heritage Commissioned Report* No. 222.

Parsons, M., Mitchell, I., Butler, A. *et al.* (2008). Seabirds as indicators of the marine environment. *ICES Journal of Marine Science*, **65**, 1520-1526.

Risely, K., Baillie, S.R., Eaton, M.A. *et al.* (2010). The Breeding Bird Survey 2009. *BTO Research Report* 559. British Trust for Ornithology, Thetford.

Rowell, T.A. (1994). *Ecological indicators for nature conservation monitoring.* JNCC, Peterborough.

Saunders, G. (2004). *Natural Heritage Trends: The Seas Around Scotland 2004.* Scottish Natural Heritage, Battleby.

Schneider, E.D. (1992). Monitoring for ecological integrity: the state of the art. In *Ecological Indicators*, ed. by D.H. McKenzie, D.E. Hyatt and V.J. McDonald. London, Elsevier Applied Science. pp 1403-1420.

Scholes, R.J., Mace, G.M., Turner, W. *et al.* (2008). Toward a global biodiversity observing system. *Science*, **321**, 1044-1045.

Scottish Executive Environment Group (2003). *Towards a strategy for Scotland's biodiversity: Biodiversity Matters!* Strategy Proposals. Paper 2003/5. Scottish Executive, Edinburgh.

Scottish Executive (2004). *Scotland's Biodiversity – It's in your hands – A strategy for the conservation and enhancement of biodiversity in Scotland.* Scottish Executive, Edinburgh.

Scottish Government (2007). *Scotland's Biodiversity Indicators.* The Scottish Government, Edinburgh.

Scottish Government (2010). *Scottish Environment Statistics Fact Card 2010.* Scottish Government, Edinburgh.

SNH (2005). *The Natural Heritage of Scotland: an overview.* SNH, Battleby.

SNH (2010). Abundance of terrestrial breeding birds. Scottish Natural Heritage, Biodiversity Indicator S003.

Singleton, P., Holbrook, J., Sargent, B. and Mackey, E.C. (2000). Potential Environmental Indicators for Scotland. *Scottish Natural Heritage Review* No 136.

UNEP-WCMC (2009). *International Expert Workshop on the 2010 Biodiversity Indicators and Post-2010 Indicator Development.* UNEP-WCMC, Cambridge, UK.

Wilson, J., Mackey, E., Mathieson, S. *et al.* (2003). *Towards a strategy for Scotland's biodiversity: Developing Candidate Indicators of the State of Scotland's Biodiversity.* Scottish Executive Environment Group, Paper 2003/6.

3 Valuing our Environment: The Economic Impact of Scotland's Natural Environment

Ralph Blaney and Claudia Rowse

Summary

1. The natural environment is one of Scotland's greatest assets, making a major contribution to economic growth and quality of life. Research commissioned by a partnership led by Scottish Natural Heritage (SNH) calculated the economic impact of Scotland's natural environment.
2. One fifth of all industry sectors depend significantly on Scotland's environment.
3. Activities making sustainable use of the natural environment are valued at an estimated £17.2 billion a year (11% of Scotland's economic output), supporting 242,000 jobs (14% of all full-time jobs in Scotland).
4. Scotland's natural environment is used for distinctive and special branding, contributes towards the health of the workforce, and attracts people to live and work here.

3.1 Introduction

Our natural environment provides numerous benefits that underpin Scotland's economy and our quality of life. It is increasingly recognised that healthy ecological systems (i.e. those that function well) deliver numerous benefits. However, the return on investment in managing and conserving nature needs to be demonstrated. Therefore, as a first step in this process SNH decided to estimate the importance of Scotland's natural environment to the economy. The study (Risk and Policy Analysts (RPA) and Cambridge Econometrics, 2008) surveyed business's perceptions of Scotland's natural environment; modelled the value of economic activity and employment generated by sustainable use of Scotland's natural

Blaney, R. and Rowse, C. (2011). Valuing our Environment: The Economic Impact of Scotland's Natural Environment – *The Changing Nature of Scotland*, eds. S.J. Marrs, S. Foster, C. Hendrie, E.C. Mackey, D.B.A. Thompson. TSO Scotland, Edinburgh, pp 39-44.

environment; and undertook an analysis of the wider benefits the natural environment provides to the economy.

3.2 Definitions

This study used the following working definition of the natural environment: *'the natural materials, processes, habitats and species, and topography that exist in Scotland'* (which includes coastal waters), and for sustainable use: *'the economic use of the natural materials and/or processes in a manner that does not have negative impacts on the quality of the environment'.*

3.3 Methodology

To gauge business perceptions an online survey was conducted of over 100 Scottish businesses between December 2007 and January 2008. For the main part of the research; estimating the impact of the natural environment on the Scottish economy; an input-output framework was used, which is a standard methodological approach widely used in economic analysis. Input-output tables are a representation of the sectoral structure of an economy at a given point in time and describe the flows of money between industries in the purchase of inputs. As there is no formal environment sector, the first task was to determine activities relying on sustainable use of the natural environment. There are 128 industry groups identified in the Standard Industrial Classification, and for each an assessment was made of how reliant it is on the natural environment and how sustainable this usage of the natural environment is. By incorporating these grouped environment activities into the input-output structure, the environment can be considered as another economic sector. This information is then used to estimate the economy-wide effect of setting the environment's demands to zero, effectively removing it from the economy. The wider analysis involved a literature review to determine the other benefits that the natural environment brings to the economy which the input-output analysis may not fully capture.

3.4 Results

3.4.1 Business survey

Analysis of survey responses indicated that two-thirds of businesses surveyed believe that Scotland's natural environment benefits their company. In addition, of the 30 factors of potential importance in determining regional locations of businesses in Scotland, quality of landscape, low levels of pollution and proximity to natural areas were all identified in the top ten factors. The only factors more important than the environment were cost/availability of premises, communications infrastructure, and proximity to customers. For businesses in the Highlands, the environmental factors were seen as even more important, with many saying that if their local environment deteriorated they would look to move elsewhere, even outwith Scotland.

Plate 3.1 Beinn Eighe National Nature Reserve. Scotland's stunning landscapes and wildlife attract tourists from near and far, and are consistently given as the top reasons for visiting Scotland.
© Lorne Gill/SNH

3.4.2 Economic modelling

The modelling process was successful and the initial impact of the environment sector, which can be thought of as the 'direct' effect, was estimated to be in the region of £4 billion a year. However, this is just the most basic, minimal impact estimate, which does not measure the full effect of environmental sector activity on the economy. Removing environment-related economic activity in Scotland would indirectly have knock-on effects across many industries through the reduction in demand for various inputs. These industry knock-on effects are known as 'indirect effects'. Moreover, it is likely that it would impact the demand for labour, which would then reduce household expenditure on goods and services. This effect is called an 'induced' effect. Multipliers can capture all of the combined direct, indirect and induced effects. When these effects are included, the economic activity dependant upon sustainable use of our natural environment was estimated at £17.2 billion a year, equivalent to 11% of total economic output. It was also estimated that this maintains almost a quarter of a million jobs, or one in seven of all full-time jobs.

3.4.3 Analysis of wider benefits

The study of wider benefits identified a number of factors that may not have been fully captured in the economic modelling. This included the value of Scotland's natural environment for branding. Scotland is closely associated with certain landscapes and wildlife. The image of Scotland is used to create brand identities, particularly by food and drink manufacturers to help differentiate their products (that has set them apart from their competition) and can provide a competitive edge within Scotland, throughout the UK, and when marketing products abroad. However, brands have to be authentic to continue working, so the reality must reflect the image. Visitors to Scotland leave with a very positive perception in relation to the scenery, wildlife, wilderness, beaches, and unspoilt environment (VisitScotland, 2002). Thus, the authenticity of the branding seems secure. The study also identified the health benefits that the natural environment of Scotland provides to be of value to the economy. The natural environment offers health

Plate 3.2 Fresh Mackerel. Scotland's natural environment provides many wild products including fish. Mackerel is estimated to be worth about £64.63 million to Scottish Fishermen.
© Laurie Campbell/SNH

benefits from pollution reduction, by encouraging exercise, and impacts positively on mental health. The Forestry Commission previously estimated the health benefits of Scottish woodlands to be worth £19 million a year (Forest Research, 2006). Another benefit not completely captured by the economic impact analysis is that provided by ecosystem services. These include flood mitigation and absorbing carbon emissions. In a previous study the Scottish Environment Protection Agency (SEPA) estimated some, but not all, of Scotland's ecosystem services to be equivalent to £21 billion per year in current prices (Williams *et al.*, 2003). Note that because of conceptual differences these values can not simply be added to the impact figure.

3.5 Conclusions

The results of this study show that the natural environment underpins the Scottish economy. Two-thirds of businesses surveyed believe that Scotland's natural environment benefits their company. Economic activity dependant upon sustainable use of our natural environment is estimated to be worth £17.2 billion a year, supporting a quarter of a million Scottish jobs. The study found that there are opportunities for further growth in many environment-related areas, such as wildlife tourism, forestry, and locally produced and marketed food. Efforts to mitigate climate change may offer potential for growth in employment based on sustainable use of the environment, such as wood biomass for fuel. Given Scottish Government climate policy commitments, this environmental employment potential is likely to be realised. Obviously, growth in each of the sectors must take place in a sustainable, environmentally sensitive way to ensure that the development of some sectors does not compromise activity in other sectors. Encouraging sustainability will develop stronger links to the environment in those industry sectors where these are weak at present. Therefore, the importance of the natural environment for Scotland's economy is likely to increase over coming decades. Of course, the environment has other values apart from the impact on the economy, such as cultural and spiritual values, and these should not be neglected when considering the total value that Scotland's natural environment has.

Acknowledgements

This work was commissioned by a research partnership led by SNH rural development team, consisting of Scottish Government, Forestry Commission, Scottish Enterprise, Cairngorms National Park Authority, SEPA and Scottish Environment Link. The economic impact analysis was undertaken by Cambridge Econometrics, and the other analysis by RPA.

References

Forest Research (2006). *A Valuation of the Economic and Social Contribution of Forestry for People in Scotland* - An Interim Report for Forestry Commission Scotland. Forestry Commission.

RPA and Cambridge Econometrics (2008). The Economic Impact of Scotland's Natural Environment. *Scottish Natural Heritage Commissioned Report* No. 304.

VisitScotland (2002). Visitor Attitudes Survey, http://www.greentourism.org.uk/default.aspx.LocID-008new097.Lang-EN.htm, accessed on 23 January 2009.

Williams, E., Firn, J.R., Kind, V., Roberts, M. and McGlashan, D. (2003). The value of Scotland's ecosystem services and natural capital. *European Environment*, **13 (2)**, 67-78.

4 Scotland's Soil Resource

Allan Lilly, Rupert Hough, Gordon Hudson and the
NSIS Sampling Team[1]

Summary

1. This paper describes the changing nature of Scotland's soils, the threats that they face and some of the work being undertaken to monitor the changes.
2. Scotland has a rich variety of soils with around 40 soil types and 800 individual soil series. Soils face a number of threats, eight major ones have been identified which range from soil sealing to climate change. To address these issues and safeguard our soils a framework has been developed by Scottish Government.
3. Very little is known about the trends in Scotland's soils and there is currently (in 2010) no single comprehensive soil monitoring system. The National Soil Inventory of Scotland (NSIS) may begin to reveal some of the changes in soils. NSIS has sampled 183 sites in Scotland.

4.1 Introduction

Although only approximately 78,000km^2 in extent, Scotland has a rich variety of soils which is due to the nature and distribution of the underlying bedrock, the humid maritime climate, a legacy of the most recent glaciation, and the wide range of above and below ground biota (including the influence of man). The Soil Survey of Scotland recognises around 40 individual soil types or major soil subgroups (Soil Survey of Scotland Staff, 1984; Lilly *et al.*, 2010) each of which is subdivided on the basis of parent material (often rock type or types) and inherent drainage characteristics, giving around 800 individual soil series (soils developed on similar parent materials and with a similar sequence of layers or horizons). Many of these soil series exist in two forms: cultivated and uncultivated, reflecting the influence of man on shaping soil development in Scotland.

Lilly, A., Hough, R., Hudson, G. and the NSIS Sampling Team (2011). Scotland's Soil Resource – *The Changing Nature of Scotland*, eds. S.J. Marrs, S. Foster, C. Hendrie, E.C. Mackey, D.B.A. Thompson. TSO Scotland, Edinburgh, pp 45-52.

4.2 Reasons for the diversity in Scottish soils

Why a particular soil is found at a specific site is due to a complex interaction between five main soil forming factors (Jenny, 1941); these are climate, parent material, topography, organisms and time. The combination of strong east/west gradation in rainfall and the temperature regime driven by the altitudinal range from sea level to over 1,300m affects the nature and distribution of Scottish soils with wet *gley soils* predominant in the west and drier *brown soils* and *podzolic soils* a feature of the east. *Montane soils* at high altitude are subject to freeze/thaw cycles and stone sorting reminiscent of an arctic tundra landscape (Figure 4.1). *Organic soils* are extensive in the uplands where the climate is cool and relatively wet, conditions that favour accumulation of soil organic matter.

The predominance of acid rocks in Scotland means that the soils are relatively poor in base cations such as calcium, magnesium and potassium. Many Scottish soils that are freely draining are also strongly leached due to the cool, wet climate. These leached soils form distinctive grey layers from which they derive their name, *podzol* – *zol* comes from the Russian for ash, (IUSS Working Group WRB, 2006) and have an accumulation of iron and aluminium in the subsoil. The Soil Survey of Scotland (Soil Survey of Scotland Staff, 1984) identified nine different podzolic soils covering approximately 25% of Scotland. This type of soil is typical of those under remnant Scots pine (*Pinus sylvestris*) woodland and dry heaths although many podzolic soils are now cultivated, particularly in the lowlands of north east Scotland and this grey layer (and the surface humus layer) has been lost.

The 13 types of *gley soils* mapped in Scotland (including *strongly gleyed brown earths*, *mineral gleys* and *peaty gleys*) occupy around 30% of Scotland. They are found predominantly in the north and west in high rainfall areas and through the Midland Valley where the last Ice Age (which ended in Scotland about 10,000 years ago) left a legacy of consolidated glacial drift. Rainfall percolates through this drift slowly giving rise to a perched water table for much of the year. The resulting anaerobic conditions lead to the development of gley features such as iron rich nodules and dull soil colours. In the uplands, the anaerobic conditions can also lead to the development of organic surface layers.

Glaciation also removed much of the pre-existing weathered mantle from Scotland exposing the bedrock in many areas. But, as well as eroding, the glaciers deposited a wide range of substrates as they flowed across the country and as they melted. The resulting mixture of different types of glacial and post-glacial substrate left a complex pattern of materials in which the soils of Scotland began to form. If we add the additional soil forming factors of climate, biota, relief and nutrient status on to this post-glacial complexity, it is easy to see why Scotland has a wide diversity

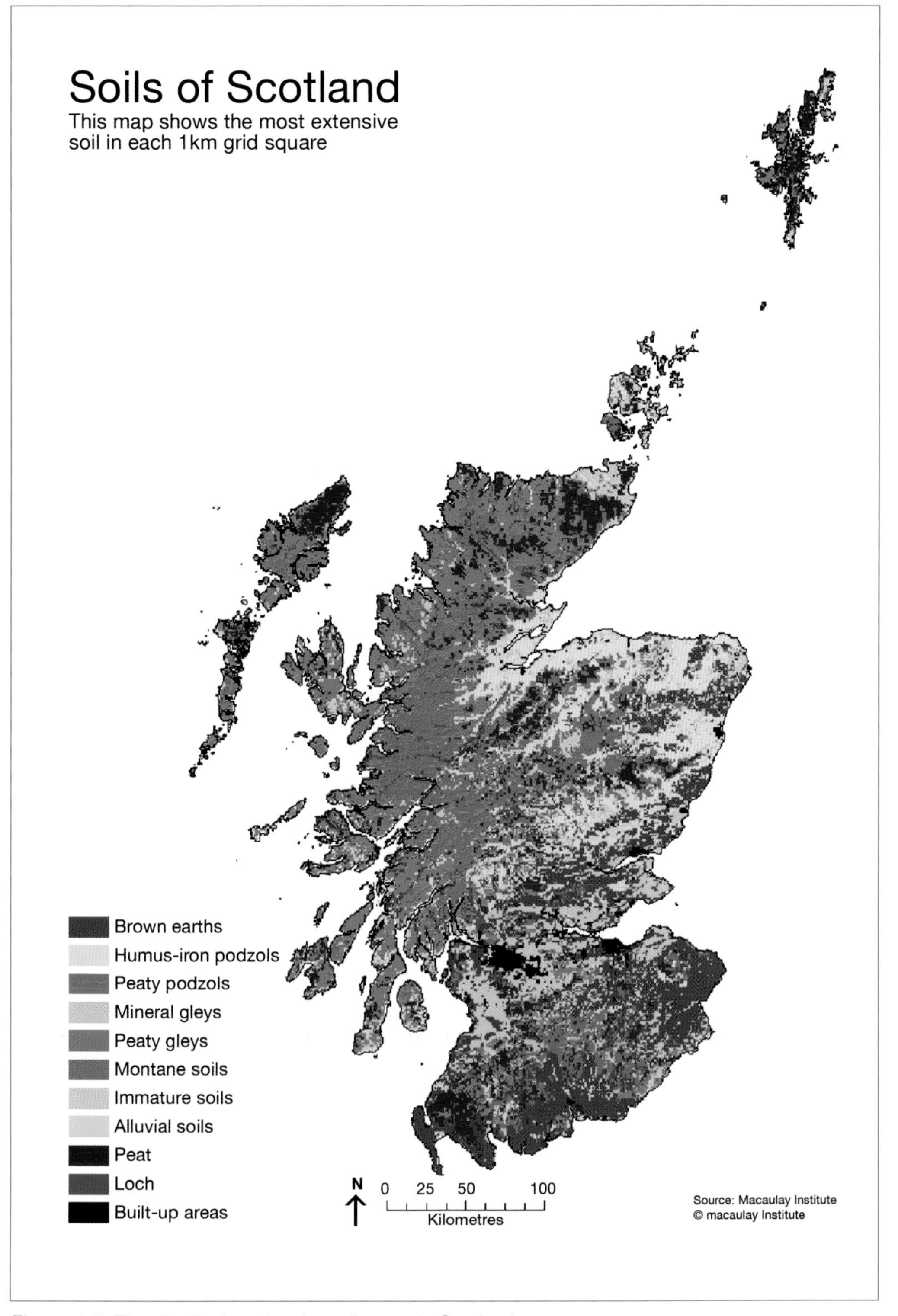

Figure 4.1 The distribution of major soil types in Scotland.

of soil types, often in close proximity. For example *peaty gleys*, *peaty podzols* and *peat* are found in a recurring pattern in moundy morainic landscapes.

One of the most striking features of Scottish soils is that they are rich in organic carbon. About 32% of Scotland has soils with an organic surface layer up to 50cm thick and often comprising around 50% organic carbon. A further 22% of Scotland has peat soils where the organic surface layer is more than 50cm thick and with around 50% carbon. This makes Scotland a significant store of carbon in UK, and possibly in European, terms. Various studies have attempted to calculate the amount of carbon stored in Scottish soils and the most recent estimate of carbon stock in the upper 1m of all the soils in Scotland, based on the Scottish Soils Knowledge and Information Base (SSKIB), is around 2,700 mega tonnes of carbon (Lilly *et al.*, 2004).

4.3 Threats to Scottish soils

Soils and, in particular, the ecosystem goods and services they provide, are under pressure from economic, social and biophysical drivers. The Scottish Government have recognised this and have developed a framework to safeguard soils (Scottish Government, 2009). They identified eight threats to soil quality from soil sealing to climate change. Soil erosion, loss of organic matter and biodiversity, compaction, contamination and atmospheric deposition were also identified as potentially detrimental to Scotland's soil resource. Towers *et al.* (2006) concluded that climate change and loss of soil organic matter were the two most substantial threats to the health and functioning of Scottish soils. This reflects the ubiquitous effects of climate change on all of Scotland's soils and the key role that soil organic matter plays in regulating many soil processes. A key aspect of soil protection is being able to identify detrimental changes in the soil resource at an early stage before significant harm is done. Black *et al.* (2008) identified two 'canary' indicators, soil organic carbon and pH, that would be key soil properties in any soil monitoring system as they influence many soil processes. Should detrimental changes be observed in these properties, it can be assumed that there would be consequences for soil health in general. As the two main threats identified by Towers *et al.* (2006) will impact on all Scottish soils, some form of national scale monitoring is required and is indeed one of the actions identified in the Scottish Soil Framework (Scottish Government, 2009).

4.4 Soil monitoring

Although some soil monitoring takes place via the Environmental Change Network, (NERC, 2001), the Countryside Survey (Firbank *et al.*, 2003; Emmett *et al.*, 2008) and Trends In Pollution of Scottish Soils (TIPSS, 2010) there is currently no single and comprehensive soil monitoring system specifically for Scottish soils that encompasses all the main soil/land use combinations found in Scotland. However, it is possible to use the National Soil Inventory of Scotland to at least examine potential changes in the two canary indicators proposed by Black *et al.* (2008).

4.5 National Soil Inventory of Scotland (NSIS)

Between 1978 and 1988, soil profiles were described and sampled at 721 sites throughout Scotland and a wide range of soil properties, including soil pH and soil organic carbon were determined. These sites were distributed on a grid pattern and were 10km apart. From 2007 until 2009, a subset of sites were revisited and new samples taken from similar soils to allow the determination of the magnitude and direction of change. This subset comprised 183 sites where a soil profile could be excavated and on the same grid pattern but at 20km intervals (Figure 4.2).

These sampling frameworks encompass most of the main soil/land use combinations found in Scotland (for example *brown earths* under arable production or *peaty podzols* under dry heathland) but do not cover some of the more iconic Scottish landscapes and soils such as the *machair* or *montane soils*; these have been sampled separately. Although the NSIS is not a soil monitoring scheme, one of its key objectives was to examine and test methods most suitable for soil monitoring in Scotland. For example, it has been used to compare the determination of soil carbon concentration from a composite sample taken by auger to a depth of 15cm against the more traditional soil survey approach of sampling the soil layers (or horizons). Figure 4.3 shows the results from the NSIS sampling. If there was no

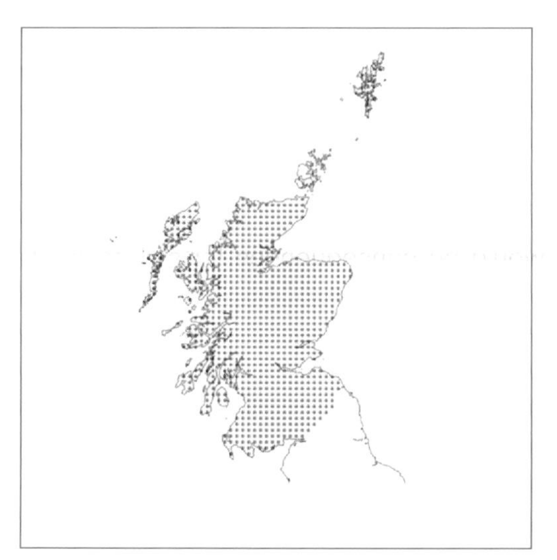

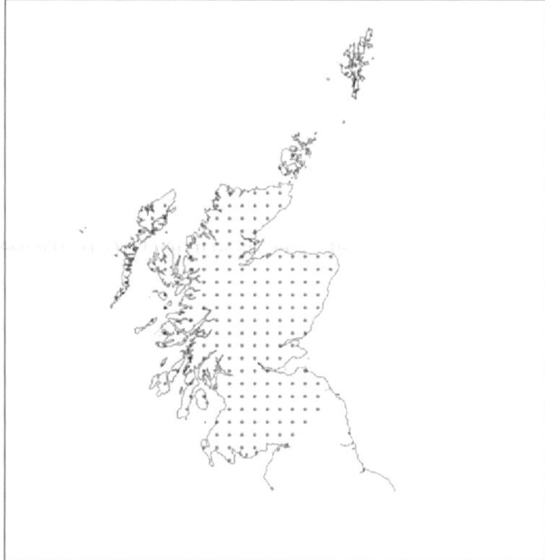

Figure 4.2 Original (1978-1988 sampling campaign) 10km grid (left) and the new (2007–2009) 20 km grid (right).

difference between these sampling methods, the measured carbon content would lie along the 1:1 line shown. This holds true for the cultivated soils where ploughing provides a reasonably well mixed layer to around 30cm in most soils. There is less agreement in the results where samples are taken from organic soils. This probably indicates that there is some spatial variability in the soils at each sample location. The main differences in the results, however, lie with the organo-mineral soils which have variable thicknesses of organic surface layers overlying mineral layers as well as inherent soil variability at the sampling sites. It is clear that composite sampling to a fixed depth in these soils leads (in many cases) to an under-estimate of the carbon concentration compared with sampling by pedological horizon. Other preliminary results from the first year of sampling suggest that changes in analytical techniques can have a major impact on change detection. When the results of the carbon concentrations from the original analyses were compared with the new soil samples, it was found that the carbon contents appeared to have declined but, by re-analysing the stored soil, the change was not statistically significant. This was attributed to the change in analytical methods but work is ongoing to test this hypothesis.

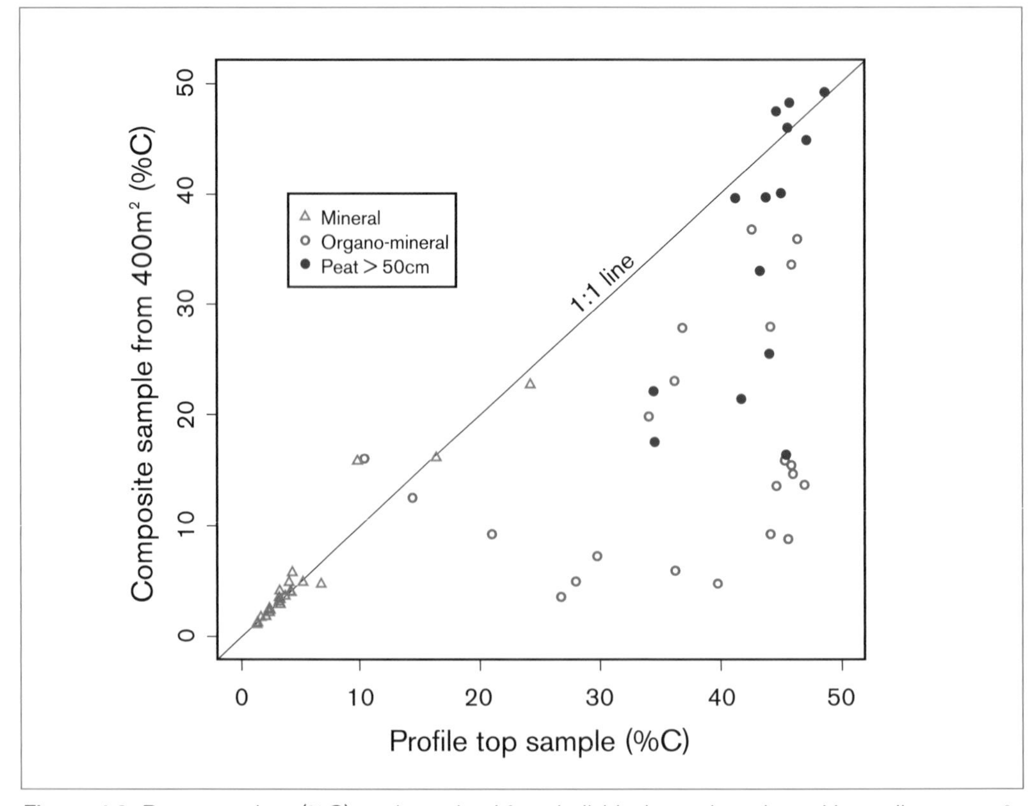

Figure 4.3 Percent carbon (%C) as determined from individual samples taken with a soil auger at 0-15cm depth over a $400m^2$ area and from profile topsoil samples.

4.6 Conclusions

Scottish soils exhibit a high degree of spatial variability and diversity, and they are under pressure from a range of climatic, socio-economic and biophysical factors. This presents a unique challenge to develop methods of detecting change that are applicable and appropriate to Scottish conditions. In 2010, work is on-going to identify suitable indicators of soil health, to identify the most appropriate methods for sampling Scottish soils and to establish the magnitude and direction of change in some key indicators such as soil pH, soil organic carbon and concentration of base cations. This is not a trivial task and requires robust and critical analyses of the data, field and laboratory techniques. However, the outcome of these analyses will help inform any future soil monitoring network that may be put in place in order to protect Scotland's soil resource.

Acknowledgements

The financial support of the Scottish Government Rural and Environment Research and Analysis Directorate (RERAD) for this work is gratefully acknowledged.

[1] The NSIS sampling team comprises over 20 staff including research staff who devised and implemented the sampling procedures, field staff who assisted with soil sampling and laboratory staff who prepared and analysed the soil. Their contribution is also gratefully acknowledged.

References

Black, H.I.J., Bellamy, P.H., Creamer, R. *et al.* (2008). *Design and operation of a UK soil monitoring network*, Environment Agency, Bristol, UK.

Environmental Change Network. December 2001. *Soils*, Ver 1.1 http://www.ecn.ac.uk/protocols/Terrestrial/S.pdf, accessed on 15 June 2010.

Emmett, B.A., Frogbrook, Z.L., Chamberlain, P.M. *et al.* (2008). *CS Technical Report No. 3/07. Soils manual.* Centre for Ecology & Hydrology. Wallingford. UK.

Firbank, L.G., Barr, C.J., Bunce, R.G.H. *et al.* (2003). Assessing stock and change in land cover and biodiversity in GB: an introduction to Countryside Survey 2000. *Journal of Environmental Management*, **67**, 207-218.

Jenny, H. (1941). *Factors of Soil Formation, A System of Quantitative Pedology.* McGraw-Hill, New York.

IUSS Working Group WRB (2006). World reference base for soil resources 2006. 2nd edition. *World Soil Resources Reports* No. 103. FAO, Rome.

Lilly, A., Towers, W., Malcolm, A. and Paterson, E. (2004). *Report on a workshop on the development of a Scottish Soils Knowledge and Information Base (SSKIB).*

Proceedings of a Workshop, Macaulay Institute, 22nd September 2004. http://www.macaulay.ac.uk/workshop/SSKIB/SSKIBWorkshop_Report.pdf

Lilly, A., Bell, J.S., Hudson, G., Nolan, A.J. and Towers, W. (2010). National Soil Inventory of Scotland 1 (NSIS_1): Site location, sampling and profile description protocols. (1978-1988). Technical Bulletin. Macaulay Land Use Reasearch Institute. Aberdeen.

NERC (2001). Soils. http://www.ecn.ac.uk/protocols/Terrestrial/S.pdf

Scottish Government (2009). *The Scottish Soil Framework*. The Scottish Government. Edinburgh.

Soil Survey of Scotland Staff (1984). *Organisation and methods of the 1: 250 000 soil survey of Scotland*. Macaulay Institute for Soil Research.

Towers, W.I.C., Grieve, I.C., Hudson, G. *et al.* (2006). *Scotland's Soil Resource Current State and Threats*. Environmental Research Report, Scottish Government, Edinburgh.

Trends in Pollution of Scottish Soils (TIPSS). 31 March 2010. http://www.macaulay .ac.uk/tipss/, accessed on 29 June, 2010.

5 Wild Deer Population Trends in Scotland

Fiona Newcombe

Summary

1. Since 2000, the emphasis on understanding wild deer populations has focused on local counts to inform management to reduce negative impacts. It is very difficult to use existing information to estimate national wild deer populations.
2. Statistical analyses show that populations of hill deer increased from 197,600 (+/-35,000) in 1967 to 350,900 (+/-33,300) in 2000. However, there are limitations to this approach which are described in the paper.
3. The ranges of all four wild deer species in Scotland increased between 1972 and 2002.
4. The importance of understanding regional and national populations and trends is recognised and research is being undertaken to ascertain if and how data can be analysed to understand this further.

5.1 Introduction

Wild deer are found throughout the hills, woodlands and urban areas of Scotland. They are iconic symbols of Scotland and play an important role in rural communities and the economy of the countryside. Deer are a key part of Scotland's wildlife and affect its landscape. They provide us with healthy food and recreational opportunities.

This paper sets out the information to date on the trends in population of the four wild deer species in Scotland: fallow deer (*Dama dama*); red deer (*Cervus elaphus*); roe deer (*Capreolus capreolus*) and sika deer (*Cervus nippon*). Red and roe deer are native to Scotland. Sika escaped from deer parks approximately 100 years ago where they were imported from Asia. Fallow deer were introduced approximately 1,000 years ago from the Mediterranean.

Newcombe, F. (2011). Wild Deer Population Trends in Scotland – *The Changing Nature of Scotland*, eds. S.J. Marrs, S. Foster, C. Hendrie, E.C. Mackey, D.B.A. Thompson. TSO Scotland, Edinburgh, pp 53-58.

At the time of writing, the Deer Commission for Scotland (DCS), the organisation responsible for promoting conservation and sustainable management of deer in Scotland, was in the process of being merged with Scottish Natural Heritage (SNH). This process was completed on 1 August 2010. The newly merged organisation, SNH, now has all the powers and functions previously available to the DCS.

The wild deer strategy *Scotland's Wild Deer: A National Approach* (Scottish Government, 2008) identifies the need for sound science and the best available evidence when managing deer populations. This paper focuses on population trends only and does not include trends in the impacts of wild deer, for example the number of road traffic accidents involving the animals.

5.2 Trends in populations of wild deer in Scotland

The total populations of the four species of wild deer present in Scotland are not fully understood and nor are their trends. The woodland-dwelling deer species (roe deer, sika deer, fallow deer and red deer) are extremely difficult to count and numbers are not known with any precision. However, the following data represent the best available estimates for red deer on the open hill.

Hill red deer were counted initially by the Red Deer Commission and then by its replacement, the DCS, between 1961 and 2000. Analyses of these data requires great caution, as only a sample of areas were counted each year and individual counts are subject to error due to the terrain covered and limitations to methodology. There is considerable geographic variation. Standardised figures derived from the multiple regression model which includes correction for area and year effects suggests an increase in hill deer from 197,600 (+/- 35,000) in 1967 to 350,900 (+/- 33,300) in 2000 (Clutton-Brock and Albon, 1989; Clutton-Brock *et al.*, 2004). However, the researchers noted that the confidence intervals are very large. Counts since 2000 (by deer practitioners, DCS and Forestry Commission Scotland) on open-hill habitat and woodlands have focused on specific areas identified as priorities for understanding and preventing negative deer impacts.

It has been estimated that red deer populations in the Scottish Highlands increased from 300,000 in 1989 to 450,000 by 2002 (Hunt, 2003). However, Clutton-Brock *et al.* (2004) noted that this estimate includes tripling the number of deer living in woodland where they cannot be counted accurately.

The DCS is currently undertaking some work to ascertain whether it is possible to use statistical techniques on existing data to develop a methodology to describe regional and national deer populations and trends in open-hill and woodland habitats in Scotland. Regional populations and their trends are informative in supporting practitioners to deliver sustainable management of populations. Initial work (MLURI and BIOSS, 2009) indicates the complexity of the task and highlights the need for caution when trying to use current data to calculate regional and national populations. The work is currently being developed further.

5.3 Distribution of wild deer species in Scotland

The distribution or range of a species is related to but different from its population size. This is because it may be possible to have a large number of individuals in a small area, or a small number of individuals widely dispersed. Nevertheless, information on distributions and their trends are needed to support the understanding and delivery of sustainable management of wild deer. For example, the local approach to the management of sika deer is likely to differ where they are expanding their range compared with where they are well established. The current understanding of the distribution of the four species of deer in Scotland is shown in Figure 5.1.

Plate 5.1 Red deer grazing on Rum. © Laurie Campbell/SNH

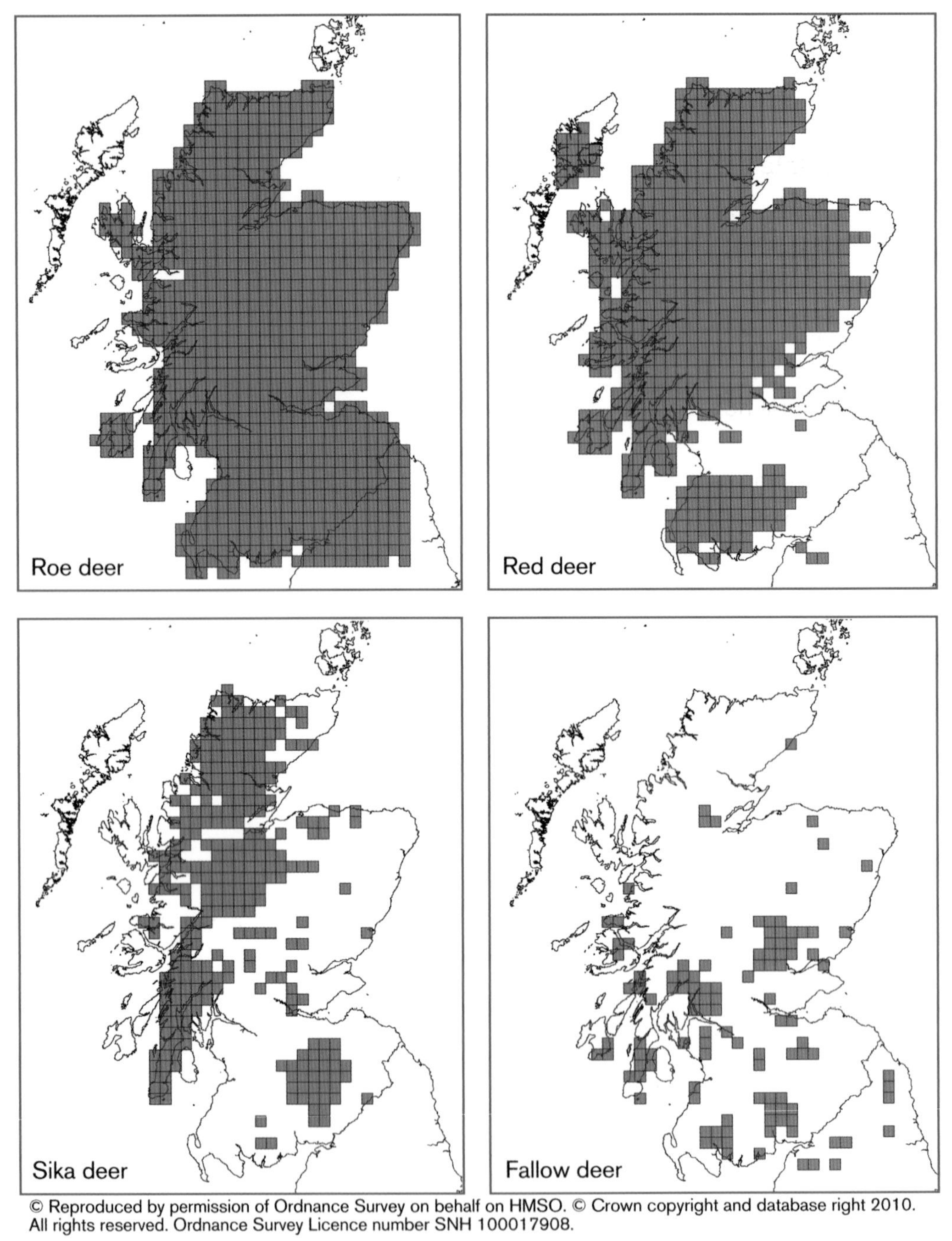

Figure 5.1 Distribution of wild deer populations in Scotland.
Source: National Biodiversity Network Gateway
Data providers: Mammal Records from Britain from the Atlas of Mammals; Highland Biological Recording Group

Between 1972 and 2002 roe deer, sika deer and fallow deer increased their range in Scotland (Ward, 2005), partly in association with the expansion of forestry and woodland planting.

5.4 Cull data

Deer are humanely shot or culled by practitioners for a variety of reasons.

For landowners, deer may represent a hunting asset – people pay an owner to visit his or her land to hunt and shoot deer. Culling may also be undertaken to identify and remove unhealthy stock that are suffering from disease, malnourishment, and/or injury. Culling also occurs to protect forestry, agriculture and the natural heritage from damage. It may also be undertaken to improve road traffic safety.

The DCS annually gathers data across Scotland on the number of deer culled. The cull data for the last 10 years for roe and red deer are presented in Table 5.1. This shows that the number of deer culled per year for each species has been fluctuating within a range of 57,363 to 70,962 for red deer and 26,214 to 33,597 for roe deer.

Table 5.1 The cull return data for red and roe deer from 1999/2000 to 2008/2009

Year	Red deer cull returns	Roe deer cull returns
1999/2000	70,962	30,222
2000/2001	66,931	26,214
2001/2002	67,282	29,392
2002/2003	57,363	31,117
2003/2004	61,957	32,913
2004/2005	68,610	32,264
2005/2006	63,611	33,597
2006/2007	62,563	31,808
2007/2008	61,354	32,058
2008/2009	58,496	32,626

Note: Data for 2009/2010 were not available at the time of writing.

The number of sika and fallow deer culled is low (fewer than 10,000 for each species per annum) but has been increasing slightly for the last 10 years. The cull data presented may be an under-recording, particularly of roe deer in the south of Scotland. DCS are continuing to review data collection and develop proposals for more effective and efficient data collection at both a national and local level. This will help inform the implementation of the wild deer strategy (Scottish Government 2008) and the Code of Sustainable Deer Management under the Wildlife and Natural Environment (Scotland) Act 2011.

5.5 Conclusion

The paper has summarised knowledge to date on the population of wild deer species in Scotland. Counting wild deer is a resource intensive process. It relies on significant public, private and/or voluntary effort and resources. Accurate national and regional population trends are also challenging to calculate. In recent years, counts have been focused on specific areas where deer are causing damage, for example to the natural heritage. More work is being undertaken at present to give a better understanding for the future of trends at a national and regional level. This would enable deer practitioners to manage deer populations sustainably and provide useful information for the general public.

References

Clutton-Brock, T.H. and Albon, S.D. (1989). *Red Deer in the Highlands.* Blackwell Scientific Publications, Oxford.

Clutton-Brock, T.H., Coulson, T. and Milne, J.M. (2004). Red deer stocks in the Highlands of Scotland. *Nature*, **429**, 261-262.

Hunt, J.F. (2003). *Impacts of Wild Deer in Scotland: How Fares the Public Interest?* Report for WWF Scotland and RSPB Scotland.

MLURI and BIOSS (2009). *A methodology to describe regional and national deer populations and trends in Scotland.* Report to Deer Commission for Scotland.

Scottish Government (2008). *Scotland's Wild Deer: A National Approach.*

Ward, A. I. (2005). Expanding ranges of wild and feral deer in Great Britain. *Mammal Review*, **35**, 165-173.

6 Trends in Scotland's Butterflies

Tom Brereton, Richard Fox, Paul Kirkland, David Roy and
Simon Foster

Summary

1. Butterflies in Scotland are monitored largely through the efforts of volunteer recorders *via* two different recording schemes, the Butterflies for the New Millennium Project and the UK Butterfly Monitoring Scheme.
2. Two different types of trend are calculated, namely distribution (31 species), and abundance (20 species).
3. The results show that the trends for Scotland's butterflies are mixed. Some species have undergone substantial range contractions, whilst other species have expanded in range. The abundance trends show that overall generalist species that occur in a wide range of habitats have increased, whilst specialist species that are largely restricted to semi-natural habitats have declined.
4. The range of many butterfly populations is determined by climate. Three new species have already colonised Scotland since 2000 and in the future we may see more changes as a result of predicted climate change.

6.1 Introduction

Butterflies are an important part of Scotland's fauna; they perform a range of ecosystem services including pollination and provide a food source for other wildlife. Many of them have very precise requirements including the need for specific food plants in a particular growth form for development of the immature stages. Knowing what is happening to butterflies is important to our understanding of ecosystem function; any changes to butterfly populations can indicate problems with habitats or climate. Continued fragmentation, deterioration and loss of wildlife habitats, pollution and predicted climate change pose considerable challenges for

Brereton, T., Fox, R., Kirkland, P., Roy, D. and Foster, S. (2011). Trends in Scotland's Butterflies – *The Changing Nature of Scotland*, eds. S.J. Marrs, S. Foster, C. Hendrie, E.C. Mackey, D.B.A. Thompson. TSO Scotland, Edinburgh, pp 59-66.

biodiversity. Butterflies are no exception and have arguably fared worse than birds and flowering plants in Britain over recent decades (Thomas *et al.*, 2004). Butterflies have a long history of recording in Scotland and Great Britain (Pollard and Yates, 1993). They are relatively conspicuous, easy to record and have high public appeal. In addition there is detailed information on their distribution and ecology dating back over many decades. Their short lifecycles and, in many cases, high sensitivity to habitat and climatic conditions make them biologically suitable as indicator species of the state of Scotland's biodiversity (Thomas, 2005).

Scotland supports about half of Britain's butterfly species and many are of conservation importance and interest. All of Britain's populations of the chequered skipper (*Carterocephalus palaemon*) occur in Scotland, along with the majority of colonies of northern brown argus (*Aricia artaxerxes*), mountain ringlet (*Erebia epiphron*), Scotch argus (*Erebia aethiops*) and large heath (*Coenonympha tullia*). In addition, the pearl-bordered fritillary (*Boloria euphrosyne*), small pearl-bordered fritillary (*Boloria selene*) and marsh fritillary (*Euphydryas aurinia*), are UK Biodiversity Action Plan priority species, and have strongholds in Scotland.

In this paper we describe butterfly trends in Scotland. We also look at possible changes in populations of butterflies as a consequence of climate change.

6.2 Butterfly monitoring schemes

Two different, but complementary, schemes exist to monitor butterflies: a distribution recording scheme (Butterflies for the New Millennium) and a population monitoring scheme (UK Butterfly Monitoring Scheme). Many hundreds of volunteer recorders contribute to these schemes in Scotland every year.

There have been three comprehensive national distribution surveys across Britain and Ireland for the periods 1970-82, 1995-99 and 2000-04; the latest of these is known as Butterflies for the New Millennium (BNM). Changes to butterfly status have been determined by comparing their distributions in these surveys (Asher *et al.*, 2001; Fox *et al.*, 2006). The distribution trends reported here have been calculated using methods that take variation in recording effort into account (Warren *et al.*, 2001; Fox *et al.*, 2006). Distribution trends are calculated for 31 of 34 species that regularly occur in Scotland.

The UK Butterfly Monitoring Scheme (UKBMS) provides data on short and long-term population trends, based mainly on transect counts. These data can be used to provide information on the effectiveness of biodiversity action plans, agri-environment schemes or nature reserve management (Brereton *et al.*, 2006). In Scotland monitoring has been carried out at over 120 sites and in 2009 was undertaken at 70-80 sites.

Abundance trends were calculated for 21 of 34 species regularly occurring in Scotland. Transect monitoring provides an annual estimate of the abundance of butterfly species at a site (site indices) (Pollard and Yates, 1993). Collated indices were calculated for each year that a species was recorded from a minimum of five sites. Trends are calculated using methods which take into account site and year effects of butterfly populations (Brereton and Roy, 2010).

6.3 Trends in Scotland's butterflies

The trends of Scotland's butterflies are mixed. Some species associated with special ('semi-natural') wildlife habitats such as unimproved grassland, open woodland and bog, have shown declines, whilst other species, which are capable of breeding in a wider range of habitats including highly modified ones (such as field margins and gardens), have increased significantly in range and abundance. The number of resident butterfly species has increased, yet many species that are important to Scotland's distinctive natural heritage are under threat. The destruction and deterioration of habitats remain primary causes of butterfly declines in Scotland (Kirkland, 2006).

Plate 6.1 Orange-tip, a butterfly species expanding in range and abundance in Scotland. © Dean Morley

6.3.1 Distribution trends

The distribution of butterflies in Scotland since the 1970-82 survey has shown that 22 species have declined and nine have increased in range (Figure 6.1). Several have undergone considerable declines in range in Scotland and are a cause for conservation concern. These include the dingy skipper (*Erynnis tages*), already one of Scotland's rarest butterflies, the large heath, grayling (*Hipparchia semele*) and

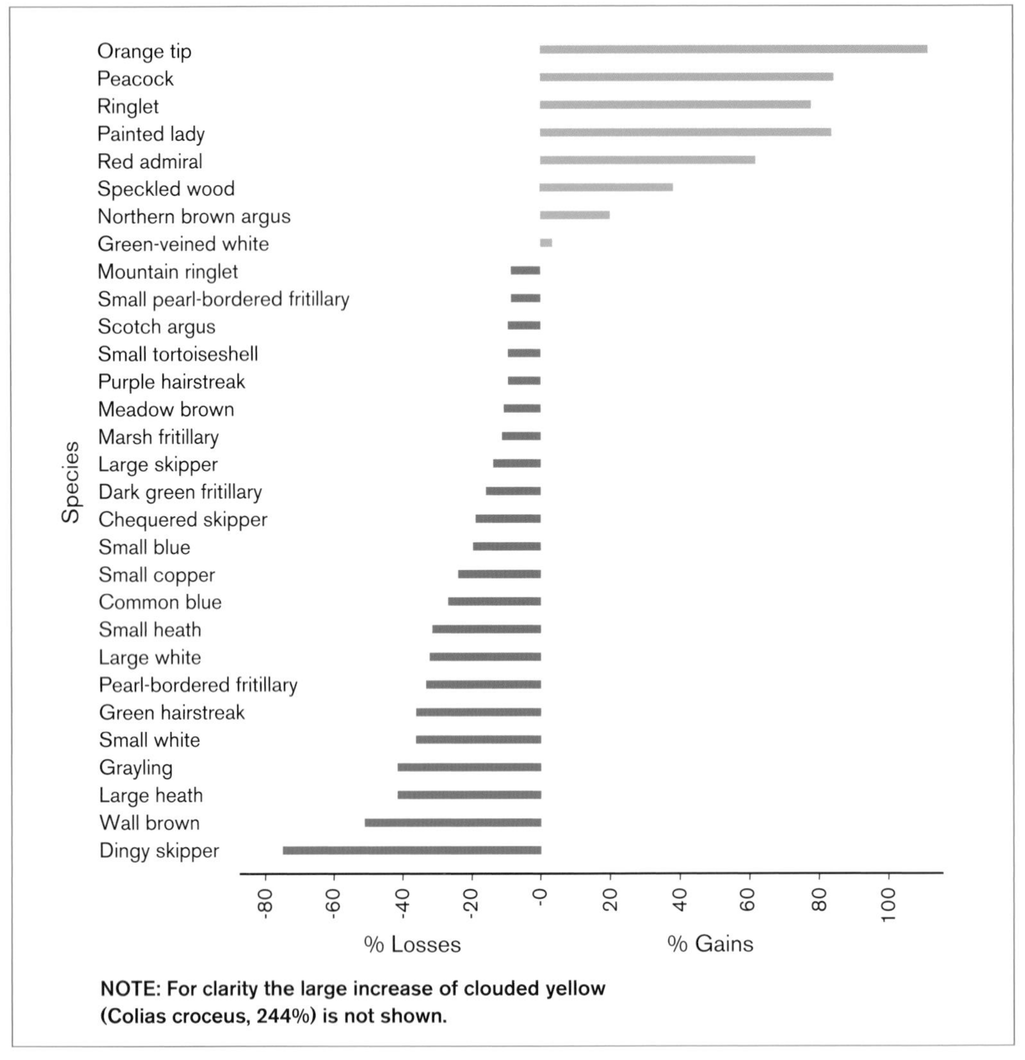

Figure 6.1 Changes in distribution for butterflies in Scotland between 1970-82 and 1995-2004.

pearl-bordered fritillary. These four Biodiversity Action Plan (UK BAP) Priority Species have declined substantially across the UK.

Four resident species show a large increase in distribution in Scotland since the 1970-82 survey: the orange-tip (*Anthocharis cardamines*), peacock (*Aglais io*), ringlet (*Aphantopus hyperantus*) and speckled wood (*Pararge aegeria*).

6.3.2 Abundance trends

As of 2009 the UKBMS transect network was still not sufficient in Scotland to provide good national trends for all species. It is likely that trends will become available for more species in the future as the monitoring network improves and more years of data are available. Reliable trends can be calculated for nearly two-thirds of species and they present a similar picture of change to the distribution data. Species that have shown significant increases include the migratory red admiral (*Vanessa atalanta*), and orange-tip (a common resident), whilst decreasing species include grayling (a specialist).

Scottish Government uses butterflies as one of the indicators measuring the state of Scotland's Biodiversity (Anon., 2007). The all-species trend in butterfly abundance shows that numbers have fluctuated in Scotland over the last 27 years, according to weather patterns and natural variability; however the overall trend is stable (Figure 6.2). The *generalist* species smoothed trend has remained stable. However the *specialists'* smoothed trend showed a moderate decline from 1979-85,

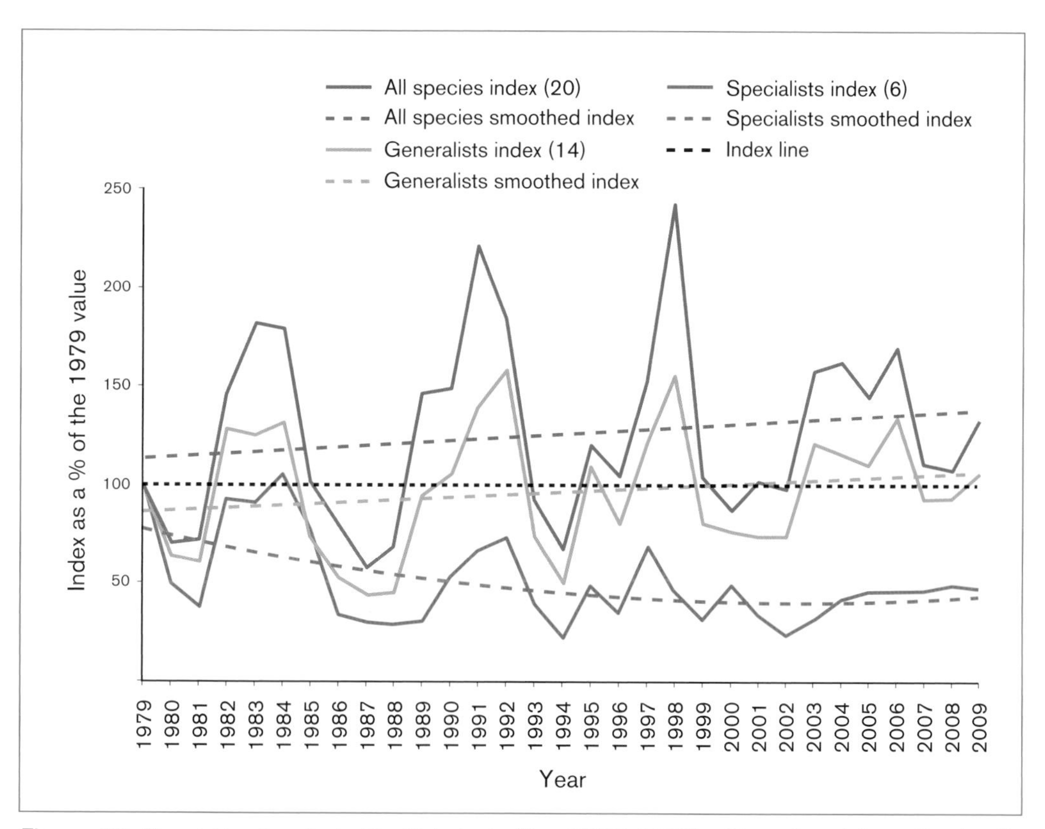

Figure 6.2 Population trends in Scottish butterflies (1979-2009). Reproduced from Scotland's Biodiversity Strategy state indicator No. 8 Terrestrial insect abundance: butterflies; annual updates are available at www.snh.gov.uk. Since 1979 the distribution and abundance of butterflies in Scotland have been recorded, primarily using results from the UK Butterfly Monitoring Scheme (www.ukbms.org). This assessment is based on an analysis of the underlying smoothed trend (Brereton and Roy, 2010). The indicator describes trends for 20 out of the 34 regularly occurring butterfly species in Scotland; the remaining 14 species are not included due to insufficient data. The number of species in each category is shown in brackets.

thereafter the trend stabilised until 2001. From 2002 the trend became uncertain due to large variations in the data. However, between 1979 and 2009 there has been a 44% decline in *specialist* species' numbers, most of which occurred during the early 1980s.

6.4 Climate change and butterflies

Some butterflies in Scotland may benefit from increased temperatures predicted under current climate change scenarios. Butterfly populations are controlled by a number of internal and external factors including climate (Dennis, 1993). Climate can limit the latitudinal and altitudinal range within which butterflies may be able to breed, by the temperature, number of frost-free days, day length, hours of sunshine, and suitable habitat for breeding. Rapid range changes (both positive and negative) have been documented in recent years in accordance with the predictions of climate change (Warren *et al.*, 2001; Franco *et al.*, 2006). Already, three butterfly species have colonised Scotland during the twenty-first century; the small skipper (*Thymelicus sylvestris*), the Essex skipper (*Thymelicus lineola*), and the holly blue (*Celastrina argiolus*). In contrast, mountain ringlet and Scotch argus which occur at higher latitudes and altitudes have experienced declines in their geographic ranges (Franco *et al.*, 2006).

6.5 The future for butterflies in Scotland

Although UKBMS data enables trends to be calculated for the majority of species, there is still a significant gap in our knowledge of some scarce species, whilst wider countryside species trends are calculated using data which is mostly collected on semi-natural sites. These data gaps and biases are currently being addressed. Volunteer recorders are being encouraged to fill coverage gaps of specialist species in target areas through workshops supported by SNH. Furthermore, Butterfly Conservation (BC) and the Centre for Ecology and Hydrology (CEH) in partnership with the British Trust for Ornithology (BTO) have developed a less intensive field method which requires fewer site visits (Roy *et al.*, 2007) and is aimed at improving wider countryside species monitoring. The Wider Countryside Butterfly Scheme (WCBS) was launched across Scotland in 2009, with butterflies sampled in 57 randomly selected 1km squares. The scheme will continue in 2010 and in subsequent years subject to resourcing.

Targeted conservation and research work is ongoing on populations of some of Scotland's threatened species. The Species Action Framework, developed by SNH to provide a strategic approach to species management in Scotland has enabled conservation work on marsh fritillary and pearl-bordered fritillary populations. BC is working with landowners, Scottish Agricultural College and others through the Scottish Rural Development Programme, which funds environmentally-friendly management specifically for marsh fritillary. This involves developing site specific management plans in agreement with the landowners aimed at restoring and maintaining marsh fritillary populations in Scotland (SNH, 2010). Similar targeted advisory work is due to be undertaken on pearl-bordered fritillary in 2010. In addition, volunteers and BC staff have been studying mountain ringlet populations in Scotland. Targeted research, advisory work and monitoring schemes such as UKBMS and WCBS are vital if we are to understand and measure the changes happening to Scotland's butterflies.

Acknowledgements

We would like to thank all of the volunteers without whom this work would not be possible. We are indebted to all who coordinate and record butterflies throughout the United Kingdom, as well as to those who allow access to their land. We are grateful to the Vincent Wildlife Trust, Esmée Fairburn Foundation and ICI for sponsoring the BNM. The UKBMS project was co-funded by BC and CEH and a multi-agency consortium led by the Department of the Environment, Food and Rural Affairs and including the Countryside Council for Wales, Forestry Commission, Joint Nature Conservation Committee, Natural England, Northern Ireland Environment Agency, and Scottish Natural Heritage. We gratefully acknowledge comments from Sue Marrs and Claire McSorley which improved this manuscript.

References

Anon. (2007). *Scotland's Biodiversity Indicators.* The Scottish Government, Edinburgh.

Asher, J., Warren, M., Fox, R. *et al.* (2001). *The Millennium Atlas of Butterflies in Britain and Ireland.* Oxford University Press, Oxford.

Brereton, T., Roy, D. and Greatorex-Davies, N. (2006). Thirty years and counting. The contribution to conservation and ecology of butterfly monitoring in the UK. *British Wildlife*, **17**, 162-170.

Brereton, T. and Roy, D. (2010). *Technical annex – Assessing change in England, Scotland and UK Butterfly Indicators.* http://www.jncc.gov.uk/docs/biyp2010_1bTechBackground.doc, *accessed 26 May 2010.*

Dennis, R.L.H. (1993). *Butterflies and Climate Change.* Manchester University Press, Manchester.

Fox, R., Asher, J., Brereton, T., Roy, D. and Warren, M. (2006). *The State of Butterflies in Britain and Ireland.* Pisces Publications, Newbury.

Franco, A.M.A., Hill, J.K., Kitschke, C. *et al.* (2006). Impacts of climate warming and habitat loss on extinctions at species' low-latitude range boundaries. *Global Change Biology*, **12**, 1545-1553.

Kirkland, P. (2006). *Butterflies.* Scottish Natural Heritage, Battleby.

Pollard, E. and Yates, T.J. (1993). *Monitoring Butterflies for Ecology and Conservation.* Chapman and Hall, London.

Roy, D.B., Rothery, P. and Brereton, T. (2007). Reduced-effort schemes for monitoring butterfly populations. *Journal of Applied Ecology*, **44**, 993-1000.

SNH (2010). *Species Action Framework – Scottish Forestry Strategy Action for Priority Lepidoptera Annual Summary Report – 2008/2009.* http://www.snh.gov.uk/docs/B620296.pdf, accessed 05/08/2010.

Thomas, J.A. (2005). Monitoring change in the abundance and distribution of insects using butterflies and other indicator groups. *Philosophical Transactions of the Royal Society B*, **360**, 339-357.

Thomas, J.A., Telfer, M.G., Roy, D.B. *et al.* (2004). Comparative losses of British butterflies, birds, and plants and the global extinction crisis. *Science*, **303**, 1879-1881.

Warren, M.S., Hill, J.K., Thomas, J.A. *et al.* (2001). Rapid responses of British butterflies to opposing forces of climate and habitat change. *Nature*, **414**, 65-69.

7 Bird Atlas 2007-11: Measuring Change in Bird Distribution and Abundance

Simon Gillings, Bob Swann, Dawn Balmer and Chris Wernham

Summary

1. Bird Atlas 2007-11 is an ambitious four-year project, undertaken largely by volunteers, to update knowledge of bird distributions in Britain and Ireland.
2. Casual records and fixed effort sample surveys are collected largely through a web application; this improves data quality and enables instant feedback to observers.
3. The methods allow comparisons with previous breeding (1968-72 and 1988-91) and wintering (1981/2-1983/4) atlases to identify areas and species undergoing changes over a 40-year period.
4. The results will provide key insights into changes in range and abundance of birds in Scotland. These will help to set conservation and research priorities and develop our understanding of the consequences of recent and future policies.

7.1 Introduction

Mapping bird distributions is an invaluable step towards understanding what can have an impact on bird populations. Identifying which parts of the country support important species, assemblages or high diversity is central to many conservation planning policies. Tracking distributions over time allows the identification of areas of recent, current and possible future changes in bird diversity. Bird atlases, of which over 400 had been published by 2007 (Gibbons *et al.*, 2007), play a central role in providing such information for conservation and academic uses (Donald and Fuller, 1998).

In Britain and Ireland the first breeding bird atlas was compiled during 1968-72 (Sharrock, 1976) followed by a winter atlas in 1981/82-1983/84 (Lack, 1986).

Gillings, S., Swann, B., Balmer, D. and Wernham C. (2011). Bird Atlas 2007-11: Measuring Change in Bird Distribution and Abundance – *The Changing Nature of Scotland*, eds. S.J. Marrs, S. Foster, C. Hendrie, E.C. Mackey, D.B.A. Thompson. TSO Scotland, Edinburgh, pp 67-72.

In 1988-91 a second breeding bird atlas (Gibbons *et al.*, 1993) updated distribution maps and for the first time produced patterns of relative abundance and changes in range. These range changes, along with population trend data, helped demonstrate the scale of farmland bird declines (Fuller *et al.*, 1995) and helped diagnose the causes (Gates *et al.*, 1994; Chamberlain and Fuller 2000, 2001). They are still used for subjects as diverse as conservation planning (Franco *et al.*, 2009) and assessments of ecosystem services (Anderson *et al.*, 2009).

Twenty years on from the last breeding atlas, and 30 since the last winter atlas, this paper describes the current efforts to produce a new bird atlas for Britain and Ireland.

7.2 Bird Atlas 2007-11

Bird Atlas 2007-11 is run in partnership between the British Trust for Ornithology (BTO), BirdWatch Ireland and the Scottish Ornithologists' Club. The fieldwork spans four winters (November to February; 2007/08 to 2010/11) and four breeding seasons (April to July; 2008 to 2011). The majority of the fieldwork is undertaken by volunteer observers using two complementary field methods. The simple aim of 'roving records' is to produce complete species lists for every 10km square in Britain and Ireland. During the breeding season there is a particular emphasis on collecting standard evidence of breeding, such as records of adults carrying food or newly fledged and dependent young, to determine which species are possibly, probably or confirmed to breed. Timed Tetrad Visits (TTVs) provide standardised measures of abundance in a sample of eight or more tetrads (2km×2km squares) in each 10km square. Each tetrad receives two winter and two breeding season visits; each visit lasts one hour with the option of a second hour to improve the species list and abundance information.

These methods have been designed to maximise volunteer involvement and allow comparison with previous Atlases, whilst also improving the quality of data collected (Gillings, 2008). The first hour of TTVs will allow direct comparison with data from Gibbons *et al.*, (1993) for effort-controlled measures of range and relative abundance change. Methodological improvements in winter can be seen as 'catching up' with Gibbons *et al.*, (1993) in using a structured sampling approach with standardised effort and, though they will present analytical challenges for making comparisons with Lack (1986), they will provide a wealth of new information and a stronger basis for future monitoring.

A major change since previous Atlases is the advent of the internet. State-of-the-art web technology (www.birdatlas.net) was built into the Bird Atlas 2007-11 from the outset. Web data capture ensures the completeness of survey returns and improves data quality, for example using interactive maps to handle grid references. The success of surveys involving volunteers relies on regular feedback to maintain motivation. BirdAtlas.net provides instant feedback to participants. In sparsely populated areas where surveyors often work in apparent isolation this feedback connects them with the results of others, allowing evaluation of records in the light of local, regional and national results. Record validation occurs both at the point of input, whereby the observer is prompted upon entering unusual records, and subsequently using a network of experienced validators drawn from the local ornithological community. This process aims to improve confidence in the data and provide positive feedback in data collection and the support of local expertise.

Bird Atlas 2007-11 is being run in close partnership with over 40 regional bird clubs, including those in Caithness, Clyde, Kinross, Lothian, Borders and the Isles of Arran and Bute, each aiming to produce fine scale (2km resolution) local atlases.

7.3 Progress and provisional results

Throughout Britain and Ireland over 90 million birds have been counted via 3.6 million casual records and over 100,000 TTVs after two years of atlas surveying. In Scotland *c.*3,000 volunteers have submitted over 11,000 TTVs in 6,400 tetrads, amounting to *c.*70% of the target coverage of eight tetrads per 10km square.

The project still has two years of fieldwork to run so incomplete coverage may explain some gaps in species maps. However for certain species, for example the common buzzard (*Buteo buteo*), the changes have been so great that there is already little uncertainty over current distribution (Figure 7.1 on following page). Changes in Scotland mirror those in the rest of Britain: over the last 40 years the common buzzard population has expanded eastwards and into many lowland areas. From 1968-72 to 1988-91 the Scottish range increased by 10% from 694 to 764 occupied 10km squares. In the following 20 years the range has extended at least a further 14% to 874 occupied 10km squares.

7.4 Future uses of Bird Atlas data

The comprehensive coverage, both in terms of species and space, allows analysis of species, functional groups and habitat specialists. With increasing interest in ecosystem function it may be possible to assess how bird communities change in terms of guilds or niches rather than simply species composition. Atlas data will be invaluable for monitoring and predicting the consequences of land-use change in Scotland. For example, it can be used to illustrate how bird populations react to the changes put in place by the new Scottish Rural Development Programme, Common Agricultural Policy (CAP) reform and the new Scottish Forestry Strategy. Has climate change already impacted upon arctic-alpine birds such as dotterel (*Charadrius morinellus*) and ptarmigan (*Lagopus mutus*) and what future impacts can be expected? The Atlas data will continue to underpin the identification of key sites for

Figure 7.1 Provisional breeding distribution of common buzzard in Scotland. Black dots show 10km squares occupied in the 2008 and 2009 breeding seasons. Grey background shading shows 10km squares occupied in 1968-72 (Sharrock, 1976).

conservation designation, and for targeting management for species of current conservation importance, such as red-throated diver (*Gavia stellata*) and golden plover (*Pluvialis apricaria*). National and regional measures of range change will complement population trends to update conservation status e.g. Red and Amber lists (Eaton *et al.*, 2009) and interpret bird indicators. Atlas data will be invaluable for assessing development applications, including risk mapping for onshore wind farms, urban development and forestry expansion. These and many other applications of Atlas data will help to inform key conservation issues in Scotland in the coming years.

Acknowledgements

Bird Atlas 2007-11 would not be possible without the dedication of tens of thousands of volunteer observers and local organisers to whom we are very grateful. Bird Atlas 2007-11 is funded by donations and grants including those from a small number of Scottish charitable trusts. We thank John Calladine and referees for comments on a previous draft of this paper.

References

Anderson, B.J., Armsworth, P.R., Eigenbrod, F. *et al.* (2009). Spatial covariance between biodiversity and other ecosystem service priorities. *Journal of Applied Ecology*, **46**, 888-896.

Chamberlain, D.E. and Fuller, R.J. (2000). Local extinctions and changes in species richness of lowland farmland birds in England and Wales in relation to recent changes in agricultural land-use. *Agriculture, Ecosystems and Environment*, **78**, 1-17.

Chamberlain, D.E. and Fuller, R.J. (2001). Contrasting patterns of change in the distribution and abundance of farmland birds in relation to farming system in lowland Britain. *Global Ecology and Biogeography*, **10**, 399-410.

Donald, P.F. and Fuller, R.J. (1998). Ornithological atlas data: a review of uses and limitations. *Bird Study*, **45**, 129-145.

Eaton, M.A., Brown, A.F., Noble, D.G. *et al.* (2009). Birds of Conservation Concern 3: the population status of birds in the United Kingdom, Channel Islands and the Isle of Man. *British Birds*, **102**, 296–341.

Franco, A.M.A., Anderson, B.J., Roy, D.B. *et al.* (2009). Surrogacy and persistence in reserve selection: landscape prioritization for multiple taxa in Britain. *Journal of Applied Ecology*, **46**, 82-91.

Fuller, R.J., Gregory, R.D., Gibbons, D.W. *et al.* (1995). Population declines and range contractions among lowland farmland birds in Britain. *Conservation Biology*, **9**, 1425-1441.

Gates, S., Gibbons, D.W., Lack, P.C. and Fuller, R.J. (1994). Declining farmland bird species: modelling geographical patterns of abundance in Britain. In *Large-scale Ecology and Conservation Biology*, ed. by P.J. Edwards, R.M. May & N.R. Webb. British Ecological Society 35th symposium 1993. Oxford. Blackwell, pp 153-177.

Gibbons, D.W., Donald, P.F., Bauer, H.-G., Fornasari, L. and Dawson, I.K. (2007). Mapping avian distributions: the evolution of bird atlases. *Bird Study*, **54**, 324-334.

Gibbons, D.W., Reid, J.B. and Chapman, R.A. (1993). *The New Atlas of Breeding Birds in Britain and Ireland: 1988-1991*. T. & A. D. Poyser, London.

Gillings, S. (2008). Designing a winter bird atlas field methodology: issues of time and space in sampling and interactions with habitat. *Journal of Ornithology*, **149**, 345-355.

Lack, P.C. (1986). *The Atlas of Wintering Birds in Britain and Ireland.* T. & A.D. Poyser, London.

Sharrock, J.T.R. (1976). *The Atlas of Breeding Birds in Britain and Ireland.* T. & A. D. Poyser, Calton.

8 Natural Heritage Futures: A Strong Vision for the Natural Heritage

Emma Jordan and Mary Christie

Summary

1. Scottish Natural Heritage's Natural Heritage Futures (NHF) prospectuses, published in 2002, set out a vision of what Scotland's environment could be like in 2025 based on sustainable management and use.
2. Considering new policy and legislative drivers, we reviewed the prospectuses and their visions in 2009. This highlighted that the visions were still deliverable, with the new drivers contributing to sustainable management of the natural heritage.
3. This paper outlines some of the new drivers for change influencing the visions for the national prospectuses of Farmland, Settlements, Coasts & Seas, Forests & Woodlands, Hills & Moors, and Fresh Waters.

8.1 Natural Heritage Futures

Scottish Natural Heritage (SNH) has set out a vision of what Scotland could be like in 2025, based on sustainable use and management of the natural heritage. Natural Heritage Futures (NHF) (SNH, 2002) were first developed in 2002 to promote an integrated approach to the sustainable management of the natural heritage for SNH and external partners. NHF consists of six National Prospectuses – Farmland, Settlements, Coasts & Seas, Forests & Woodlands, Hills & Moors and Fresh Waters – and Local Prospectuses for 21 areas of Scotland with distinctive character (Figure 8.1). This is supported by a description of the current state of the natural heritage and its use, an analysis of key influences, and a set of objectives and priority actions over the short (0 to 5 years), medium (5 to 15 years) and long term (15 to 25 years), for SNH and others to deliver the vision.

Jordan, E. and Christie, M. (2011). Natural Heritage Futures: A Strong Vision for the Natural Heritage – *The Changing Nature of Scotland*, eds. S.J. Marrs, S. Foster, C. Hendrie, E.C. Mackey, D.B.A. Thompson. TSO Scotland, Edinburgh, pp 73-82.

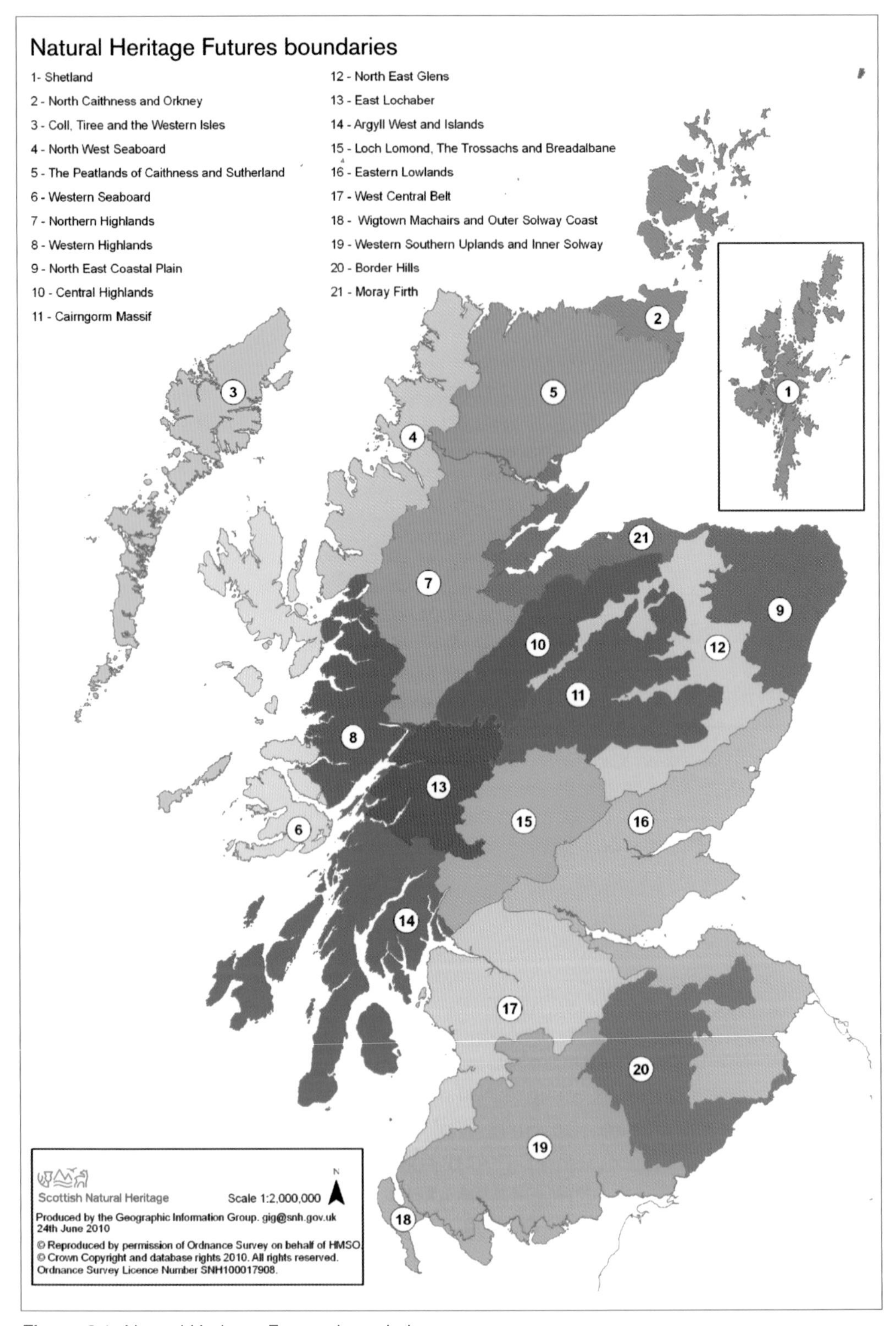

Figure 8.1 Natural Heritage Futures boundaries.

In 2009 all 27 documents were reviewed and updated to reflect changes in policy and progress towards achieving the objectives identified in the prospectuses since 2002 (SNH, 2009). In this paper we consider the effect recent policy and legislative changes have had on the visions outlined in the six national NHF prospectuses over the last five years.

8.2 The vision's relevance in a changing environment

As part of the NHF update in 2009 a number of new policy or legislative drivers affecting management of the natural heritage were reviewed (see Table 8.1) alongside other drivers, and changes were made to reflect the new key influences on the natural heritage within the various prospectuses. There were also changes to some of the objectives and actions to reflect these new drivers: such as flood management; Scotland Rural Development Programme (SRDP); and marine spatial planning.

The vision statements were also reviewed at this time and despite the various new drivers these were still found to represent relevant and achievable aspirations for the natural heritage.

Table 8.1 Key policy and legislative drivers considered while undertaking the update of the NHF prospectuses in 2009.

Policy
A Forward Strategy for Scottish Agriculture: Next Steps (2006)
A Strategic Framework for Scottish Freshwater Fisheries (2008)
Better Health, Better Care (2007)
Consolidated Scottish Planning Policy (SPP) (2010)
European Landscape Convention (2006)
National Planning Framework for Scotland 1 (2004) & 2 (2008)
Planning Advice Note (PAN) 45 - Planning for Micro Renewables (2006)
Planning Advice Note (PAN) 65 - Planning and Open Space (revised) (2008)
Physical Activity Strategy (2003)
Rural Development Programme for Scotland 2007-2013. The Strategic Plan (2008)
Scotland's Biodiversity Strategy (2004)
Scotland's Climate Change Adaptation Framework (2009)
Scotland's Climate Change Delivery Plan (draft)
Scotland's Sustainable Development Strategy (2005)
Scottish Forestry Strategy (revised 2006)
Scottish Government Economic Strategy (October 2007)

Scottish Government Strategy for Wild Deer in Scotland (2008)
Scottish Planning Policy 6: Renewable Energy (2006)
Scottish Planning Policy 11: Physical Activity and Open Space (2007)
Scottish Planning Policy 21: Green Belts (2006)
Scottish Soil Framework (2009)
Species Action Framework (2007)
Strategic Framework for Scottish Aquaculture (2003)
Sustainable Framework for Scotland's Sea Fisheries (2005)
Strategic Framework for Inshore Fisheries in Scotland (2005)

Legislation

Aquaculture and Fisheries (Scotland) Act 2007
Climate Change (Scotland) Act 2009
EU Common Fisheries Policy (2002)
EU Floods Directive (2007)
EU Water Framework Directive implemented through the Water Environment and Water Services (Scotland) Act 2003 and CAR regulations
EU Integrated Maritime Policy (2007)
EU Marine Strategy Framework Directive (2008)
EU Soil Thematic Strategy (2006)
Flood Risk Management (Scotland) Act 2009
Land Reform (Scotland) Act 2003 & Scottish Outdoor Access Code
Local Government in Scotland Act 2003
National Parks (Scotland) Act 2004
Nature Conservation (Scotland) Act 2004
Planning etc (Scotland) Act 2006
Scottish Marine Bill (2009) – now Act (2010)
UK Marine & Coastal Access Bill (2008) – now Act (2009)

8.2.1 Farmland

The vision developed for farmland in 2025 describes a confident agricultural sector which is willing to invest to meet the challenges of sustainable development. It outlines a sector committed to farm assurance standards, quality branding and meeting multiple objectives in relation to rural development, public access and management of the natural heritage.

Since 2002 we have seen changes to existing agricultural support mechanisms under the Common Agricultural Policy (CAP). These changes have resulted in a stronger focus on meeting the needs of environmental protection and tools to help deliver better integration between rural development, agriculture and natural heritage objectives. This has been seen most recently with the introduction of the Scotland Rural Development Programme (SRDP) in 2008 (Scottish Government, 2008). The need to address climate change through land management is a greater political priority since 2002, with a need to encourage farmers to contribute towards mitigation and adaptation measures, including: better retention of carbon in vegetation and soils; the development of renewable energy generation where appropriate; low-carbon management practices; the development of new habitats on farmland; and management strategies for invasive species. Changes in the way land is managed through the loss of the set-aside subsidy has also put a new emphasis on the need to manage some areas to increase their value for wildlife.

These changes have provided new drivers for delivering the Farmland vision, with the ongoing focus on delivering multiple benefits through integration of agriculture with natural heritage objectives.

8.2.2 Settlements

The 2025 Settlements vision focuses on increased provision of greenspace for people and wildlife, more community involvement in the management of local natural heritage, and a greater importance placed on quality of life. In 2025 we envisage good provisions for access to countryside around towns and more emphasis on sustainable settlements, with facilities in place for active transport options like cycle pathways.

Plate 8.1 Forth and Clyde Canal. A canal footpath demonstrates a vision for greener settlements, with opportunities for access to nature. © George Logan/SNH

Since this vision was first published, there has been an increasing focus on improving natural heritage provision in settlements (Procter and Johnston, Chapter 39). This has been influenced by rising populations, land and resource use pressures and climate change threats. Recent changes include the need to create options for wildlife to move unhindered between areas, and the drive to develop settlements based on sustainable principles. The role of greenspace and communities in planning has also increased, with a focus on greenspace helping to empower local communities through regeneration of deprived areas and the provision of services such as local food and health.

The changing policy drivers, with a focus on quality greenspace, sustainable settlements, good access to the countryside around towns and the involvement of communities, are helping to ensure progress towards meeting the Settlements vision.

8.2.3 Coasts and Seas

The 2025 vision for the Coasts and Seas describes an integrated approach to the management of the marine environment. It details a high level of awareness and knowledge about the value of the natural heritage in the coastal and marine environment across all stakeholders and an agreement to manage the resource within sustainable limits. The vision describes thriving coastal communities having an active role in the management of coastal and marine environments, with a local

Plate 8.2 Bottle-nosed dolphin in the Moray Firth. There is increasing recognition of the need to protect the natural heritage as a key asset of a sustainable tourism industry, as demonstrated by the lure of the bottlenose dolphins in the Moray Firth. © Lorne Gill/SNH

economy based on a mix of sustainable fishing, aquaculture and diversification into leisure and tourism.

Since 2002 there have been significant changes in the marine regulatory environment. This includes new legislation from Europe under the EU Marine Strategy Framework Directive (EC, 2008). In the UK, there has been new UK - based legislation, Marine and Coastal Access Act 2009 (House of Commons, 2009), and a Scottish Marine Act (Scottish Parliament, 2010). The new legislative framework focuses on improved marine conservation through Marine Protected Areas (MPAs) and marine spatial planning. There is also a stronger focus on climate change, with concerns about the trend of ocean acidification and its possible effects on marine organisms and ecosystems. The marine environment also has a role in climate change mitigation and adaptation, through marine renewable energy production, offshore carbon storage and through the use of managed coastal realignment and ecosystem management.

The vision statement has been expanded to more explicitly reflect these changes: achievement of *good environmental status* as required under the new EU Marine Strategy Framework Directive and the success of a marine spatial planning system based on environmental limits and quality. There is also a greater focus on adaptive management in response to climate change. However, the main thrust of the Coasts and Seas vision, based on integrated management and sustainable resource use, remains a relevant ambition for the marine environment.

8.2.4 Forests and Woodlands

The 2025 vision for Forests and Woodlands describes a successful multi-benefit forestry industry which contributes to sustainable development at a local and national level. The vision envisages diverse woodlands, with high biodiversity value, playing a key role in the development of habitat networks. There is also a good mix of forestry and open ground, maximising the benefits to landscape, biodiversity and amenity.

Since the original publication, changes to forestry and woodland management include a greater emphasis on their role in climate change mitigation (including biomass energy production and low carbon planting strategies) and adaptation (habitat networks). The Scottish Forestry Strategy (FCS, 2006) now has a vision to increase forest cover in Scotland from 17% to 25%. There is also a greater role for woodlands in delivering community health and well-being (for example green gyms), education, and in delivering a range of biodiversity benefits including the management of invasive species.

Based on these changes to woodland management and priorities the 2025 vision for Forests and Woodlands still represents a desirable and achievable aim.

8.2.5 Hills and Moors

The 2025 vision for Hills and Moors describes sustainable management of the uplands, based on a common agreement to safeguard nationally important flora and fauna. It also envisages significant restoration of upland habitats and a greater role for recreation and tourism, mixed with traditional uses, ensuring the viability of upland communities.

Since 2002 the management pressures on the uplands have changed, with an increased focus on the links between land management and climate change; including the role of the uplands in carbon storage and sequestration. Other pressures on upland areas include afforestation, renewable energy developments and changes in livestock grazing patterns. As a result of changes to agricultural support through the CAP reform there have been reductions in the numbers of hill sheep and cattle. This may have implications for the natural heritage and the local economy. The ability to safeguard nationally and internationally important features has been strengthened through the Planning etc. (Scotland) Act 2006 (Scottish Parliament, 2006), with new provisions for National Scenic Areas (NSAs), and the implementation of the Nature Conservation (Scotland) Act 2004 (Scottish Parliament, 2004).

These new drivers have resulted in changes to the objectives and actions for managing the natural heritage, which will help to deliver the Hills and Moors vision for 2025.

8.2.6 Fresh Waters

The 2025 vision for Fresh Waters focuses on the sustainable management and use of fresh waters and wetlands at an ecosystem level, managed through catchment initiatives. Fresh water management has close links to land management strategies, with effective controls in place to minimise pollution and practices that do not detrimentally affect the riparian zone. It also envisages stakeholders and communities working together to provide an integrated approach to fresh water management, including sustainable fisheries, with a high level of public awareness about the key products and services provided by a healthy fresh water environment.

Since 2002 there have been a number of changes, most notably the transposition of the EU Water Framework Directive in Scotland (EC, 2000). This requires EU member states to ensure that all water bodies achieve *good ecological status*, and has led to the development of river basin management planning. In 2009 the Flood Risk Management (Scotland) Act (Scottish Parliament, 2009) was published with the need to assess flood risk and develop area flood risk management plans. Effective flood management strategies, incorporating natural flood management techniques, will help to ensure community resilience to flooding events. These events are expected to be more frequent as a result of predicted climate change. In addition new controls for aquaculture and fresh water fisheries which are now in place, should assist in protecting wild fish populations and help towards achieving sustainable management of the resources.

The changes to fresh water and fisheries management will help to deliver fresh waters which are healthy and sustainable, reflecting the aspirations of the Fresh Waters vision.

8.3 Conclusion

Since Natural Heritage Futures were first published in 2002 there has been a number of changes (including political and legislative) which have affected Scotland's natural heritage. Despite these changes the visions are still as relevant as when they were first written. Indeed, many of the new drivers are helping to deliver the inspirational and achievable visions for the sustainable management of the natural heritage in 2025.

The vision statements are intended to act as an inspirational basis for developing a shared vision between everyone with a responsibility for, or an interest in, the natural heritage, and, supported by the objectives and actions, to guide planning in the shorter term. By working together towards the vision SNH and its partners in the public, private and third sectors can help achieve this ambition for sustainable management of the natural heritage – which underpins the health and prosperity of Scotland.

References

Defra (2009). *Marine and Coastal Access Act 2009.* Defra, London.

European Commission (2008). Council Directive (EC) 2008/56/EC of 17 June 2008 establishing a framework for community action in the field of marine environmental policy. European Commission, Brussels.

European Commission (2000). Council Directive 2000/60/EC of the European Parliament and of the Council establishing a framework for the Community action in the field of water policy. European Commission, Brussels.

Forestry Commission Scotland (2006). *The Scottish Forestry Strategy.* Forestry Commission, Edinburgh.

Scottish Government (2008). *Rural Development Programme for Scotland 2007-2013. The Strategic Plan.* Scottish Government, Edinburgh.

Scottish Natural Heritage (2002). *Natural Heritage Futures.* Scottish Natural Heritage, Perth.

Scottish Natural Heritage (2009). *Natural Heritage Futures Updates.* Scottish Natural Heritage, Perth.

Scottish Parliament (2010). *Marine (Scotland) Act 2010 (asp 5).* Scottish Government, Edinburgh.

Scottish Parliament (2004). *Nature Conservation (Scotland) Act 2004.* Scottish Government, Edinburgh.

Scottish Parliament (2006). *Planning etc. (Scotland) Act 2006.* Scottish Government, Edinburgh.

Scottish Parliament (2009). *Flood Risk Management (Scotland) Act (asp 6).* Scottish Government, Edinburgh.

9 Identifying the Special Qualities of National Scenic Areas

James H.C. Fenton, Krystina Campbell and Alastair H. Simmons

Summary

1. This paper describes recent work to identify the special qualities of Scotland's National Scenic Areas (NSA).
2. Potential developments can be tested against the NSA's identified list of special qualities to determine whether they would have a beneficial, neutral or adverse impact on the landscape of an NSA.

9.1 The National Scenic Area designation

A National Scenic Area (NSA) is a formal designation to safeguard Scotland's finest landscapes. In many respects NSAs are equivalent to the Area of Outstanding Natural Beauty designations found in England, Wales and Northern Ireland. NSAs were created in 1980 and there are 40 covering 13% of Scotland's land mass (Figure 9.1). Recent legislation defines an NSA as *'an area of outstanding scenic value in a national context'* (Scottish Government, 2006).

9.2 Special qualities of National Scenic Areas

9.2.1 Background history

To date the only descriptions for most NSAs are the short paragraphs given in the 1978 report *Scotland's Scenic Heritage* (Anon., 1978) which formed the basis for their subsequent designation. A few NSAs have more detailed descriptions from later work. For example, the then Countryside Commission for Scotland in a pioneer report on Loch Rannoch and Glen Lyon NSA (Anon., 1987) included a heading '*What makes the Landscape Special*', and identified five main qualities:

Fenton, J.H.C., Campbell, K. and Simmons A.H. (2011). Identifying the Special Qualities of National Scenic Areas – *The Changing Nature of Scotland*, eds. S.J. Marrs, S. Foster, C. Hendrie, E.C. Mackey, D.B.A. Thompson. TSO Scotland, Edinburgh, pp 83-90.

- Setting and physical grandeur;
- Glacial landforms;
- Natural beauty and tranquillity;
- Cultural heritage; and
- Man-made resources.

In 2002 the production of management strategies was piloted in Wester Ross NSA (Highland Council, 2002) and in the three NSAs in Dumfries and Galloway (Dumfries and Galloway Council, 2002). The resultant management strategies included a list and description of the special qualities of each NSA.

However for most NSAs there had only been the original descriptions in *Scotland's Scenic Heritage* (Anon., 1978). Therefore in 2006 SNH considered it was time to revisit these early descriptions, take on board the findings of any later work, and identify in a systematic manner what particular aspects contribute to the special qualities of each NSA.

SNH commissioned David Tyldesley and Associates to devise such a systematic methodology, resulting in the report *Identifying the Special Qualities of Scotland's National Scenic Areas* (Tyldesley and Associates, 2007). SNH used this report to produce guidance (SNH, 2008) which was subsequently applied to produce a list of the special qualities of every NSA (SNH, 2010).

9.2.2 Definition of a special quality

A given NSA will have many qualities, some special and some not. The guidance defined special qualities as *'the characteristics that, individually or combined, give rise to an area's outstanding scenery'* (SNH, 2008).

It should be emphasised that a given NSA may well have other special qualities, for example related to culture, history, archaeology, geology or wildlife, but this paper only analysed the qualities of the landscape.

9.2.3 Difference between a description and a quality

It is useful to differentiate between a description and a quality. For example, a given view might contain a loch and a mountain, and an objective description of the view would be:

OBJECTIVE DESCRIPTION: *'A loch and a mountain.'*

However, such views are common in Scotland, and this does not convey what is special about this particular juxtaposition of loch and mountain. The conversion of a description to a quality involves a value judgement, that is making a subjective assessment and, following the definition above, a quality is special if it is judged to be one that gives rise to the area's outstanding scenery. Hence, a special quality might appear as follows:

SPECIAL QUALITY: *'Massive mountain towering above a long, sinuous, gloomy loch.'*

It should be noted, however, that in practice the distinction between a description and a special quality is not always clear cut. For example, while the phrase 'a loch' or a 'mountain' is relatively objective, it does implicitly include a value judgement: the feature has been judged to be bigger than a lochan and higher than a hill – it already incorporates a quality of 'bigness'. Likewise, the phrase 'a long loch' can be seen both as an objective description and as a value judgement, whereas the word 'gloomy' would be seen as pure value judgement, with the word 'sinuous' somewhere in between.

Although it is relatively easy to produce a description of a landscape, sometimes it can be difficult to express a given special quality in words. Where this is the case, a good description may serve the purpose in that it creates a strong mental image of the scene that evokes a special quality or qualities. For example, the description 'an indented rocky coast with many islands' can create an appealing seascape in the mind, giving to the landscape a special quality which it is hard to express.

In summary, although ideally it is important in this work to identify the special qualities of the landscape rather than produce an objective description of the landscape, in some cases this can be difficult to achieve. Hence some of the special qualities derived by this method contain more objective description than others, in which case the 'specialness' is derived from the presence of the particular described feature or features.

9.3 Method used to determine the special qualities

The method that has been developed to identify the special qualities follows a similar approach to that used when carrying out a Landscape Character Assessment (SNH and Countryside Agency, 2002) and could in theory be used in any area whose landscape has special qualities. It has been a nationally-led process, designed to produce a national overview of the NSAs using a standard, transparent method.

In summary, the method has the following stages – see (SNH, 2008) for the full details:

1) A desk study to collect background information on the NSA, including the relevant description in *Scotland's Scenic Heritage*, Landscape Character Assessment, Historic Land Use Assessment (HS and RCAHMS, 2009) and other literature.

2) A familiarisation visit to the NSA, and the identification of key viewpoints that will give full, representative coverage.

3) Fieldwork at each key viewpoint, where three field sheets are completed as follow:

   i. an objective description of the landscape;
   ii. a visual analysis; and
   iii. a personal response.

4) Analysis and collation of viewpoint information.

5) Combining of viewpoint information and background information to determine what is special about the landscape.

9.4 Application of the method

SNH employed two fieldworkers to apply the method during 2007 and 2008 and the following principles were followed.

9.4.1 Existing sites and boundaries

This work made the assumption at the outset that, as the NSAs had previously been identified as worthy of a national designation, they all had special qualities that could be determined. The work also made the assumption that the qualities were contained within the existing NSA boundaries, and fieldwork was confined to these.

9.4.2 No comparisons

The identification of the qualities that came across as special were made without reference to other locations. Hence there was no attempt to compare one NSA with another, or with the undesignated surrounding areas.

9.4.3 No ranking of landscape types

During the fieldwork there was no preconceived notion that one landscape type was more special than another. For example, mountainous terrain was not necessarily judged more special than lowland terrain, or wooded areas more special than open landscapes.

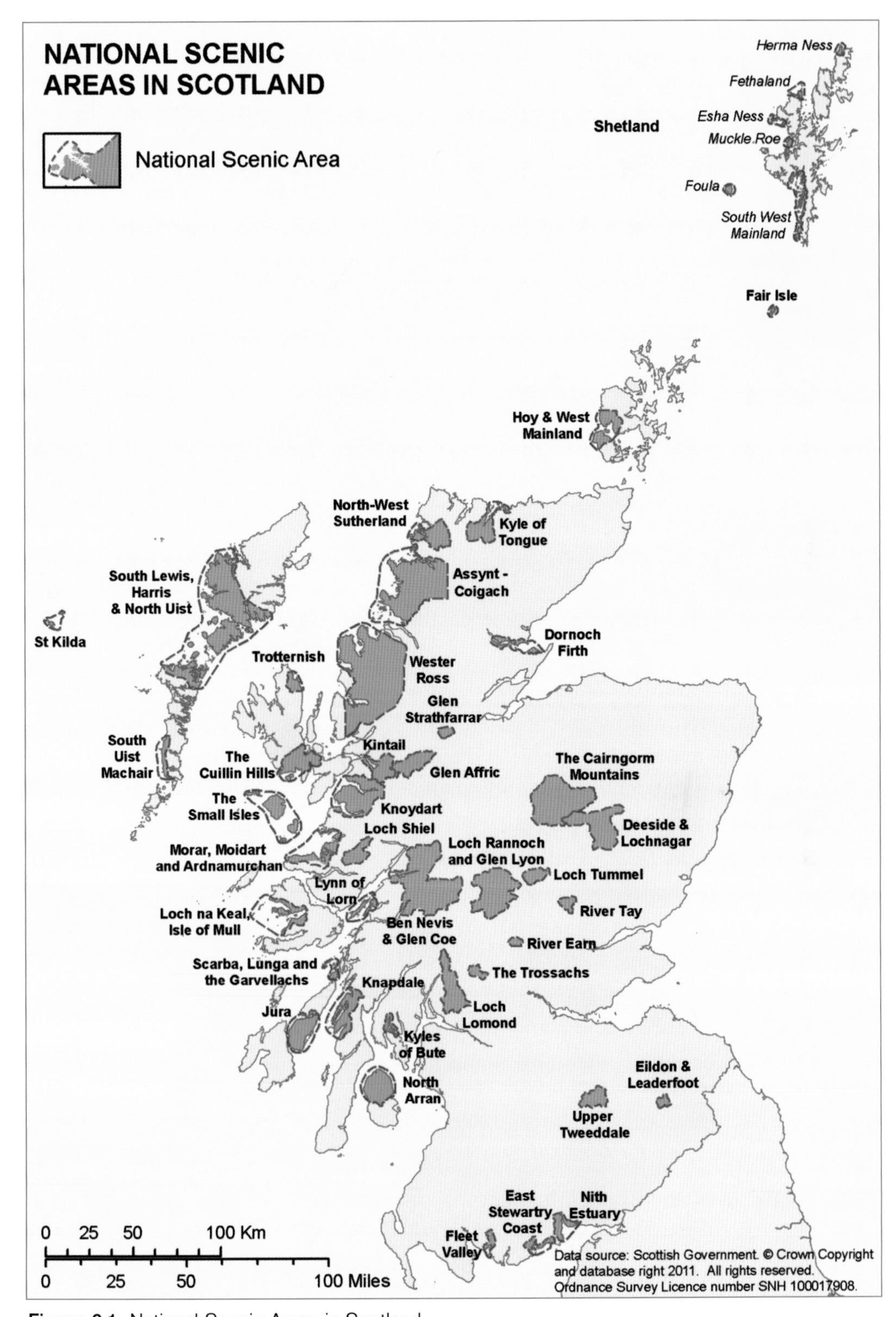

Figure 9.1 National Scenic Areas in Scotland.

9.4.4 No ranking of special qualities

On completion of the list of the special qualities for each NSA, there was no subsequent ranking, that is stating that one special quality is any more or less important than any other. The disaggregation of the landscape into separate qualities is to some extent an artificial exercise because it is the combination and integration of all the individual special qualities which creates the appealing landscapes deemed worthy of national designation. However the disaggregation does help us understand what is special about a given NSA, and makes it easier to plan future management in keeping with individual qualities.

9.5 Output

The report *The Special Qualities of the National Scenic Areas* (SNH, 2010) presents the special qualities for every NSA in a standard format, involving a bulleted headline quality followed by a more expansive textual description of the quality in a language designed to be both evocative and specific. A succinct overview of the special qualities of an NSA can be derived by combining all the headline qualities, which, for the South Uist Machair NSA, would be as follows:

- White, shell-sand beaches and turquoise seas;
- The profusion of flowers;
- Distinctive scenery between the mountains and the sea;
- Extensive, traditionally-managed machair;
- Birds and song at every step;
- An indigenous, South Uist settlement pattern;
- A scalloped coastline;
- 'The land of the bent grass';
- A host of lochs and wetlands;
- Wide, open horizons and skies;
- The force of nature and elemental beauty; and
- Deserted beaches, remoteness and solitude.

Alternatively, the headline qualities and text can be run together:

- *White, shell-sand beaches and turquoise seas.*

  Wide, soft, white shell-sand beaches and dunes sweep South Uist's Atlantic coast. Their comparative flatness leads to a great feeling of expansive linear

space at the sea's side, their appearance continually changing with the light and the tide.
In good weather, when the turquoise seas contrast with the white sands, there can be the feeling of being on an exotic island. But in storms and winds, there is a sense of exposure and danger, with the beaches' long, linear form appearing never ending.

The headline qualities can be omitted resulting in a more flowing description of the NSA which can be useful in promotion and tourist literature.

9.6 Use of the special qualities

Scotland's finest landscapes, as represented by the suite of NSAs, are highly valued by residents and visitors alike. The work described here (SNH, 2010) identified the qualities that make each NSA special, which is another way of saying it identified the qualities of the area that people value. With a listing of the special qualities, potential developments within an NSA can be tested against each quality to see whether they would have a beneficial, neutral or adverse impact. This should make it easier to direct future landscape change in such a way that we pass on the appeal and value of our finest landscapes to future generations.

During this work it has emerged that there are different types of quality. Some are immutable, for example the arrangement of an island group, or abstract qualities such as historical associations. Others though, are capable of being changed by human action, such as the balance between woodland and open ground, the wildness of an area, or a cherished view. It is this latter group that has most relevance to future management. For a given NSA, the next stage from the work described here is to identify these mutable qualities and list the policy implications that follow.

In summary, the listing of the special qualities of each NSA clarifies the features that need safeguarding and will be used to:

- Help planners, communities and land managers ensure development is sensitively planned;
- Provide the starting point for any locally-produced management strategies or plans;
- Promote these outstanding landscapes to residents and visitors alike; and
- Raise awareness of the importance of the NSA designation generally.

During 2010 SNH will issue guidance on how these qualities can be used to achieve the above.

References

Anon. (1978). *Scotland's Scenic Heritage.* Countryside Commission for Scotland.

Anon. (1987). *Loch Rannoch & Glen Lyon National Scenic Area: Policies for Landscape Conservation & Management.* Countryside Commission for Scotland.

Dumfries and Galloway Council (2002). *Management Strategies for East Stewartry Coast, Fleet Valley and Nith Estuary National Scenic Areas.* http://www.dumgal.gov.uk/index.aspx?articleid=1991, accessed on 12 December 2009.

Highland Council (2002). *Wester Ross Revised Draft Management Strategy November 2002.* http://www.highland.gov.uk/yourenvironment/planning/developmentplans/westerrossnationalscenic.htm, accessed on 9 April 2010.

Historic Scotland and Royal Commission on the Ancient and Historical Monuments of Scotland (RCAHMS) (2009). *The historic land use assessment data for Scotland*, http://jura.rcahms.gov.uk/HLA/start.jsp, accessed on 12 December 2009.

Scottish Government (2006). *Planning etc. (Scotland) Act 2006*, http://www.opsi.gov.uk/legislation/scotland/acts2006/asp_20060017_en_13#pt10, accessed on 12 December 2009.

Scottish Natural Heritage (2010). The special qualities of the National Scenic Areas. *Scottish Natural Heritage Commissioned Report* No. 374.

Scottish Natural Heritage (2008). Guidance for identifying the special qualities of Scotland's National Scenic Areas, http://www.snh.gov.uk/doc/B232041.pdf, accessed on 12 December 2009.

Scottish Natural Heritage and The Countryside Agency (2002). *Landscape Character Assessment – Guidance for England and Scotland*, http://www.landscapecharacter.org.uk/lca/guidance, accessed on 12 December 2009.

Tyldesley, D. and Associates (2007). Identifying the special qualities of Scotland's National Scenic Areas. *Scottish Natural Heritage Commissioned Report* No. 255.

10 Using Rephotography to Record Changes in Scotland's Natural and Cultural Heritage

Peter R. Moore

Summary

1. Rephotography is the process of taking a photograph, then re-taking it from the exact same place after a given time period, to reveal the sometimes dramatic and sometimes unnoticed changes that take place in our natural and cultural heritage.
2. In this paper two examples of rephotography show the changes that can be revealed through interrogation of replicate pairs of images.

10.1 Introduction

Rephotography provides ways to explore impacts of the passage of time and the ensuing changes taking place. The process requires that the vantage point (that is the place where the original photograph was taken) is replicated precisely. The repeated photograph can be compared on like-for-like terms with the original, either by direct comparison of printed output or using other techniques which can allow images to be layered over one another. Some techniques allow detailed comparisons to be made between the constant elements contained within the images and the 'space' that may have been occupied previously, by an ephemeral feature.

The process of rephotography allows additional information to be collected. When re-visiting the original vantage point the area outside the frame of the view can be scrutinised and features examined; some of the choices made by the photographer when making the original image provide interesting insights. Perhaps the most significant benefit of re-visiting the original vantage point, is the opportunity it presents to examine and 'ground-truth' the area, validating or refuting perceptions that may be formed through scrutiny of the original image.

Moore, P.R. (2011). Using Rephotography to Record Changes in Scotland's Natural and Cultural Heritage – *The Changing Nature of Scotland*, eds. S.J. Marrs, S. Foster, C. Hendrie, E.C. Mackey, D.B.A. Thompson. TSO Scotland, Edinburgh, pp 91-96.

'Rephotography' was a term coined in the late 1970s by American photographer Mark Klett, during the Rephotographic Survey Project (Klett *et al.*, 1984). This meticulous study set a new standard of precision and which, some 20 years later, was expanded to embrace technological advances and consideration of the concepts of space and time (Klett *et al.*, 2004). Repeat photographs of people or places contribute to constructing the narratives of change through which we understand something about ourselves, our circumstances and our relations within the social and natural world of which we form a part.

Rephotography is also known as repeat or retake photography. Typically, it repeats photographs of locations that were not taken for that purpose. However, fixed point and photo-point photography, which are similar, can be distinguished by their initiation through a conscious decision to document a scene for monitoring or other purposes. Repeated images may be made at a regular frequency – sometimes seconds, minutes or hours, and in other instances months, years or decades. However, all of these techniques have in common, the reference to an earlier photographic image and the return to the original location.

10.2 Rephotography – documenting short-term change

Figure 10.1 shows four pictures taken over 13 years as part of an on-going study of change in the Cairngorms. Initiated casually in the mid 1990s, the early repeated images depicted seasonal change or local weather events. Over time, changes, such as the introduction of fencing, footpaths and trees, were also documented from the same vantage point and supporting information, such as their influence on vegetation and nesting birds noted.

In 2005, a planned housing development (The Highland Council, 1997) was commenced on the field forming the majority of the view and the frequency of picture taking was increased. Photographs were made at different times of day, weather and season and when defining events in the housing development, took place.

The hundreds of images collected – four of which are reproduced here – provide a structured narrative of change to which other narratives may be appended. The loss of song and wading birds from the foreground area, the increase of some species such as starlings (*Sturnus vulgaris*), the impression of social and economic prosperity or the reality of figures measuring permanent house occupancy and the success of the planting schemes introduced to landscape and disguise the development.

May 1998 © Peter R. Moore

July 2005 © Peter R. Moore

June 2006 © Peter R. Moore

July 2010 © Peter R. Moore

Figure 10.1 Development at Aviemore 1998 to 2010.

10.3 Rephotography – documenting long-term change

Rephotography is perhaps most associated with 'then and nows', often using decades-old photographs as the source. It is these comparisons that provide the rephotographer with the greatest challenges and potentially, the highest rewards.

Images come from many and varied sources. In Scotland, the prolific photographic studios of Valentines of Dundee and George Washington Wilson of Aberdeen offer a remarkable documentary, but perhaps the most meticulous and extensive coverage of landscape is the work of Robert M. Adam whose collection of *c.*15,000 negatives, is now held at the University of St Andrews Library Special Collection.

In a 1958 interview, Adam explained the motive behind his photography saying that he had set out to catalogue '[Scotland's] wildlife and its topography as a permanent record against industrial and other changes in the future' (Smart, 1996).

Figure 10.2 is a series of four photographs revealing the changes in Invereshie and Inshriach National Nature Reserve, as shown by rephotography, since the scene was initially captured by Adam in 1946.

To speculate briefly about the reason for the 1946 photograph, is to investigate some of Adam's psyche; the vast majority of his images depict the beauty and majesty of Scotland, here, it seems reasonable to imagine his concern at this scar through the landscape and his desire to document it.

Dominating this scene, taken on 15 April 1946, is a poorly engineered track, cutting across a heather (*Calluna vulgaris*) clad slope, wooded with mature Scot's pine (*Pinus sylvestris*) above and below. Loose glacial rubble has fallen across the track surface. Two silver birch (*Betula pendula*) trees are visible below the track.

Exactly fifty years on (April 1996), the scene is readily identifiable and shows remarkably little change. The mature pine trees have changed shape almost imperceptibly, with rounded tops signifying a cessation to growth. One of the two birch trees is missing. The distinctly twisted Scot's pine tree on the slope above the track – key to the relocation of the vantage point and clearly a veteran tree when originally photographed – has neither grown nor regressed noticeably in the five decades between the photographs. The double-wheel track indicates continued regular vehicle use.

Some regeneration is occurring with Scot's pine, heather, and broom (*Cytisus scoparius*) colonising and providing mechanical support to the loose gravel and the slope has acquired some stability. However, regrowth is being held in check by grazing or browsing pressure with saplings mostly multi-headed and only just growing above the height of surrounding vegetation. There are no records of domestic stock grazing in this area and mountain hare (*Lepus timidus*) occurs infrequently. Browsing can be attributed to wild populations of red deer (*Cervus elaphus*) and roe deer (*Capreolus capreolus*).

A decade later (April 2006), the regenerating Scot's pine have established, due to a number of factors, principally through the cooperative control of red deer on this estate and adjacent land units but also coinciding with a period of milder climatic conditions, with less severe winters and wetter, warmer summers permitting fast and strong growth from the young trees (Moore, 2010).

In the most recent image (April 2008), the twisted pine is obscured from view by regenerating trees. It has however, died suddenly in the interim. The track has narrowed and a wider, single-track footpath formed. This reflects not only a change in the type of vehicles being used for deer recovery to either quad bike or all terrain vehicles with smaller wheelbase and lower ground pressure – but also a perceived increase in the number of hill walkers using the track as an access or egress route from popular hilltops.

Robert M. Adam Scotspine wood, hill track in Coire Ruadh, Glen Feshie 15 April, 1946 RMA 8307 Courtesy of St Andrews Special Collection.

15 April 1996 © Peter R. Moore

15 April 2006 © Peter R. Moore

28 April 2008 © Peter R. Moore

Figure 10.2 Hill track, Inshriach and Invereshie National Nature Reserve.

These images also demonstrate the limitations of remote photographic analysis and the additional information available to the rephotographer. Fieldwork to 'ground-truth' these images across a wider area at this site in 2008 indicated that the regeneration evident within the repeated images, was in fact, very localised and associated in particular with the disturbed ground at the sides of the engineered tracks. While there is logic to the claim that the tracks themselves and their regular use by visitors, helps to reduce grazing pressure through displacement, the thick overlying surface layer of mosses and organic litter in the adjacent clearfell areas – evident on examination – is also impeding seed-setting and regeneration. There is visual evidence of this lack of recovery, discernible at centre right of the images.

10.4 Conclusion

Rephotography is a powerful medium for documenting change. The presentation of replicate pairs of images provides a graphic reference that can be interrogated at all levels. The making of rephotographs at a location, allows considerably more information to be collected which adds value and broadens the application of the record.

As such, rephotography can be as much an interactive experience as an interpretive and documentary narrative. The process can be used to explore the changes to locations for which earlier images exist and act as a stimulus to document current schemes and landscapes for future rephotography projects.

References

Klett, M., Manchester, E., Verburg, J. *et al.* (1984). *Second View: The Rephotographic Survey Project.* University of New Mexico Press, Albuquerque.

Klett. M., Bajakian, K., Fox, W., *et al.* (2004). *Third Views, Second Sights: A Rephotographic Survey of the American West.* University of New Mexico Press, Albuquerque.

Moore, P.R. (2010). Photography and Rephotography in the Cairngorms, Scotland, UK. *In Repeat Photography; Methods and Applications in the Natural Sciences*, ed by R.H. Webb, D.E. Boyer and R.M. Turner. Island Press, Washington DC.

Smart, R. (1996). Robert Moyes Adam. Unpublished flyer to accompany "The Landscape Photographs of R. M. Adam" exhibition at University of St. Andrews. University of St. Andrews, St. Andrews.

The Highland Council (1997). Badenoch and Strathspey Local Plan. Adopted Plan. p50 section 6.1.2 (a) Aviemore North.

The Changing Nature of Scotland

People and nature

People and nature

Scotland's prosperity and culture are linked intimately with nature. From the 'Order of the Thistle' (a Scottish symbol of Knighthood) – which rallied the nation to the unofficial 'Flower of Scotland' – through to countless writings, paintings, works of music and even company brands and logos we find nature taking centre stage. Our natural heritage is rich and diverse, and we increasingly see the links and dependencies between people and nature.

In this section, the Chapters look at how human populations interact and connect with nature. The first of these (Chapter 11 by Marrs and Foster) summarises the five indicators produced as part of Scotland's Biodiversity Strategy. The indicators reflect our involvement and engagement with biodiversity in Scotland. The indicator on *Visits to the Outdoors* shows that around 78% of Scotland's adult population made at least one visit to the outdoors within a year of the survey period. Marrs and Foster reference an interesting study which suggests that the 'younger generation' are more familiar with computer games than with the natural environment – something many of us have probably suspected, but for which there is now evidence.

In Chapter 13, Scotland's Chief Medical Officer, Harry Burns, looks at the extent to which our health is determined by our external environment. This is timely and important. The word 'environment' is used in the wide sense of the meaning and does not exclusively refer to the natural environment. Through presenting some key studies, Burns points to Aaron Antonovsky's conclusion that good health is related to the feeling of control, or as Antonovsky states 'a sense of coherence'. This sense is often determined by the interactions we experience in our childhood years. Poor health has been related to deprivation, and a study by Mitchell and Popham (2008) reported that health inequality due to deprivation was less marked in areas where there was good access to greenspace. However, Burns suggests that 'if we want to use our natural environment to generate good health we need to do more than say it's available – proactive action is required to create something that makes people *want* to go out and participate in it.'

Based on the assumption that 'getting outside improves your health and wellbeing', Crawford *et al.* (Chapter 12) look at data which could be used to

surveyor studies plants with her faithful
ompanion looking on. © Sue Marrs

develop indicators to monitor levels and opportunities to participate in outdoor activities. They stress that more research is required to demonstrate the link between improved health and getting outside. Nevertheless, they show that since 1985, the percentage of children walking to school has decreased whilst the percentage of children being driven to school has increased. This tallies with a report by William Bird (Bird, 2007), one of Natural England's strategic health advisors, describing how in four generations children have lost the 'right to roam' and play outdoors. Given that Burns suggests the experiences we face in our childhood years help influence our adulthood, it begs the question about how adults of the future will view their environment.

The final two chapters look at specific projects which help people connect with nature. Mitchell and Bushby (Chapter 14) concentrate on the attitudes, aspirations and experiences of children aged 8 to 18 years who have taken part in the John Muir Award scheme. They conclude that 86% of participants had a 'positive experience', with 79% indicating that as a result of doing their award they were more likely to seek opportunities to get outdoors.

In Chapter 15, Cook *et al.* stress the importance of volunteers to nature conservation, notably bird monitoring schemes in Scotland. Although the British Trust for Ornithology (BTO) cite an impressive number of volunteers – 54,000 contributing to over 40 BTO led surveys each year – more are needed. The authors describe innovative schemes which the BTO have adopted to recruit and sustain members of the public in volunteer recording schemes, we sense many other organisations could learn from this.

References

Bird, W. (2007). *Natural Thinking.* Royal Society for the Protection of Birds, Bedfordshire.

Mitchell, R. and Popham, F. (2008). Effects of exposure to natural environment on health inequalities: an observational populations study. *The Lancet*, **372**, 1655-1660.

11 Measuring our Attitudes to Scotland's Biodiversity

Susan J. Marrs and Simon Foster

Summary

1. Improving engagement with biodiversity (in conjunction with awareness, understanding and enjoyment) is one of the objectives of Scotland's Biodiversity Strategy (SBS).
2. Progress in meeting this objective is monitored by five SBS engagement indicators: changing attitudes to biodiversity; greenspace; visits to the outdoors; involvement in biodiversity conservation; and membership of biodiversity non-governmental organisations.
3. These, and initiatives to improve public engagement with biodiversity, are described.

11.1 Background

Ten years after the UK signed the Convention on Biological Diversity, Balmford *et al.* (2002) published an intriguing, but stark, warning on the level of engagement of Britain's children with the environment. They reported that young children could identify more than 100 synthetic species from the game Pokémon (a popular games franchise originating in Japan) but could barely identify common real species in their own back yard; this, they argued, represented a serious alienation from nature. Ironically, the inspiration for the game came from the creator's (Satoshi Tajiri) passion for collecting insects as a child (Anon., 1999). Eye-catching studies such as this help stimulate debate, but how can we systematically measure how people engage with Scotland's biodiversity?

Chapter seven of the UK Biodiversity Action Plan (Defra, 1994), the UK's strategy for implementing the objectives of the Convention, focuses on the importance of public understanding of the environment. Among the five objectives

Marrs, S.J. and Foster, S. (2011). Measuring our Attitudes to Scotland's Biodiversity – *The Changing Nature of Scotland*, eds. S.J. Marrs, S. Foster, C. Hendrie, E.C. Mackey, D.B.A. Thompson. TSO Scotland, Edinburgh, pp 101-108.

of Scotland's Biodiversity Strategy (Scottish Executive, 2004a) is the need 'to increase awareness, understanding and enjoyment of biodiversity, and engage many more people in its conservation and enhancement'. A suite of indicators has been developed to gauge progress (Scottish Executive, 2004b). Five of the 22 indicators relate to how involved and engaged Scotland's people are with biodiversity (Scottish Executive, 2007; Scottish Natural Heritage (SNH), 2010a).

11.2 The indicators

Indicators should be based on a consistent, credible and quantifiable data series collected over time that can be subjected to statistical analyses. In addition, the subject matter of the indicators should be relevant and responsive to policy, be easily communicated and understood, and have public resonance. The five indicators which measure involvement and engagement with biodiversity in Scotland are:

- E1 Attitudes to biodiversity;
- E2 Extent and composition of greenspace;
- E3 Visits to the outdoors;
- E4 Involvement in biodiversity conservation; and
- E5 Membership of biodiversity non-governmental organisations.

11.3 What do the indicators tell us?

11.3.1 Attitudes to biodiversity

What people think and understand about biodiversity is critical to the level in which they support or become involved in nature conservation. Everyone is reliant on biodiversity to deliver ecosystem services such as clean water, food and climate regulation. If people are poorly informed they are unlikely to be supportive of protecting biodiversity when faced with competing concerns affecting their daily lives, such as financial or job security. This indicator is a measure of whether a key aim of SBS, to increase awareness of biodiversity, is being realised.

Representative samples of Scotland's population were asked questions in relation to their interest in, the relevance of, and concern about biodiversity in 2006 and 2009 (Progressive Partnership Ltd., 2009). In both years more than 68% of adults responded positively to questions on interest, relevance and concern about Scotland's biodiversity. There were however small, but notable, decreases between the surveys in the proportion of adults who were interested in biodiversity (which dropped from 83% to 75%) and who were concerned about biodiversity loss (83% to 71%). This result was attributed to competing concerns about the state of the economy from 2009 onwards.

11.3.2 Extent and composition of greenspace

Greenspace in and around towns and cities is where the majority of people in Scotland can enjoy being outside, connect with nature and experience biodiversity (see Procter and Johnson, Chapter 39). The importance of greenspace is recognised through various planning policies (Scottish Government, 2008; 2010). Policies relating to the provision of greenspace (for a definition see Scottish Executive, 2003) are described in Local Plans; these, together with supporting information, were interrogated to identify and measure greenspace. Approximately 25% of the total area of 171 settlements (towns or cities with a population of 3,000 or more) in Scotland is greenspace, such as urban parks and playing fields, although much of it is countryside at the outer edge of settlements.

11.3.3 Visits to the outdoors

A growing body of evidence supports outdoor recreation as good for health and well-being (Bell, 2008; Maller *et al.*, 2008). The Scottish Recreation Survey (TNS Research International, 2010a) is a monthly survey of a demographically representative sample of 1,000 adults (age 16 and over) in Scotland. The numbers of adults who made at least one recreational visit to the outdoors in the preceding 12 months has been fairly consistent, at around 78% from September 2005 to November 2008 (TNS Research International, 2010b). Although this headline figure remained relatively constant, the number of adults who made at least one trip per week increased from 44% in 2006 to 47% in 2008. The most commonly visited areas were parks and open spaces, which accounted for 37% of the visits. The main reasons for not visiting the outdoors were ill health (31%) and lack of time (29%). Old age (13%), no reason (14%) and no interest (8%) were also given as reasons for not visiting. Forty-one percent of visits are associated with dog walking.

11.3.4 Involvement in biodiversity conservation

The work of biodiversity NGOs (Non-Governmental Organisations) is founded on the commitment of volunteers. Volunteers provide essential skills and time, but benefit from learning and experience, and a sense of personal reward and achievement. Volunteering demonstrates a considerable commitment to biodiversity and this is a strong measure of the value that people put on the natural environment (Volunteer Development Scotland, 2006). Between 2005 and 2008 the total number of volunteers from 82 organisations surveyed increased by 43%.

11.3.5 Membership of biodiversity non-governmental organisations

Many people give active support for biodiversity conservation, without necessarily getting directly involved, through membership of biodiversity NGOs. Funds generated *via* membership are vital to support the activities of NGOs; in return members receive information and a greater understanding of the threats facing biodiversity and the need to protect species and habitats. Between 2007 and 2009 membership to eight main biodiversity NGOs surveyed increased by 15% from 137,798 to 161,140.

Results from 2009 are summarised in Table 11.1.

Table 11.1 The five engagement indicators developed to underpin Scotland's Biodiversity Strategy. Updates can be viewed online (see SNH, 2010a).

The indicators	How do we measure them?	What do they show us?
E1 Attitudes to biodiversity (2006 - 2009)	A representative sample of over a 1,000 people were asked questions about biodiversity attitudes.	Three-quarters of people surveyed responded positively to interest, relevance and concern about Scotland's biodiversity.
E2 Extent and composition of greenspace (2007 - 2009)	The proportion of the total area of 171 towns and cities in Scotland with a population over 3,000 which are covered by greenspace policies in Local Plans.	25% (36,787 ha) of the total area of towns and cities is covered by greenspace policies. The area of Green Belt fell by over 9% from 10,844 ha to 9,849 ha since 2007.
E3 Visits to the outdoors (2005 - 2008)	The Scottish Recreation Survey is a demographically representative sample of 1,000 adults each month who live in Scotland.	Over 75% of Scotland's adult population made at least one visit to the outdoors for leisure and recreation in the previous 12 months since September 2005.
E4 Involvement in biodiversity conservation (2005 - 2008)	Data are gathered from responses to questionnaires collated by Volunteer Development Scotland.	The total number of volunteers in 82 surveyed organisations increased by 43% between 2005 and 2008.
E5 Membership of biodiversity NGOs (2007 - 2009)	Eight prominent biodiversity NGOs were asked their membership figures. The organisations contacted were Bat Conservation Trust, Butterfly Conservation, Plantlife, RSPB, Scottish Wildlife Trust, Woodland Trust, WWF and Wildfowl and Wetland Trust.	From 2007 to 2009 the membership of eight biodiversity NGOs in Scotland increased by 15% to 161,140.

11.4 Current initiatives to foster engagement in biodiversity

The indicators act as a kind of barometer, showing how engaged and involved people are with biodiversity in Scotland. They do not identify the underlying drivers that change behaviour, but they can identify areas where more targeted action may be of value. The relatively short time series means that the trends should be interpreted with caution; however the figures provide a factual point of reference.

There is evidence that adults are more likely to visit the outdoors if they did so as children (*inter alia* Palmer and Suggate, 1996). First hand experience is crucial to understanding and awareness of the natural heritage and this tenet is central to the plethora of organised activities designed to encourage engagement in the outdoors and wider. Scottish Biodiversity week, held each May since 2001, delivers a host of exciting and innovative events that engage both children and adults. The year 2010 has been declared International Year of Biodiversity by the United Nations General Assembly; throughout this year it is intended that awareness of biodiversity will be raised across the world. An account of Scotland's contribution to halting biodiversity loss has been published (Mackey and Mudge, 2010). Scotland's biodiversity will be celebrated through a series of campaigns and the public understanding will be monitored through a quarterly omnibus survey commissioned by SNH (Primrose and Granville, 2009).

Outdoor learning is now embedded in the Curriculum for Excellence, with guidance developed by a partnership between Learning Teaching Scotland, SNH, Forestry Commission Scotland and the Scottish Advisory Panel for Outdoor Education. Eco-schools is an international initiative designed to encourage whole-school action for the environment. To date over 3,500 schools have registered to take part in this initiative in Scotland (Anon., 2010). The Deer Commission (incorporated into SNH August 2010) and the Royal Highland Education Trust (working with SNH) both encourage young people to experience rural activities such as deer management and farming.

These organised activities have proved to be an excellent way of encouraging people to enjoy biodiversity. The SNH campaign *Simple pleasures: easily found* (SNH, 2010b) takes an alternative approach and focuses on how easy it is to enjoy nature as part of daily life. For those of us whose experience of biodiversity is one of unfettered joy, it can be difficult to communicate the importance of biodiversity effectively. New approaches to communicating biodiversity that focus on psychological and sociological responses (e.g. Futera, 2010) may prove to a powerful tool in improving our understanding of and increasing our engagement with biodiversity.

Whichever mechanisms we use to communicate the importance of biodiversity, it is essential that the message is conveyed successfully. Scotland's Biodiversity Strategy engagement indicators provide a factual measure of how effective the combined effect of these activities is.

Plate 11.1 Waxwings feeding out of the hand. Not all experiences of wildlife are as intimate, but they do leave a lasting impression. These birds arrived on Fair Isle in autumn 2010 as part of an influx of waxwings around the British Isles. © Tommy Hyndman

Acknowledgements

This paper draws on the activities of a large number of people in Scottish Natural Heritage. In particular we would like to thank Scott Ferguson, David Rodger and Fiona Cunninghame who worked on delivery of the indicators. Richard Davison provided valuable direction to an early draft of the manuscript. Ed Mackey, Claire McSorley, Catriona Hendrie and Rebecca James all provided valuable input.

References

Anon. (1999). The ultimate game freak. *Time Asia*, **154(20)**, http://www.time.com/time/asia/magazine/99/1122/pokemon6.fullinterview1.html accessed from online archive.

Anon. (2010). Eco-schools. http://www.ecoschoolsscotland.org/ accessed 20 August 2010.

Balmford, A., Clegg, L., Coulson, T. and Taylor, J. (2002). Why scientists should heed Pokémon. *Science*, **295**, 2367.

Bell, S. (2008). *Design for outdoor recreation (2nd Edition).* Taylor and Francis, Abingdon.

Defra (1994). *Biodiversity: The UK Action Plan.* Her Majesty's Stationery Office: London.

Futera (2010). *Branding Biodiversity. The new nature message.* Futera Sustainability Communications.

Mackey, E.C. and Mudge, G. (2010). *Scotland's Wildlife: An assessment of biodiversity in 2010.* Scottish Natural Heritage, Inverness.

Maller, C., Townsend, M., St Leger, L. *et al.* (2008). *Healthy parks, healthy people – The health benefits of contact with nature in a park context – A review of relevant literature (2nd Edition).* Deakin University, Melbourne.

Primrose, D. and Granville, S. (2009). *Evaluating the effectiveness of Scottish Natural Heritage's communications.* George Street Research Ltd., Edinburgh.

Progressive Partnership Ltd. (2009). National baseline survey of biodiversity awareness and involvement. *Scottish Natural Heritage Commissioned Report* No. 334.

Palmer, J.A. and Suggate, J. (1996). Influences and experiences affecting the pro-environmental behaviour of educators. *Environmental Education Research*, **2**, 109-121.

Scottish Executive (2003). *Planning Advice Note 65 - Planning and open space.* Scottish Executive, Edinburgh.

Scottish Executive (2004a). *Scotland's Biodiversity It's in your hands. A strategy for the conservation and enhancement of biodiversity in Scotland.* Scottish Executive, Edinburgh.

Scottish Executive (2004b). *Developing an Indicator Set. Scotland's Biodiversity - It's in your hands. A strategy for the conservation and enhancement of biodiversity in Scotland.* Scottish Executive, Edinburgh.

Scottish Government (2008). Planning and Advice Note 65. Planning and open space. Scottish Executive, Edinburgh.

Scottish Government (2010). Scottish Planning Policy 11. Open space and physical activity. Scottish Executive, Edinburgh.

SNH (2010a). http://www.snh.gov.uk/publications-data-and-research/trends/scotlands-indicators/biodiversity-indicators/engagement-indicators/ accessed on 31 March 2010.

SNH (2010b). http://www.snh.gov.uk/enjoying-the-outdoors/simple-pleasures/ accessed 02 August 2010.

TNS Research International (2010). Scottish Recreation Survey: technical report 2007. *Scottish Natural Heritage Commissioned Report* No. 357.

Volunteer Development Scotland (2006). Volunteering in the natural heritage: an audit and review of natural heritage volunteering in Scotland. *Scottish Natural Heritage Commissioned Report* No. 219.

12 Healthy Activities in the Natural Outdoors: Proposed Indicators and Key Data Sets

Fiona Crawford, Ian McKenzie, Scott Ferguson and Jo Kennedy

Summary

1. This paper proposes a set of indicators to track participation in health promoting activity in the natural outdoors.
2. A pragmatic approach is taken to identifying a small basket of 'fit for purpose' indicators associated with national level data sets.
3. Gaps in the data are identified, including the need for further work that focuses on data sets that record children's use of the outdoors.

12.1 Introduction

There is increasing interest in the impacts the natural environment can have on individual, community and population health and well-being. While it is widely recognised that the outdoor environment and human health are closely related, the evidence-base in relation to specific health benefits from contact with the natural environment is still developing (Scottish Natural Heritage, 2009; Marrs and Foster, Chapter 11).

This paper describes the development of proposed national level indicators to monitor levels of participation in, and opportunities to participate in, outdoor activities which promote better health and well-being. It also examines opportunities to develop indicators to track progress on the contribution that the natural environment makes to improved health and well-being. It emerged from work (Crawford *et al.*, *in press*) undertaken to inform approaches to strengthen the evidence-base regarding the impacts that contact with natural environments can have on health and wellbeing.

Crawford, F., McKenzie, I., Ferguson, S. and Kennedy, J. (2011). Healthy Activities in the Natural Outdoors: Proposed Indicators and Key Data Sets – *The Changing Nature of Scotland*, eds. S.J. Marrs, S. Foster, C. Hendrie, E.C. Mackey, D.B.A. Thompson. TSO Scotland, Edinburgh, pp 109-124.

12.2 Policy relevance in Scotland

The importance of the environment in health improvement and reducing health inequalities is now recognised at a policy and strategy level in Scotland, and there is growing awareness of the relationship between place and health. *Good Places, Better Health* (Scottish Government, 2008a) sets out a commitment to creating and shaping places that nurture positive health and well-being. *Healthy Eating, Active Living* (Scottish Government, 2008b) also recognises that increasing physical activity and tackling obesity in Scotland requires action to create, improve and maintain the supply of natural and built environments encouraging more active lifestyles.

12.3 Approach

Our approach to developing the indicator set drew on that used by Parkinson and colleagues in the establishment of a set of national, sustainable mental health indicators for adults in Scotland (Parkinson, 2007) although their initial step, the determination of a desirable set of defined indicators, was omitted. It also drew on work undertaken by SNH and others to develop Engagement Indicators for the Scotland's Biodiversity Indicators set (Scottish Government, 2007a).

We used the following outcomes identified within the health and well-being theme of SNH's corporate strategy (SNH, 2008) as the framework for developing the indicator set:

- Greater and wider participation in enjoying the outdoors;
- Adequate good quality greenspace in towns;
- More sustainable patterns of travel, especially walking and cycling, close to where people live; and
- Greater involvement by communities in managing their local environment including the landscapes around them.

We sought to identify a small 'fit for purpose' basket of indicators that could be used to monitor trends. Work by the Glasgow Centre for Population Health (GCPH) to develop health and well-being indicators for Glasgow city recommends a small set of indicators based on data that can track change over time (GCPH, 2010).

A stakeholder workshop[1] concluded that there were limitations to available data sources that could inform the measurement of agreed indicators. It was agreed that a pragmatic approach, focusing on indicators to measure levels of participation in, or

[1] Participants in the workshop were: Glasgow Centre for Health Population; NHS Health Scotland; SNH; Health Protection Scotland; Ramblers Scotland; Scottish Government; Edinburgh University; Forestry Commission Scotland; SEPA; SNIFFER and Greenspace Scotland.

Plate 12.1 Exercising outdoors does not have to involve 'extreme' activities; a walk in the countryside can be just as rewarding. Children visiting Vane Farm RSPB reserve at Loch Leven. © George Logan/SNH

opportunities to participate in, outdoor activities which promote better health and well-being, should be adopted. Criteria agreed to identify useful data sources included:

- The 'fit' between identified survey questions and the strategic outcome of interest;
- The frequency of surveys identified as potential data sources;
- Sample sizes and potential for disaggregation of data to local authority level;
- Comprehensiveness and quality of geographical information system data; and
- Potential of other data sources to provide indicators.

12.4 Proposed indicators and accompanying data sources

A set of proposed indicators and data sources for each of the four outcomes is given in Table 12.1. It should be noted that some of the proposed indicators are already used elsewhere. For example 'proportion of adults making one or more visits to the outdoors per week' is one of the National Indicators in the Scottish Government's 'Scotland Performs' outcomes framework, while the 'number of volunteers involved in biodiversity conservation', is used in the Scotland's Biodiversity Indicators set.

Table 12.1 Summary of proposed indicators and relevant data sources.

SNH Corporate Outcome	Proposed Indicator	Data sources
Greater and wider participation in enjoying the outdoors	Proportion of people using the outdoor environment for physical activity, frequency of use and demographic breakdown of users.	Scottish Recreation Survey Scottish Health Survey Scottish Environmental Attitudes and Behaviours Survey Public Attitudes to the Environment in Scotland Survey
Adequate good quality greenspace in towns and cities	Amount, type, quality and spatial distribution of urban greenspace, and levels of access to greenspace.	The State of Scotland's Greenspace GIS Mapping Scottish Vacant and Derelict Land Survey
More sustainable patterns of travel, especially walking and cycling, close to where people live	Proportion of people using walking and cycling as a main mode of transport, and frequency of walking and cycling.	Scottish Household Survey National Travel Survey
Greater involvement by communities in managing their local environment including the landscapes around them	Involvement in volunteering in the outdoors. The number of people who are informed about changes to their local landscape, and the number of people who feel they can contribute by having a say on local changes.	Scottish Biodiversity Strategy Indicator E4 Scottish Household Survey Scottish Nature Omnibus

The following sections examine how the data sources identified could be used to define indicators to report progress towards the outcomes identified. Full descriptions of each data source are given, as well as analysis of the sample size, potential for geographic and demographic disaggregation, and other relevant information in relation to each data source. Examples of graphical presentation illustrate how user-friendly monitoring reports could be produced. Gaps and opportunities to develop further indicators are identified.

12.4.1 Greater and wider participation in enjoying the outdoors

12.4.1.1 Proposed indicator

Proportion of people using the outdoor environment for physical activity, frequency of use and demographic breakdown of users.

12.4.1.2 Rationale

Physical activity contributes to well-being and is essential for good health (NHS Health Scotland, 2008). There is additional evidence that regular outdoor activity and contact with nature offers a range of physical and mental health benefits (Bowler *et al.*, 2010).

12.4.1.3 Source data

Source data for this indicator:

- Scottish Recreation Survey. This is a representative sample of around 1,000 Scottish adults interviewed each month. It examines how often, on average, respondents have visited the outdoors for leisure and recreation in Scotland in the previous 12 months.
- Scottish Health Survey. This has run continuously from 2008 to 2011, based on an annual sample of 6,400 adults and 2,000 children. It examines places used for physical activity, including the outdoor environment, over a 4 week period, and frequency of use.
- Scottish Environmental Attitudes and Behaviours Survey. Carried out in 2008 this survey of 3,054 adults examined how often respondents visited public gardens, parks, countryside or other greenspaces on foot or by bike, and how important it was for people to have public gardens, parks, countryside or other greenspaces nearby.
- Public Attitudes to the Environment in Scotland Survey. This 2002 survey of 4,119 adults examined how often respondents took part in a range of activities, including physical activity in the outdoors.

12.4.1.4 Commentary

The Scottish Recreation Survey can be used to derive the proportion of people making one or more visits to the outdoors per week, accurate to around +/-5% at the 95% confidence interval. This is used as the Scotland Performs Indicator No 41 (Figure 12.1). Data from this survey can also be used to show overall frequency of visits to the outdoors (Figure 12.2) although accuracy diminishes with small sample sizes and care needs to be taken when comparing variables of interest.

These surveys can be used to examine trends in more detail, for example for

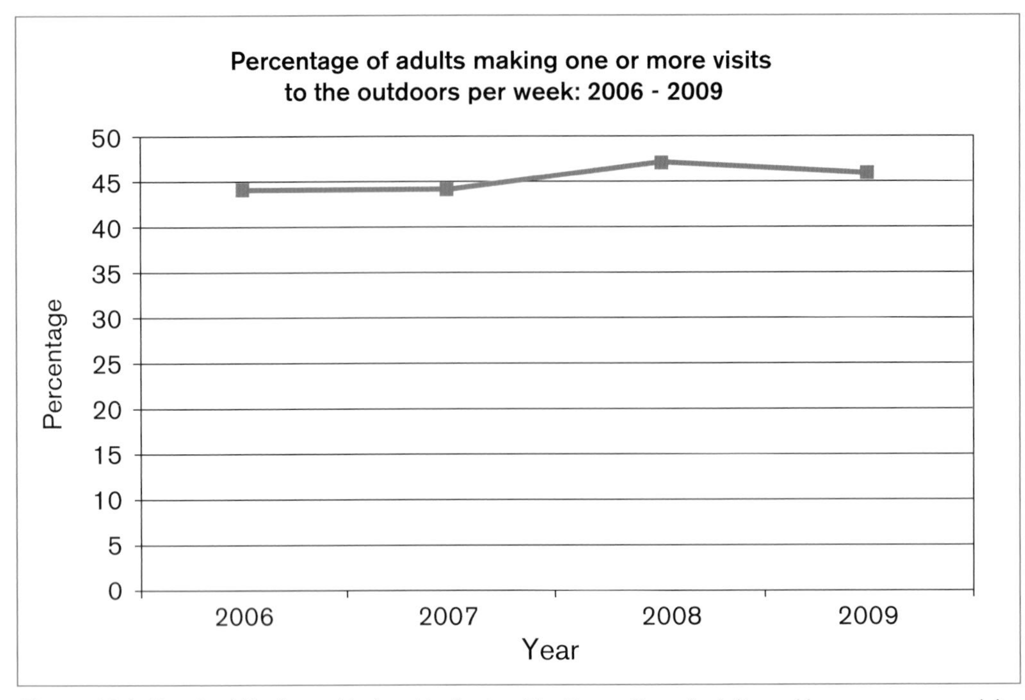

Figure 12.1 Scotland Performs National Indicator 41: Proportion of adults making one or more visits to the outdoors per week.

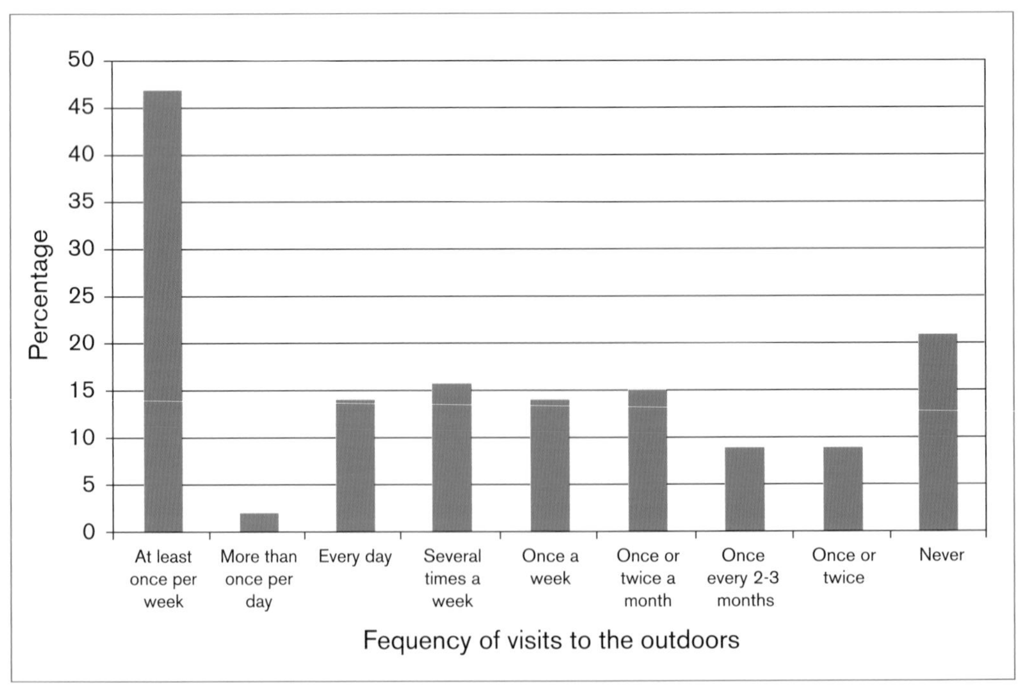

Figure 12.2 Scottish Recreation Survey 2008: Frequency of visits to the outdoors for leisure and recreation in the last 12 months.

specific geographical areas or for specific sectors of the population. The Scottish Health Survey can also be used to examine trends in frequency of use of outdoor spaces for physical activity amongst men, women and children. While the sample size is too small to disaggregate to a local authority level at present, the Scottish Government has published information in relation to analysing the data at sub-Scotland geographies (Scottish Government, 2009). Further disaggregation of the Scottish Health Survey and the Scottish Recreation Survey to examine trends for different socio-economic groups may be possible over a three year cycle. The Scottish Environmental Attitudes and Behaviours Survey is designed to enable disaggregation of information in terms of sub-groups and to detect trends over time, although the sample size is too small to allow disaggregation to local authority level. If repeated it provides robust data source to measure trends in both the proportion of the population, and of specific sub-groups, visiting the outdoors, frequency of use, and how important these places are to them. It can also be used to examine the relationship between frequency of use of the outdoor environment and reported well-being/life satisfaction.

Some areas covered in the Public Attitudes to the Environment in Scotland Survey were also included in a 1991 survey of public attitudes to the environment, allowing some comparisons to be made. It provides a reasonably robust data source which can contribute to information about levels of participation and the type of activity undertaken, although it would need to be repeated to examine trends over time.

12.4.1.5 Gaps and opportunities

The surveys reviewed primarily focus on adults. Research shows that engagement with the outdoors as a child is a significant predictor of continued engagement as an adult (Ward Thompson *et al.*, 2008). Given this there is a clear rationale for including levels of participation in outdoor activity by children in the indicator set.

There is also increasing interest in the scope for reporting participation in 'therapeutic' programmes associated with activities in the natural heritage, that is health walks and 'green gyms', as interest in 'greenspace on prescription' increases. Paths for All and British Trust for Conservation Volunteers (BTCV) Scotland have developed databases to allow better monitoring and reporting of participation in these initiatives which offer the potential to report trends in future.

12.4.2 Adequate good quality greenspace in towns and cities

12.4.2.1 Proposed indicator

The amount, type, quality and spatial distribution of urban greenspace in Scotland, and levels of access to greenspace.

12.4.2.2 Rationale

Research shows that the amount of greenspace in an area impacts upon population health (Mitchell and Popham, 2008). Additionally, proximity to greenspace, and the quality of greenspace, are significant factors in determining people's use of greenspace (Greenspace Scotland, 2007).

12.4.2.3 Source data

Source data for this indicator:

- The State of Scotland's Greenspace Report (Greenspace Scotland, 2009). This comprehensive survey of greenspace in Scotland, carried out in 2009, presents GIS data on greenspace for settlements of over 3,000 people for 20 of Scotland's 32 local authorities.
- Landmark local plans data. Local Plans provide comprehensive coverage across all of Scotland. The digitised plans can be analysed to derive information about the area of land in and around settlements of over 3,000 people covered by greenspace policy designations. The analysis has been carried out in 2007 and 2009, and is used to report a Scottish Biodiversity Strategy indicator on the extent and composition of greenspace (Scottish Government, 2007a).
- Scottish Vacant and Derelict Land Survey (Scottish Government, 2010). This collates and presents GIS data on vacant and derelict land in all local authorities. The survey is a co-operative effort between local authorities and the Scottish Government to record the extent and state of vacant and derelict land in Scotland and the amount of land that has been reclaimed.

12.4.2.4 Commentary

The State of Scotland's Greenspace Report 2009 establishes a baseline on the amount and type of greenspace in 20 local authority areas, covering 70% of Scotland's population. A second report, covering all 32 local authorities in Scotland, is expected in 2011. This will establish a national baseline, and allow trends and changes to be examined at a local authority level, and also for individual settlements. The Landmark local plans data will also be analysed again in 2011, allowing Scotland-wide and regional trends to be examined. Limitations of these data are the inconsistent classification of some greenspace policy areas and the currency of plans. Seventy percent of Local Plans are more than five years old and 20% are over 15 years old.

Further analysis of both these data sources could be undertaken to examine levels of access to greenspace against population and population health data and

Plate 12.2 Sea kayakers exploring the Scottish coastline of Elgol on Skye. © George Logan/SNH

socio-economic data at a local authority, settlement and neighbourhood level, and for areas with different demographic and social characteristics.

An alternative approach is to examine proximity to negative dimensions of the physical environment such as derelict land, landfill sites and areas with reported industrial pollution. The Vacant and Derelict Land survey provides a robust dataset which can be analysed at a regional and local authority level, and against socio-economic data. The data can also be used to derive figures for the proportion of people in each local authority area who live within 500m of any vacant or derelict site. In 2009 30% of Scotland's population lived within 500m of a vacant or derelict site.

12.4.2.5 Gaps and opportunities

Greenspace Scotland is now working with a range of partners to create a national greenspace map which will allow the amount, type and distribution of urban greenspace to be tracked over time. While current data on greenspace examine spatial distribution and type, it is widely recognised that the quality of greenspace is a key factor in delivering health benefits (Greenspace Scotland, 2008). Guidance has been published to encourage a consistent approach to quality assessment in Scotland (Greenspace Scotland and Glasgow and Clyde Valley Green Network, 2008). A comprehensive national dataset on greenspace quality, combined with new paths and routes information, could be used to monitor trends in peoples' access to good quality greenspace.

In addition to mapping greenspace, a number of studies examine perceptions of the quality of the local environment. The Scottish Household Survey is used to monitor a National Indicator to 'increase the percentage of adults who rate their neighbourhood as a good place to live', and the report 'Scotland's People Annual report: results from 2007/2008' (Scottish Government, 2007b) examines quality of life in Scotland's neighbourhoods and communities. Greenspace Scotland has commissioned surveys in 2004, 2007 and 2009 to investigate people's use of greenspaces and their attitudes towards the availability and quality of greenspace in their communities (Progressive Partnership, 2009). Survey data could be combined with spatial data to develop a comprehensive indicator of provision of adequate good quality greenspace.

12.4.3 Sustainable patterns of travel

12.4.3.1 Proposed indicator

Proportion of people using walking and cycling as a main mode of transport, and frequency of walking and cycling.

12.4.3.2 Rationale

Walking and cycling are a major component of outdoor physical activity, and research shows that the quality of the environment affects levels of walking and cycling (Sustrans, 2007).

12.4.3.3 Data sources

Source data for this indicator:

- Scottish Household Survey. Started in 1999, this continuous cross-sectional survey interviews 14,000-15,000 households annually. The Travel Diary component of the SHS collects a broad range of information about travel.
- National Travel Survey. Since 1988, this continuous cross sectional survey of between 3,000 and 8,000 households per year (8,300 in 2006) has gathered a range of data regarding travel patterns and use of transport infrastructure and services.

12.4.3.4 Commentary

These surveys offer a comprehensive and robust data source in relation to Scottish travel patterns (Figures 12.3 and 12.4) and provide long term trends in travel patterns which can be disaggregated both geographically, to a local authority level, and demographically.

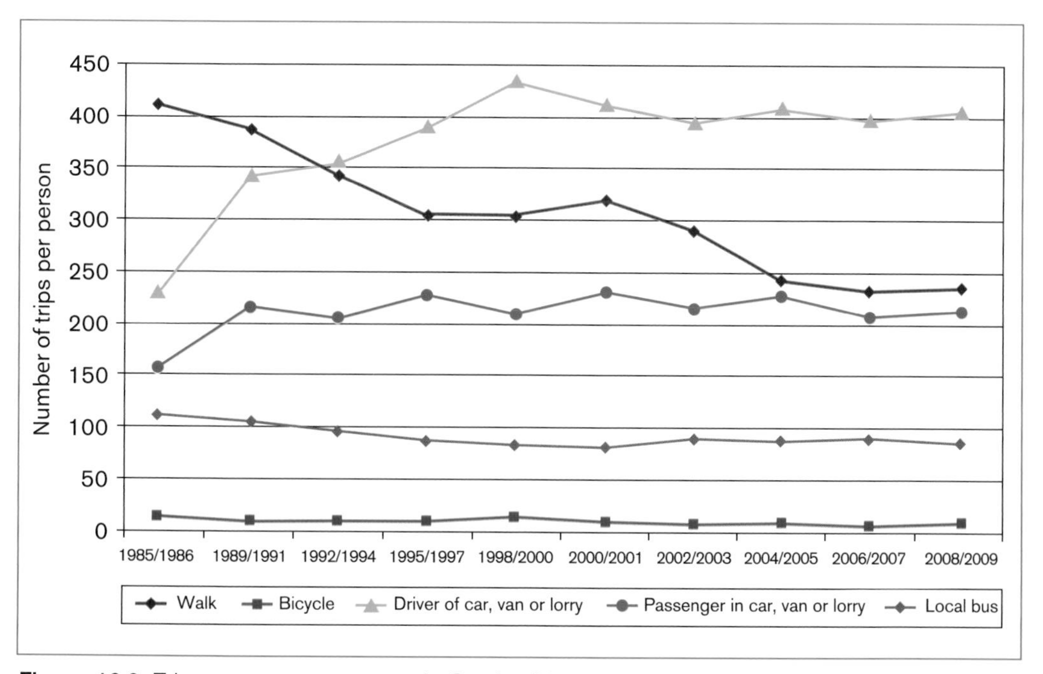

Figure 12.3 Trips per person per year in Scotland by main mode of transport between 1985 and 2009. Source: Scottish Transport Statistics Website

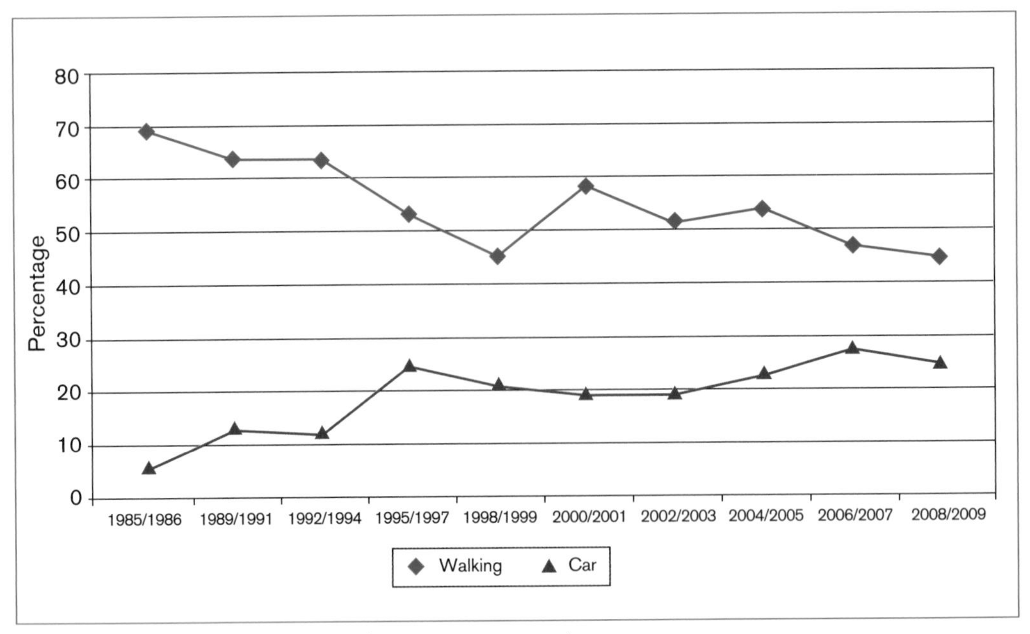

Figure 12.4 Travel to/from school (pupils aged 5 to 16).

12.4.3.5 Gaps and opportunities

National surveys offer good data source on travel patterns, and how these are changing. In 2008 Sustrans also undertook a 'Hands Up' Survey to examine how children normally travel to school. The survey involved primary and secondary schools in 29 Local Authority areas, although not all schools in any one authority took part. If continued this survey will provide a detailed breakdown of trends in school travel over time at national, regional and local level.

12.4.4 Involvement by communities in managing their local environment

12.4.4.1 Proposed indicators

Involvement in volunteering in the outdoors.

The number of people who are informed about changes to their local landscape, and the number of people who feel they can contribute by having a say on local changes.

12.4.4.2 Rationale

Active participation in outdoor volunteering contributes to physical activity, and surveys of environmental volunteers report increased health and well-being as an impact of volunteering (Scottish Natural Heritage, 2007). The degree to which people feel they can influence things that affect their lives, including changes to the local environment, impacts upon health and well-being (see Burns, Chapter 13).

12.4.4.3 Data sources

Source data for this indicator:

- Scottish Biodiversity Strategy Indicator E4. This survey of volunteer-involving organisations, carried out in 2005 and 2008, examines the number of volunteers involved in each organisation, and the number of hours volunteered. In 2008, 90 organisations responded to the questionnaire compared to 204 organisations in 2005.
- Scottish Household Survey. Started in 1999, this continuous cross-sectional survey interviews 14,000-15,000 households annually. It examines volunteering across a range of activities, including 'environment/animals'.
- Scottish Nature Omnibus. A quarterly survey (March 2009, June 2009 and Dec/Jan 2009-10) of 1,100 adults. The sample is representative of the Scottish Government's six-fold urban/rural classification (Scottish Government, 2008d). The survey examines how well informed people feel about proposed changes in the environment close to where they live, and whether they feel they have an opportunity to have a say in the proposed changes.

12.4.4.4 Commentary

The data supporting SBS indicator E4 are classed as good/satisfactory but a number of cautionary factors were highlighted in the baseline survey (Volunteer Development Scotland, 2006). Whilst the number of hours volunteered is a more reliable indicator of volunteer effort, an indicator examining the health impact of volunteering should examine both the number of volunteers and volunteering hours. Disaggregation to local authority level is not possible, but some larger volunteer involving organisations can examine the socio-economic characteristics of volunteers. The Scottish Household Survey (SHS) offers a robust dataset of participation in volunteering, although a category for 'improving the environment' would be better than the current 'environment/animals' category in monitoring involvement in active volunteering in the outdoors.

The Scottish Nature Omnibus data provides a baseline on how informed and engaged people feel in decisions about their local environment, but falls short of a measure of involvement that would be useful in monitoring impacts on health and well-being. The survey shows that while people report a high level of care for nature in general and want to see Scotland's nature protected, they are less engaged in decisions about their local environment at a local level.

12.4.4.5 Gaps and opportunities

Participation in volunteering is just one aspect of involvement in managing the local environment. While continued surveys of participation in volunteering in the outdoors may be used in future to measure health and well-being, other aspects of involvement should be considered too. A broader measure of participation in decision making about the local environment should be developed to examine trends in levels of community involvement in changes to the local environment.

12.5 Conclusions

This paper has presented a number of existing indicators and highlighted several data sources that could be utilised to monitor the level of healthy activities undertaken by Scotland's people to provide baseline data or examine recent trends. Taken together, they will provide a picture of progress over time in relation to some of SNH's corporate outcomes for health and well-being.

The study also examined gaps and opportunities. For some data sources the sample size limits opportunities for disaggregation, and there is uncertainty regarding whether or not certain surveys will be repeated. A number of key challenges therefore remain, including:

- Many data sources focus on adults. Additional data sources that record children's use of, and involvement with, the outdoors are required;
- New approaches to collecting the recommended data, and establishing data collection systems for desired indicators where they do not currently exist need to be explored. This includes the need for greater standardisation and harmonisation of data collection at a local authority level, perhaps linked to the development of Single Outcome Agreements; and
- Data must continue to be collected for the current and developing indicator sets. This includes tracking and monitoring review processes and coordinating lobbying to maintain and develop the various national surveys and data sets.

This paper has also highlighted the data which exist on levels of participation in healthy activities in the outdoors, the type of activities being undertaken, and access to opportunities to participate. Opportunities to use, and further develop, this data to underpin indicators to track progress on participation have been highlighted. However, if more specific indicators of the contribution the natural heritage makes to health and well-being are to be developed more evidence of the specific health benefits from contact and engagement with the natural outdoors is needed.

References

Bowler, D., Buyung-Ali, L., Knight, T. and Pullin, A.S. (2010). *The importance of nature for health: is there a specific benefit of contact with green space?* Environmental Evidence: www.environmentalevidence.org/SR40.html .

Crawford, F., McKenzie, I, and Kennedy, J. (in press). What do we know about the health impacts of contact with nature? What works in engagement with and use of natural environments? How best can we support and measure this? Scottish Natural Heritage, Inverness.

Glasgow Centre for Population Health (2010). *The development of health and wellbeing indicators for Glasgow.* http://www.gcph.co.uk/work_programmes/understanding_glasgows_health/development_of_health_and_wellbeing_indicators_for_gla, accessed on 5 November 2010.

Greenspace Scotland (2007). *The links between greenspace and health: a critical literature review.* Greenspace Scotland, Stirling.

Greenspace Scotland (2008). *Health Impact Assessment of Greenspace; a Guide.* Greenspace Scotland, Stirling.

Greenspace Scotland (2009). *State of Scotland's Greenspace 2009.* Greenspace Scotland, Stirling.

Greenspace Scotland and Glasgow and Clyde Valley Green Network Partnership (2008). *Greenspace Quality – a Guide to Assessment, Planning and Strategic Development.* Greenspace Scotland, Stirling.

Mitchell, R. and Popham, F. (2008). Effect of exposure to natural environment on health inequalities: an observational population study. *The Lancet*, **372**, 1655-1660.

NHS Health Scotland (2008). NHS Health Scotland Commentary on NICE Public Health Guidance on promoting and creating built or natural environments that encourage and support physical activity. http://www.healthscotland.com/uploads/documents/7280-NICEPHG008HScommentaryFullText27Jun08.pdf, accessed on 5 November 2010.

Parkinson, J. (2007). *Establishing a core set of national, sustainable mental health indicators for adults in Scotland: Rationale paper.* NHS Health Scotland, Glasgow.

Progressive Partnership (2009). *Greenspace Scotland – Omnibus Survey Final Report.* Greenspace Scotland, Stirling.

Scottish Government (2007a). *Scotland's Biodiversity Indicators.* Scottish Government, Edinburgh.

Scottish Government (2007b). *Scotland's People Annual report: results from 2007/2008.* Scottish Household Survey.

Scottish Government (2008a). *Good places, better health: a New Approach to Environment and Health in Scotland.* Scottish Government, Edinburgh.

Scottish Government (2008b). *Healthy Eating, Active Living: An Action Plan to Improve Diet, Increase Physical Activity and Tackle Obesity (2008-2011).* Scottish Government, Edinburgh.

Scottish Government (2008c). *Planning Advice Note 65: Planning and open space*. Scottish Government, Edinburgh.

Scottish Government (2008d). *Urban Rural Classification, 2007-2008*. Scottish Government, Edinburgh.

Scottish Government (2009). *Scottish Health Survey Analysis by Local Authority or Health Board*. Scottish Government, Edinburgh.

Scottish Government (2010). *Scottish Vacant and Derelict Land Survey 2009*. Statistical Bulletin, PLG/2010/1.

SNH (2007). Volunteering Impact Assessment. Internal report.

SNH (2008). *Scottish Natural Heritage, Corporate Strategy 2008 – 2013*. Scottish Natural Heritage, Perth.

SNH (2009). *Developing the contribution of the natural heritage to a healthier Scotland*. Scottish Natural Heritage, Perth.

Sustrans (2007). Creating the environment for active travel. *Information Sheet FH09*. Sustrans, Bristol.

Volunteer Development Scotland (2006). Volunteering in the natural heritage; an audit and review of natural heritage volunteering in Scotland. *Scottish Natural Heritage Commissioned Report*. No. 219.

Ward Thompson, C., Aspinall, P. and Montarzino, A. (2008). The Childhood Factor: adult visits to green places and the significance of childhood experience. *Environment and Behavior*, **40**, 111 – 143.

13 How Supportive Environments Generate Good Health

Harry Burns

Summary

1. This paper explores the principles underling how our health is affected by the environment.
2. Our early year experiences are likely to determine the extent to which we engage with nature; those who would benefit the most are often less likely (or able) to seek out opportunities for themselves.
3. If we want to use our natural environment to generate good health we need to do more than say it is available; proactive action by public bodies is required.

13.1 The relationship between nature and health

To what extent is our health determined by our external environment? There is suggestive evidence that exposure to nature improves human health, but the scientific literature that explores the relationship between nature and health is not completely compelling and many of the published papers are flawed in some way. Most studies are undertaken in high income countries and participants are usually fit, middle class adults; this is highly selective. Studies very rarely have control stimuli - is there an alternative way of stimulating a sense of well-being? It is very difficult to screen out confounding variables, for example some neurologists believe that the continued exposure to traffic noise from living close to a motorway will lower the IQ of children, however if you cannot afford to move your home away from the motorway there may be other social factors present.

This paper considers some of the key underlying principles linking health and the human external environment and provides food for thought on how planners can devise urban environments that will generate good health.

Burns, H. (2011). How Supportive Environments Generate Good Health – *The Changing Nature of Scotland*, eds. S.J. Marrs, S. Foster, C. Hendrie, E.C. Mackey, D.B.A. Thompson. TSO Scotland, Edinburgh, pp 125-132.

To set the work in context we should first compare the health of Scotland's people to those in the rest of Europe. At the start of the twentieth century, life expectancy in Scotland was higher than the European average and was comparable with countries such as France, Spain, Germany, Italy and in Scandinavia. During the first half of the twentieth century life expectancy in all countries increased at roughly the same rate. This improvement slowed in the middle of the century for all countries, but was particularly marked for Scotland, so that at the end of the century the only European country with a lower life expectancy was Portugal. If we look at life expectancy by local government district we see that most of Scotland has a similar life expectancy to the rest of Western Europe. However there are eight districts in Scotland where life expectancy is noticeably lower. These districts are the Clydeside conurbation plus Dundee city and the Western Isles.

Why might this be? In the 1950s the districts on either side of the Clyde suffered the most from the collapse of ship-building, heavy engineering and steel working. These parts of central Scotland have for three of four generations suffered from the psychological, social and physical dereliction that comes from loss of skilled employment. Although the same thing happened in the Midlands of England, people living there were able to find employment in car manufacturing, electronics and consumer goods.

Most people would accept there is a relationship between dereliction and poor health. You are more likely to die 10 to 15 years earlier if you are born in the Clydeside conurbation plus Dundee City and the Western Isles than in other parts of Scotland; however what appears on your death certificate is a molecular cause, not a sociological one. You never see a death certificate that says he died from poor housing or because he was unemployed. What happens is that you die because the protein molecules in your blood coagulate and form a clot and you get a stroke or a heart attack, or free radicals damage your DNA and you develop a cancer.

So what is the link between molecules in the body and the sociological and psychological consequences of being in that sort of environment? The history of health improvement is full of well intentioned failure. We do the right things: for example, we plant trees but unless planting trees actually changes what goes on inside individuals physiologically, it is unlikely to influence the atoms and molecules that are going to kill them.

13.2 A sense of coherence

Aaron Antonovsky was an American sociologist, who studied women who had been through the holocaust as children and had survived the concentration camps. His study on the mental and physical health of these women showed that 29% had absolutely no ill health whatsoever - he was astonished that it was so high. How could anyone come through that experience and be physically and mentally intact? Antonovsky concluded that the children coped because they had developed what he described as a sense of coherence (Antonovsky, 1979).

A sense of coherence is the feeling of confidence that you get once you have learned that external environments are structured, predictable and explicable. That you have the resources, psychologically and physically to meet the demands posed by stimuli and finally that you see the demands as challenges to be overcome. If you develop that kind of psychological view of the outside world, Antonovsky argued, you can cope with things as terrible as being in a concentration camp. You can make sense of what is happening to you. You trust yourself to cope and you want to cope.

13.3 Stress and social hierarchy

The impact of social inequality on health has been recognised since the nineteenth century when accurate mortality data first became available. People higher up the social hierarchy tend to live longer healthier lives. Prior to the 1970s socioeconomic differences were controlled for as confounding variables rather than being studied in their own right. However, in the 1960s a study of British civil servants from all grades, in stable secure jobs, demonstrated that people at lower grades had a higher risk of premature death from cardiovascular disease and diabetes (Marmot and Brunner, 2005). The studies came to be known as the Whitehall study. Whitehall II started in the 1980s with a new cohort of civil servants and aimed to determine the biological mechanisms that underpin this 'social gradient' in health. A study of salivary cortisol levels (elevated levels are indicative of stress) showed that higher-grade civil servants were significantly less stressed through the day than lower-grade civil servants (Steptoe *et al.*, 2003). One of the conclusions reached was that more senior staff are able to delegate undesirable tasks to lower-grade staff and therefore have more control over their working lives. Whereas the grades at the bottom of the hierarchy are characterised by high demand, low control jobs, where staff tend not to have as much control and are therefore prone to increased stress levels.

So the sense of control in daily life, to a large extent, determines the body's physiological response to the psychological position you find yourself in by regulating the stress response. Similar responses have been detected in babies when placed in orphanages. It seems that very early on in life we seem to be able to set our stress response in light of things that are happening to us externally.

The impact of a lack of control in life can be scaled up to a country level. After the breakdown of the Soviet-block men and women from across Eastern Europe were asked questions about health, socioeconomic circumstances, perceived control over their lives and a range of aspects relating to their work. The results showed a strong correlation between health and the balance between effort and reward at work (Pikhart *et al.*, 2001). Studies such as these do not allow us to reach any firm conclusions about cause and effect; for that we need to look to some controlled experiments on primates.

Rhesus macaque (*Macaca mulatta*) monkeys have been studied in detail to determine the effects of social stress on behaviour and neural biology. The experiments involve controlling the access the female monkey has to food for her young. Where food is plentiful the mother finds it easy to locate and feed her baby monkey. If food is scarce the mother may have to search and compete with other monkeys, which means she is away from her baby for a much longer period. You might think that this would result in stress for the baby monkey, however cortisol levels are the same in both groups of monkeys. It is okay for the baby monkey to be left on its own, so long as it knows that it is going to be left on its own. However, if sometimes it is easy for the mother to get food but other times it is hard, the baby monkey does not know whether it will be left for a long time or a short time or even if it will get food – it is this inconsistency that results in stress for the baby (Stevens *et al.*, 2009).

Inconsistency of early years is an extremely powerful driver of stress in young infants. It is also a driver of obesity, because cortisol blocks the entry of the hormone leptin, which is released by adipocytes (fat cells), into the satiety centres of the brain, so hunger is never switched off. This is a perfectly reasonable evolutionary response. If the baby receives signals that feeding is inconsistent it starts to store food; a good survival response. What we have established here is the importance of the brain in shaping our response to stress.

Dr Bruce McEwen from the Rockefeller University in New York has shown that the brains of stressed young animals develop in a completely different way from those that are nurtured consistently. The areas of the brain that change are the prefrontal cortex (where decision making happens), the hippocampus (where short and long term memory are integrated) and the amygdala (where you generate emotional responses). The number of cells in the prefrontal cortex and the hippocampus decreases but shows an increase in the amygdala, because the baby is receiving signals that the outside world is an inconsistent and possibly dangerous place. Essentially the brain is switching from intellectualising the world to surviving it – aggression, fear and anxiety are being sharpened.

Another key element is that the hippocampus and the amygdala both regulate the stress response. The hippocampus suppresses it, while the amygdala up regulates it. In babies that receive inconsistent care the hippocampus gets smaller and the amygdala gets larger. In evolutionary terms this is precisely what is needed for survival. We are hunter gatherers and babies need to learn to defend themselves early on, so they need an accentuated stress response and they need to be emotionally aware of danger. Infants adopt behaviours that optimally enhance their own chances of survival in whichever environment they find themselves.

The idea is explained by the concept of attachment theory, developed by the British psychiatrist and psychoanalyst John Bowlby and published in his trilogy *Attachment and Loss* (1969/1982, 1973, 1980). Attachment behaviour gives the baby an internal working model of what the outside world is and what it can expect from adults. If the infant does not attach to adults early on in life, this is a predictor of poor social and emotional outcomes in later life (Balbernie, 2001). A baby that is nurtured and develops a consistent relationship with its primary caregiver will develop executive function in the prefrontal lobes, build memory in the hippocampus and suppress the relatively negative effects of the amygdala, reduce aggression and dampen stress responses.

Contrast that with the baby whose feeding is inconsistent and who is alone when he cries, or even worse who experiences violence. The baby gets the message that the world is not only inconsistent, but is a dangerous place. In this scenario the amygdala will be more developed as the baby needs to respond to danger, there is a reorientation of nerve growth in the direction of the fight or flight response and so a chronic up-regulation of stress results. Chronically elevated stress response leads to higher levels of circulating fatty acids in the blood, which can be deposited in the lining of the arteries. When associated with increased inflammatory processes the rupture of these plaques leads to an increased risk of heart attack and stroke.

13.4 Physical responses to external environments

Does this theory translate into what is observed in the wider world? Recent work undertaken by the University of Glasgow using an MRI (Magnetic Resonance Imaging) scanner at Southern General Hospital has suggested that there are significant differences in the hippocampus volume in affluent and deprived Glaswegians. In the same study, psychometric tests have produced results consistent with damage to the prefrontal cortex and hippocampus in subjects from deprived areas. The differences have been subtle, but they are measureable and statistically significant and the early results are beginning to show that the complex environments in which people live have a very profound influence on their ability to function (unpublished data).

The hypothesis that we have outlined is being played out in real time through the different life routes of children taking part in the Dunedin Study. In the early 1970s 1,000 children from Dunedin, South Island of New Zealand, were recruited for a longitudinal study of health and development. The children have been monitored periodically since they were three years old to the present day (Silva and Stanton, 1996) and are considered representative of the New Zealand population as a whole

Plate 13.1 A sense of coherence can be established from knowing what to expect and having boundaries. We develop this sense as children often from simple things like taking a regular walk with our families. © Kelly Matheson

(Poulton *et al.*, 2006). A number of children who at three years old were indentified as living in a chaotic environment have demonstrated adverse social outcomes such as long-term unemployment; criminal convictions (especially violence); teenage pregnancy and substance abuse. They are also showing the metabolic abnormalities that we would predict from chronic elevation of cortisone, insulin resistance and metabolic syndromes that will lead to early heart disease, stroke and cancer as we have predicted from data elsewhere.

So where does that leave us? Consistent parenting, safe nurturing in early years and a supportive education build a sense of understanding and help make the world comprehensible. The opportunity to escape poverty, decent housing, social networks and a sense of control make life manageable. The third limb of Aaron Antonovsky's work, that life must be meaningful, needs iconic buildings and places that make people feel good about themselves. The ability to get outdoors is really important. Scotland's fascination with mountaineering took off during the 1920s and 1930s when unemployed ship yard workers travelled to the mountains of Glencoe. People from deprived areas are not doing this now. They stay at home and are much less resilient in making choices about their life. Planners need to think about how they can plan environments that create space for people to make choices. It is very clear that people who are being most harmed by their environment are least likely to go out and, for example, climb mountains.

> *'We are coming to understand health not as the absence of disease, but rather as the process by which individuals maintain their sense of coherence (i.e. sense that life is comprehensible, manageable, and meaningful) and ability to function in the face of changes in themselves and their relationships with their environment.'*
>
> Aaron Antonovsky

13.5 Conclusion

In the past public health authorities thought that health could be improved by tackling health related behaviours such as smoking or diet. We have known for some years now that you are more likely to engage in healthy behaviour if you have the opportunity to escape poverty, decent housing, good social networks, a sense of self esteem and a sense of control over your life. In addition to this Aaron Antonovsky has demonstrated that consistent parenting and supportive education in early years allows you to make sense of the world, which in turn helps you to manage your problems in a more effective way. If we can create something with our environment that is meaningful, something that makes people *want* to go out and participate in it, this is how we will generate good health.

Perhaps one the reasons we have found it so difficult to describe the link between greenspaces and health is that we have been providing greenspaces to people who already have all of these things. The challenge is to focus on people who can neither find their lives comprehensible, manageable or meaningful.

Acknowledgement

I would like to thank Sue Marrs who helped prepare this manuscript.

References

Antonovsky, A. (1979). *Health, stress, and coping: New perspectives on mental and physical wellbeing.* San Francisco. Jossey-Bass.

Balbernie, R. (2001). Circuits and circumstances: the neurobiological consequences of early relationships and how they shape later behaviour. *Journal of Child Psychotherapy*, **27**, 237-255.

Bowlby, J. (1969/1982). *Attachment and loss: Vol. 1. Attachment.* New York. Basic Books.

Bowlby, J. (1973). *Attachment and loss: Vol. 2. Separation.* New York. Basic Books.

Bowlby, J. (1980). *Attachment and loss: Vol. 3. Loss.* New York. Basic Books.

Marmot, M. and Brunner, E. (2005). Cohort profile: the Whitehall II study. *International Journal of Epidemiology*, **34**, 251-256.

Pikhart, H., Boback, M., Siegrist, J. *et al.* (2001). Psychosocial work characteristics and self related health in four post-communist countries. *Journal of Epidemiology and Community Health*, **55**, 624-630.

Poulton, R., Hancox, R., Milne, B. *et al.* (2006). The Dunedin multidisciplinary health and development study: are its findings consistent with the overall New Zealand population? *Journal of the New Zealand Medical Association*, **119**.

Silva, P.A. and Stanton, W.R. (ed.) (1996). *From child to adult: the Dunedin multidisciplinary health and development study.* Auckland. Oxford University Press.

Steptoe, A., Kunz-Ebrecht, S., Owen, N. *et al.* (2003). Socioeconomic status and stress-related biological responses over the working day. *Psychosomatic Medicine*, **65**, 461-470.

Stevens, H.E., Leckman, J.F., Coplan, J.D. and Suomi, S.J. (2009). Risk and resilience: early manipulation of macaque social experience and persistent behavioural and neurophysiological outcomes. *Journal of the American Academy of Child and Adolescent Psychiatry*, **48**, 114-127.

14 The Impact of John Muir Award Experiences on the Health-related Behaviours, Attitudes and Aspirations of Participants

Richard Mitchell and Rob Bushby

Summary

1. The John Muir Award encourages people of all ages and backgrounds to connect with, enjoy, and care for the planet's wild places. This involves meeting four challenges: discovering a wild place; actively exploring it; doing something to conserve it; and sharing these experiences.
2. There are positive impacts arising from involvement, not least high levels of enjoyment and direct engagement with groups ordinarily less likely to undertake outdoor experiences.
3. Once introduced to natural environments, there is a heightened aspiration by participants to revisit them; however, evidence of longer term behaviour change was not identified in follow-up surveys.

14.1 Study aim

This paper is based on a study conducted by Glasgow University's Public Health and Health Policy Unit. The aim of the study was to assess the impact of the John Muir Award on the health-related behaviours, attitudes and aspirations of participants and determine what they thought of their Award experience. The study targeted participants aged 8 to 18, drawn primarily from west and central Scotland. There was a flexible interpretation of 'wild places', and this included everything from parks to remote wilderness settings.

14.2 Background

There is growing interest in the role outdoor environments play in improving health and well-being (Bell *et al.*, 2007; Mitchell and Popham, 2007; van den Berg *et al.*,

Mitchell, R. and Bushby, R. (2011). The Impact of John Muir Award Experiences on the Health-related Behaviours, Attitudes and Aspirations of Participants – *The Changing Nature of Scotland*, eds. S.J. Marrs, S. Foster, C. Hendrie, E.C. Mackey, D.B.A. Thompson. TSO Scotland, Edinburgh, pp 133-138.

2007). Although the body of evidence which shows that the outdoors really can help make everyone healthier is growing, this is more anecdotal rather than rigorous scientific work (Mitchell and Popham, 2008).

We know that people who spend time in natural environments as children are more likely to do so as adults, with their own children (Ward Thompson *et al.*, 2008). We also know that these environments promote physical activity and relaxation, and that they might also have other health benefits (Mitchell and Popham, 2008; van der Berg *et al.*, 2007). Encouraging young people to take an interest in wild places could have long term benefits for both their development and health.

The Award is the main educational initiative of the John Muir Trust and is particularly adept at including young people from disadvantaged backgrounds (Bushby, 2003). At least 30% of the year-on-year uptake were in this category (6,919 of the 21,829 Awards achieved across the UK in 2009). This category can be difficult to connect with and inspire, and are more likely to experience health problems in later life (Mitchell and Popham, 2007; 2008).

14.3 Approach and methods

The study collected data in two ways: questionnaires and focus groups. Detailed questionnaires were received from an initial sample of 326 participants before their Award experiences. The same participants were contacted just after (205 valid responses received) and approximately 18 months after Award experiences (69 valid responses received). The questionnaires covered health-related behaviours and opinions, experiences of wild places and aspirations for the future. Participants were also asked detailed questions about what they had done for their Award, their attitudes to it and how the experience might have changed their opinions and behaviours.

The average age of the sample was 13, with a spread from 8 to 18 years and evenly balanced between boys and girls. It was possible to establish whether a respondent was resident in an area which was part of the most deprived 15% of the Scottish population by matching postcodes with the Scottish Index of Multiple Deprivation (SIMD). Just over 20% of our respondents were from these areas.

A number of Award participants who had not been part of the survey took part in focus groups to discuss their own Award experiences and attitudes in relation to survey findings. This allowed the research team to explore some of the results from the questionnaires in more detail.

14.4 Key findings

We were interested to find out about participants' experience of wild places. Nearly one in ten had never visited what they understood to be a 'wild place' before their

Award. The chances of being in this minority were significantly increased by being in socio-economically deprived backgrounds – those living in the 15% most deprived areas, according to the SIMD, were over six times more likely to have had no previous experience of wild places.

We also wanted to know about their attitudes towards their Award experiences, and what they did or didn't like about them. The vast majority (95%) of respondents enjoyed their Award experience and felt they had achieved something by doing it (92%); see Figure 14.1. Specific themes identified within these findings included conservation activities, the chance to do new things, and mixing with existing friends and making new ones.

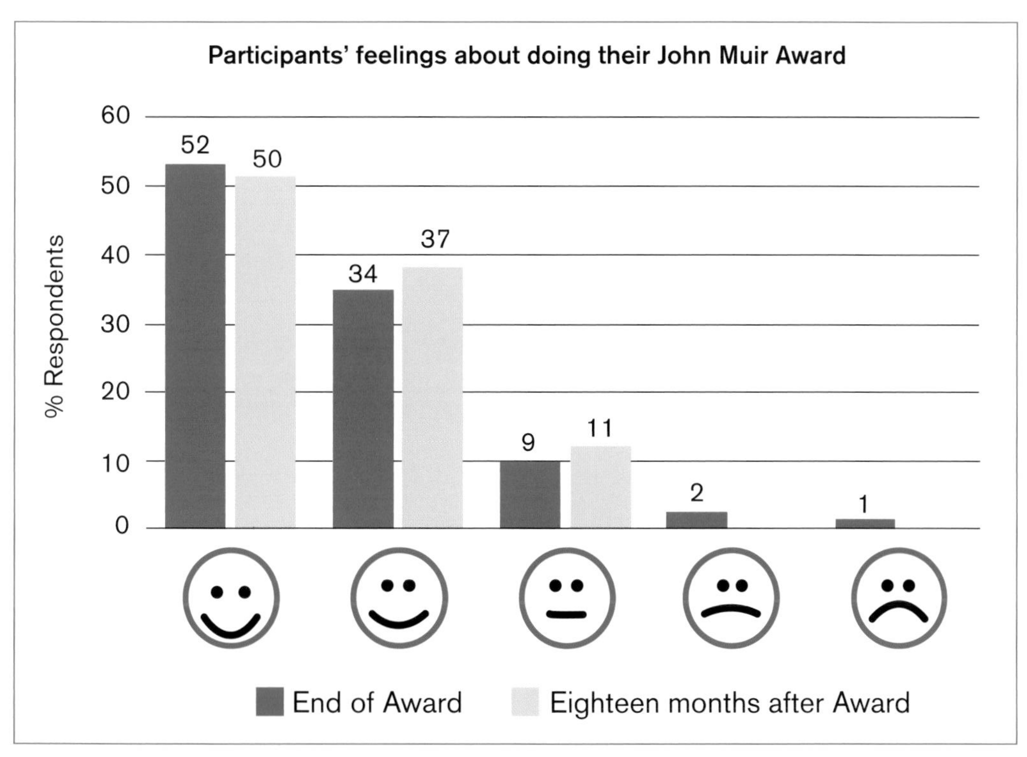

Figure 14.1 Opinions of John Muir Award participants on how much they enjoyed taking part in the Award. The categories were: very much enjoyed; enjoyed; were indifferent to; disliked; or hated their experience of the John Muir Award.

Participants were asked about their aspirations for future contact with natural environments. The majority of respondents (Figure 14.2) reported that their Award involvement made them want to spend more time outdoors, and to visit natural environments more, with 44% agreeing 'a lot' and 35% agreeing 'a bit'. This was a sustained effect among those responding a further 18 months after completing their John Muir Award, with 71% of these respondents still in agreement. This

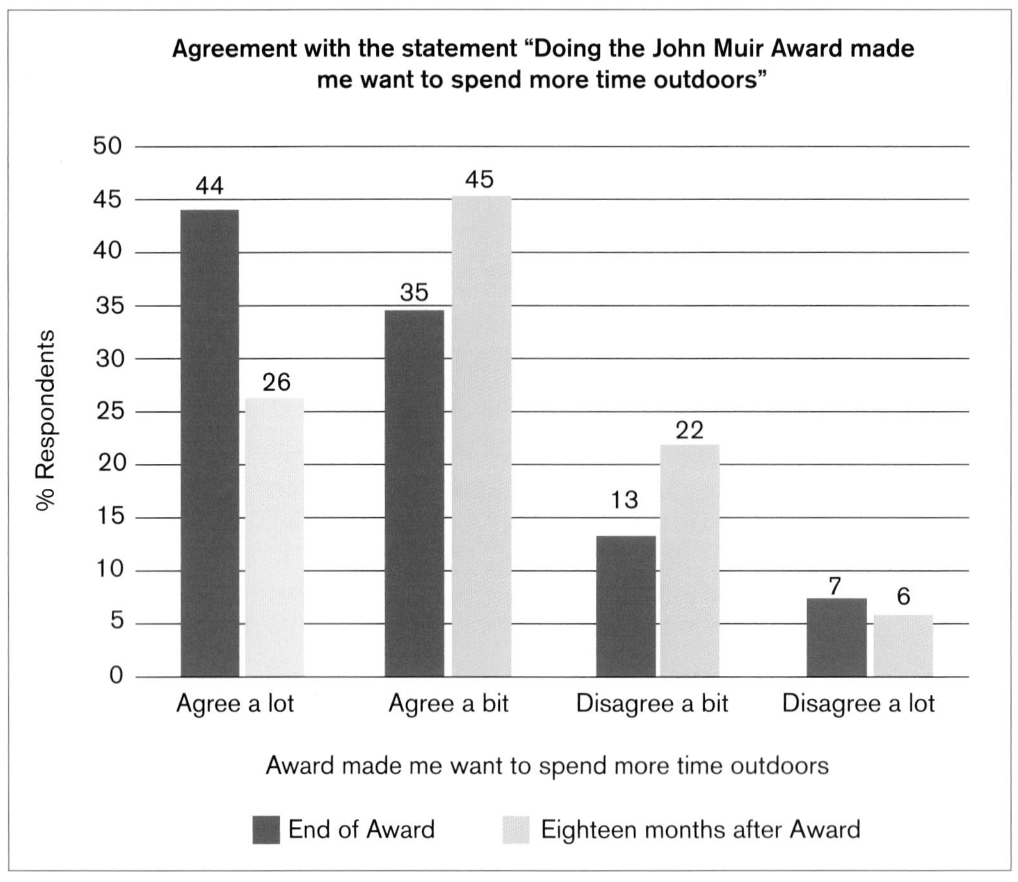

Figure 14.2 Responses of participants who were asked whether they agreed with the statement 'Doing the John Muir Award made me want to spend more time outdoors', directly after the award and after a period of 18 months.

impact was particularly strong for Award participants from Scotland's most deprived neighbourhoods.

The Award experience had no clearly identifiable impact on self esteem amongst the participants as a whole; variations occurred within subgroups but could not be attributed directly to Award involvement. There was no observed difference between boys and girls in terms of attitude to, enjoyment and impact of their Award experience.

Participation in the Award had no clear impact on how often young people subsequently visited wild places; 18 months after their Award experience 62% of respondents continued to visit wild places with the same frequency as before, 15% more often and 15% less often. This is highly likely to reflect the fact that most respondents are not in control of their visits to these environments; it requires some combination of time, parental permission, company and perhaps transport.

14.5 Conclusions

The results from our study show that participants overwhelmingly enjoyed and valued their John Muir Award experience. Their aspirations for visiting wild places also increased, particularly among those from the most deprived backgrounds. The study showed that those in the poorest circumstances were much less likely to have visited wild places before their Award experience, and that perhaps this group was most positively affected by the experience.

Whilst the Award experience was successful at introducing people to wild places and helping to establish aspirations for healthy behaviours this did not appear to translate into longer term behaviour change. The implication is that further support is required to convert aspiration into actual behaviour, either by the John Muir Award itself or other agencies.

With the increased recognition and profile of links between health and outdoor experiences, the study findings indicate that the impact of John Muir Award experiences on the health-related behaviours, attitudes and aspirations of participants has both value and further potential. The implications are clear: more young people should have the chance to have this kind of experience, and efforts should continue to reach the least advantaged.

Plate 14.1 Wild Rum - John Muir Award participants enjoying a sunset on 'Wild Rum'. © Dave Pyper/ George Watson's College

Acknowledgements

Glasgow Centre for Population Health (GCPH) funded this research which was conducted by Richard Mitchell and Rebecca Shaw of Glasgow University's Public Health and Health Policy Unit. A full research report is available to download from www.gcph.org.uk or from info@johnmuirward.org.

References

Bell, S., Montarzino, A. and Travlou, P. (2007). Mapping research priorities for green and public urban space in the UK. *Urban Forestry and Urban Greening*, **6**, 103-115.

Bushby, R. (2003). *An investigation into the John Muir Award and its relationship with outdoor education and environmental education.* MSc. University of Edinburgh.

Kaczynski, A.T. and Henderson, K.A. (2007). Environmental correlates of physical activity: A review of evidence about parks and recreation. *Leisure Sciences*, **29**, 315-354.

Mitchell, R. and Popham, F. (2007). Greenspace, urbanity and health: relationships in England. *Journal of Epidemiology and Community Health*, **61**, 681-683.

Mitchell, R. and Popham, F. (2008). Effect of exposure to natural environment on health inequalities: an observational population study. *The Lancet*, **372**, 1655-1660.

Van den Berg, A.E., Hartig, T. and Staats, H. (2007). Preference for nature in urbanized societies: stress, restoration, and the pursuit of sustainability. *Journal of Social Issues*, **63**, 79-96.

Ward Thompson, C., Aspinall, P. and Montarzino, A. (2008). The Childhood Factor: Adult visits to green places and the significance of childhood experience. *Environment and Behavior*, **40**, 111-143.

15 Why Bird Monitoring in Scotland Needs More Volunteers

Mandy Cook, Chris Waltho, Ieuan Evans and Chris Wernham

Summary

1. Over 5,000 volunteers provide scientifically rigorous and cost-effective information for bird conservation science purposes in Scotland.
2. Volunteers indicate how much they benefit from involvement in bird recording, enhancing their appreciation of being outdoors.
3. Scotland's low and aggregated human population, remote and challenging terrains, and varied climate and land-uses give rise to considerable challenges when seeking representative monitoring by volunteers.
4. We describe recent attempts to increase the volunteer base and provide the enhanced biodiversity monitoring that is needed to underpin policy decisions relating to Scotland's changing nature into the future.

15.1 Introduction

UK bird populations are some of the most effectively monitored in the world, thanks to more than 54,000 dedicated volunteer birdwatchers who contribute to over 40 British Trust for Ornithology (BTO)-led surveys annually. The effort of over 5,000 Scottish volunteers represents a huge input of manpower and has proved to be a productive and cost-effective way of monitoring wild birds. It is the only feasible means of achieving the geographically broad, and regular, monitoring of the wide range of species and habitats in Scotland, and involves many people in practical conservation. In this paper we describe why the need for volunteer bird recorders to increase understanding of Scotland's biodiversity has never been greater, and how we are attempting to increase the volunteer base for the future.

Cook, M., Waltho, C., Evans, I. and Wernham, C. (2011). Why Bird Monitoring in Scotland Needs More Volunteers – *The Changing Nature of Scotland*, eds. S.J. Marrs, S. Foster, C. Hendrie, E.C. Mackey, D.B.A. Thompson. TSO Scotland, Edinburgh, pp 139-144.

15.2 Current volunteering in Scotland: value, needs and initiatives

Volunteers are vital for collecting biodiversity information in Scotland. They generously give their own time to a broad range of recording activities that produce scientifically robust information on: bird populations, distributions, trends and conservation alerts; demography (productivity and survival); phenology (timing of breeding and movements); and migration (movement routes and patterns) (see www.bto.org/survey/). The funding that underpins monitoring activities delivered by volunteers thus represents phenomenal value for money.

15.2.1 Skills and needs of volunteers

Volunteers in Scotland have a wide range of expertise: many are highly skilled, often contributing years of experience, whilst others have basic bird identification skills or are starting off with little or no survey experience. BTO and Scottish Ornithologists' Club (SOC) work to ensure that surveys exist for everyone and have a long-term commitment to: providing training to volunteers for specific surveys matching the right people with the right type of survey for their current skill levels; and empowering volunteers to progress from entry-level recording (e.g. BTO Garden BirdWatch; Toms *et al.*, Chapter 41) to the systematic recording schemes that provide the highest quality information for conservation science use. Through these approaches, an appropriate balance is struck between the need to maintain high data quality whilst involving as many people as possible in bird surveying.

Volunteers need well designed and enjoyable surveys. It is important to provide timely feedback on their efforts and suitable recording facilities such as bespoke online applications for their data.

15.2.2 Why are more volunteers needed in Scotland?

Scotland's generally low and clustered human population, remoteness and demanding terrains in many areas, present considerable challenges when seeking representative bird monitoring by volunteers. Survey coverage is very low or absent over large areas of Scotland (Figure 15.1).

Birds can respond quickly to variation in habitat quality and other environmental variables and are therefore often used as indicators of environmental change. 'Increasing the Index of Abundance of Terrestrial Breeding Birds' is a National Biodiversity objective for the Scottish Government. The BTO/JNCC/RSPB Breeding Bird Survey (BBS; see www.bto.org/bbs) is the principal means of monitoring change in breeding numbers of widespread terrestrial birds in Scotland, contributing information on 56 of the 65 species in the terrestrial bird indicator (see www.snh.gov.uk/docs/B536405.pdf). As the numbers of volunteers increase, the

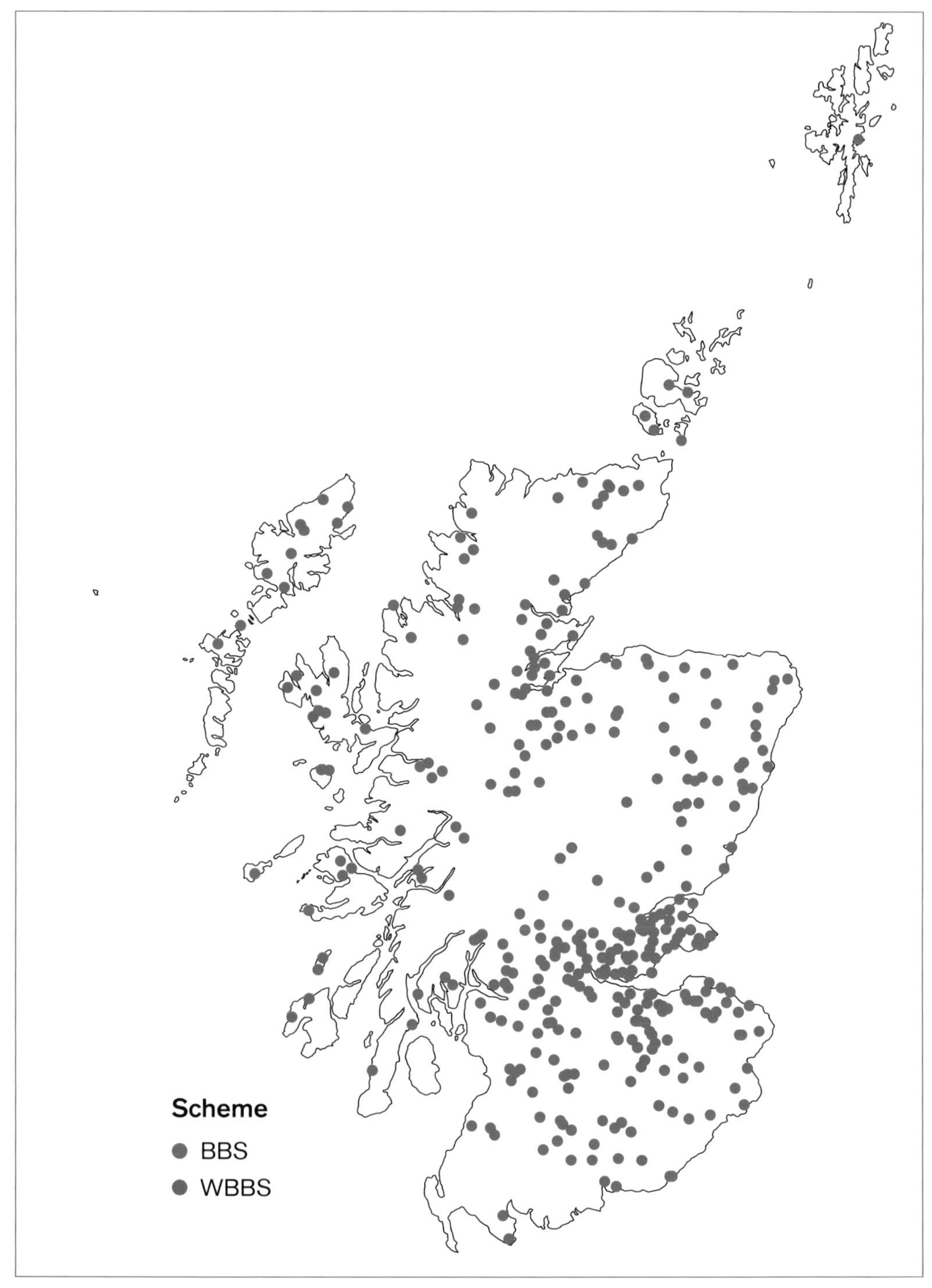

Figure 15.1 Breeding Bird Survey (BBS) and Waterways Breeding Bird Survey (WBBS) squares surveyed in Scotland in 2009. Areas with low monitoring coverage by volunteers include parts of Argyll, the central Highlands, Ross-shire and Sutherland. Similar areas have low coverage by other bird monitoring schemes (for example, inland WeBS (Wetland Bird Survey) sites).

precision of trends and the number of species that are monitored improves. In Scotland, some habitats and geographical areas remain under-represented (particularly the uplands).

Another of Scotland's Biodiversity Indicators is the 'Abundance of Wintering Waterbirds', based on BTO/RSPB/JNCC Wetland Bird Survey (WeBS; see www.bto.org/webs) data collected largely by volunteers. Coverage in Scotland is generally very good for large estuaries, but there are a number of other sites (lochs, rivers, ponds or even burns) used by many species of waterbirds, which are not currently surveyed. Recently a decline in mallard (*Anas platyrhyncos*) numbers of 33% since the mid 1980s has been shown by WeBS data. The reasons behind this decline are unclear, but might include poor breeding success or milder winters which could allow birds to remain on smaller waterbodies instead of being forced to congregate at larger sites. In order to be sure whether mallard are declining, improved monitoring of smaller waterbodies is needed, and is one of the aims for WeBS in Scotland.

Scotland is experiencing a range of new challenges that will require an enhanced and robust biodiversity evidence base. For example, climate change is already markedly altering Scotland's river flows (Spray, Chapter 21), yet there is inadequate monitoring in place to assess the impacts on riverine birds. Our northerly-distributed upland birds are regarded as sensitive to predicted changes in Scotland's climate (Pearce-Higgins, Chapter 33). Currently widespread upland species are poorly covered by monitoring schemes. Rigorous bird monitoring of representative habitats across Scotland is vital to better understand ecological principles and functions of Scotland's natural heritage, and for testing and refining current change predictions.

15.2.3 Recent volunteer initiatives

With these needs in mind, we have run a number of projects aimed at enhancing monitoring coverage by increasing the numbers, geographical distribution, and types of people involved in voluntary bird survey work.

In 2006, *Project Ptarmigan* asked hillwalkers if they would record ptarmigan (*Lagopus mutus*) and other montane birds across Scotland. Over 140 volunteers covered 614 transect routes across an impressive 3,212km of Scotland's arctic-alpine zone. Not only did they prove they had the knowledge to identify and record a range of upland birds, they also provided a test of suitably rigorous scientific survey methods that were attractive to hillwalkers rather than traditional birdwatchers. Their experiences are contributing to plans for improving monitoring coverage of Scotland's uplands (Calladine and Wernham, 2007, 2009).

The BTO/SOC *Building Bird Monitoring in Scotland* project (with support from SNH and the Gillman Trusts) involves working with the BTO and SOC regional volunteer coordinators to offer enhanced bird survey training: ranging from introducing basic bird identification skills to complete beginners, to courses to build confidence and encourage highly experienced birdwatchers to undertake systematic surveys. Over three years, 350 people have attended training events across Scotland, including audiences new to bird recording (e.g. hillwalkers, land owners and land managers). The project has included detailed monitoring of the success of training events and feedback on the needs and aspirations of volunteers (Cook *et al.*, in press).

The current SOC/BTO *Integrated Bird Recording in Scotland* project (supported by SNH) aims to mobilise bird records, collected across Scotland by volunteer Scottish Local Bird Recorders and their observer networks, by enhancing the current BTO/RSPB/BWI/SOC BirdTrack system (see www.bto.org/birdtrack) to make it more attractive for the volunteers to use. It will: allow the system to store more information that volunteers wish to record; provide enhanced on-line feedback and facilities for the volunteers to analyse their records for their own purposes (e.g. for Local Recorders when they need to summarise records for their local bird reports); and provide bespoke guidance to encourage as great an uptake by the Scottish birding community as possible, making their records available for conservation use.

15.3 Future priorities to enhance volunteer involvement and monitoring coverage

In the future our priorities include:

- Continued consideration of enhanced survey approaches to improve coverage of key under-surveyed habitats (e.g. uplands and rivers) and geographical areas;
- Continued promotion of bird recording to new groups of potential volunteers (e.g. countryside users), and working with partner organisations to access appropriate volunteer groups;
- Increasingly recognising the needs of 'entry-level' volunteers and the support required to progress them to systematic bird recording (e.g. one-to-one mentoring and regular personal encouragement);
- Further enhancement of on-line recording and support/feedback tools to maximise their attractiveness and usefulness for volunteers; and
- Increased partnership working with organisations that monitor taxa other than birds, to facilitate efficient skills transfer and provide appropriate tools for multi-taxa monitoring where possible.

Some targeted research will be needed to meet the future challenges of managing the nature of Scotland. Without the long-term bird monitoring undertaken in Scotland, largely by volunteers, we would not know how Scotland's biodiversity has altered already or be able to predict the implications of future policy and management action.

Acknowledgements

We thank all those volunteers who have given so much to assist BTO and SOC in bird recording activities over the years, and especially our regional coordinators for their commitment. We also thank all those organisations and individuals who have funded us to develop and support our volunteer base, only some of whom are mentioned in this paper.

References

Calladine, J. and Wernham, C. (2007). Extensive monitoring of arctic-alpine birds in Scotland: a pilot survey to test the potential for using volunteers. *BTO Research Report* No. 473. BTO Scotland, Stirling.

Calladine, J. and Wernham, C. (2009). Extensive monitoring of rock ptarmigan *Lagopus mutus* in Scotland: a pilot to test the efficacy of using volunteer surveyors for monitoring arctic-alpine birds. *Avocetta*, **33**, 217-224.

Cook, M. *et al.* (In press). The Building Bird Monitoring in Scotland Project: final report. *BTO Research Report* No. 564. BTO Scotland, Stirling.

The Changing Nature of Scotland

Surrounding seas and coast

Surrounding seas and coast

Despite the many connections between habitats and species throughout the world's seas, the waters around Scotland support a characteristic and diverse flora and fauna. Many species are either at the northern or southern edges of their range. The chapters within this section demonstrate the interconnectivity of life in marine systems and give a flavour of how important the surrounding seas and coast are to Scotland. We have already seen in the early part of this book that much monitoring is underway; the status of commercial fish stocks and the changes to plankton are tracked and updated annually through two of the Scottish Biodiversity Indicators (Foster *et al.*, Chapter 2).

Some key events concerning nature in Scotland's marine environment since 1970

1971	Advisory Committee on Fisheries set up (now also covers aquaculture – ACFA) to provide industry advice to the European Commission
1975	Bathing Water Directive (76/160/EEC)
1976	North Sea oil production began
1978	Grey seal cull on Orkney and Western Isles reduced significantly due to public outcry
1979	*Nature Conservation and the Marine Environment* published by the NCC
1981	Wildlife and Countryside Act – allows for the designation of Marine Nature Reserves
1983	The Marine Conservation Society formed
1984	Inshore Fishing (Scotland) Act
1985	The North Sea Forum (later Marine Forum) established
1986	The Seabird Monitoring Programme (SMP) established
1987	Tri-butyl-tin (TBT), the causative agent of anatomical deformations in a number of marine molluscs, is banned in antifouling paints in vessels under 25m and aquaculture equipment
1988	Phocine distemper virus affects common seals in Scotland

or cod, bloody Henry starfish and soft corals
Loch Carron, Strome © Sue Scott/SNH

1990	Shetland sand eel fishery suspended in response to seabirds' breeding failure
1992	Habitats and Species Directive – Directive 92/43/EEC
1993	The oil tanker *Braer* ship-wrecked off Shetland, resulting in a major oil spill
1995	Environment Act – enabled fishery restrictions to be applied for biodiversity reasons
1997	Isle of Eigg bought by residents in partnership with SWT and Highland Regional Council
1998	Darwin Mounds (almost 100 miles off north west Scotland) discovered
1999	JNCC commences survey of offshore sites for Habitats and Species Directives. Completed in 2002
2000	Water Framework Directive – Directive 2000/60/EC
2000	Start of the global census of marine life – a ten year project with the aim of systematically recording all that is known about the oceans
2002	Common Fisheries Policy (CFP) reform (EC)2371/2002
2003	First offshore fisheries closure for nature conservation purposes in the EU – an emergency closure of the fisheries around the Darwin Mounds enabled by the reformed CFP. The closure was made permanent in 2004
2003	First allocation in Europe of quotas for deep sea fish species
2004	Creation of Regional Advisory Councils (RACs) to foster stakeholder engagement in the management of marine fisheries
2005	First marine Special Areas of Conservation designated under the Habitats Directive
2006	Launch of the Marine Wildlife Watching Code
2006	Scotland's first offshore wind turbine is sited in the Moray Firth
2008	EC 1005/2008 Council Regulation to deter illegal, unreported and unregulated fisheries
2008	Marine Strategy Framework Directive – Directive 2008/56/EC
2009	Marine Scotland formed
2009	Marine and Coastal Access Act
2010	Marine (Scotland) Act
2011	Scotland's Marine Atlas published

Beth Scott, Selina Stead and Sue Marrs (Chapter 16) describe some of the changes taking place in the waters around Scotland, largely due to climate change. Changes to sea temperature, frequency of storms, and sea water acidity all have an impact on species' life histories, which can have repercussions through the food chain as demonstrated by a case study of black-legged kittiwakes (*Rissa tridactyla*). The composition of plankton has shown a shift to 'warmer water' species, indicating that increased sea water temperature has already had an impact. Looking to the future, the impact of predicted climate change on cetaceans is modelled in a short paper by Emily Lambert and co-workers from Aberdeen University (Chapter 19).

Increased temperatures have had surprising impacts on the distribution of marine biota. The North West passage, once the sought after jewel of navigation for trade routes, was eventually discovered at the beginning of the 20th century. Now it is free from ice in summer months and has become a tourist destination. In May 2010 a grey whale (*Eschrichtius robustus*) appears to have navigated the North West passage from the Pacific Ocean, where it normally resides, to the Atlantic. Pacific diatom species, such as *Neodenticula seminae*, have been observed in the Labrador Sea since 1999; again the opening of the North West passage is implicated. Whilst the opening of the seaway, due to a reduction in the icecap, may bring exciting opportunities for commerce, the implications for marine biota, particularly with the potential for the spread of invasive non-native species, is difficult to predict. Indeed, the transport of these through human activity probably poses one the greatest threats to biodiversity in Scottish waters (Donnan and Manson, 2010).

Although commercial fishing has been practiced since the fourteenth century, technological advances mean that our ability to harvest fish far outstrips the capacity of the marine environment to recover. Of all human activities, fishing is the most pervasive. Indeed, the environmental 'footprint' of commercial fishing has continued to grow over time. Developments in electronics, fishing gear and operations have made it possible for fishers to target areas of seabed previously untouched, including deep-sea waters. As a result, fishing has significantly modified marine ecosystems through, for example, the removal of top predators and impacts on sea bed habitats. Given that we cannot manage the marine environment *per se* Scott *et al.* (Chapter 16) end with a call for greater efforts to improve the management of people and their activities through, for example, participatory fora.

In Chapter 17, Bill Turrell demonstrates the extent of Scotland's marine resources and how important these are to society through the provision of food and generation of income, as an energy source, and indeed as a regulator of our climate through complex patterns of oceanic circulation. The quality of shellfish waters around Scotland is generally high, and Judy Dobson and colleagues from SEPA

(Chapter 20) explain how they monitor designated sites for the protection of shellfish. Competition for sea space is a major challenge for the future of the marine environment, which must include provision for a network of Marine Protected Areas. The Scottish and UK Marine Acts provide a regulatory framework, but there is also a need for new scientific tools and continued research to fill the gaps in our knowledge of the marine environment.

To date, most of the human impacts have been in shallow seas, but as competition for space increases and resources become reduced, or even depleted, human activities increasingly move into deeper waters. Although worldwide around 80% of the ocean has been surveyed to some extent, vast areas remain unexplored. Even though we have considerable knowledge of our seas around Scotland (Saunders *et al.*, 2004; Baxter *et al.*, 2008) new areas, habitats and species are still being found. The Darwin Mounds are an exceptional example of cold water coral (*Lophelia pertusa*) formations located 185km from the north-west coast of Scotland. When discovered in 1998 they were already damaged by the emerging deep water trawler fishery in the area. This led, as a result of intense lobbying, to the first offshore fisheries closure for nature conservation purposes in the European Union in 2003 (De Santo and Jones, 2007). Scott *et al.* (Chapter 16) demonstrate that even close to shore there is still much to discover. In 2000, an ambitious ten year project to create a baseline of our understanding of marine biodiversity began (Ausubel *et al.*, 2010). Ten years on, it has recorded a staggering 244,000 marine species, and for the first time we at least have a feel for the extent of the resource we do not know.

At around 16,500km in length (MLURI, 1993), Scotland's coastline covers a vast range of habitats supporting a diverse flora and fauna. There are internationally important numbers of breeding seabirds – with 6.6 million recorded in the last survey (around 76% of the UK seabird population) (Mitchell *et al.*, 2004). Against a marked increase in UK numbers since 1970, seabird abundance in Scotland has declined since 1991; by 2008 it had fallen to 79% of the survey baseline recorded in 1986. Breeding productivity has declined since 2000, to 58% in 2008. Their fate is tracked through Scotland's Biodiversity Indicator S5 (see Foster *et al.*, Chapter 2). The coast is home to one of Scotland's rarest endemic plants the Scottish primrose (*Primula scotica*), and is one of the few places in the world where machair exists. In Chapter 18, Stewart Angus, Jim Hansom and Alistair Rennie comprehensively explore some of the challenges of monitoring change in coastal habitats where there is a paucity of baseline data. The authors describe the changes to key coastal habitats attributed to human impacts.

Scotland's estuaries are important for many reasons. They serve as an important refuge for hundreds of thousands of migrating waders and wildfowl every year, are vital nurseries for many fish and support several rare habitats such as eel grass beds. Fish diversity is recovering in the estuaries of the Forth and Clyde, and is tracked through Scottish Biodiversity Indicator S15 (Foster *et al.*, Chapter 2). Historically, the main pressures on Scotland's estuarine water quality came from sewage discharge, pollution and agricultural run-off. The water quality of the Forth and Clyde estuaries is substantially dependent on river flows, influenced by weather and a legacy of historically polluted sediments. However, investment by Scottish Water and industrial dischargers are delivering cleaner estuarine waters. Further improvements are expected as the contaminant load from diffuse sources carried by inflowing rivers (e.g. nutrients from agricultural activities) is reduced as a consequence of the implementation of the EU Nitrates and Water Framework Directives. Nitrates can have devastating impacts on estuaries, with excess nutrients encouraging smothering growth of algae which reduces the available extent of important mudflats to wildlife. Several areas have been identified as Nitrate Vulnerable Zones, for example the Ythan estuary in Aberdeenshire; these are now the focus of concerted management action in a bid to reduce the effects of nitrification.

Addressing our knowledge gaps in the marine environment can only be done through a collaborative approach. It is clear that there will be increasing pressure on our seas in the future in terms of predicted impacts of climate change, fisheries, renewables and oil exploration. Skillfully led and managed joint working will be needed to ensure a better future for Scotland's seas.

References

Appeltans, W., Bouchet, P., Boxshall, G.A. *et al.* (eds.) (2010). World Register of Marine Species, accessed at http://www.marinespecies.org

Ausubel, J.H., Crist, D.T. and Waggoner, P.E. (2010). *First Census of Marine Life 2010. Highlights of a Decade of Discovery.* Census of Marine Life, Washington, USA.

Baxter, J.M., Boyd, I.L., Cox, M. *et al.* (eds.) (2008). *Scotland's Seas towards understanding their state.* Fisheries Research Services, Aberdeen.

De Santo, E.M. and Jones, P.J.S. (2007). The Darwin Mounds: from undiscovered coral to the development of an offshore marine protected area regime. In *Conservation and Adaptive Management of Seamount and Deep-sea Coral Ecosystems*, ed. by R.Y. George and S.D. Cairns, Rosenstiel School of Marine and Atmospheric Science, University of Miami.

Donnan, D.W. and Manson, F. (2010). Invasive non-native species in Scotland's seas: risk and reality. In *Species Management: Challenges and Solutions for the 21st Century*, ed. by J.M. Baxter and C.A. Galbraith. TSO Scotland, Edinburgh. pp 265-282.

Mitchell, I.P., Newton, S.F., Ratcliffe, N., and Dunn, T.E. (2004). *Seabird Populations of Britain and Ireland.* T. and A.D. Poyser, London.

MLURI (1993). *The Land Cover of Scotland 1988.* Final Report. Macaulay Land Use Research Institute, Aberdeen.

Saunders, G. (2004). *Natural Heritage Trends. The Seas Around Scotland.* Scottish Natural Heritage, Perth.

16 Changes to Scotland's Surrounding Seas

Beth Scott, Selina M. Stead and Susan J. Marrs

Summary

1. We rely on healthy seas to supply us with a wide range of ecosystem goods and services, including food, social well-being and income generated from employment.
2. Climate change has been shown to be associated with increases in temperature, summer storm activity and acidity of our seas. The sea surface temperature in the North Sea is estimated to have risen from between 0.2°C to 0.6°C per decade since the 1980s. Such changes can affect the timing of spring and autumn blooms of plankton, which in turn can influence the abundance of important fish like the sandeel (e.g. *Ammodytes marinus*) and seabird populations. The effects of increased acidity in our seas are not yet fully understood.
3. Devising management measures that can reconcile conservation needs with sustainable livelihoods, especially in coastal communities who are socially and economically dependent on the marine environment for food and income, remains an under researched but key challenge for Scotland.

16.1 A brief history of our relationship with and understanding of the sea

The seas around Scotland have provided food, access to transport routes and generated wealth for millennia. Archaeological evidence points to fish as a vital source of food in Scottish coastal communities dating back over 10,000 years. Herring (*Clupea harengus*) bone remains have been found in excavations of Roman encampments in Britain and there is evidence of early man building weirs to capture fish over 6,000 years ago (Smylie, 2004). The Viking era saw an increased consumption of deep water fish species. Scotland was probably exporting species such as Atlantic cod (*Gadus morhua*) in the 1300s (Barrett *et al.*, 1999).

Scott, B., Stead, S.M. and Marrs, S.J. (2011). Changes to Scotland's Surrounding Seas – *The Changing Nature of Scotland*, eds. S.J. Marrs, S. Foster, C. Hendrie, E.C. Mackey, D.B.A. Thompson. TSO Scotland, Edinburgh, pp 153-166.

The potential for wealth creation available from the sea has shaped our settlement patterns and many communities are located next to sheltered anchorages to allow fishing or shipping. The foundation of Ullapool, in Wester Ross, is attributed to the work of the British Fisheries Society (Dunlop, 1978); a society established in 1786 to compete with the highly successful Dutch herring merchants. The city of Glasgow – originally a small fishing village for Atlantic salmon (*Salmo salar*) – thrived on the wealth generated from shipping imports of tobacco, sugar and rum in the eighteenth century. The 'Tobacco Lords' were responsible for building many of the finer old buildings that characterise the city today.

Commercial exploitation of fisheries is not a modern phenomenon; in the fourteenth century German and northern European fish merchants visited Shetland to barter for dried salt fish (Goodlad, 1971). The ability to cure herring, first attributed to Willem van Beukels in 1383 (Smylie, 2004), was the pivotal event that allowed the extensive development of the herring fishing industry during the following centuries. Activities associated with fish harvesting probably have the single biggest effect on the marine environment through removing key species and the direct impact of more intrusive fishing gear (e.g. bottom trawls or dredges) on habitats (Jennings and Kaiser, 1998). Fish catching technology has developed from static shore traps and baited hooks to the highly efficient mechanised and computer controlled vessels of today. As a result it is possible to catch considerably more than is sustainable and harvesting is now controlled by a system of quotas.

Much of our understanding of the sea has been driven by the desire for resource utlisation and there is still much to discover. The recent discovery of extensive cold water coral formations in Scottish waters during the latter part of the twentieth century (Rogers, 1999) illustrates this. Closer to land the Marine Nature Conservation Review (MNCR) sea loch surveys during 1987 to 1998 were one of the first coordinated explorations of the marine habitat around Scotland (Hiscock, 1998). Many of these sites have not been resurveyed since the initial study and the majority of current conservation efforts are focused in Special Areas of Conservation.

16.2 What has changed in recent times?

16.2.1 Impact of climate change on Scotland's seas

It is broadly accepted by much of the scientific community that the earth is undergoing a period of climate change caused by increases in human induced emissions of greenhouse gases such as carbon dioxide. The rate at which our seas are warming, especially coastal shallow seas such as the North Sea, is causing mounting concern. Studies based on long-term North Sea data-sets show that the sea surface temperature is estimated to have risen from between 0.2°C to 0.6°C per decade over the last 25 years (Hughes and Holliday, 2007). This has direct implications for biodiversity and indirect impacts on the available resources for exploitation by those that depend on the sea for food and/or income.

Measurable increases in sea level have been detected around the coast of Scotland and are predicted to continue to rise. The main reason for this is thought to be a combination of an increase in the volume of water due to melting glaciers and the thermal expansion of water as temperatures rise. However the estimates for sea level rise are highly uncertain as rates of melting are higher in some regions (such as Greenland) than earlier models have predicted. The predicted range of relative sea-level rise by the 2080s (relative to the 1961-1990 mean) is 20cm to 80cm in south-west England and 0cm to 60cm in Scotland (MCCIP, 2008).

The 'greenhouse effect' is not the only consequence of elevated atmospheric carbon dioxide. Carbon dioxide is a very soluble gas and the oceans and seas play a major role in the Earth's carbon cycle with much of the carbon dioxide that has been emitted due to human activity being absorbed therein. As more carbon dioxide is absorbed by water the more acid the water becomes. In the last 200 years, ocean pH has decreased by 0.1 units (equivalent to a 30% increase in H^+ ions), a rate that is much greater than at any time in the last 65 million years. Predictions suggest the pH levels could fall by 0.5 units by 2100, which will be the lowest level of pH (and therefore most acidic) for millennia. We still do not fully understand the effects of acidification but early studies have indicated that there will be negative effects on egg development of many species (Turley *et al.*, 2009).

Winds are generally stronger in winter, with weaker wind speeds and fewer storms in summer months. However, wind patterns are also changing. An increased incidence of severe storms and an increase in wave height have already been recorded. Predictions suggest there will be fewer storms overall but there will be an increase in the incidence of severe winds, which will lead to larger mean wave heights in western and northern UK waters (MCCIP, 2008). Therefore the mean annual wind speed is not changing vastly, but the variance is increasing rapidly. The increased frequency of severe storms, now occurring during summer periods, is changing the seasonal patterns of maximum wind strengths; an effect that has important biological consequences, discussed in more detail below.

To understand how climate change will affect an ecosystem such as a shallow sea, one has to appreciate the normal seasonal cycle and how it interacts with species life histories. Figure 16.1 is a simple representation of the bio-physical seasonal cycle of a shallow sea (less than 200m deep). During the winter months, the lower levels of sunlight together with the stronger winds and tidal friction leave

General seasonal pattern

Primary production/ Biweekly Production in the summer months.

Sea temperature

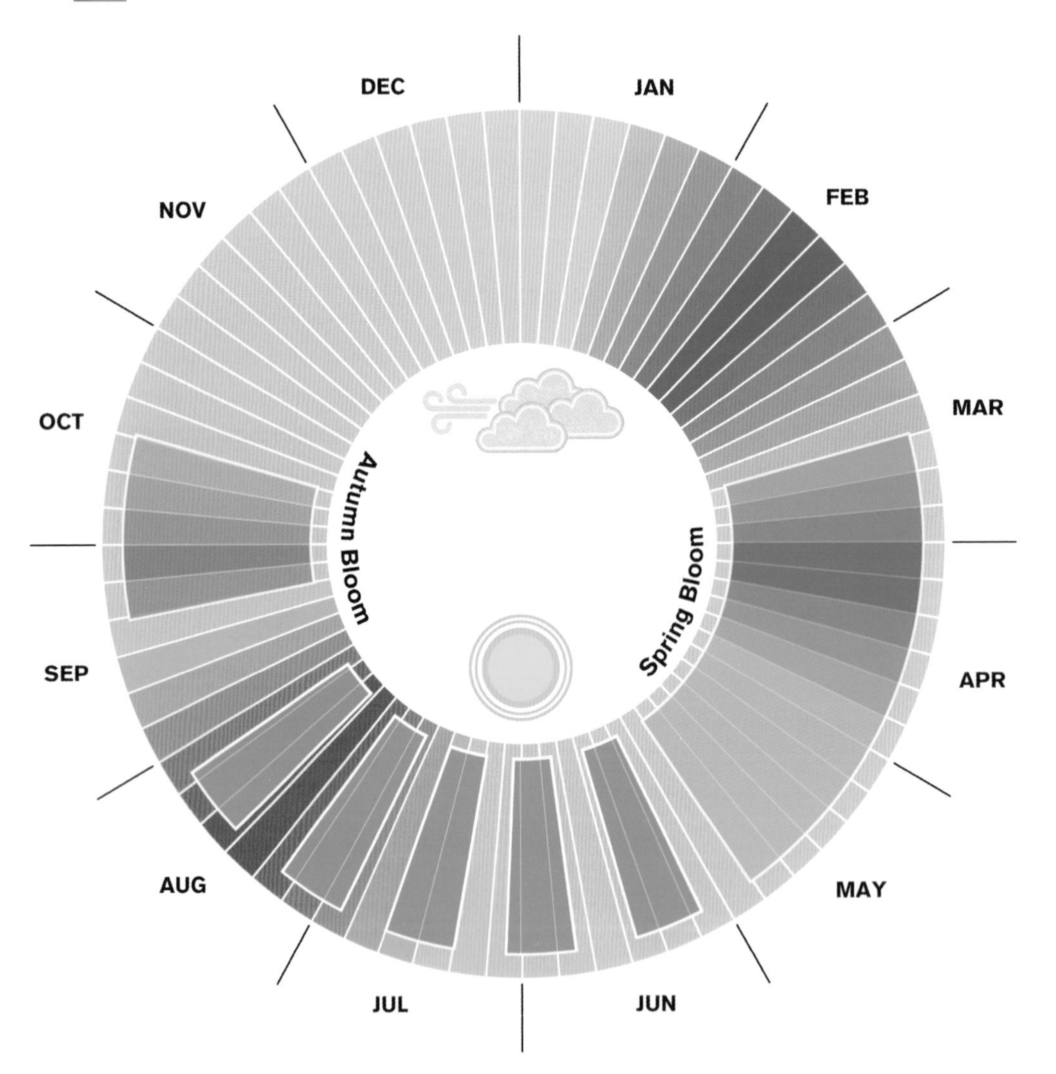

Figure 16.1 Seasonal changes in northern hemisphere physical and biological conditions in a shallow sea. The outer ring represents water temperature with the coldest month in the UK seas being February and the warmest August. Winds are generally stronger in winter, with weaker winds in summer. Heating from the sun is strongest in the summer months. The patterns of seasonal production in plankton are shown in green by the overlaying inner ring, highlighting the spring bloom and autumn blooms; in addition the thin green wedges during the summer represent the increase in production due to biweekly changes from strong to weak tides.

the water column completely mixed. In the spring, increasing amounts of sunlight and less windy conditions result in a decrease in vertical mixing. In areas that are deep enough or have weaker tidal currents the effect of tidal mixing does not reach the surface and the surface layer begins to warm up (Mann and Lazier, 1996).

This warming creates a difference in density between the upper and lower layers of the water column called stratification (Sharples, 2008). The onset of stratification allows plankton to remain above the critical depth where there is enough light for population growth. Consequently, the timing of stratification heralds the beginning of the seasonal flush of primary production, referred to as the spring bloom (Miller, 2004). In Figure 16.1 the patterns of seasonal production in plankton are shown in green – highlighting the spring and autumn blooms when the winter winds die down or strengthen, to either stratify or remix the water column respectively. The green wedges during the summer represent the biweekly production pulses caused by changes from strong to weak tides (spring to neap), which provide conditions that first mix nutrients into the upper water column and then, as tidal mixing decreases, allows the plankton populations to increase in the calmer conditions (Pingree *et al.*, 1975).

North Sea surface temperatures are coldest in February and warmest in August. However, bottom temperatures can be more than 2°C warmer in October than they are during the summer as the heat from warm surface water is transferred to the whole water column via turnover by strong autumnal winds. As the North Sea has warmed up, mean winter temperatures have increased more than the summer ones (Hughes and Holliday, 2007).

16.2.2 Effects of physical ('bottom up') changes on organisms from plankton to seabirds

What do these physical changes mean for marine life in the waters around Scotland? Increases in seasonal temperature and wind produce changes to the expected seasonal productivity throughout the ecosystem from phytoplankton to seabirds. Overall increases in phytoplankton biomass are found where there has been a rise in temperatures in cooler regions but not warmer regions (Barton *et al.*, 2003). As a result the geographic distribution of warm temperate plankton species has moved much farther north (Beaugrand *et al.*, 2002). When there are sunny calm conditions early in the year the spring bloom may happen earlier but there may be overall less production as nutrients are used up and sink out of the system before they can be recycled by zooplankton. Certain species such as, Coccolithophores which do well in such conditions can dominate and may represent up to 90% of plankton by sea surface area.

Extreme winds during the spring and summer months can result in reduced overall primary production as the conditions are never calm enough for the plankton to utilise all the available nutrients. Greater water mixing and therefore turbulence can also result in a switch to smaller plankton species that do well in more mixed conditions. Within the two main groups of phytoplankton, in general, the smaller species made up of diatoms will do better in rough conditions whereas the larger dinoflagellate species prosper in calmer conditions (Miller, 2004).

Large changes in zooplankton species have occurred over the last 30 years with an overall decrease in biomass and a dramatic change from a cold water species (*Calanus finmarchicus*), which annually increases in abundance in the North Sea in the spring, to a warmer water species (*Calanus helgolandicus*) that increases later in the year (Beare and McKenzie, 1999; Hays *et al.*, 2005).

These changes in turn have an impact on sandeel, seabird and marine mammal populations. Sandeels (mainly *Ammodytes marinus*) are unusual fish in that they spend most of their lives (up to 10 months of the year) buried in the sand. Individuals will not leave the protection of the sands until there is sufficient food, thus offsetting the risk of predation. The timing of the spring bloom therefore has a large influence on when sandeels are in the water column and available to predators. The wind regime of the spring and early summer, as explained above, will not only affect the timing of the spring bloom (Sharples *et al.*, 2006) but will also affect the levels of primary productivity and will determine which plankton species are available for the sandeels to eat.

Sea temperatures also affect the time it takes for fish eggs to hatch; in other well studied pelagic fish such as herring, warmer temperatures speed up developmental rates considerably (Blaxter and Hempel, 1966). In general warmer temperatures speed up enzyme reaction rates in cold blooded animals and one could expect faster growth and possibly larger individuals in warmer conditions. However the size-at-age of sandeels has been steadily decreasing over the last 30 years (Wanless *et al.*, 2004). Heath *et al.* (1997) demonstrated that ingestion rates decreased and metabolic costs increased when sea temperatures rose resulting in slower growth of herring. If sandeels prove to have a similar functional response of metabolic costs to increases in temperatures, then northern North Sea sandeel populations will experience a slow down in growth in conditions where sea water temperature is over 9°C.

The warmer winter sea temperatures can be attributed to warmer summers and more frequent strong winds which combine to increase the mixing of warm water into deeper layers, retaining more heat over the winter. This is a critical time. Sandeels need enough reserves to survive the winter without feeding and there is a trade off between survival, growth and reproductive success (Figure 16.2).

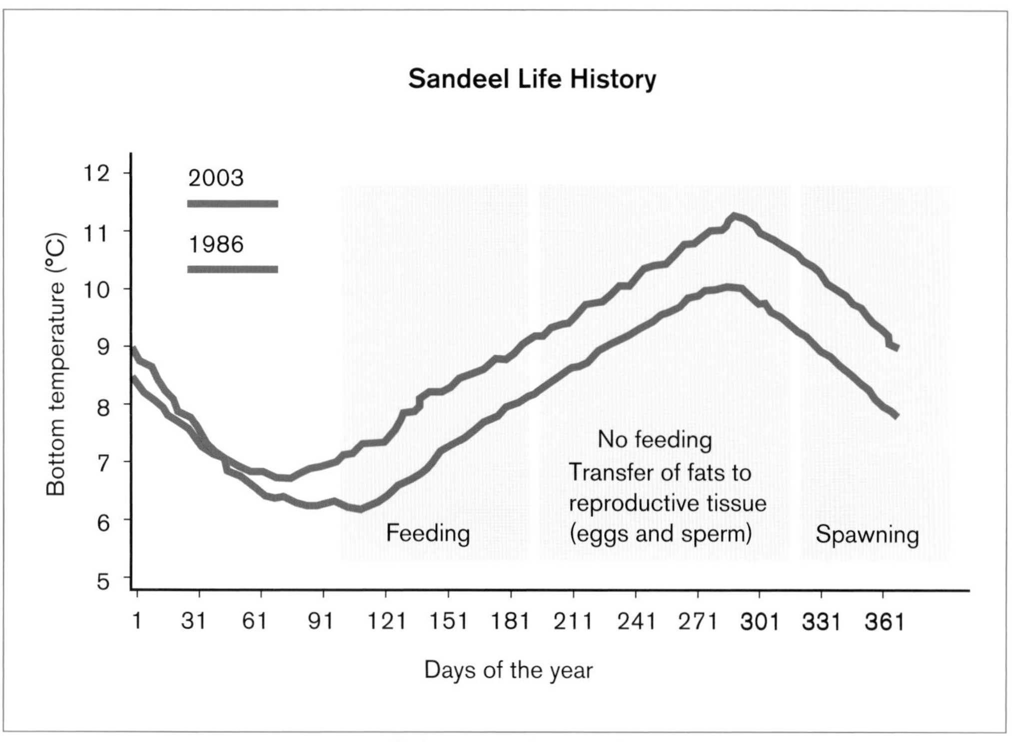

Figure 16.2 Sea bottom temperature (°C) in 1986 (blue line) and 2003 (green line) throughout the year from modelled data (Sharples *et al.*, 2006), overlaid with seasonal behaviour of sandeels.

Current collaborative research between the University of Aberdeen and Marine Scotland Science (Dr Peter Wright, *pers comm.*) has shown that this is not a simple relationship and spawning will depend on both the condition of the fish and the sea temperature.

Breeding success in black-legged kittiwakes (*Rissa tridactyla*) is linked to the timing of the spring bloom (Scott *et al.*, 2006b), which in turn is impacted by the changing climatic conditions. Kittiwakes on the east coast of Scotland feed predominantly on sandeels and the condition of the adult and therefore that of the egg will depend to a large extent on the timing of the spring bloom. Adult kittiwakes rely heavily on the availability of adult sandeels for food while the egg is developing. However chick growth and fledging success depend on the availability of juvenile sandeels that hatched early in the winter. Therefore, annual kittiwake breeding success is not only dependent on weather conditions during the months of June and July, when the young are being fed, but is also dependent on the conditions during the early winter – especially the timing of the spring bloom as this will determine the size, condition and availability of juvenile sandeels.

Plate 16.1 Pollack stalking sandeels in Loch Carron, Scotland. The availability of sandeels, dependent on the timing of the spring bloom, is in turn critical to the breeding success of many marine species around Scotland. © Sue Scott

16.3 Anthropogenic ('top down') changes to fish abundance and population structure

We have already reported that there is evidence that humans have harvested from the seas for millennia, however the reality that we can have a significant impact on marine populations and habitats is a more recent and increasingly acknowledged fact with measures used to address this, such as Marine Protected Areas (MPAs), remaining highly contentious. There is increasing evidence that whole ecosystem changes are related to heavy decreases in common species for example Atlantic cod in Canadian waters (Frank *et al.*, 2005). Part of the problem has been that of a 'shifting baseline' where our expectations for abundance levels or species diversity are lowered as we get used to current standards and are unaware of superior past levels (Pauly, 1995; Pinnegar and Engelhard, 2008). Within the UK territorial waters North Sea herring and Atlantic cod are good examples of such a problem.

The wide spatial distribution of North Sea herring has not truly recovered from the crash in the 1970s, with many spawning areas never being re-colonised. Intriguing theories on the reasons for this lack of spatial recovery are put forward by McQuinn (1997) and Corten (2002) who suggest that meta-population structure, the need to learn migration routes from other members of the population and destruction of so many sub-populations are the mechanisms for the lack of a full recovery.

The age structure of cod populations, a longer lived species, has been shown to be an important factor in its ability to recover from fishing practices which generally target the larger, older and consequently more reproductively able members of the population (Marteinsdottir and Thorarinsson, 1998; Trippel *et al.*, 1997; Scott *et al.*, 2006a). In fact one of the clearer signals of long term effects of fishing is the decline of species which are longer lived and less fecund (e.g. sharks and rays) as well as the lack of older, larger age classes within a species (Jennings and Kaiser, 1998; Jennings *et al.*, 2002). This has resulted in size indices to be considered important indicators for the health of ecosystems (Greenstreet and Rogers, 2006).

Many studies have shown links to the role that climate change has played in the massive declines of species such as cod as well as other species and attempts have been made to try and assess what stock recruitment relationships might look like in the future with a functional link to rising temperatures (Cook and Heath, 2005). Fishing, especially techniques which run heavy gear over the seabed, can cause extensive habitat damage for many species but have been shown to be particularly harmful to maerl beds and bivalve mollusc species such as native oyster (*Ostrea edulis*) and the nest-building gaping fileshell (*Limaria hians*) (Hall-Spencer and Moore, 2000; Kaiser *et al.*, 2006).

These issues need to be dealt with in the coming era of comprehensive marine spatial planning which will include a proliferation of marine renewable developments and the addition of a network of MPAs. Overall the goal is to return our seas to healthy and productive ecosystems.

16.4 Changes in the marine aquaculture and fisheries sectors

Two main drivers of global trends in demand for food are income and population growth. More than 60% of the global population lives within 100km of the coast and some predictions estimate the world's coastal population will exceed 6 billion by 2025 (UNEP, 2007) thus food security, both for Scotland and globally, especially in communities socio-economically dependent on declining fisheries, is high on all political agendas.

The fishing industry (aquaculture, capture and processing) accounts for a relatively small proportion of the overall Scottish workforce (0.9%). However in specific locations, such as the Western Isles, the Shetland Isles and parts of north east Scotland where opportunities for diversification may be limited, these sectors can directly account for 10 to 19% of total employment (Jamieson *et al.*, 2009). The importance of this is explored later in this volume (Turrell, Chapter 17); however these statistics set the value of fisheries to Scotland in context.

Aquaculture is the fastest growing food production sector worldwide with an average growth rate of over 8% per annum for the past 10 years. More than half of all aquatic species consumed are now produced from aquaculture. Current trends of per capita consumption and falling fish capture indicate 40 million tonnes of aquatic food will be required by 2030 to supply increasing demand for fisheries products (FAO, 2009).

Marine aquaculture has not yet realised its full growth potential and is arguably a twenty-first century opportunity and solution for achieving food security from marine environments (Stead, 2009). To date, a major constraint to developing coastal aquaculture is a lack of marine interdisciplinary scientists who understand landward (human coastal communities) and seaward (marine ecosystems) processes that drive marine resource users' behaviour (Stead *et al.*, 2002).

There is a growing demand to provide decision makers with the best information to effectively manage and protect vital marine ecosystem services through evidence based studies that involve stakeholders and can inform policy debate and people's choices. In the UK, management of the marine environment has traditionally been dominated by fisheries-related research; however the growth in demand for seafood, which cannot be matched by the fisheries sector, has forced aquaculture up the political agenda.

16.5 Conclusions

In this paper we have summarised some of the recent changes in the marine environment, which have been largely driven by human activity. Relatively little research has been done on understanding this human dimension, which is surprising when you consider that you cannot manage marine environments *per se*. Greater effort needs to be placed on managing people, especially through participatory fora that focus on identifying how best to manage marine resource users behaviour, ideally by including those who are targeted. This can help improve compliance with regulations, for example, fishers observing areas closed to fishing. The majority of marine research concentrates on a few commercially exploited species. It is therefore arguably relatively easy to focus research effort to observe changes in populations of species such as cod or herring, however it is inevitable that changes are also taking place in less well studied species and their habitats. Applying local stakeholder (e.g. divers, fishers) knowledge is one way to help address this gap in current information (Stead *et al.*, 2006).

We have demonstrated that organisms in the marine environment are inextricably linked; with the breeding success of kittiwakes in a given year being dependent on the timing of abundant numbers of microscopic plankton. This is just one illustrative example; it is well documented that the timing of plankton abundance controls the success of reproduction of many species (*inter alia* Cushing, 1990; Platt *et al.*, 2003). Climate change is not only increasing the temperature of the seas but also increasing its acidity. The combined effects of winds and temperature will affect the timing of seasonal events in species in different ways and may result in more years where food supplies are not synchronised with predator needs. Many predators in the marine environment are long-lived and have evolved to cope with periodic years of breeding failure; however they may not endure this indefinitely.

Fishing (whether for food, income or recreational pursuits) probably has the greatest direct impact on marine life in comparison to any other activity; largely due to its ubiquitous nature. The longevity of fishing as an activity and the relative youth of marine science as a discipline mean that we will probably never fully understand the impact of fishing on pristine habitats. We must however act to ensure that our marine environment has the resilience to adapt to the wider changes that we are currently observing and adopt management approaches that take account of both the human and scientific components in a climate change context (McClanahan *et al.*, 2009). SNH and the other UK conservation agencies are currently developing a network of Marine Protected Areas around the UK in an attempt to secure the future of our marine environment. In doing this, reconciling conservation needs with sustaining traditional livelihoods like fishing remain key challenges.

References

Barrett, J.H., Nicholson, R.A. and Cerón-Carrasco, R. (1999). Archaeo-ichthyological evidence for long-term socioeconomic trends in northern Scotland: 3500BC to AD1500. *Journal of Archaeological Science*, **26**, 353-388.

Barton, A.D., Greene, C.H., Monger, B.C. and Pershing, A.J. (2003). The Continuous Plankton Recorder survey and the North Atlantic Oscillation: Interannual- to multidecadal-scale patterns of phytoplankton variability in the North Atlantic Ocean. *Progress in Oceanography*, **57**, 337-358.

Beare, D.J. and McKenzie, E. (1999). Temporal patterns in the surface abundance of *Calanus finmarchicus* and *C. helogolandicus* in the northern North Sea (1958-1996) inferred from Continuous Plankton Recorder data. *Marine Ecology Progress Series*, **190**, 241-251.

Beaugrand, G., Ibañez, F., Lindley, J.A. and Reid, P.C. (2002). Diversity of calanoid copepods in the North Atlantic and adjacent seas: Species associations and biogeography. *Marine Ecology Progress Series*, **232**, 179-195.

Blaxter, J.H.S. and Hempel, G. (1966). Utilisation of yolk by herring larvae. *Journal of the Marine Biological Association of the UK*, **46**, 219-234.

Cook, R.M. and Heath, M.R. (2005). The implications of warming climate for the management of North Sea demersal fisheries. *ICES Journal of Marine Science*, **62**, 1322-1326.

Corten, A. (2002). The role of "conservatism" in herring migrations. *Reviews in Fish Biology and Fisheries*, **11**, 339–361.

Cushing, D.H. (1990). Plankton production and year class strength in fish populations: an update of the match/mismatch hypothesis. *Advances in Marine Biology*, **26**, 249-293.

Dunlop, J. (1978) *The British Fisheries Society 1786-1893.* John Donald, Edinburgh.

FAO (Food and Agriculture Organization of the United Nations) (2009). *The State of World Fisheries and Aquaculture – 2008.* FAO, Rome.

Frank, K.T., Petrie, B., Choi, J.S. and Leggett, W.C. (2005). Trophic cascades in a formerly cod-dominated ecosystem. Science, **308**, 1621-1623.

Goodlad, A. (1971). *The Shetland Fishing Saga*. Shetland Times, Lerwick.

Greensteet, S.P.R. and Rogers, S.I. (2006). Indicators of the health of the North Sea fish community: identifying reference levels for an ecosystem approach to management. *ICES Journal of Marine Science*, **63**, 573-593.

Hall-Spencer, J. and Moore, P.G. (2000). Scallop dredging has profound, long term impacts on maerl habitats. *ICES Journal of Marine Science*, **57**, 1407-1415.

Hays, G.C., Richardson, A.J. and Robinson, C. (2005). Climate change and marine plankton. *Trends in Ecology and Evolution*, **20**, 337-344.

Heath, M., Scott, B. and Bryant, A.D. (1997). Modelling the growth of herring from four different stocks in the North Sea. *Journal of Sea Research*, **38**, 413-436.

Hiscock, K. (1998). *Biological monitoring of marine Special Areas of Conservation: a review of methods for detecting change.* JNCC Report No. 284, Peterborough, Joint Nature Conservancy Committee.

Hughes, S.L. and N.P. Holliday (eds.) (2007). ICES Report on Ocean Climate 2006. *ICES Cooperative Research Report* 289.

Jamieson, L., Munro, G. and Perrier, M. (2009). *Social change in Scottish Fishing Communities: a brief literature review and annotated bibliography.* Scottish Government Social Research.

Jennings, S. and Kaiser, M.J. (1998). The effects of fishing on marine ecosystems. *Advances in Marine Biology*, **34**, 201-352.

Jennings, S., Greenstreet, S.P.R., Hill, L. *et al.* (2002). Long-term trends in the trophic structure of the North Sea fish community: evidence from stable-isotope analysis, size-spectra and community metrics. *Marine Biology*, **141**, 1085-1097.

Kaiser, M.J., Clarke, K.R., Hinz, H. *et al.* (2006). Global analysis of response and recovery of benthic biota to fishing. *Marine Ecology Progress Series*, **311**,1-14.

MCCIP. (2008). *Marine Climate Change Impacts. Annual Report Card 2007-2008*, Marine Climate Change Impacts Partnership.

Mann, K.H. and Lazier, J.R.N. (1996). *Dynamics of Marine Ecosystems.* Blackwell Science, Oxford.

Marteinsdottir, G. and Thorarinsson, K. (1998). Improving the stock-recruitment relationship in Icelandic cod (*Gadus morhua* L.) by including age diversity of spawners. *Canadian Journal of Fisheries and Aquatic Science*, **55**, 1372-1377.

McClanahan, T.R., Cinner, J.E., Graham, N.A.J. *et al.* (2009). Identifying reefs of hope and hopeful actions: Contextualizing environmental, ecological, and social parameters to effectively respond to climate change. *Conservation Biology*, **23**, 662-671.

McQuinn, I.H. (1997). Metapopulations and the Atlantic herring. *Reviews in Fish Biology and Fisheries*, **7**, 297-329.

Miller, G.B. (2004). *Biological Oceanography.* Blackwell Science, Oxford.

Pauly, D. (1995). Anecdotes and the shifting base-line syndrome of fisheries. *Trends in Ecology and Evolution*, **10**, 430.

Pingree, R.D., Holligan, P.M., Mardell, G.T. and Head, R.N. (1975). Summer phytoplankton blooms and red tides along tidal fronts in the approaches to the English Channel. *Nature*, **258**, 672-677.

Pinnegar, J.K. and G.H. Engelhard. (2008). The 'shifting baseline' phenomenon: A global perspective. *Reviews in Fish Biology and Fisheries*, **18**, 1-16.

Platt, T., Fuentes-Yaco, C. and Frank, K.T. (2003). Spring algal bloom and larval fish survival. *Nature*, **423**, 398-399.

Rogers, A.D. (1999). The biology of *Lophelia pertusa* (Linnaeus 1758) and other deep-water reef-forming corals and impacts from human activities. *International Review of Hydrobiology*, **84**, 315-406.

Scott, B.E., Marteinsdottir, G., Wright, P. and Kjesbu, O.S. (2006a). Effects of population structure, condition and temporal dynamics of flexible life history traits on reproductive output in Atlantic cod (*Gadus morhua*). *Ecological Modelling*, **191**, 383-415.

Scott, B.E., Sharples, J., Wanless, S. *et al.* (2006b). The use of biologically meaningful oceanographic indices to separate the effects of climate and fisheries on seabird breeding success. In *Top predators in marine ecosystem. Their role in monitoring and management, Conservation Biology No. 12*, ed. by I.L. Boyd, S. Wanless & C.J. Camphuysen, Cambridge University Press, Cambridge.

Sharples, J., Ross O.N., Scott, B.E. *et al.* (2006). Inter-annual variability in the timing of stratification and the spring bloom in the north-western North Sea. *Continental Shelf Research*, **26**, 733–751.

Sharples, J. (2008). Potential impacts of the spring-neap tidal cycle on shelf sea primary production. *Journal of Plankton Research*, **30**, 183-197.

Smylie, M. (2004). *Herring. A history of the silver darlings.* Tempus Publishing Ltd., UK.

Stead, S.M., Burnell, G. and Goulletquer, P. (2002). Aquaculture and its role in Integrated Coastal Zone Management. *Aquaculture International*, **10**, 447-468.

Stead, S.M. (2009). Future of marine aquaculture in a changing fisheries environment (plenary paper). *Proceedings of AQA Marine aquaculture – the 21st century opportunity and challenge for world fishing conference*, 18 September, Vigo. pp 14-17.

Stead, S.M., Daw, T. and Gray T.S. (2006). Uses of fishers' knowledge in fisheries management. *Anthropology in Action*, **13**, 77-86.

Trippel, E.A., Kjesbu, O.S. and Solemdal, P. (1997). Effects of adult age and size structure on reproductive output in marine fishes. In *Early life history and recruitment in fish populations, Fish and Fisheries Series 21*, ed. by R.C. Chambers & E.A. Trippel. Chapman and Hall, London, U.K. pp 31-62.

Turley, C., Findlay, H.S., Mangi, S., Ridgwell, A. and Schimdt, D.N. (2009). CO_2 and ocean acidification. In *Marine Climate Change Ecosystem Linkages Report Card 2009*, ed. by J.M. Baxter, P.J. Buckley and M.T. Frost, Online science reviews. www.mccip.org.uk/elr/acidification

UNEP (United Nations Environment Programme) (2007). *Global Environment Outlook GEO-4 environment for development.* UNEP, Malta.

Wanless, S., Wright, P.J., Harris, M.P. and Elston, D.A. (2004). Evidence for decrease in size of lesser sandeels (*Ammodytes marinus)* in a North Sea aggregation over a 30-yr period. *Marine Ecology Progress Series*, **279**, 237-246.

17 Our Surrounding Seas – Why do they Matter?

William R. Turrell

Summary

1. Our surrounding seas control our climate, provide wealth, employment and food; yet there is still much to discover.
2. The area of Scotland's surrounding seas is approximately 470,000km^2; some six times that of the land.
3. Oceanic circulation maintains the climate of Scotland at 5°C to 10°C warmer than the average temperature for our latitude.
4. Nutrient rich oceanic water, complex and varied seabed habitats, and relative warmth combine to make our waters some of the most biologically productive in the world.
5. The seas provide Scotland with approximately £15,560 million in income and 49,200 jobs. This is in the region of 19% of the total Scottish annual income and 3% of total employment.
6. Decommissioning of oil platforms, deep water exploration for fuel, the growth of offshore renewable energy, space for fisheries, new deep water aquaculture, and demands for new levels of nature conservation present significant challenges to the future management of our surrounding seas.

17.1 Introduction

Our Surrounding Seas – why do they matter? To address this deceivingly simple question this paper focuses on three principle aspects; Our Surrounding Seas – what are they, where are they and what oceanic processes influence them? Goods and Services – what do our surrounding seas provide us with? Can we place a value on the benefits from our seas? Change and Challenge – how are our seas changing and how may these changes affect us?

Turrell, W.R. (2011). Our Surrounding Seas – Why do they Matter? – *The Changing Nature of Scotland*, eds. S.J. Marrs, S. Foster, C. Hendrie, E.C. Mackey, D.B.A. Thompson. TSO Scotland, Edinburgh, pp 167-182.

17.2 Our surrounding seas

To understand our surrounding seas we can first set their size in context. The area of sea bed within the Scottish share of the UK Exclusive Economic Zone (EEZ) (Figure 17.1) is approximately 470,000km^2 (see Appendix for all data sources and calculations). This may be compared to Scotland's land area of approximately 79,000km^2. To put this into more human terms, each Scot (at the 2007 population of about five million) 'owns' two football pitches of land, and just over 12 football pitches of sea bed.

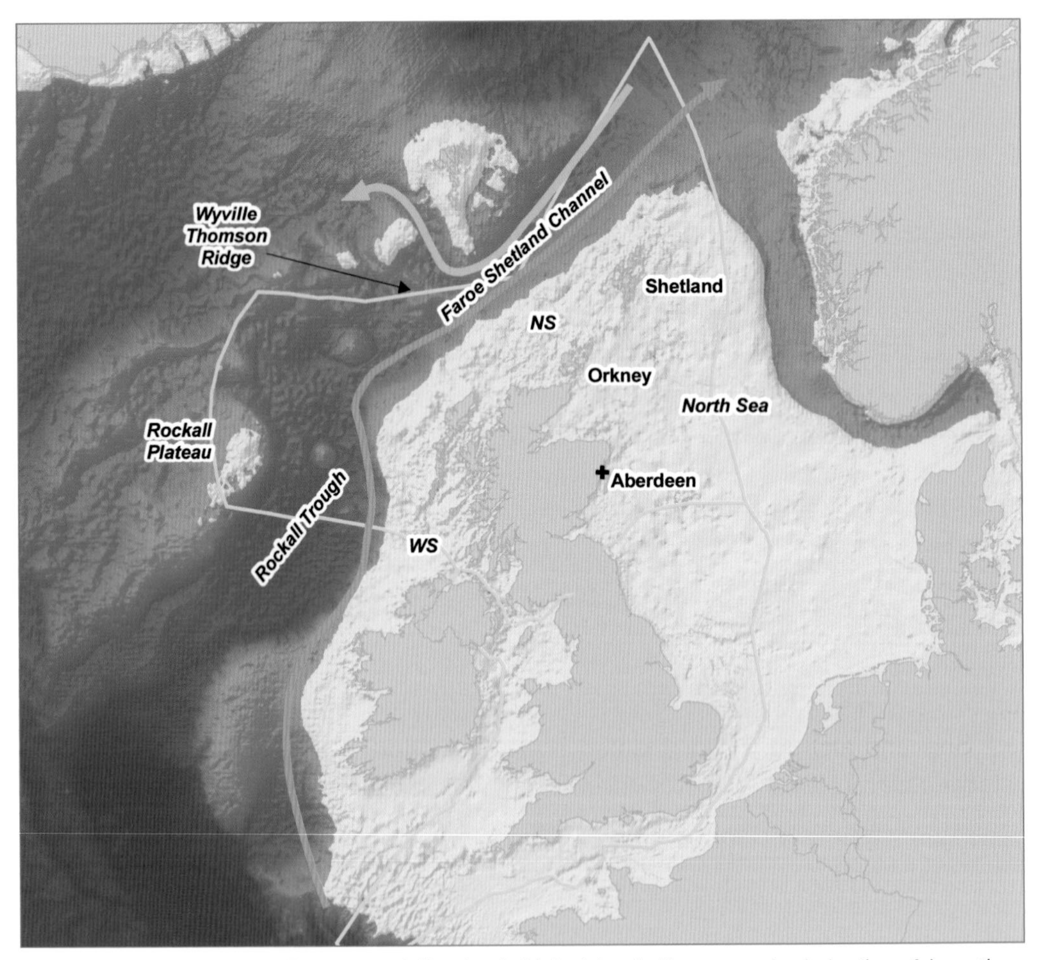

Figure 17.1 The surrounding seas of Scotland. Light blue indicates seabed depths of less than approximately 200m, i.e. the Continental Shelf. WS – western shelf. NS – northern shelf. Blue arrow – outflow of cold deepwater from the Arctic basins. Red arrow – surface flow of warm, salty Atlantic water in the Slope Current. The thin yellow line indicates the extent of the UK fishery limit, as well as the Scottish Adjacent Waters Boundaries Order (1999) line, which together form the outline of 'Scottish waters'.

A great variety of sea bed shapes, depths and types exist within Scotland's surrounding seas. A fundamental division of the nature of our seas exists along the line where the water depth is about 200m. Inshore from this depth contour, and so shallower than 200m, lies the Continental Shelf which for Scotland has three principle regions; the western shelf, the northern shelf and the northern North Sea. Offshore from the 200m depth contour lies the deep ocean.

On the Scottish Continental Shelf, the western shelf is characterised by small scale, complex sea bed depth changes including a multitude of peaks and gullies lying between island chains. Bare rock supporting unique rocky reef habitats lie side by side with patches of sand and mud. The complexity of habitats found within west coast sea lochs adds to the rich mosaic of habitats which make up the western shelf.

The northern shelf has less variation in sea bed depths overall, although recent surveys have revealed the presence of detailed sea bed features in some areas, such as large scale moraines left behind by the retreating ice sheets of the last glacial period.

The northern North Sea is more homogeneous in its character, dominated by sandy sediments, but also with large areas of mud created, for example, by circulating gyres of water retaining fine sediments in the central basin.

Offshore from the 200m isobath, water depths rapidly increase down the Continental Slope to depths greater than 1,000m. Two principal regions exist in the deep waters around Scotland; the Faroe Shetland Channel and the Rockall Trough. These two deep trenches are separated by a narrow submarine ridge – the Wyville Thomson Ridge.

The Faroe Shetland Channel is the deepest connection between the Arctic basins and the Atlantic, and water colder than -1°C flows out from the Norwegian Sea into the Atlantic at the bottom of this channel. To replace this cold deep water outflow, a continual flow northwards of warm (8°C) salty surface water is drawn past Shetland along the Continental Slope. This northward flux of warm Atlantic water is partly supplied by the Slope Current, a flow of water in a continuous ribbon that extends along the continental slope from the Bay of Biscay to the north of Shetland. The northward flow of warm surface water and the outflow of cold Arctic water is the northern limb of the Global Conveyor Belt; a system of ocean currents which is crucial to the maintenance of the world's climate system.

The Rockall Trough has less extreme variations of temperature within the water column, but contains several seamounts and the Rockall Plateau itself, each of which support a variety of sea bed habitats and species. In summary, the deep oceanic waters in Scotland's territorial seas are diverse, contain fascinating oceanographic, geological and biological features, processes and habitats and are of global importance in terms of the world's climate system.

The flow of oceanic warm water past Scotland, combined with the predominant westerly winds, maintains the climate of Scotland, and of northern Europe and Scandinavia, on average between 5°C to 10°C warmer than the average temperature of our latitude. Each second approximately 3.8 million cubic metres of water flows past the northern tip of Shetland; equivalent to the flow of approximately 22 Amazon rivers, by far the largest flow of freshwater on earth. The oceanic flow carries northwards 156TW of thermal power (heat), providing the northern oceans with energy equivalent to the output of around 340,000 Hunterston B (in Ayrshire) nuclear power stations. This is approximately half of the total flow of thermal power the ocean supplies the Arctic.

The presence of the steep division between ocean depths and Continental Shelf depths is itself an important feature for the oceanic characteristics of our waters as the difference in water depth across the slope keeps the Slope Current confined as a narrow persistent flow of water all year round separating our shelf waters from the offshore waters. Contrary to popular belief, it is the Slope Current which provides the source of oceanic water which flushes our Continental Shelves, not the Gulf Stream.

The supply of nutrient rich oceanic water from the Slope Current, the complex and varied seabed habitats provided by our continental shelves and the warmth supplied to the region by the ocean combine to make our waters some of the most biologically productive in the world. It is in the context of this biologically rich setting that we may go on to examine the 'goods and services' the ocean provides us with.

We must not forget, however, that all of the goods and services provided by northern European terrestrial ecosystems depend on the mild climate provided courtesy of our surrounding seas.

17.3 Goods and services

The economic value of goods and services supplied by our surrounding seas has proved difficult to assess, and there are currently some discrepancies among the different estimates (see Appendix). However, for the purposes of this chapter a recent Scottish Government report has been used which is consistent across different sectors of our marine industries.

Our surrounding seas provide Scotland with approximately £15,560 million in income (Gross Value Added, or GVA, in 2004) and 49,200 jobs. This is approximately 19% of the total Scottish annual income, and 3% of the total employment. When split between the principal industry sectors, we find the following (Table 17.1).

Table 17.1 Income and employment generated by the principal marine industry sectors (2004 values).

	Value to the Scottish Economy GVA (£million)	**Employment (Full Time Equivalent Jobs)**
Sea Fishing	150	2,700
Aquaculture	120	2,500
Offshore oil and gas – Service + Sales	14,330	19,700
Other (fish processing, ship building and repair, transport, civil engineering)	960	24,300
Total	15,560	49,200

It can be seen that the industry providing the highest monetary value from our surrounding seas is the oil and gas industry, which has been of great importance to the UK economy for several decades. The 'other' sector, which includes transport and shipping, fish processing, ship building and repair and civil engineering construction has the second highest monetary value, but provides the most employment.

Sea fishing and aquaculture are approximately equal in terms of economic value and employment. However, we must remember that these industries provide an additional harvest from the sea other than monetary value and employment; they provide food. Food production in the two sectors differs. The sea fisheries catching sector is a primary producer of food, while the finfish aquaculture industry principally converts lower quality (or lower value) fish (such as anchovies) and fish processing by-products into higher value fish, which currently is predominantly Atlantic salmon (*Salmo salar*). This of course does not apply to the shellfish aquaculture industry, which grows mainly common mussels (*Mytilus edulis*) which feed off plankton in the surrounding sea. Scottish sea fisheries land approximately 370,000 tonnes of fish from our surrounding seas while aquaculture produces approximately 130,000 tonnes of fish and 5,000 tonnes of shellfish annually.

Once again, to put the monetary value of the sectors and the production of food into more human terms, Table 17.2 gives the 'income' to Scotland from each sector per Scot, along with the number of 150g portions of fish or shellfish produced from the sea each year.

It is obvious we will miss the oil and gas industry when production from our surrounding seas eventually stops, although our service industry will undoubtedly continue, serving oil and gas extraction in other waters.

In terms of food, our seas could provide every Scot at least one meal a day all year round, with some to spare (Table 17.2). However, Scots would have to change our diet, as currently approximately 40% of these meals are made up from the oily fish herring (*Clupea harengus*) and mackerel (*Scomber scombrus*) for which we have lost our appetite and now go mainly for export. Similarly most of our shellfish production also goes straight to export, along with many of the fish species we no longer favour, leaving Scots with our standard haddock (*Melanogrammus aeglefinus*) suppers.

Table 17.2 Annual 'income' and number of portions of seafood generated per head of Scotland's population (2004 values).

	Annual 'income' per Scot	**Number of 150g portions of fish or shellfish**
Sea Fishing	£29	380
Aquaculture	£23	140
Offshore oil and gas – Service + Sales	£2,786	
Other (fish processing, ship building and repair, transport, civil engineering)	£187	
Total	£3,025	520

In terms of employment, the oil and gas sector has centres such as Aberdeen and Montrose on the east coast, although people from all over Scotland participate in this sector. Ship building and repair historically was centred on the Clyde, although this sector has suffered from recession over many years. Jobs in aquaculture are principally located in fragile rural communities on the west coast of Scotland, on the western Isles, Orkney and Shetland, and hence are of immense value to local communities in areas where there are few alternative sources of employment.

Sea fisheries is a complex industry, providing employment around the coasts of Scotland. The industry is split into four principal sectors, summarised in Table 17.3.

The sea fisheries sector is an extremely diverse one. In Scotland there is a tradition of skipper/owners rather than large vessel-owning companies, hence the tendency is for a heterogeneous industry with many different ideas of the best way to gain benefit from our surrounding seas.

Table 17.3 Characteristics of the principal sectors in Scotland's sea fisheries industry (2004 values).

Sector	Number of vessels	Average length and type of boat	Target species	Principal locations
Pelagic	26	60m – very modern efficient vessels	herring, mackerel	Peterhead, Fraserburgh, Shetland
Demersal White Fish	324	25m – many modern vessels	haddock, cod, monk, whiting, saithe	Peterhead, Fraserburgh, Shetland
Mixed White Fish / Prawns	385	14m – some older vessels	prawns, white fish as above	East and west coast ports
Inshore	1658	<10m – small vessels work by day	prawns and white fish	West coast and islands

(Note that 'prawns' in Scotland refers to the species *Nephrops norvegicus*, sometimes known as Langoustine or scampi).

17.4 Change and challenge

Each of the industries above that result in economic and social benefits to Scotland come with concerns and challenges we must start to address.

The early days of the oil and gas industry were characterised by a limited approach to safety and pollution. Oil-based drilling 'muds' (lubricants) were discharged into the sea, as were production waters containing low-levels of hydrocarbons. These contaminant sources posed concerns of sub-lethal effects on organisms, potentially affecting planktonic early-life phases of many species. Piles of oil-bearing drill cuttings remain under some installations, posing a long-term potential source of contamination if disturbed.

In addition to widely distributed low-level sources of contaminants, point releases of hydrocarbons have occurred following marine accidents such as Piper Alpha and the Braer tanker grounding. While every effort is made to avoid such events, we must remember that they are always possible where we extract or transport oil at sea.

Today the industry has matured, presenting much higher standards of safety and pollution control. However, as North Sea fields age and come to the end of their useful lives two changes pose a challenge to us; a move into deeper water and decommissioning.

In the last decade oil fields in water depths of 400m or more have been exploited using new floating drilling and extraction facilities, such as the Schiehallion field west of Shetland. Exploiting these new fields not only pose engineering challenges, but also may expose more sensitive deep water sea bed habitats to the effects of pollution.

In the North Sea, oil and gas fields are becoming uneconomical and are therefore being shut down. Will it be possible to keep to the promise made, at the outset of the industry, to return the sea bed to its original condition? The first contentious decommissioning was of the Brent Spar (a floating oil storage facility which was destined for deepwater disposal in 1995 when public opinion stopped this), when there was a societal debate concerning the use of our surrounding seas to dispose of inert structures. Future changes may need more such debate and discussion on how we wish to use our surrounding seas.

As the hydrocarbon-based marine energy industry withdraws from our seas, a new industry is in the throes of birth; marine renewable energy. This includes the generation of energy from offshore wind, waves and tides. The technology needed by this new industry is still very much in its infancy, so it is difficult to predict the environmental impacts the industry may have. Threats to fish migration and spawning areas, mammal and bird movements, as well as possible direct physical effects such as removal of tidal energy from areas where ecosystems have evolved expecting highly energetic conditions have been suggested. Certainly the new industry will bring competition for space, and hence possible conflict with existing marine users.

Alongside the offshore energy industries stand the two other principal users of our 'sea space'; aquaculture and fisheries. Both industries bring society social and economic benefits, but both bring environmental challenges and concerns. Change is occurring in both industries.

Aquaculture faces the continual challenge of the husbandry of animals kept at unnaturally high densities, which has in the past meant the use of chemical treatments which are then released into the surrounding environment, as well as where to obtain food from sustainable sources for a high-end marine predator such as Atlantic salmon. The industry is tending towards larger farm units, which may mean moving offshore into more exposed environments.

Fishing has historically been of great cultural, social and economic importance to Scotland, and continues to be so. However, it currently represents the single greatest impact on our marine ecosystems. Fishing impacts both the species targeted by the fishery, and hence their prey and predators, as well as the non-target species killed by the fishing process. It impacts the physical habitat of the sea bed. Changes to the industry will come from a variety of sources, including those stimulated by changes in legislation, the changing economy and by climate change altering the basic productivity of the ecosystem fishing exploits and the range of species available for exploitation.

Perhaps the greatest change and challenge in the fishing industry is brought about by its investment in science. While many fishermen would deny any benefit from science, the industry is actually wholly dependent on it. Marine architects design larger, faster, more stable and more fuel efficient vessels, marine engineers design more powerful engines, acoustic scientists design better and more accurate fish finding equipment, space scientists give the industry pin-point navigation, computer scientists give the industry ever more complex data processing and display tools such as 3D sonars and net simulation software, and chemists give the industry stronger nets which can be towed faster or with less power. All of these changes result in a phenomena known as 'technical creep' which means even if no more fishing vessels join the fishing fleet, its ability to catch and kill fish gets greater each year – probably by about 2 to 3% (COM(2009)163 - Green Paper: Reform of the Common Fisheries Policy) which means the 'effective' size of the fleet doubles every 20 years. This is a difficult challenge for fishery managers and for the industry itself.

There is much else changing in our surrounding seas and these changes matter. The climate of northern Europe is driven by the surrounding oceans, and we must consider the oceans in order to be able to predict future terrestrial climate change. We still understand very little about the physical processes controlling ocean climate change, and science is progressing in this area all the time. We do not yet have a full inventory and understanding of the habitats that exist in our surrounding seas. Recent studies have revealed remarkable glacial-origin features on our own continental shelf which we did not think existed below the sea. Surveys revealed extraordinary new habitats such as the Mingulay Reef complex (Figure 17.2). The science of marine ecosystems is progressing. We have only recently understood that our principal commercial species may exist in a complex of sub-populations which do not match large management units such as the North Sea. Ecosystem modelling is only now progressing to the point where we can manage holistically rather than in a single-species vacuum. Hence marine science itself is changing, and is constantly revealing why our surrounding seas, and changes within those seas, matter.

Finally, perhaps the largest challenge we face in the coming 5 to 10 years is how to best manage the competition for sea space. Aquaculture may move offshore, renewable energy will demand space in the sea, oil and gas may ask to move into deeper new territory, while sea fisheries expect to be able to fish where Scottish fisherman have always fished. In addition, society is now demanding new levels of nature conservation, which will include Marine Protected Areas. All of these changes increasingly compete for the same sea space. While legislation such as the Scottish and UK Marine Bills will provide the regulatory framework for managers

Figure 17.2 Close up of the cold water coral (*Lophelia pertusa*) on Mingulay Reef, April/May 2010. © Phil Boulcott, Marine Scotland Science

of the sea, we will also need new scientific tools, including better spatial data and models and better ways of judging the value and benefits from different sectors of our marine industries in more complex ways than simple monetary value.

Appendix – data and calculations

17.A1 Our surrounding seas – areas

Table 17.A1 Data and sources used in the calculation of relative areas of land and seas that surround Scotland.

Scotland: Area of land (to Mean HW) [A]	78,807 km^2
Scotland: Area of sea (Mean HW to 200nm) [A]	467,458 km^2
UK: Area of land (to Mean HW) [A]	244,168 km^2
UK: Area of sea (Mean HW to 200nm) [A]	768,068 km^2
Scottish land as % of total UK land	32%
Scottish sea as % of total UK sea	61%
Current (2007) population of Scotland [B]	5,144,200
Area of a football pitch [C]	0.0074 km^2 (105m x 70m)
Scotland: Area of land per Scot (to Mean HW)	0.0153 km^2 (2.07 football pitches)
Scotland: Area of sea per Scot (Mean HW to 200nm)	0.0909 km^2 (12.3 football pitches)

Sources:
A – Data courtesy of Scottish Government GI-SAT (Geographic Information Science and Analysis Team).
B – Scottish Government (2008a). C – Average size of a pitch for international play (FIFA, 2009).

17.A2 Our surrounding seas – oceanic fluxes

Table 17.A2 Data and sources used to demonstrate the scale of oceanic fluxes that influence Scotland's climate.

Flow of Atlantic water northwards past Shetland per second [A]	3.8 million cubic metres
Flow of water in the Amazon River (average) per second [B]	170,000 cubic metres
Thermal power (heat) delivered by Atlantic water [A]	156 TW
Thermal power (heat) delivered by Atlantic water in a year	1,366,560 TWh
Electrical energy output of Hunterston B over the year ending 31 March 2008 [C]	4 TWh

Sources:
A – Østerhus *et al.* (2005). B – Dodds (2002). C – www.british-energy.com

17.A3 Goods and services – GVA and employment

The principal source for data on the economic and social, in terms of employment, 'value' of Scottish surrounding seas has been the recent Scottish Government publication edited by Baxter *et al.* (2008). Within this publication, Chapter 5 – Productive Seas, presents a detailed examination of the contribution various marine industries make to the Scottish economy, both in terms of economic value (by industry in the form of contribution to Gross Domestic Product (GDP) at basic prices (Gross Value Added, GVA – i.e. before taxes applied or Government subsidies removed) using values published by the Scottish Government in Input-Output tables, re-compiled using the 1995 European System of Accounts (European Commission, 1996) and in terms of employment (calculated based on estimated output share applied to employment figures for the whole input-output industry category). The table below is an extract from Table 5.3 of Baxter *et al.* (2008). Note that values and employment are for 2004. While economic data from single sectors may be available more recently than 2004, this is the last year where economic and employment data across sectors are currently (2009) available.

Table 17.A3 Economic value and employment generated by the principal marine industry sectors.

	Value to the Scottish Economy GVA (£m)	**Employment (Full Time Equivalent Jobs)**
Sea Fishing	149.4	2,684
Aquaculture	121.7	2,468
Service Industry to offshore oil and gas	1,011.6	19,661
Other – Fish processing	481.4	14,104
Other – Ship building and repair	312.9	7,216
Other – Marine civil engineering	4.2	94
Other – Transport	160.6	2,896
Other – Total	959.1	24,310

Note that the 'value' of sea fishing and aquaculture in the table above differs from the 'first point of sale' values normally quoted for these industries (approximately twice the GVA values) as when estimating the GVA of an economic sector the costs incurred by that sector must first be removed from the primary income to the sector.

The actual GVA from the sale of offshore oil and gas is not listed in the table above. Estimation of the contribution of offshore oil and gas to Scotland's economy is harder to estimate, as in UK Government statistics oil and gas sales and revenues are aggregated and compiled as *Extra Regio* income and not allocated to the UK region which generated them.

However, for this paper an estimate has been derived as follows:

1. The Scottish Government (2008b) analysed the tax revenue raised from the UK offshore oil and gas industry in some detail. In 2004-2005 (in order to compare to the 2004 values above) this was £5,183 million. The paper goes on to estimate two methods of allocating this revenue to Scotland. One is based on a per capita estimate, while the other is a geographical share based on analysis of the location of oil and gas fields. The per capita share of revenue to Scotland for 2004-2005 was £440 million (8.5% of the UK total), while the geographic share was £4,328 million (83.5%). For the purposes of this paper the geographic share of revenue is used.
2. The UK Government publishes its headline regional GVA estimates as the NUTS tables (NUTS, or Nomenclature of Units for Territorial Statistics, is a European classification system which provides a breakdown of regions and countries to give a comparable view of economic activity across the European Union). These tables state that the total GVA generated by the *Extra Regio* category of industries was £20,269 million in 2004 and £25,201 million in 2005.
3. Pugh (2008) estimated that in 2005 78.7% of the *Extra Regio* income was generated by the UK offshore oil and gas industry.
4. Thus, the GVA generated in Scottish waters by the offshore oil and gas industry for 2004 was (£20,269 million x 0.787 x 0.835) = £13,320 million.

Thus, in summary the GVA for all marine industries, plus the tax revenue from offshore oil and gas, is as follows (with some rounding applied):

Table 17.A4 GVA and employment generated by all marine industries.

	Value to the Scottish Economy GVA (£million)	**Employment (Full Time Equivalent Jobs)**
Sea Fishing	150	2,700
Aquaculture	120	2,500
Offshore oil and gas – Service + Sales	14,330	19,700
Other	960	24,300
Total	15,560	49,200

Baxter *et al.* (2008) note that for 2004 the total Scottish economy was approximately £83 billion, and the total employment figure was two million in full time employment.

As a note of caution it is clear that the estimation of the contribution of a sector of the economy to its overall value is difficult and depends on the methodology employed. For example, an alternative estimate of the value of Scottish marine fisheries in terms of GVA and employment is given in a report commissioned by Seafish (Fraser of Allander Institute, 2007). This study uses a different method of estimation by calculating the impact of the complete removal of the fish catching sector from Scotland on the Scottish economy. The study uses 2002 figures. The results indicated that Scottish GDP would decrease by £302.9 million and employment by 10,472 jobs if sea fisheries ended. This differs from the Baxter *et al.* (2008) estimates by factors of two in value and five in employment. However, Baxter *et al.* (2008) use the same method across the different marine sectors, hence their values are used in this paper.

17.A4 Goods and services – food

Estimates of the amount of food produced by sea fishing were calculated using figures published in Scottish Government (2008c) and summarised in Turrell (2009). The estimates are:

Table 17.A5 Scottish Sea Fisheries Landings, 2007.

Fishing Sector	**Landed Weights (tonnes)**
Total demersal (e.g. cod, haddock, whiting, monk)	89,230
Total pelagic (e.g. herring, mackerel)	213,404
Total shellfish (e.g. nephrops, crab, lobster, scallops)	66,862
Total landings	369,496

Taking the total output from the industry of 369,496 tonnes which, assuming 20% wastage in processing, is the equivalent to 383 150g food portions per head of Scottish population (using population figure quoted above).

Estimates for the amount of food produced by Scottish aquaculture were taken from Scottish Government (2009). This document estimates the amount of farmed salmon produced by the Scottish industry (in 2007) was 130,000 tonnes, along with 5,000 tonnes of shellfish. Adding these values gives a total output from the industry of 135,000 tonnes which, assuming 20% wastage in processing, is the equivalent to 140 150g food portions per head of Scottish population (using population figure quoted above).

Hence, of the 523 150g portions of fish or shellfish per Scot that could be produced if the total output from Scottish aquaculture and sea fisheries went to human consumption by our own population, 42% would be made up of the oily pelagic fishes herring and mackerel, 26% by farmed salmon, 18% by demersal white fish, 13% by wild caught shellfish and 1% by farmed shellfish.

17.A5 Goods and services – industry sectors

The report Scottish Government (2005) *A Sustainable Framework for Scottish Sea Fisheries*, described the basic aspects of the principal sectors of Scottish sea fisheries. These were as follows:

Table 17.A6 Basic aspects of the principal sectors of Scotland's sea fisheries.

Sector	Number of Vessels	Average Length (m)
Pelagic	26	62
Demersal	324	23
Mixed Demersal/Shellfish	385	14
Inshore/Shellfish	1658	<10

References

Baxter, J.M., Boyd, I.L., Cox, M. *et al.* (eds.) (2008). *Scotland's Seas: Towards Understanding their State*. Fisheries Research Services, Aberdeen.

British Energy (2010). Our nuclear power stations [online]. Available at http://www.british-energy.com/pagetemplate.php?pid=82, accessed on 10 September 2010.

Dodds, W.K. (2002). *Freshwater Ecology: concepts and environmental applications*. London Academic Press.

European Commission (1996). *European System of Accounts (ESA 1995)*. Eurostat, Brussels-Luxembourg.

FIFA (2009). *Laws of the Game 2009/2010*. Federation Internationale de Football Association, Zurich, Switzerland.

Fraser of Allander Institute (2007). *The economic impacts of the UK sea fishing and fish processing sectors: An input-output analysis*. Seafish, Edinburgh.

Østerhus, S., Turrell, W.R., Jónsson, S. and Hansen, B. (2005). Measured volume, heat, and salt fluxes from the Atlantic to the Arctic Mediterranean. *Geophysical Research Letters*, **32**, L07603.

Pugh, D.T. (2008). Socio-economic indicators of marine-related activities in the UK economy. *Marine Estate Research Report*, The Crown Estate, March 2008.

Scottish Government (2005). *A Sustainable Framework for Scottish Sea Fisheries.* The Scottish Government, Edinburgh.

Scottish Government (2008a). *Scottish Economic Statistics*. The Scottish Government, Edinburgh.

Scottish Government (2008b). *Government Expenditure & Revenue Scotland 2006-2007*. The Scottish Government, Edinburgh.

Scottish Government (2008c). *Scottish Sea Fisheries Statistics 2007.* The Scottish Government, Edinburgh.

Scottish Government (2009). *A Fresh Start: The renewed Strategic Framework for Scottish Aquaculture.* The Scottish Government, Edinburgh.

Turrell, W.R. (2009). Review of the Scottish Marine Fisheries Sampling Programme – Basic description of the Programme. *Marine Scotland Science Internal Report* No. 12/09.

18 Habitat Change on Scotland's Coasts

Stewart Angus, Jim Hansom and Alistair Rennie

Summary

1. Scotland has approximately 71% of Britain's dunes (including machair) by area, 60% of sea cliff by length, 13% of saltmarsh by area and less than 5% of shingle by length. Information on lagoons is currently deficient.
2. Coasts are dynamic habitats where change is inevitable. However, difficulties associated with establishing baseline data in terms of either length or area mean that any meaningful measurement of coastal change is challenging.
3. We explore some of the issues and present a synopsis of the available information on key coastal habitats. We also consider recent drivers of coastal change: sea level rise; sediment deficit and human intervention in coastal systems.
4. We argue that the need to monitor coastal change is a problem that must be addressed strategically, not only in respect of coastal habitats, but also in respect of the immense investment in settlement and infrastructure on Scotland's coasts.

18.1 Introduction

It is said that there are only two certainties in life: death and taxes. There is a third: coastal change. Most coasts composed of sediment will undergo change on every tide, and individual storms can exert significant foreshore change within a few hours. Large, storm-related change will be widely noticed, whereas the gradual erosion and accretion of beach and dunes will not. Such changes are daily, event-based, or seasonal, but they are not the subject of this paper, which deals instead with the direct human impact and longer term changes that affect Scotland's coastline. Paleao-environmental and historical data indicate that there have been extensive

Angus, S., Hansom, J.D. and Rennie, A. (2011). Habitat Change on Scotland's Coasts – *The Changing Nature of Scotland*, eds. S.J. Marrs, S. Foster, C. Hendrie, E.C. Mackey, D.B.A. Thompson. TSO Scotland, Edinburgh, pp 183-198.

changes to Scotland's coast in the past, as at Skara Brae in Orkney (Vega Leinert *et al.*, 2000), and on the west coast of North Uist, where the township of 'Hussaboste', mentioned in the Charter of Inchaffrey of 1389, is now visible only as a heap of stones at low tide (Angus, 1997). The scale of these past changes may serve as a warning of the possibility of future changes of equal or greater magnitude, particularly in view of the more recent shifts in the drivers of coastal change such as sea level rise, sediment deficit and human intervention in coastal systems.

18.2 Measuring the coast

It is notoriously difficult to assess coastal change when establishing the physical baseline is problematic.

Official figures for the length of Scotland's coast range from 'over 10,000km' (Scottish Office, 1997) or 'over 11,000km' (Scottish Executive, 2005) to 13,115km (Scottish Development Department (SDD), 1998). Scottish Natural Heritage's (SNH) measurement of the Ordnance Survey's 1:25,000 coastal outlines yielded a total coastal frontage (length at Mean High Water Springs) of 16,490km (Angus, 2001) while more recent SNH measurement of the Ordnance Survey's 1:10,000 coastal outline using ArcGIS gave a figure of 18,670km.

Attempts have been made to subdivide these national figures into habitat components (cliffs, dunes, shingle, saltmarsh, etc.) by the Joint Nature Conservation Committee (JNCC, unpublished) and (for SNH) by Posford Duvivier Environment (1998). However, the fact that the conservation agencies rarely employ these statistics serves to acknowledge the difficulties involved in the subdivision of the coast into particular habitats, and recognises that any use of such numbers should be accompanied by lengthy definitions of habitats and methodology, as well as caveats about use and accuracy. If linear measurement of the coast is difficult, obtaining figures for areas of coastal habitats presents even greater challenges, given the absence of any agreed definition of the coastal zone in terms of inland (and sometimes seaward) extent, as well as the problem of delineating boundaries between diffuse habitats. Additionally, much of the habitat area of cliff slopes has a strong vertical component that is neither measured by conventional technologies nor displayed on maps or vertical aerial photography. When establishing a baseline is problematic, meaningful measurement of change becomes particularly challenging, and responses include a sampling approach, use of environmental proxies, or falling back on expert knowledge. The legal requirement to report on the extent of habitats as part of Favourable Conservation Status reporting within the Habitats Directive, and current work on the National Ecosystem Assessment have recently emphasised the extent of such problems.

Sediment-based habitats are usually distinguished by sediment size rather than by the vegetation they support, but sediments can be borderline or mixed, or can be zoned in relation to distance from the sea, so that allocation to one category in preference to another can be arbitrary. Even the classification of saltmarsh, which given its intertidal position should be straightforward, presents difficulties. For example: on exposed hard coasts, cliff-tops high above the sea may be subject to such marine spray or even inundation that they support functional saltmarsh vegetation – should these 'perched saltings' be catalogued as saltmarsh or cliff-top habitat? All sand dune habitat (including machair) has been mapped to a high standard by the Sand Dune Vegetation Survey of Scotland (SDVSS) (Dargie, 2000), and this provides an excellent basis for monitoring change in these habitats.

Though a range of remote sensing technologies is now available, and studies using satellite imagery and airborne sensors exist, they tend to be localised, and national assessments such as Countryside Survey (Norton *et al.*, 2009) designed to monitor change in the countryside, accept that they lack a facility to distinguish between coastal habitats and are thus unable to report on their changes. The problem of establishing baselines is not merely a bureaucratic issue for formal reporting. The pressing need to monitor change in order to identify trends arising from climate change is a very real practical problem that has to be addressed at a strategic level, not only in respect of coastal habitats, but also in respect of the immense investment in settlements and infrastructure around Scotland's coasts.

18.3 Cliffs and rocky coasts

Scotland's cliffs are generally composed of durable, hard rock, and even the soft cliffs of till are generally underlain by rock at or near sea level, so that there are no Scottish counterparts for the rates of cliff recession experienced in parts of eastern and southern England (May and Hansom, 2003). Hard coasts are perceived as the least dynamic of coasts, but this is not to say they are not subject to change, simply that change is slow. The Old Man of Hoy in Orkney is a mere 600 years old and had two 'legs' until one was removed in early nineteenth century storms (Hansom and Evans, 1995).

The JNCC Coastal Directories give a length of 4,061km for sea cliffs (in reality hard coasts) in Britain, of which 2,455km (60.5%) are in Scotland. Posford Duvivier Environment (1998) give a cliff length for Scotland of 1,778km, based on steeper slopes, but even this figure includes rock slopes that many would not regard as true cliff. In any case, when does a sloping rocky coast become a cliff, and how is a cliff-girt bay backed by cliffs classified? By their very existence, a spurious precision is afforded to such statistics.

Although the coasts of the Northern and Western Isles and the northern mainland were known to experience infrequent episodic change, recent research has questioned the assumed slow rate of change. In all of these areas large blocks of rock are known to have been quarried by large waves at altitude and moved tens of metres inland many times a year (Hansom *et al.*, 2008). Exposed cliffs and cliff-tops may be completely stripped of soil and vegetation by wave wash with transitional areas supporting only soil and a few hardier, salt-tolerant plants. These extreme habitats are not endangered by increasing wave action or sea level rise – their zone merely moves inland; the high wind speeds and salt spray in such situations tend to preclude types of land use that would inhibit such movement. In contrast, some deep clefts in cliffs in more sheltered situations may be entirely non-maritime and support woodland. However, in many situations land use changes pose a more widespread threat to cliff habitats than storm waves. A few ungrazed, inaccessible cliff ledges may constitute the most natural habitat in the UK, but in general a reduction or cessation in grazing poses problems by allowing taller grasses to shade out the many cliff-top plants with rosette growth forms, including the endemic Scottish primrose (*Primula scotica*), which requires grazing that is close without being excessive. Studies in Orkney have demonstrated that it is possible to adjust grazing to encourage a very high level of biodiversity on cliff-tops, allowing even maritime heath to be restored (Harris and Jones, 1998). However, over much of Scotland, decades of heavy grazing, sometimes with the addition of artificial fertiliser, have led to the displacement of maritime heath by grassland, the Mull of Galloway being a notable example. In eastern Scotland, cultivation close to the cliff edge creates the possibility of spray drift or run-off of agricultural chemicals to the cliff slope habitats.

Introduced species also pose problems. On Craigleith Island in the Firth of Forth, the spread of tree mallow (*Lavatera arborea*) resulted in puffins (*Fratercula arctica*) abandoning their burrows (CEH, 2005). On Mull and Ulva, the remaining cliff sites for the endemic slender Scotch burnet moth *(Zygaena loti scotica*) are subject to invasion by introduced *Cotoneaster* species as well as native bracken (*Pteridium aquilinum*) (SNH, 2007).

18.4 Shingle

Though it is known that the area of coastal shingle in Scotland is in excess of 700 ha, the distribution is poorly known except for deposits on the coasts of the Moray and Solway Firths and larger deposits elsewhere. On the Solway, Randall and Doody (2001) identified a total of 39.7km of shingle between Stranraer and the English border. Nevertheless the total length of shingle shoreline probably represents less than 5% of the coastal length of Scotland, in sharp contrast to

England and Wales where 30% of the coast is shingle (Randall and Doody, 1995). Much of Scotland's shingle area is on emerged beaches now so far removed from maritime influence that they support woodland or non-maritime grassland, while shingle deposits close to the tideline are often so mobile that little can grow. Thus the extent of true 'maritime vegetated shingle' is comparatively low in Scotland, and often restricted to annuals on strandlines, where deposits of seaweed may provide a local growing medium in an otherwise hostile environment. Some of the more stable sections of the shingle deposits on the Moray Firth as at Culbin consist solely of large gravels, so that there is no growing medium for higher plants; instead lichens flourish on the undisturbed shingle surfaces.

On some shingle systems in the Moray Firth, adjacent conifer plantations have spread onto the shingle expanse by self-sowing (Figure 18.1). West of the Spey, within 1-4 km of the river mouth, hitherto bare areas of shingle have been colonised by successive waves of scrub and tree growth. As each tree grows it provides a litter layer on and between the gravels that allows new growth, and so the process continues. The Forestry Commission has embarked on a tree and scrub removal programme to restore parts of the original surface, in close co-operation with SNH.

Figure 18.1 Extensive relict shingle at Spey Bay, Moray, showing scrub invasion of the type now being cleared by the Forestry Commission, September 2006. © Stewart Angus

Active shingle is associated with high mobility, so significant shifts occur within a single storm: Spey Bay is arguably the most dynamic section of Scotland's coast, subject to onshore storms and river floods.

18.5 Dunes, including machair

Scotland is fortunate in having a comprehensive inventory survey of all coastal sand-based habitat, the *Sand Dune Vegetation Survey of Scotland* (SDVSS) (Dargie, 2000), which found around 50,000ha of 'potentially vegetated sand'. Scotland has 71.4% of Britain's dunes by area but some 9,127ha (18%) of the Scottish resource has been lost to development and plantations. Nevertheless, Scotland is believed to have retained a high proportion of its dune resource in good condition compared with other countries in the UK, Ireland and mainland Europe.

Of the 40,875ha of sand dunes (including machair) in Scotland, that have not been afforested or developed, 8,487ha (21%) has been converted to improved grassland, where natural species have been displaced by sown perennial rye-grass (*Lolium perenne*) and crested dogstail (*Cynosurus cristatus*). The areas involved can be extensive, with 43% of the dune/machair area of Orkney affected. In southern Scotland improved grassland may be for amenity rather than agriculture (Dargie, 2000). The impact of grassland improvement varies greatly: on Tiree, grassland improvement has had a comparatively low impact, whereas on Scotland's many links golf courses, there are strong contrasts between the intensively managed areas of play and the 'rough', where the latter can retain high conservation interest, albeit as a highly fragmented version of the original habitat.

The colonisation of dune systems (mainly the larger, acid systems) by self-sown conifers from nearby plantations, native trees and scrub, and bracken, is an issue and is particularly serious at Torrs Warren, Barry Links and Tentsmuir, where a reduction in, or cessation of, grazing has allowed trees to spread, leading to water table lowering that promotes further expansion of tree cover. The excavation of drains is believed to have exacerbated the problem at Barry Links, where SNH has negotiated some scrub clearance and the introduction of cattle to maintain dune grassland. In the acid systems of the Grampian coast, trees are present, but do not spread, even in the absence of stock grazing. This may be determined by the water table, but whether or not a fall in the water table is the control, any existing water table issues will be exacerbated by any further changes in summer temperature or precipitation associated with climate change.

Although immensely valuable, parts of the SDVSS date from the mid-1980s. If this resource is to retain its full value as a portrayal of a highly dynamic habitat, there is now an imperative need for a rolling programme of re-mapping of at least the more important dune systems.

Machair can be regarded as an extreme form of dune grassland, and some aspects of the habitat have been included within the above sand dune analysis. Though an expanded definition of machair habitat in respect of its listing on Annex I of the EU Habitats Directive is now available (Angus, 2006), this has not yet been applied throughout the range of the habitat, so there is no official figure for its extent, but it is believed to be in the order of 17,500ha (included within the 50,000ha figure above).

Machair has been affected to a lesser extent by many of the land uses listed above, although the windy climate has limited the amount of forestry. Tiree and parts of Orkney are particularly affected by grassland improvement, which tends to be more intensive in Orkney. Though most machair areas are believed to have been cultivated to some extent in the past, this is now confined to the islands of North and South Uist, Benbecula and Berneray, with a small area on Oronsay managed by the Royal Society for the Protection of Birds (RSPB). However, machair is a habitat that has never been entirely natural, having evolved in tandem with human settlement (Angus, 1994). The cultivation is unusual in being rotational and in delivering high biodiversity in both crop and fallow. The first cycle of SNH's Site Condition Monitoring identified a dramatic loss of biodiversity in 2004, but subsequent work suggests that this was unrepresentative and that biodiversity has substantially recovered. Nevertheless there are issues that need to be addressed regarding the relationships between land use, funding measures and biodiversity to ensure that both the crofting system and the biodiversity it supports are maintained (Angus, 2009).

18.6 Saltmarsh

The whole of the UK saltmarsh was surveyed at a basic level in the 1980s and there was found to be 6,089ha of saltmarsh in Scotland, 13% of the British resource (Burd, 1989); but gaps in the survey and known under-estimates mean that the total area in Scotland could be as much as 7,000ha. A major inventory survey of the entire Scottish saltmarsh resource, jointly commissioned by SNH and SEPA, commenced in summer 2010 and will report on vegetation and condition by 2012.

Scottish saltmarshes differ from their southern counterparts in terms of substrate and species composition. There are fewer muddy saltmarshes and most Scottish saltmarshes are sandy (May and Hansom, 2003). Scottish saltmarshes are also less likely to include a pioneer zone, terminating instead in an abrupt scarp (Burd, 1989).

The invasive cord-grasses (*Spartina spp.*) form extensive patches only in the Solway, though there are outliers elsewhere. There is little information on how much, if at all, *Spartina* has spread in recent years within sites, and opinions differ as to its impact on pre-existing coastal habitats (Lacambra *et al.*, 2004).

The main firths have been subject to extensive land claim in the past; it has been calculated that 2,860ha (51%) of the saltmarsh and mudflat area of the Forth were lost to land claim over the last 400 years (Hansom *et al.*, 2001). The loss in the Tay over the period 1800-1900 was 150ha (1% of intertidal area) (Buck, 1993). RSPB has successfully undertaken a managed realignment project at Nigg in the Cromarty Firth and has recently (2009 to 2010) initiated a tidal exchange scheme at Skinflats in the Firth of Forth.

There has been very little land claim in recent years, although some claim in the Moray Firth for the expansion of Inverness harbour and industrial estates has affected mainly mudflats. Though embankments were built on the Solway Firth, these were for flood protection rather than land claim (Geodata Institute, 2003). The extent to which the landward transition has been truncated by embankments and other infrastructure is believed to be less than elsewhere in the UK.

18.7 Lagoons

Low-lying areas of the Scottish coast where water-filled rock basins exist are frequent in the Outer Hebrides and the north-western mainland. Where these are coastal, flooding by salt water can occur on some or even all high tides, forming brackish lochs or 'saline lagoons'. Elsewhere on the coast, but particularly in Orkney and Shetland, banks of shingle have impounded water bodies in such a way as to promote brackish conditions.

Though a national UK inventory of saline lagoons has been published by the JNCC (Covey *et al.*, 1998; Thorpe, 1998; Thorpe *et al.*, 1998), the Scottish reports are more accurately described as accounts of sites surveyed as potential lagoons. More rigorous application of habitat criteria to this dataset has proved problematic: only 23 sites out of 139 give records of diagnostic lagoon 'obligates', and the total number of records is only 40, possibly because most obligates belong to difficult groups (Charophytes, Gammarids, Mysids and Hydrobiids). The study also failed to take account of the variability of salinity in each water body. The functionality of the habitat is poorly known and improvements in monitoring are currently being explored at UK level.

Many lagoons have been altered by construction of roads, the installation of culverts and sluices. Charophytes have disappeared from some lagoons, notably the Loch of Stenness, Orkney, and this loss has been attributed to inflow of artificial fertilisers, though changes in salinity could also be involved (Stewart *et al.*, in press).

18.8 Future change

Though there continues to be localised pressure on coastal habitat from development, impacts can usually be mitigated by conservation advice and significant direct threats to coastal habitats from development are uncommon. By far the most significant driver of change on coasts in the coming decades will be climate change, but the human response to climate change will itself bring coastal change. The impact of the latter will depend on the extent to which adaptation is adopted as opposed to structural intervention and defence. There is a clear case for defending major existing infrastructure such as the refinery installation at Grangemouth, but less of a case for permitting new coastal development in similar situations. Similarly, localised iconic features like Skara Brae may be defended by structures but all such sea defences have a knock on effect on adjacent coastlines that must be considered in strategic planning.

One of the main drivers for climate-related change on the coast is relative sea level, and this has been rising in all parts of Scotland, with recent tide gauge data revealing an increase in the pace of the rise (Rennie and Hansom, 2011). Although rising sea level will have a gradual impact on all coasts, impacts associated with single storm events could bring long term changes to sediment coasts. Coastal flood risk has been mapped, but there are problems of vertical resolution as well as uncertainty regarding storminess (Ball *et al.*, 2008). Although the evidence for increasing storminess is inconclusive (Dawson *et al.*, 2007), there is a mounting case for increasing storm severity evidenced by increasing storm wave heights (Hansom *et al.*, 2008). Rising sea level is cumulative and storms – occasionally severe storms – will act in concert with rising sea level, so that coasts will experience increased marine flooding, erosion, and deposition. Redistribution of sediment will occur, but the rate and pattern will be influenced by any vegetation present. Marram (*Ammophila arenaria*) has an extensive rooting system and is able to adjust rapidly to sediment movement, so that where space exists to landward or downdrift mobile dune habitat will quickly align itself to any new dune landform. Where such space is absent, there will be a loss of habitat. Atlantic saltmarsh in Scotland (i.e. all Scottish saltmarsh except the pioneer zone) tends to form a very dense mat with a strong, resistant rooting system, which in turn will affect erosion patterns within estuaries. In the Solway, however, where marsh surfaces are the most extensive in Scotland, physical change in the form of frequent erosion and redeposition may be more related to changing channel patterns as sea level rise alters the lower courses of rivers.

It is possible that high-energy systems based on shingle, such as the mouth of the Spey, could become increasingly mobile, with these rolling inland where space is available, to create new coastal habitat inland by displacing existing habitat. The more exposed beaches of the outer Firths could be the first mainland dune systems to mobilise (Pethick, 1999) and recent observations by the authors at the Morrich More in the Dornoch Firth suggest that this process may already be under way. In many cases beach sediments that were once available to support developing dune habitats are now much depleted and many Scottish coasts are now affected by coastal steepening where Low Water Spring Tide advances landward at a faster pace than High Water Spring Tide (Hansom, 2010).

In the Outer Hebrides as sea level rises, lagoons within rock basins will become increasingly saline, and eventually fully saline, but replacements will be created as rising seas flood fresh-water lochs. In the Northern Isles, the same process will operate on existing lagoons, possibly with an additional role played by storms whereby shingle barriers will be dismantled or rolled landward. Again, numerous coastal shingle-bound fresh water lochs will become increasingly saline, as has already been observed as a result of rapid relative sea level rise in Nova Scotia (Carter *et al.*, 1989). Individual saline lagoons must be regarded as ephemeral habitats due to sea level rise: even management of the inflow/outflow may only delay the inevitable. The lagoon 'obligate' species of these water bodies are rare because they have limited dispersal powers, but will they make their own way to their analogue sites as sea level rises, or should conservationists intervene in this process?

One of the greatest issues, however, could be on the flatter, outlying islands, where relative sea level rise has been in progress for several thousand years, and is now accelerating. Preliminary analysis of the topography of South Uist derived from airborne LiDAR (Light Detection and Ranging) remote sensing suggests that there are extensive inland machair areas below the altitude of Mean High Water Springs on adjacent beaches (Figure 18.2). However, the nearest tidal reference ports are too far away from this coastline to be reliable, and work by SNH and the UK Hydrographic Office is progressing to obtain better correlations between Chart Datum and Ordnance Datum in these areas. These low-lying areas are separated from the sea by a semi-continuous low dune cordon; gaps in which will allow overwash and marine flooding which would then spread laterally across the low-lying hinterland, infiltrating significant areas with saline water.

Work by SNH following the severe storm of January 2005 suggested a relationship between the salinity of surface water in seasonal lochs and the fresh water table, so that the water table restored low salinity levels following a short-term marine inundation. Such inundations are short-lived because an extensive and complex artificial drainage network established prior to 1805 allows the drains to discharge at low tide, when inland loch levels are higher than sea level. However, sea level has been rising over the intervening 200 years, and the drains have now lost the most

Figure 18.2 Digital Elevation Model (DEM) from, LiDAR, super-imposed on Ordnance Survey map of southern South Uist. The gradual narrowing and lowering of the dune reach towards Cille Pheadair is clear, as is the extensive low-lying area inland of the dune ridge, which is the bed of a drained loch. LiDAR data captured November 2005. High to low DEM scale is: red, orange, green, beige, pale yellow. © SNH for Western Isles Data Partnership, map base Crown Copyright and database right 2010. All rights reserved. Ordnance Survey licence number SNH 100017908.

efficient part of their tidal discharge range. SNH is conducting further work to identify the inter-relationship of sea level rise and the drainage network, and SEPA has commissioned a study of the machair water table (Johan Schutten, *pers. comm.*).

Overall, in both North and South Uist, it is possible that sea level rise will result in the net displacement of machair (an uncommon habitat) by saltmarsh (a more widely distributed habitat), and a reduction in the area of high-biodiversity machair cropping if the water table becomes increasingly saline.

18.9 Conclusions

Almost all of the impacts of climate change on terrestrial habitats will also apply to coastal habitats, with the added complication that coastal sediments will mobilise and sea level will rise, both at faster rates than before. There will be impacts on the built heritage as well as the natural heritage, and conservationists, planners and politicians will be under intense pressure to 'do something' about coastal change and the associated degradation of habitats and infrastructure.

It is critically important that any intervention is designed to work in concert with natural processes, in view of the long history of ill-planned intervention at the coast

Plate 18.1 At Eshaness and the adjacent Villians of Hamnavoe, Shetland high energy storm waves impact the coast so that in places, the cliff-top vegetation is stripped away at altitude. Cliff top wave quarrying may also result in cliff-top storm deposits formed of individual blocks that are transported landward into boulder beaches and spreads. © Lorne Gill/SNH

making matters worse, not only at the pressurised location but also on adjacent coasts both up and down drift. Such planning requires reliable data, information and knowledge, such as beach and habitat configuration via remote sensing, at both local and synoptic levels, that are presently either scarce or non-existent. Storm-based events may be one-off impacts or they could contribute to, or exacerbate, long-term trends. Long-term datasets are required to separate events from trends and at the synoptic level these are most effectively obtained by remote sensing, to enable rapid identification of low-lying and/or particularly vulnerable sections of coast. SNH and its partners have begun this process for parts of the Outer Hebrides, Tiree and Coll, along with targeted commissioned research projects that review the implications of climate change for a range of coastal situations. It is already clear that a systematic and coordinated rolling programme of such work is required and that Scotland needs to increase its capacity to gather and analyse such datasets and address the emerging problems described above.

Close liaison between all the organisations involved will be required to address the multiple problems of coastal change. The primary role of conservation should be to facilitate natural adaptation, with a secondary role of investigating the options for the limited number of sites where a range of intervention processes may be justified and appropriate. The coastal environment has never been static, and temporary attempts to stabilise this dynamism must be carefully evaluated and implications understood. Conservationists need to accept that change-related pressures from people will have impacts on the natural heritage that raise fundamental questions. If, for example, geomorphological features and the habitats they support, are allowed to 'roll back', as part of an 'adaptive management' response to sea level rise, what are the implications for owners and occupiers, whose holdings do not 'roll back'?

Acknowledgments

We are grateful to James Dargie of Scottish Natural Heritage for calculating the coastal length for Scotland. The later part of the SNH work on the impacts of climate change on the habitats of the Uists was supported by CoastAdapt, funded by the Northern Peripheries Programme. We also thank Professor Robert Duck of the University of Dundee and Dr Susan Watt of SNH for their comments on a previous draft of this paper.

References

Angus, S. (1994). The conservation importance of the machair systems of the Scottish islands, with particular reference to the Outer Hebrides. *The islands of Scotland: a living marine heritage*, ed. by M.B. Usher and J. Baxter. HMSO, Edinburgh. pp 95-120.

Angus, S. (1997). *The Outer Hebrides: the shaping of the islands.* White Horse Press, Harris and Cambridge.

Angus, S. (2001). *The Outer Hebrides: moor and machair.* White Horse Press, Harris and Cambridge.

Angus, S. (2006). De tha machair? Towards a machair definition. *Sand Dune Machair*, **4**, 7-22. Aberdeen Institute for Coastal Science & Management, Aberdeen.

Angus, S. (2009). Dé tha cearr air a'mhachaire? Biodiversity issues for Scottish machair: an initial appraisal. *Glasgow Naturalist*, **25 (Supplement)**, 53-62.

Ball, T., Werrity, A., Duck, R.W. *et al.* (2008). Coastal flooding in Scotland: a scoping study. Report to SNIFFER by University of Dundee, SNIFFER Report FRM10.

Buck, A.L. (1993). *An inventory of UK estuaries. Volume 4. North and east Scotland.* Joint Nature Conservation Committee, Peterborough.

Burd, F. (1989). The saltmarsh survey of Great Britain – an inventory of British saltmarshes. *Research and Survey in Nature Conservation* **No. 17**. Nature Conservancy Council, Peterborough.

Carter, R.W.G., Forbes, D.L., Jennings, S.C. *et al.* (1989). Barrier and lagoon coast evolution under differing relative sea-level regimes: examples from Ireland and Nova Scotia. *Marine Geology*, **88**, 221-242.

Centre for Ecology and Hydrology (CEH) (2005). Relationship between tree mallow (*Lavatera arborea*) and Atlantic puffin (*Fratercula arctica*) on the island of Craigleith, Firth of Forth (Forth Islands Special Protection Area). *Scottish Natural Heritage Commissioned Report*, No. 106. Scottish Natural Heritage, Battleby.

Covey, R., Fortune, F., Nichols, D. and Thorpe, K. (1998). *Marine Nature Conservation Review Sectors 3, 4, 12, 13 & 15. Lagoons in mainland Scotland and the Inner Hebrides: Area summaries.* Joint Nature Conservation Committee, Peterborough (Coasts and Seas of the United Kingdom. MNCR Series).

Dargie, T.C.D. (2000). *Sand Dune Vegetation Survey of Scotland: National Report.* 2 vols. Scottish Natural Heritage, Battleby.

Dawson, A., Dawson, S. and Ritchie, W. (2007). Historical climatology and coastal change associated with the "Great Storm" of January 2005, South Uist and Benbecula, Scottish Outer Hebrides. *Scottish Geographical Journal*, **123**, 135-149.

Geodata Institute (2003). *Use of GIS to map land claim and identify potential areas for managed realignment in the Inner Solway Firth.* Report to Solway Firth Partnership by GeoData Institute, University of Southampton.

Hansom, J.D. (in press). Coastal steepening in Scotland. *Scottish Natural Heritage Commissioned Report.*

Hansom, J.D. and Evans, D.J.A. (1995). The Old Man of Hoy. *Scottish Geographical Magazine*, **111**, 172-174.

Hansom, J.D., Maslen J., Lees G., Tilbrook, C. and McManus J. (2001). Sea level changes and sustainable management of the coast: the potential for managed realignment in the Forth estuary. In *Earth Science and the Natural Heritage of Scotland*, ed. by J.E. Gordon and K. Leys. The Stationery Office, London. pp148-160.

Hansom, J.D., Barltrop, N. and Hall, A. (2008). Modelling the processes of cliff-top erosion and deposition under extreme storm waves. *Marine Geology*, **253**, 36-50.

Harris, R.A. and Jones, M. (1998). *The nature of grazing: farming with flowers at Loft and the Hill of White Hamars.* Scottish Wildlife Trust, Edinburgh.

Lacambra, C., Cutts, N., Allen, J., Burd, F. and Elliott, M. (2004). *Spartina anglica*: a review of its status, dynamics and management. *English Nature Research Reports* No. 527. English Nature, Peterborough.

Leach, S.J. and Kinnear, P.K. (1985). Scrub and woodland management Tentsmuir Point NNR: Fife. *Sand dunes and their management. Focus on Nature Conservation* **No. 13**, ed. by P. Doody, Nature Conservancy Council, Peterborough. pp 239-241.

May, V.J. and Hansom, J.D. (2003). *Coastal Geomorphology of Great Britain. Geological Conservation Review,* Volume 28. Joint Nature Conservation Committee, Peterborough.

Norton, L.R., Murphy, J., Reynolds, B., Marks, S. and Mackey, E.C. (2009) *Countryside Survey: Scotland Results from 2007.* NERC/Centre for Ecology & Hydrology, The Scottish Government, Scottish Natural Heritage. (CEH Project Number: C03259).

Pethick, J. (1999). Future sea level changes in Scotland: options for coastal management. In *Scotland's Living Coastline*, ed. by J.M. Baxter, K. Duncan, S.M. Atkins and G. Lees. The Stationery Office, London. pp 45-62.

Posford Duvivier Environment (1998). Distribution of coastal habitats in Scotland. *Unpublished report to SNH Maritime Group.* Contract No. BAT/97/98/11.

Randall, R.E. and Doody, J.P. (1995). Habitat inventories and the European Habitats Directive: the example of shingle beaches. In *Directions in European coastal management*, ed by M.G. Healy and J.P. Doody. Samara Publishing Limited, Cardigan. pp 19-36.

Randall, R.E. and Doody, J.P. (2001). Shingle vegetation survey of the Solway Firth. *Report to Scottish Natural Heritage*, contract No. R/AA4/B/00/26.

Rennie, A.F. and Hansom, J.D. (2011). Sea level trend reversal: land uplift outpaced by sea level rise on Scotland's coast. *Geomorphology*, **125**, 193-202.

Scottish Executive (2005). *Seas the opportunity. A strategy for the long-term sustainability of Scotland's coasts and seas.* Scottish Executive, Edinburgh.

Scottish Development Department (SDD) (1998). *Scottish Environment Statistics 1998.* The Scottish Office, Edinburgh.

Scottish Natural Heritage (2007). *A Five Year Species Action Framework: Making a difference for Scotland's Species.* Scottish Natural Heritage, Battleby.

Scottish Office (1997). *National Planning Policy Guideline (NPPG) 13 Coastal Planning.* The Scottish Office (Development Department), Edinburgh.

Stewart, N.F., Darwell, A. and Scott, S. (in press). Bird's nest stonewort *Tolypella nidifica* in Loch an t-Sruith Mhoir and Loch an Duin, North Uist. *Commissioned Research Report*, Scottish Natural Heritage, Inverness.

Thorpe, K. (1998). *Marine Nature Conservation Review Sectors 1&2. Lagoons in Shetland and Orkney: area summaries.* Joint Nature Conservation Committee, Peterborough. (Coasts and Seas of the United Kingdom. MNCR Series.).

Thorpe, K., Dalkin, M., Fortune, F. and Nichols, D. (1998). *Marine Nature Conservation Review Sector 14. Lagoons in the Outer Hebrides: area summaries.* Joint Nature Conservation Committee, Peterborough. (Coasts and Seas of the United Kingdom. MNCR Series).

Vega Leinert, A.C. de la, Keen, D.H., Jones, R.L., Wells, J.M. and Smith, D.E. (2000). Mid-Holocene environmental changes in the Bay of Skaill, Mainland Orkney, Scotland: an integrated geomorphological, sedimentological and stratigraphical study. *Journal of Quaternary Science*, **15**, 509–528.

19 The Future of Cetacean Watching in Scotland under Different Climate Change Scenarios

Emily Lambert, Colin D. MacLeod, Colin Hunter and
Graham J. Pierce

Summary

1. Global climate change is expected to affect the distribution and range of cetacean species, with implications for cetacean watching tourism in Scotland.
2. The distributions of a representative warm water species (common dolphin, *Delphinus delphis*) and a representative cold water species (white-beaked dolphin, *Lagenorhynchus albirostris*) were modelled for the time period 2010 to 2099, based on predicted future sea surface temperatures. These models suggest substantial contractions in the range of cool water species and substantial northwards expansion of warm water species.
3. Tourist questionnaires suggest that the effect of future changes in cetacean distribution on cetacean watching in Scotland will vary according to trip type and the expectations of tourists. However, from the results obtained so far, it appears that an overall decline in the likelihood of observing any cetacean on a trip (regardless of species) is more likely to affect cetacean watching in this area than a reduction in the likelihood of observing individual species *per se*.

19.1 Introduction

Cetacean watching tourism is a significant economic sector of Scotland's wildlife tourism industry. On the west coast alone, there are about 26 operators advertising opportunities to see cetaceans (whales, dolphins and porpoise), each of which offer one or more different types of trip (see Table 19.1). However, the future sustainability of this industry is dependent upon the continued presence of

Lambert, E., MacLeod, C.D., Hunter, C. and Pierce, G.J. (2011). The Future of Cetacean Watching in Scotland under Different Climate Change Scenarios – *The Changing Nature of Scotland*, eds. S.J. Marrs, S. Foster, C. Hendrie, E.C. Mackey, D.B.A. Thompson. TSO Scotland, Edinburgh, pp 199-204.

cetaceans, whose geographic ranges are expected to be affected by global climate change (Learmonth *et al.*, 2006; MacLeod, 2009).

Table 19.1 Definition of trip types generated for the west coast of Scotland.

Trip type	Trip definition
A	Dedicated day trip, where the primary aim is to search for and see cetaceans.
B	A day trip which aims to search for and see cetaceans and other wildlife equally.
C	A day trip which predominantly aims to search for other wildlife, although seeing cetaceans is still important.
D	Cruise trip which lasts a number of days whereby passengers sleep on board. Seeing cetaceans is important, however, it is not the primary aim of the trip.

Global climate change is expected to result in increases in water temperature across the NE Atlantic, including Scottish waters (Lowe *et al.*, 2009). The range of cetacean species is expected to alter in response, as species track changes in the spatial distribution of their preferred temperature ranges, either due to direct effects on the cetaceans themselves or due to the effects of water temperature on the distribution of preferred prey (MacLeod, 2009). However, little work has been conducted to quantify the likely extent of such changes in species ranges, or the potential effect of these changes on cetacean tourism. We present a subset of results from a study which seeks to address this issue in relation to cetacean watching in Scotland.

19.2 Predicting future cetacean distribution

Data on cetacean sightings, sea surface temperature (SST) and sea bed topography were used to create a spatial model of habitat suitability under specific temperature conditions. These models were then used to predict how the distribution of species is likely to change for each decade between 2010 and 2099, based on projected SST data generated from the HadCM3 climate model (Johns *et al.*, 2003). To account for some of the uncertainty associated with emission projections, three different IPCC scenarios were applied for each time period (Nakicenovic and Swart, 2000).

We illustrate the model outputs generated for two of the 11 species examined: common dolphin (*Delphinus delphis*, a warm water species) and white-beaked dolphin (*Lagenorhynchus albirostris*, a cool water species), (Figure 19.1: 1a & 2a). Distributional shifts are more likely for these two species given that the edge of their range (northern and southern respectively) occurs within the study area.

By comparison, range shifts are less likely to be observed for those species within the study area which occupy the centre of their thermal niche.

Our results predict the range of common dolphin to expand under all emission scenarios, while the range of white-beaked dolphin is predicted to significantly decline (Figure 19.1: 1b & 2b). While the predicted rate of range expansion/reduction differed according to the scenario applied, the direction of this change was constant.

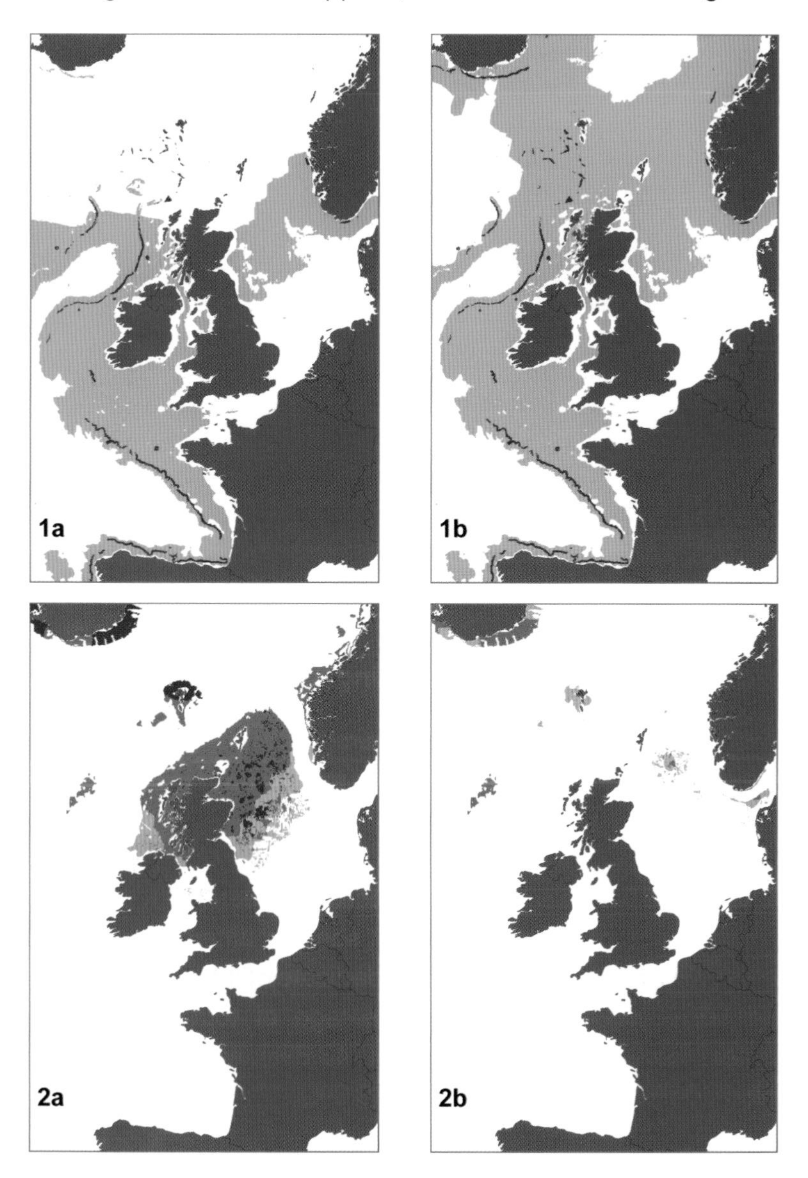

Figure 19.1 Predicted distribution of (1) common dolphin and (2) white-beaked dolphin based on (a) present sea surface temperature and (b) projected sea surface temperature for 2040-2049 applying the A1b (medium) emission scenario. White shading indicates unsuitable habitat, while deep red shading indicates the highest suitability of habitat.

Plate 19.1 Common dolphin breaching in the Minch, West of Scotland, June 2009. This species is predicted to expand its range in the NE Atlantic under future climate change scenarios. © Sue Scott

19.3 Implications for cetacean watching

During the summer of 2008, 225 questionnaires were completed by tourists on the west coast of Scotland from a representative sample of different trip types. Three key questions were asked:

(1) *Is it important which species of cetacean is seen?*
The importance of seeing a specific species differed significantly with trip type (χ^2, $P<0.001$). Trip type A (dedicated cetacean watching trip, see Table 19.1) had the highest percentage of tourists who considered it important to see a specific cetacean (43.8%), while trip type D (residential general wildlife trip) had the lowest (3.3%).

(2) *Which species of cetacean are the most important to see?*
Of the seven species identified by tourists as being the most important to see (Table 19.2), common dolphin was the second highest (19.6%), while white-beaked dolphin was the second lowest (3.8%).

Table 19.2 Cetacean species considered important to see by tourists on boat trips. Data are derived from questionnaires completed by tourists on the west coast of Scotland during 2008 in response to the question "which species of cetacean are the most important to see?"

Species	Frequency (%)
Minke whale (*Balaenoptera acutorostrata*)	33.2
Common dolphin (*Delphinus delphis*)	19.6
Bottlenose dolphin (*Tursiops truncatus*)	15.2
Killer whale (*Orcinus orca*)	13.6
Harbour porpoise (*Phocoena phocoena*)	12.0
White-beaked dolphin (*Lagenorhynchus albirostris*)	3.8
Risso's dolphin (*Grampus griseus*)	2.7

(3) *If there were less variety of species to see, would tourists still want to go on a trip? (This question used a Likhert scale from 1 to 5, where 1 was 'Definitely No' and 5 was 'Definitely Yes')*
Where a reduction in diversity did not affect the chances of seeing a cetacean (regardless of species), tourists would still want to go on a trip (modal average response = 5; grouped median = 4), with no difference between trip type. Where a reduction in variety was associated with an overall reduction in the chances of seeing a cetacean, the response of tourists differed between trip types (Kruskal-Wallis, $P<0.001$). Tourists from trip type C (general wildlife trip) expressed the most positive response (mode = 4; grouped median = 3), followed by type D (mode = 3; grouped median = 3), and type A (mode = 2 & 3; grouped median = 3), with the most negative response expressed by tourists on trip type B (semi-dedicated cetacean watching trip, mode = 2; grouped median = 2).

19.4 Conclusion

While warm water cetacean species, such as common dolphin, are likely to benefit from global climate change, cool water species, such as white-beaked dolphin, are likely to be adversely affected.

Assessing the potential impacts of these changes on cetacean watching in Scotland must also take into account how other cetacean species are likely to be affected (including those which are limited by both cooler and warmer water temperatures and those which are cosmopolitan species). Further to this, it is important to consider that some species are more popular than others (see

Section 19.3), due perhaps to differences in behaviour towards boats (e.g. tendency to 'bow-ride') and differences in species ecology (e.g. group size). The next phase of research will seek to examine this question in greater detail.

From the results obtained so far however, it appears that an overall decline in the likelihood of observing any cetacean on a trip (regardless of species) is more likely to affect cetacean watching in this area than a reduction in the likelihood of observing individual species *per se*.

Where the overall likelihood of observing any cetacean does decline, specialist trips (such as trip type A) are more likely to be affected than generalist trips (such as trip type C and D).

References

Johns T.C., Gregory, J.M., Ingram, W. J. *et al.* (2003). Anthropogenic climate change for 1860 to 2100 simulated with the HadCM3 model under updated emissions scenarios. *Climate Dynamics*, **20**, 583-612.

Learmonth, J.A., MacLeod, C.D., Santos, M.B. *et al.* (2006). Potential effects of climate change on marine mammals. *Oceanography and Marine Biology: An Annual Review*, **44**, 431-464.

Lowe, J.A., Howard, T., Pardaens, A. *et al.* (2009). *UK Climate Projections Science Report*: Marine and Coastal Projections. Norwich, UK: Tyndall Centre for Climatic Change Research.

MacLeod, C.D. (2009). Global climate change, range changes and potential implications for the conservation of marine cetaceans: A review and synthesis. *Endangered Species Research*, **7**, 125-136.

Nakicenovic, N. and Swart, R. (2000). *Emissions scenarios: A special report of Working Group III of the Intergovernmental Panel on Climate Change.* Cambridge, UK: University of Cambridge Press.

20 The Quality of Shellfish Waters

Judith Dobson, Graham Davies and Ann Paterson

Summary

1. Waters designated for the production of shellfish under the Shellfish Water Protection Directive are monitored by the Scottish Environment Protection Agency (SEPA) for levels of faecal coliforms and chemical contaminants.
2. The quality of shellfish waters in Scotland is good, but there is scope for improvement in reducing the levels of faecal coliforms, which are accumulated by shellfish.
3. The Water Framework Directive will revoke the Shellfish Waters Directive in 2013.

20.1 Introduction

The Scottish Environment Protection Agency (SEPA) monitors and protects, through regulation, waters designated as Shellfish Waters by the Scottish Government under the European Community Shellfish Waters Directive (2006/113/EC). The 2006 Directive (which updated and replaced the original Directive issued in 1979 (79/923/EEC)) aims to protect, and if necessary improve, water quality in areas of shellfish growth and to contribute to the quality of shellfish for human consumption. Scottish Government initially designated 20 sites in 1981 and this process has continued so that there are currently 78 designated Shellfish Waters.

Designated waters must achieve the imperative standards and aim to achieve the guideline standards set by the Directive within six years of designation (Table 20.1). Numerical standards for contaminants in waters and shellfish were established to aid the interpretation of the qualitative standards in the Directive (Table 20.2). The Directive sets the minimum sampling frequency and the reference methods of analysis; however, the frequency of monitoring can be reduced if there is no risk of failing the standards.

Dobson, J., Davies, G. and Paterson, A. (2011). The Quality of Shellfish Waters – *The Changing Nature of Scotland*, eds. S.J. Marrs, S. Foster, C. Hendrie, E.C. Mackey, D.B.A. Thompson. TSO Scotland, Edinburgh, pp 205-212.

Table 20.1 Shellfish Waters Directive imperative and guideline standards.

Parameter	Guideline Standard	Imperative Standard	Sampling Frequency
pH		7-9	Quarterly
Temperature	A discharge affecting shellfish waters must not cause a 2°C increase compared to waters not affected	(no standard set by the Directive)	Quarterly
Colour mgPt/l (after filtration)		A discharge affecting shellfish waters must not cause an increase of 10 Hazen units in filtered waters compared to waters not affected	Quarterly
Suspended Solids mg/l		A discharge affecting shellfish waters must not cause a 30% increase compared to waters not affected	Quarterly
Salinity	12-38 ppth	< 40 ppth A discharge affecting shellfish waters must not cause a 10% increase compared to waters not affected	Monthly
Dissolved Oxygen (% saturation)	> 80%	> 70% (average value) if < 70%, repeat if < 60%, there must be no harmful effects on shellfish colonies	Monthly
Petroleum Hydrocarbons		Must not produce a visible film on water surface or a deposit on the shellfish, nor have harmful effects on the shellfish	Quarterly
Organohalogenated Substances	Concentrations in shellfish flesh must be limited so that it contributes to the high quality of shellfish products	Concentrations in shellfish water or flesh must not exceed a level which gives rise to harmful effects on the shellfish and larvae	Half Yearly
Metals: Silver, Arsenic, Cadmium, Chromium, Copper, Mercury, Nickel, Lead, Zinc	Concentrations in shellfish flesh must be limited so that it contributes to the high quality of shellfish products	Concentrations in shellfish water or flesh must not exceed a level which gives rise to harmful effects on the shellfish and larvae	Half Yearly
Faecal Coliforms	< 300/100ml in the shellfish flesh and intervalvular liquid	(no standard set by the Directive)	Quarterly
Substances affecting the taste of the shellfish	Concentration lower than that liable to impair the taste of the shellfish	(no standard set by the Directive)	
Saxitoxin (produced by dinoflagellates)		(no standard set by the Directive)	

Table 20.2 Shellfish Waters Directive Standards for organochlorine compounds and trace metals in waters and shellfish flesh.

Parameter	Waters (μg/l)		Mussels (mg/kg)[1]	
	Guideline Standards	**Imperative Standards**	**Guideline Standards**	**Imperative Standards**
arsenic	n/a	20	30	100
cadmium	n/a	1.0	5	15
chromium	n/a	10	6	20
copper	n/a	5	15	30
nickel	n/a	5	5	15
lead	n/a	5	15	50
silver	n/a	0.3	1.0	3.0
zinc	n/a	10	250	500
mercury	n/a	0.1	1.0	3.0
Dieldrin			15	50
DDD			30	100
DDE			30	100
DDT			30	100
HCB			30	100
a-HCH			10	30
g-HCH			10	30
PCB			300	1000

[1] Note – mg/kg dry weight for metals and wet weight for organohalogenated substances.

SEPA monitors both water and shellfish flesh – in some areas the frequency of monitoring has been reduced where there is sufficient evidence to demonstrate that there is no risk of failing the standards. Since 2008 Food Standards Agency *E. coli* data from harvesting sites in designated shellfish waters has been used to assess compliance with the faecal coliform guideline standard. The Food Standards Agency (Scotland) monitors the microbiological quality of shellfish for human consumption under Food Hygiene (Scotland) Regulations. The Shellfish Hygiene Class A standard for *E. coli* is used to assess compliance with the Shellfish Waters Directive guideline standard (Table 20.3). SEPA produces pollution reduction programmes for shellfish waters which list actions to ensure protection and compliance with the Directive. These identify point sources of contaminants and recommend actions required to reduce impacts.

Table 20.3 Shellfish Hygiene Directive classification standards.

Classification	Permitted Levels	Requirements
A	<230 *E.coli*/100g flesh, or <300 faecal coliforms/100g flesh	Approved for direct human consumption
B	<4,600 *E.coli*/100g (in 90% of samples) or <6,000 faecal coliforms/ 100g flesh (in 90% of samples)	Must be depurated, heat treated or relayed to meet Category A
C	<46,000 *E.coli*/100g flesh	Must be relayed for 2 months then treated if necessary to meet category A.
	>60,000 faecal coliforms	Unsuitable for production

20.2 Results

In 2008 all designated Shellfish Waters complied with the imperative and guideline standards for trace metals and trace organic compounds, however 37% did not achieve the guideline standard for faecal coliforms (Figure 20.1). Trace metal concentrations in waters and shellfish flesh were low and close to background levels which reflect natural inputs from the weathering of rocks (Figure 20.2). Organochlorine concentrations in waters were below the limit of detection of the analysis (1ng/l) at all sites and well below the guideline standards in mussels. Polycylic Aromatic Hydrocarbons (PAH) in shellfish flesh were analysed to assess the impact of petroleum hydrocarbons. There is, at the time of writing, no agreed standard for PAH in shellfish however all the data were below the interim Food Standards Agency limit for benz[a]anthracene of 15µg/kg wet weight (Figure 20.3).

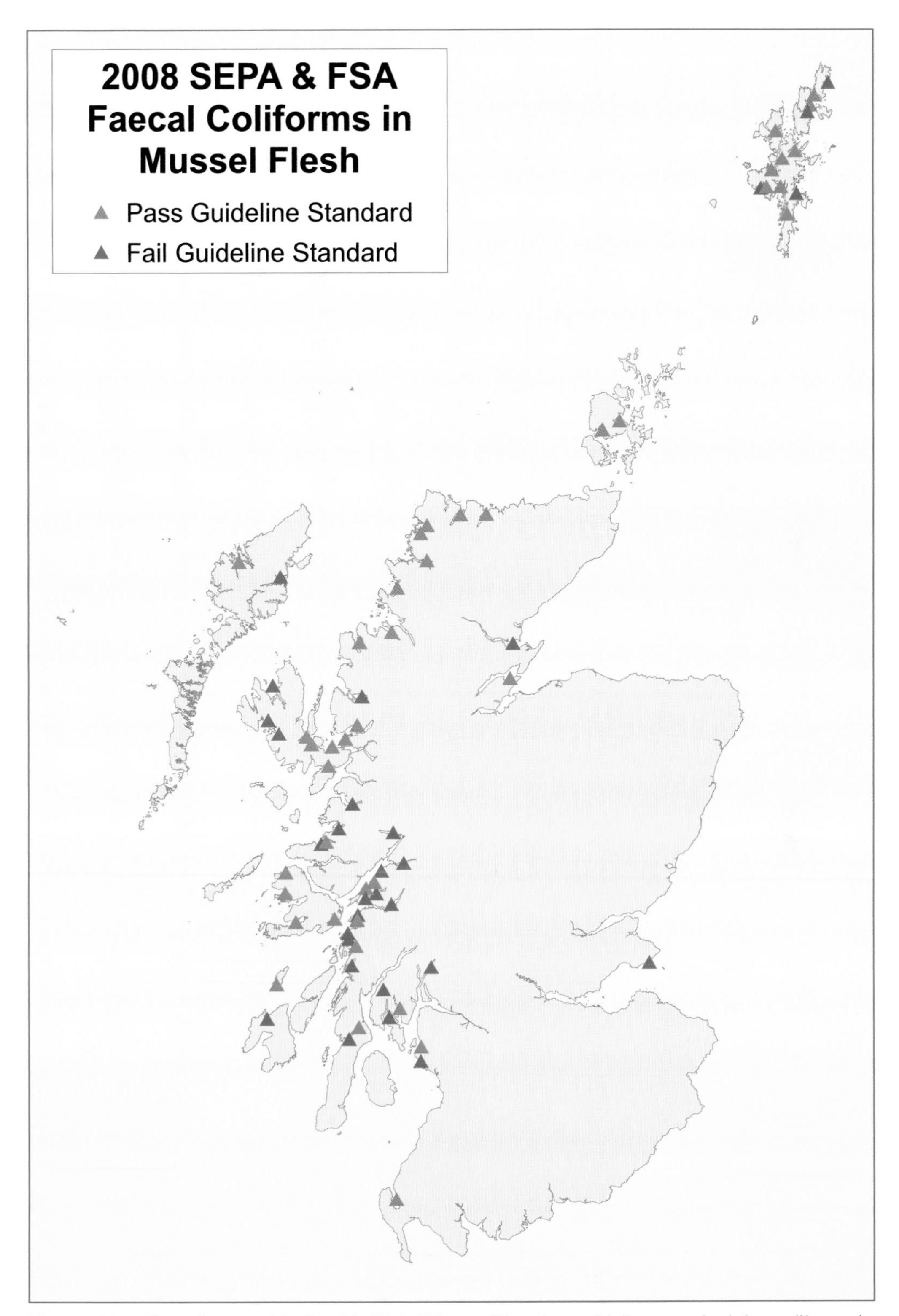

Figure 20.1 Compliance with the Shellfish Waters Directive guideline standard for coliforms in shellfish flesh.

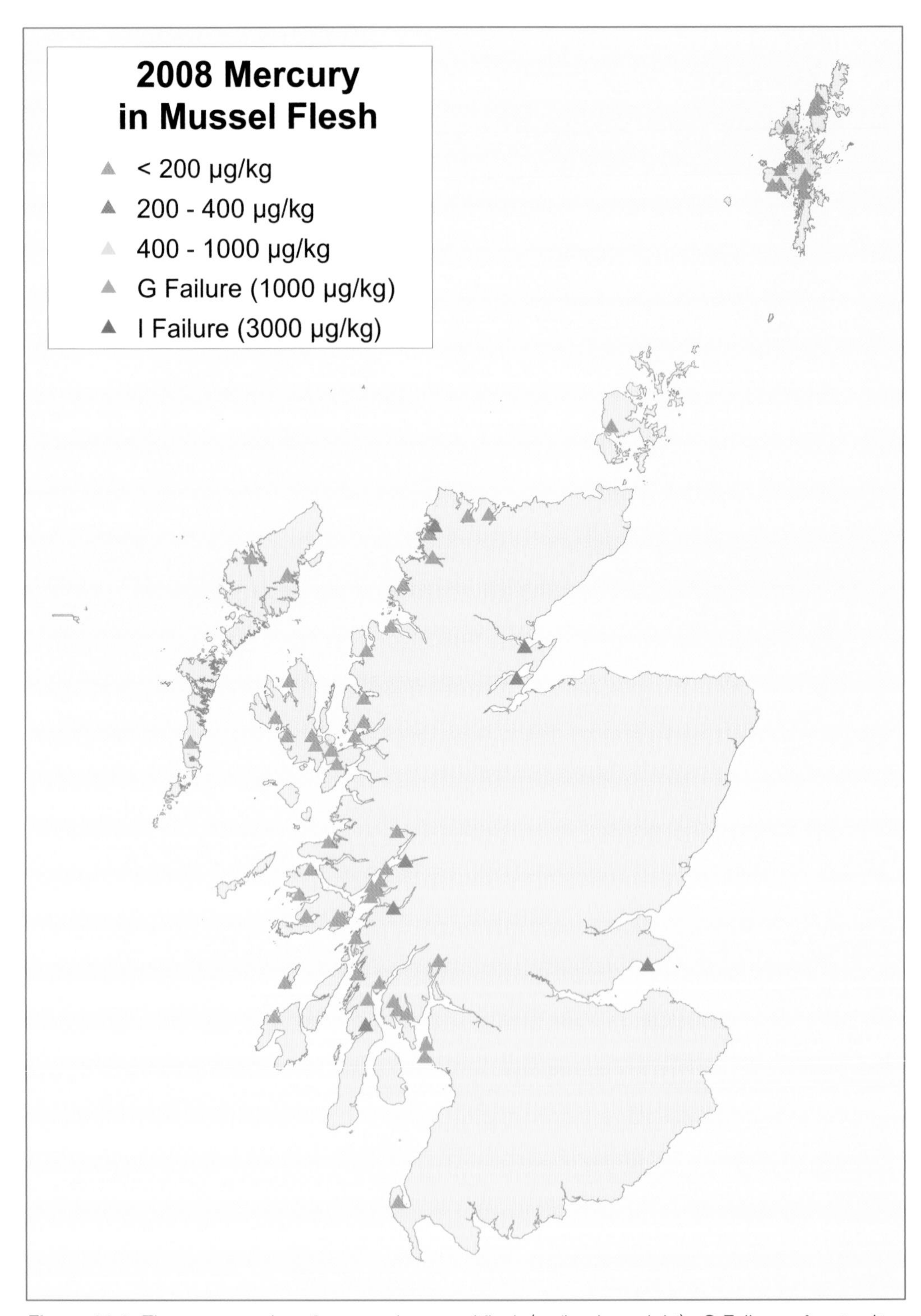

Figure 20.2 The concentration of mercury in mussel flesh (µg/kg dry weight). G Failure refers to sites that exceed the guideline standards, I Failure refers to sites that exceed the imperative standards. There are no sites in either category.

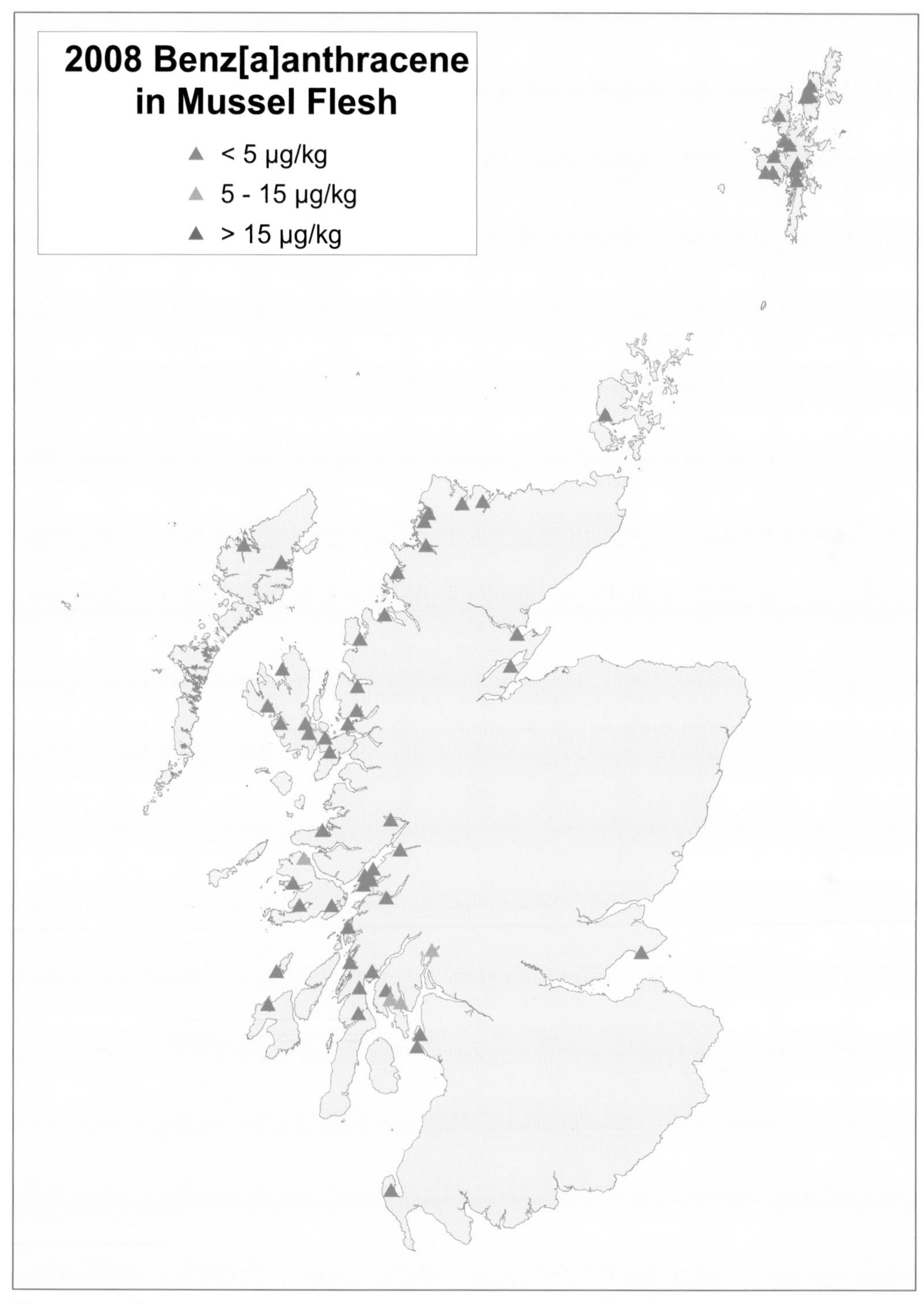

Figure 20.3 Concentration of the polycylic aromatic hydrocarbon (PAH) benz[a]anthracene in mussel flesh (µg/kg wet weight). There is no agreed standard for PAHs, which are analysed to assess the impact of petroleum hydrocarbons, however all values are below the interim Food Standards Agency limit of 15µg/kg wet weight.

20.3 Discussion

The quality of shellfish waters in Scotland is good, and all sites comply with the imperative standards. Contaminant concentrations are low in both waters and mussel flesh however many sites do not achieve the guideline standard for faecal coliforms. Shellfish accumulate contaminants from the overlying water column during filter feeding giving a flesh concentration which is considerably higher than that of the surrounding water and there is no correlation between the concentration of faecal coliforms in shellfish and waters at low concentrations. There are many sources of bacteria including wildlife, domestic animals and sewage discharges. Improvements to the sewerage network are implemented where these have been identified as causing exceedance of the guideline standard. However diffuse inputs from agriculture and wildlife are difficult to identify and require individual catchment studies. For example a study of Loch Etive identified that a high proportion of the faecal indicator organisms derived from agricultural run off during wet weather (Magill *et al.*, 2008). Diffuse inputs are more difficult to mitigate than point source discharges but improvements to the management of animal wastes may reduce inputs.

The Water Framework Directive (WFD) will revoke the Shellfish Waters Directive in 2013. Existing shellfish waters will become '*areas designated for the protection of economically significant aquatic species*' and placed on the Protected Area register. It is intended that designated waters will receive the same level of environmental protection under the WFD as applied under the Shellfish Waters Directive. The United Kingdom Technical Advisory Group (UKTAG) will produce recommendations for standards relating to faecal bacteria and other pollutants in preparation for the revocation of the Shellfish Waters Directive in 2013. The Scottish Government may then direct SEPA to adopt these standards in the regulatory framework.

Reference

Magill, S., Black, K., Kay, D. *et al.* (2008). *Risk factors in Shellfish Harvesting Areas.* SARF013/SAMS Report No. 256. Scottish Aquaculture Research Forum.

The Changing Nature of Scotland

Fresh water

Fresh water

Fresh water plays a critical role in Scotland's environment. It has shaped our landscape (see McKirdy *et al.*, 2007), driven our industrial revolution (Butt and Twindell, 1991) and forms the inspiration for poetry and prose across the world. Fresh water covers less than 1% of the world's surface, represents approximately only 2% of the whole land area in Scotland, but is vital to so much more.

Some key events for fresh waters in Scotland since 1970

1974	Control of Pollution Act (COPA)
1974	Harmonised Monitoring Scheme established
1979	Loch Dee Project established – a 10 year investigation into the impacts of acidification on the ecology of freshwaters
1980	The Water (Scotland) Act passed
1982	The otter legally protected
1983	Reasonable numbers of adult salmon reported in the Clyde from this date onwards
1988	UK Acid Waters Monitoring Network established
1990	Operation Brightwater (1990-1993) a campaign to raise public awareness of the value of Scotland's fresh water and coastal environments and the threats facing them
1991	EU Nitrates Directive
1992	Launch of the Environmental Change Network – the UK's long term environmental monitoring network
1995	SEPA (Scottish Environmental Protection Agency) formed and fully operational on 1 April 1996, so replacing the seven river purification boards in Scotland and their counterparts in the three Islands Councils and relevant functions of the 56 District and Island Councils
1995	WWF *Wild Rivers* project launched in Scotland as part of a pan-European initiative to restore rivers to a more natural state for improved water management
1995	Environment Act passed

r Livet at Tombae farm, Glen Livet. This area is of the Cairngorms Straths Environmentally sitive Area (ESA). © John MacPherson/SNH

1997	The first translocations of vendace occurred in order to save the species from extinction as a UK fish
1997	Flood Prevention and Land Drainage Act
1998	SEPA's first environmental strategy published
1998	Formation of the River Restoration Centre
1998	Habitat Enhancement Initiative launched by SEPA
1998	Freshwater pearl mussel granted full legal protection
1999	UNESCO Hydrology for Environment, Life and Policy established – a global programme to link hydrology to the needs of society
1999	Caithness and Sutherland Peatlands designated a Wetland of International Importance
2000	EU Water Framework Directive
2000	The Pollution Prevention and Control (Scotland) Regulations passed
2002	Scottish Executive publish *Scotland's Canals: an asset for the future*
2002	Forth and Clyde canal rejoined to the Union canal by the Falkirk Wheel
2002	First Nitrate Vulnerable Zones designated in Scotland
2003	Water Environment and Water Services (Scotland) Act
2004	Work began on the Conservation of Atlantic Salmon in Scotland (CASS) – a four year EU LIFE project
2005	Caithness and Sutherland Peatlands are officially designated as a Special Area of Conservation (SAC) covering over 140,000ha
2005	The Water Environment (Controlled Activities)(Scotland) Regulations passed
2006	*State of Scotland's Environment* published by SEPA
2009	Trial reintroduction of European beaver in Knapdale
2009	Flood Risk Management (Scotland) Act
2009	Climate Change (Scotland) Act
2009	Completion of Glendoe hydro-electric scheme (above Fort Augustus), possibly the last large scale dam-based project

In the first chapter in this section, Chris Spray (Chapter 21) describes the extent of Scotland's fresh water resource (90% of the UK surface water) and details a number of impressive statistics demonstrating the value of this resource in Scotland – such as the volume of Loch Ness alone exceeds the total volume of all standing waters in England and Wales combined. So perhaps inhabitants of Scotland could be forgiven for taking water for granted, despite the fact only 15% of the world's population has access to an abundance of it. However, predicted impacts of climate change mean that the distribution of water across Scotland is likely to change. Spray presents data showing that the rainfall in the north and west of Scotland has increased. Conversely, since 1961 areas in the east of Scotland have become 45% drier during the summer months. This has resulted in some rivers, such as the Dee and the Isla, experiencing longer and more severe periods of low flow and drought, which can adversely affect fish populations. Overall, however, extreme rainfall events are on the increase and since the late 1980s most of Scotland's large rivers (i.e. those with a catchment greater than $500km^2$) have recorded new maximum discharge levels and reports of damage to property from flooding have become commonplace.

In 2009, the quality of Scotland's fresh waters was generally good, and even the poorest households had access to clean water from the mains supply. The European Water Framework Directive (WFD), introduced in 2000, requires that the chemical content (i.e. cleanliness) be monitored and controlled, and the ecological status of water bodies in terms of biota and geomorphology should be assessed. The Directive states that all surface waters should achieve good ecological status by 2015. According to the WFD classification scheme, 56% of Scotland's rivers and 66% of lochs were classed as having a good overall status in 2009. Issues remain, however, with diffuse pollution from both urban and agricultural sources, climate change and alterations to patterns of river flow.

Three indicators have been developed to show trends in Scotland's fresh water quality (Otters; Fresh Water Macroinvertebrates; River Quality) (see Foster *et al.*, Chapter 2). Otters (*Lutra lutra*) are a species indicative of good environmental quality and the indicator shows that they have returned to most suitable sites throughout Scotland since the 1970s (SNH, 2007). Fresh water macroinvertebrates and river water quality indicators are tracked using data provided by SEPA. The indicator on fresh water macroinvertebrate diversity, shows that the numbers of recorded species has shown a marked upwards trend since the early 1980s. In addition the river quality indicator shows a clear improvement since the start of the time series in 1999.

The image of cleanliness and naturalness of Scotland's water plays an important part in our economy, providing income to local areas through recreation and tourism. In Chapter 22, Julie Hesketh-Laird describes the importance of good fresh water to Scotland's most iconic industry – whisky production – where the characteristics of the local water are said to impart specific qualities to the final product. Concluding that Scotland's natural environment and the whisky industry are intertwined she explains how the industry is making steps to both protect the environment and to adapt to some of the challenges posed by climate change.

Most of the fresh water in Scotland is concentrated in locations far from the centres of population and many water courses have been heavily modified to transport water or for hydro electric schemes. Dave Gilvear (Chapter 23) describes some of the major threats to fresh water biodiversity. He tracks the development of river restoration projects from small scale and fairly localised projects aimed at improving biodiversity of fisheries in the 1990s, to larger catchment scale projects which acknowledge that rivers are the product of all the land that they pass through. Over the past two centuries, Scotland's waters have been heavily modified by the urge to tame water and control where it goes. He advocates the use of natural flood control management, through for example, wet woodlands which in addition to improving biodiversity, can significantly reduce the speed at which water passes through a catchment so reducing the intensity of floods.

In the concluding paper (Chapter 24), Alastair McNeill and Paul Sutherland describe a range of practical catchment management initiatives in Dumfries and Galloway and demonstrate how requirements of the Water Framework Directive can be combined with other drivers, such as Biodiversity Action Plans, to result in improved management of Scotland's fresh water resource. Their examples of partnership working are a model for the future of fresh water management.

References

Butt, J. and Twindell, J. (1991). The power of Scotland. In: *The Nature of Scotland: Landscape, Wildlife and People*, ed. by M. Magnusson and G. White. Canongate Press, Edinburgh.

McKirdy, A., Gordon, J. and Crofts, R. (2007). *Land of Mountain and Flood. The Geology and Landforms of Scotland.* Birlinn Ltd (in association with Scottish Natural Heritage), Edinburgh.

21 The Changing Nature of Scotland's Fresh Water Environment

Chris Spray

Summary

1. Scotland has an abundance of fresh water and holds 90% of Great Britain's surface fresh water. This is a precious resource, the management of which needs to adapt to changing environmental, economic and social conditions.
2. Our fresh water and wetlands support a wide range of animals and plants, including internationally important habitats and species, such as Atlantic salmon (*Salmo salar*) and pink-footed geese (*Anser brachyrhynchus*). These wetlands can also act as natural flood defences, provide water purification services, offer places for recreation, provide food and water itself, are relied upon by industries, and form part of our landscape and cultural heritage.
3. As healthy functioning ecosystems, water and wetlands are fundamental to human well-being, and they contribute to the quality of life of all those who live in and visit Scotland.
4. This paper outlines the importance of Scotland's water resource, discusses the schemes that exist to monitor it; describes the overall status and trends in water quality and quantity, and the habitats and species it supports.

21.1 Scotland's fresh water resource – why is it important?

21.1.1 Habitats and species

Scotland's water represents more than 90% of the volume and 70% of the total surface area of fresh water in Great Britain (Smith and Lyle, 1979). More water is contained in Scotland's largest loch, Loch Ness (7.5 billion m^3), than in all the lakes in England and Wales. Overall, Scotland is estimated to hold around 30,000 fresh water lochs, ponds and lochans (representing 1.9% of Scotland's land surface).

Spray, C. (2011). The Changing Nature of Scotland's Fresh Water Environment – *The Changing Nature of Scotland*, eds. S.J. Marrs, S. Foster, C. Hendrie, E.C. Mackey, D.B.A. Thompson. TSO Scotland, Edinburgh, pp 219-236.

Scotland hosts the river discharging the greatest volume of water in the UK, the Tay; at nearly 200m^3 per second, this discharge is more than that of the rivers Thames and Severn together. On a global scale these figures are very small (UNEP, 2005), but Scotland's profusion of fresh water should not be under-valued, as in addition to supporting habitats and species, it provides critically important ecosystem services.

Scotland also hosts some 75 UKBAP priority species directly associated with fresh water and wetlands. (Table 21.1). Many of the habitats and species are of international importance, including Eurasian otters (*Lutra lutra*), Atlantic salmon (*Salmo salar*) and pink-footed geese (*Anser brachyrhynchus*).

Table 21.1 The number of fresh water species identified as UK Biodiversity Action Plan (UKBAP) priority species in Scotland

Fresh water and wetlands	UK priority species in Scotland
Algae	1
Bryophytes	7
Fungi and lichens	4
Invertebrates	24
Vascular plants	13
Vertebrates	26
Total	75

SNH's report on the State of Scotland's Biodiversity in 2010 (Mackey and Mudge, 2010) showed that the trend for these 75 priority species (based on 19 matching assessments in 2005 and 2008) was broadly stable (no change). Of the 32 species assessed in 2008, the number stable or increasing (41%) exceeded the number declining (25%).

For some species Scotland is internationally important. For example, Scotland holds the majority of the world's wintering population of migratory pink-footed geese, as well as the entire world population of wintering Svalbard barnacle geese (*Branta leucopsis*). Wintering waterbirds are reasonably well monitored, and an indicator developed for them shows that in 2007/08 abundance was 112% of the 1975/76 baseline (Mackey and Mudge, 2010).

The recovery of Scotland's otter population, a species protected under Annexes 2 and 4 of the EU Habitats Directive, is a recent success story. Occupied otter sites rose to 92% in 2004 when 1,267 sites were recorded as showing presence of otter droppings (spraints). In the past, otters have been absent from much of the central Lowlands of Scotland, largely due to the pollution of their watercourses. However, Scotland's Biodiversity Indicator on otters (Mackey and Mudge, 2010) showed the largest increases in otter populations were in Forth and Borders, from 17% in 1979 to 87% in 2004.

Scotland's river systems also play host to a variety of other species, including one of the most important populations of Atlantic salmon in Europe, with some 400 salmon rivers supporting genetically distinct populations of salmon. The lochs form a stronghold for Arctic char (*Salvelinus alpinus*) with perhaps 200 separate loch populations – again, each with their own distinct genetic characteristics.

Of increasing concern is the spread of several non-native invasive species along our waterways. Some of these, such as Himalayan balsam (*Impatiens glandulifera*) and giant hogweed (*Heracleum mantegazzianum*) are now well-established along many rivers, forming dense impenetrable stands. Others, such as North American signal crayfish (*Pacifastacus leniusculus*) are gradually spreading across Scotland, having already caused both major environmental and economic consequences elsewhere in the UK. New species can occur at any time, such as the zebra mussel (*Dreissena polymorpha*) which was recently reported on the Forth and Clyde canal. Little accurate information, however, is as yet available on changing population levels for these or other invasive species, but the Rivers and Fisheries Trusts of Scotland (RAFTS) provide details of the geographical extent and what numbers are available for some 29 such species. They estimate that in addition to environmental impacts, invasive non-native species and fish diseases already cost the Scottish economy upwards of £500 million per year (RAFTS website: www.invasivespeciesscotland.org.uk/).

The importance of Scotland's natural environment is directly recognised in four of the Government's 45 National Indicators of Performance, and in two of their 15 National Outcomes. This recognition is backed by a strong legislative framework which, for fresh water and wetlands is dominated by the EU Water Framework Directive (WFD), and the associated Water Environment and Water Services (Scotland) Act, 2003. Working through the process of river basin planning cycles, this aims to maintain or improve all water bodies to meet 'good ecological status', initially by 2015. This is complemented by key conservation legislation at both the European and Scottish level (notably the EU Habitats Directive and the Nature Conservation (Scotland) Act, 2004). Together, these provide the framework for assessing and reporting on the state of the water environment, and for the conservation management of fresh water habitats and species in Scotland.

21.1.2 The value of fresh water

The quality of Scotland's fresh water is important not just for biodiversity *per se*; it is fundamental to the delivery of the ecosystem services on which we all depend. The Millennium Ecosystem Assessment (MEA, 2005) identified four categories of service that underpin human well-being, and water and wetlands play a key role in each:

- Supporting services – functions such as nutrient cycling and water cycling, necessary to maintain life on earth;
- Provisioning services – goods derived from wetlands, such as crops, fish and fresh water itself;
- Regulating services – processes such as water quality purification, sediment, erosion, flood control, and climate regulation; and
- Cultural services – the value of wetlands to humans for recreation, leisure, spiritual and cultural activities.

Many of these services are under threat from human activities. The extent to which this occurs in Scotland will be revealed through the publication of a UK National Ecosystem Assessment in 2011. In addition it will produce scenarios and review policy options for dealing with these threats.

There is also a financial incentive to look after Scotland's fresh waters. In 2006, the income generated from tourism in Scotland was estimated at 5% of the Gross Domestic Product (GDP) equivalent to around £4.2 billion. Survey results revealed that 89% of tourists considered the natural environment as a factor in choosing Scotland as their holiday destination (SNH, 2008). Fresh water environments play a key part in this, with Loch Ness being one of Scotland's top tourist attractions.

Many of Scotland's industries rely on good quality fresh water, most notably, the whisky industry. For some, the quality of the water is the key ingredient to distilling whisky, and it is estimated that the industry uses around 62 million tonnes of water every year (Hesketh-Laird, Chapter 22). The River Spey catchment area is a good example of the value of the ecosystem services provided. Not only are over half of Scotland's malt whisky distilleries situated along the banks of the River Spey, the income generated from water-based leisure activities such as kayaking, white water rafting, bird watching and angling has increased. According to a report commissioned by SNH, fishing on the River Spey resulted in expenditure of £11.8 million by participants in 2003 (SNH, 2008). Another study showed the area had generated £1.7 million from water sports in 2004, supporting 48 jobs (Radford *et al.*, 2004). Elsewhere in the same catchment, ospreys (*Pandion haliaetus*) provide a major tourist attraction at Loch Garten (one of five major viewing sites attracting 12,500 visitors, spending some £2.2 million in 2006). The floodplain of the Insh marshes provides a good example of flood regulation through temporary storage of flood water, protecting downstream communities at an annual economic saving of more than £83,000 (Alveres *et al.*, 2007).

21.2 Monitoring Scotland's fresh water and wetlands

In 2006 SEPA produced their second comprehensive report on the State of Scotland's Environment (SEPA, 2006). They noted that 'Scotland has a generally high quality water environment'. Water quality has shown improvements but they highlighted issues around diffuse pollution from urban and agricultural sources, climate change, changing river flow patterns, widespread changes to the physical structure of rivers and the implications for biodiversity.

In this paper I describe the trends in the state of Scotland's fresh water and wetlands in terms of four key criteria:

- Water quality;
- Water quantity;
- The physical structure and condition of habitats; and
- Changes in species populations and composition.

For each of these, a range of data and trend information can be assembled, though often at differing scales and time periods.

21.2.1 Water Framework Directive (WFD) monitoring

A single comprehensive monitoring strategy for surface water bodies across Scotland was developed by SEPA in 2007 in order to address the monitoring requirements for the WFD. This built on past data as well as introducing changes in determinants, location, frequency and methodologies for sampling and analysis. Working with partners such as SNH and Environment Link, the network includes a Surveillance component (building on long-term data sets), an Operational component (risk-based monitoring of waters at risk of failing good ecological status) and an Investigative component (short-term monitoring of specific problem issues). The type of information gathered, in some cases annually, but increasingly less frequently is shown in Table 21.2. However, in terms of trends data, this monitoring system is somewhat disjointed from the previous survey networks and classification systems.

As part of a joint project between the British Geological Survey and SEPA, MacDonald and O'Dochartaigh (2005) assessed all the available chemical data from groundwater sources across Scotland and produced summaries of chemistry data for the main bedrock aquifers. Prior to this, existing information on natural groundwater chemistry was limited. SEPA have constructed and developed a large number of sampling boreholes across Scotland, as well as expanding existing sources, so that now a wider set of parameters are being recorded in a consistent and coherent manner.

Table 21.2 Data collected under the Water Framework Directive Scottish fresh water monitoring plan

Quality element	Rivers	Lochs	Groundwater
Priority substances and specific pollutants	x	x	
Macroinvertebrates	x	x	
Physico-chemical parameters	x	x	x
Phytoplankton		x	
Fish	x	x	
Diatoms	x	x	
Macrophytes	x	x	
Hydrology	x	x	x
Morphology	x	x	

Long term water quality monitoring continues directly in Scotland through the Harmonised Monitoring Scheme, undertaken by SEPA and its predecessors since 1974. This covers a set of key parameters in a standardised manner on 56 rivers. Recent analysis of these data have been jointly undertaken by SEPA and the Macaulay Institute in order to produce an online water quality atlas for Scottish rivers. Hydrology data are collected by SEPA, including information on monthly river flows, taken from over 1,300 gauging stations and fed in to the National River Flow Archive. Other data are available via the National Groundwater Level Archive, maintained by the British Geological Survey.

Another source of long-term data on water quality of relevance to the WFD is the UK Acid Waters Monitoring Network, set up in 1988 to assess the effects of acidification due largely to aerial deposition of sulphur dioxide and nitrogen oxides. The network in Scotland covers only seven lochs and three rivers, and the pattern of change is varied (Kernan *et al.*, 2010). Monitoring of invertebrates by SEPA at 56 river sites in the south west show some are improving, whilst others remain poor, possibly due to forestry effects. A total of 25 water bodies in the Solway sub-basin are still affected by acidification (Environment Agency and Scottish Government, 2009). Changes in diatom composition have also been reported in Lochs Chon and Grannoch, suggesting the beginning of a recovery (SEPA, 2006).

21.2.2 Other fresh water and wetland monitoring

Outwith the confines of the WFD, much of the data available on habitats and species has recently been brought together by SNH in *Scotland's Wildlife: An assessment of biodiversity in 2010* (Mackey and Mudge, 2010). This includes information from protected sites and the wider countryside. For protected sites, the data mainly comes from SNH's Site Condition Monitoring (SCM) programme. This covers a network of over 1,450 Sites of Special Scientific Interest (SSSIs) across Scotland, which represent some 13% of the country. Crucially, this programme only covers the 'features' (species and/or habitats) for which the site was designated, and only within *protected* areas, and so does not necessarily reflect the status of habitats and species in the wider countryside.

The Countryside Survey; a periodic UK-wide survey, which started in 1978, repeated in 1984, 1990, 1998 and 2007, assesses the status of some species and habitats in the wider countryside. Fresh waters are surveyed as part of the scheme, including samples from ponds and streams to assess their biological diversity and ecological status.

Data are also collected from voluntary bodies such as RSPB, BTO, WWT, Plantlife and others. Although these voluntary bodies have information on the state of species and habitats of direct relevance to their own interests, the majority of these surveys do not cover population trends in any systematic manner. The best data sets come from the work of the BTO and WWT covering both breeding and wintering populations of wetland birds across Scotland (e.g. Austin *et al.*, 2007).

Of increasing interest and importance has been the spread of invasive non-native species, and their impact on native species and local ecosystems, and on social and economic interests. Whilst monitoring of such populations is not formally organised as yet, action is increasing to collect such data and the Wildlife and Natural Environment (Scotland) Act takes this further.

21.3 Overall quality of rivers, lochs and groundwater in Scotland

The overall status of waters in Scotland is determined using a classification scheme that takes into account a range of quality elements. For rivers and lochs, this is done using five broad classes (High, Good, Moderate, Poor and Bad), for groundwater only two classes are used (Good or Poor). Water bodies in the highest category are assessed as being in nearly 'natural' condition; a state that is then used as a reference against which degradation in quality can be measured. The status for fresh water bodies in Scotland for 2008 is shown in Table 21.3.

Table 21.3 The overall status of water bodies in the Scottish River Basin District 2008

				% by length / area				
Category	**no.**	**area (km²)**	**length (km)**	**high**	**good**	**moderate**	**poor**	**bad**
Groundwater	284	66,568			83		17	
Loch	309	961		20	46	15	13	6
River	2,013		20,817	10	46	20	14	10

Source: Scottish Government (2009). The river basin management plan for the Scotland river basin district 2009-2015.

Table 21.3 shows that some 56% of rivers and 66% of lochs are currently classed as having at least good overall status. Whilst this analysis relates to water bodies that are essentially still natural in character, others, such as canals have been recognised as being 'artificial'. Many more though have been 'heavily modified' – through, for example, man-made changes to flow regimes or to the physical structure of their banks – for hydropower, water supply or other uses. So altered are these, that they are unable at present to achieve full good status, so whilst chemical quality standards have still to be met, their condition has been assessed against ecological *potential* instead.

The WFD monitoring programme covers 2,392 rivers and 334 lochs using one monitoring point per water body, with the exception of Loch Lomond which has two. Figure 21.1 illustrates the ecological classification of all rivers and lochs in Scotland.

Generally, the more intense agricultural areas and urban centres have a lower percentage of 'good' water quality than other parts of Scotland. There are fewer data on groundwater status in Scotland. However, data from the 284 groundwater bodies sampled by SEPA for the WFD classification in 2008 showed that 226 (80%), have good chemical status, covering some 86% of the 66,568 sq kms surveyed. Most of these water bodies are showing continuing upward trends in the concentrations of pollutants recorded.

Modification of hydromorphology, much of it historic in origin, is one of the main reasons for failure of water bodies in Scotland to reach good ecological status. Rivers like the Eddleston Water in the Borders were straightened almost 200 years

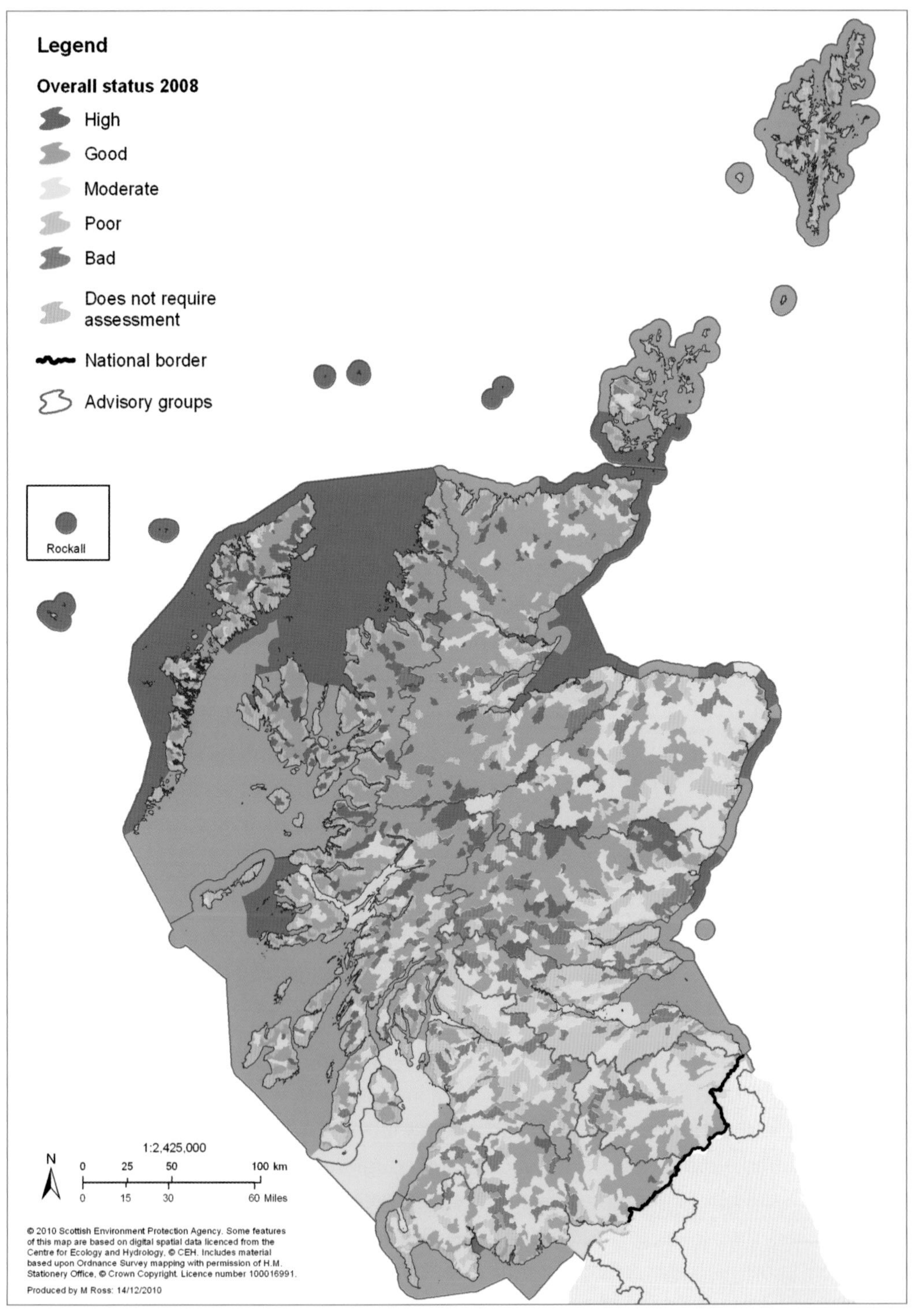

Figure 21.1 Overall classification of the status of water bodies in the Scottish River Basin district, 2008. Source: Scottish Government (2009). The river basin management plan for the Scotland river basin district 2009–2015.

ago for agricultural improvement, losing almost 40% of their original course, and still run almost straight today. This speeds run off from the catchment downstream – in part, one of the causes of flooding down-stream in Peebles (Werritty *et al.*, 2010).

21.4 Changes in water quality

Prior to the WFD, SEPA produced classifications of river water quality annually, and every five years for lochs. The number of poor and seriously polluted rivers has gradually declined since 1995, and in 2005 some 78% of rivers were classed as either excellent or good (SEPA, 2006). Although the overall classification system changed with the new regulations, this picture of gradual water quality improvement has been maintained. For lochs (larger than 1km^2) data from 2000 also showed 78% in excellent/good condition (SEPA, 2006), though this represented a slight worsening since 1995.

Data from the Harmonised Monitoring Scheme are analysed for annual, seasonal and monthly trends and initial results produced for suspended solids, biochemical oxygen demand (BOD), ammoniacal nitrogen and phosphorus. These parameters, along with information on water temperature and flow characteristics can be used to indicate the impact of activities such as land management (rural and urban) on water quality. Thus high levels of BOD are usually associated with industrial and urban pollution, high ammoniacal nitrogen with sewage, livestock and fertiliser use. Suspended solids are more general, and reflect the impacts of soil erosion and run off (agricultural and urban), whilst phosphorus concentrations can also reflect a range of pollution sources.

The data for river water temperature shows that annual average levels are increasing across Scotland, with the rising trend most marked in winter. For instance, the mean spring temperature in Loch Leven increased by 1.5°C between 1970 and 2000 (Ferguson *et al.*, 2008). This fits well with the observed changes in air temperature in Scotland over the last 40 years (Barnett *et al.*, 2006). There is likely to be an element of warming in lowland urban streams due to increased air temperatures experienced in towns and cities, overall however, the picture is one reflecting wider climatic changes. These changes may have implications for the phenology of many fresh water invertebrates and knock on effects further up the food chain.

The trend in suspended solids shows a gradual decline in levels across most of Scotland, as might be expected from the investment in improved sewage treatment facilities and the focus of regulatory pressure on point sources of pollution. This trend in the more urban and industrial locations is in contrast to an increase being observed in more rural catchments, such as the Grampian region, where it appears there is a rise, possibly associated with greater erosion in spring and more diffuse run-off from agricultural land. The BOD results show a similar trend with reductions generally across the country, particularly in the urban and industrial areas, although odd 'hot spots' still remain.

It is estimated that some 74% of nitrogen and 52% of phosphorus inputs to surface and groundwaters in Scotland come from agricultural land (SEPA, 2006). Ammoniacal nitrogen levels have declined, though the absolute loads may not have to such an extent. Total phosphorus levels have declined in urban areas, due to improved sewage treatment and reduced use of phosphates in detergents, but again there appears to be a difference with some agricultural areas seeing no such decline, especially in the north.

For lochs, the data are less comprehensive, a 2005 assessment of eutrophication in Scottish inland waters found that 17 out of some 200 water bodies examined were eutrophic or potentially eutrophic (SEPA, 2006), based on phosphorus and chlorophyll-***a*** concentrations.

Another aspect of water quality that is receiving increasing attention is the rising levels of dissolved organic carbon (DOC) in waters across the UK (Worrall and Burt, 2007). Scotland holds significant stores of carbon in upland peat soils, and warmer, drier summers may lead to the break down of the peat and higher rates of decomposition of soil organic matter. Recent analysis by SEPA (Moxley, 2009) showed a similar rising trend for DOC in Scottish rivers, where concentrations have approximately doubled in the last 20 years. Some of this could also be due to a response to declining levels of sulphur deposition since the 1980s (Evans *et al.*, 2006). Lochs shows a similar rising trend across the whole UK and for specific lochs in Scotland, such as Lochnagar, Loch Chon and Round Loch of Glenhead (Kernan *et al.*, 2010), even if there has possibly been a recent decrease in levels over the last five years. Overall though, whatever the determining factors, the picture appears to be one where the levels now recorded in waters are starting to reflect the conditions of pre-industrialised Britain.

Changes in groundwater quality have largely been focussed on monitoring of nitrate levels at some 200 sites across Scotland. Monitoring since 2002 showed elevated levels in areas of intense agricultural land use, particularly in the east. This is despite the creation of four 'Nitrate Vulnerable Zones' covering some 14% of Scotland's land area. Concentrations of over 25mg/l (as nitrate) occur across the east and southwest, compared to less than 10mg/l elsewhere (MacDonald and O'Dochartaigh, 2005)

21.5 Changes in water quantity

The ultimate factors controlling the quantity of water received in fresh water bodies and wetlands are global and local climatic conditions, in conjunction with meteorological and hydrological cycles. Scotland's temperature is undergoing a recent and rapid warming trend, with the most marked changes in the south east of the country, especially in winter (Barnett *et al.*, 2006). The evidence for this in Scotland has been brought together by SNIFFER in their *Patterns of Climate Change Across Scotland: Handbook* (Barnett *et al.*, 2006) and, more recently at a UK scale in the UKCP09 programme.

Changes to the pattern of precipitation are evident, varying both seasonally and across the country. Since 1961, the north and particularly the west of Scotland have seen increases in average winter precipitation by up to 60% in places, whereas there has been little change in the Grampian region. By comparison, the Grampian region has become up to 45% drier in summer (Barnett *et al.*, 2006).

Alongside this, there have been two other climatic changes that are influencing the water environment: an increase in the occurrence of extreme rainfall events and a drop in the number of days of lying snow (Figure 21.2).

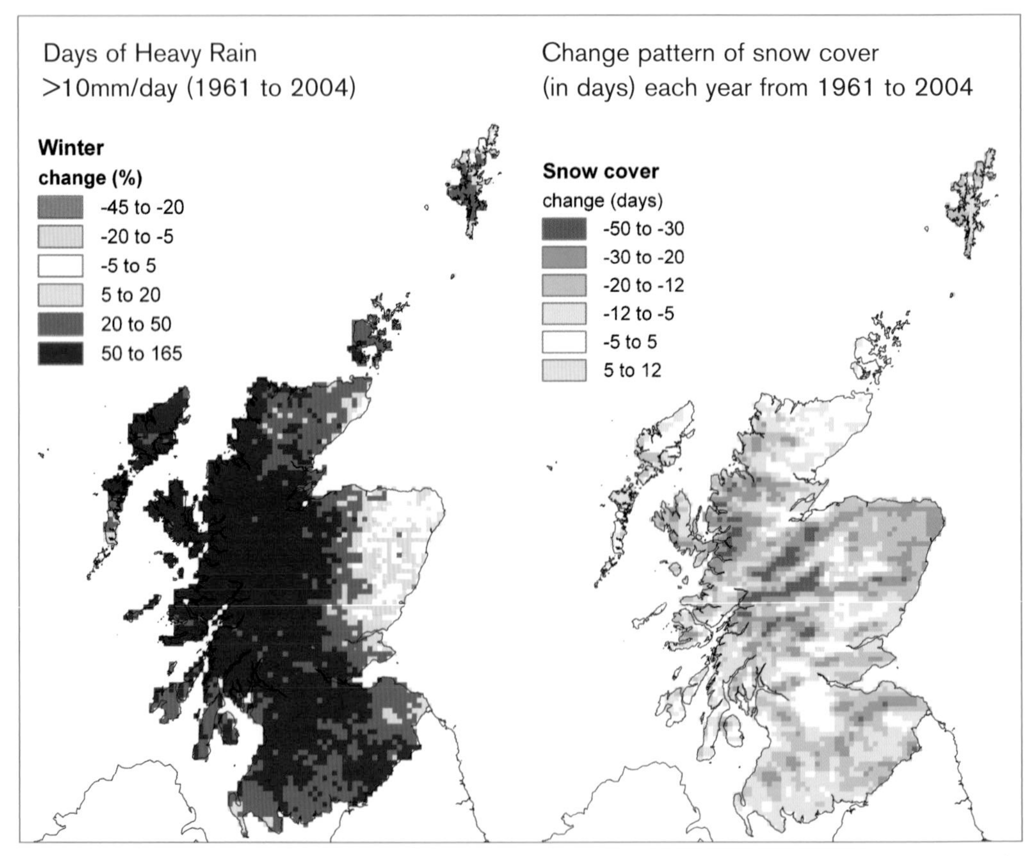

Figure 21.2 Changes in the frequency of extreme rainfall events and in the pattern of snow cover in Scotland 1961 – 2004. Source: Barnett, C. *et al.*, 2006. Patterns of climate change across Scotland. SNIFFER report.

Together with the changes in temperature already noted, this has led to dramatic changes in river flows across Scotland. Whilst the most significant changes are increases in winter peak flows, of increasing importance is the growing variability of flows between years and within years. Rivers in the north east, such as the Dee and Isla, are experiencing longer and more severe periods of low flow under drought conditions in summer (SEPA, 2006).

Using data from six catchments in north east Scotland between 1961 and 2008, Gosling (2009) showed that decreased snow accumulation led to an increase in the quick (overland flow) component of the hydrological cycle in some catchments. At three Highland sites there was a significant increase in flash floods, with higher flood flows but lower base flows, a situation not evident in lowland sites. Thus some rivers experienced increased flows in spring, as a result of changing temperature and earlier, more rapid snow melt, irrespective of any other changes in rainfall.

Data on loch levels and on groundwater resources are less available. There are estimated to be over 4,000 boreholes in Scotland, in addition to thousands of springs and wells used for private supply, and the amount used for water supply is growing annually. Along with that used by industry and agriculture, this accounts for at least 330 megalitres per day (MacDonald *et al.*, 2005). The environmental 'use' of groundwater is seldom recorded but represents an essential component of many fresh water and wetland habitats. In upland streams groundwater is responsible for up to 30% of base flow (Soulsby *et al.*, 2000). Over abstraction of groundwater is currently not a major issue in most parts of Scotland, and SEPA reported that 88% of the 284 groundwater bodies surveyed in 2008 were of good status (Scottish Government, 2009). Whilst abstraction for food and drink, water supply and mining were recognised as issues, the main impact on groundwater levels comes from agricultural irrigation.

Life in rivers can be adversely affected by changes in water quantity, making them inhospitable to species like trout (*Salmo trutta*) and salmon through rising temperature, low flows in summer and flash floods in winter. Wetlands may dry out in summer, allowing woody species to colonise or cause peat to erode. Changes in precipitation and temperature will compound the effects of existing pressures, such as eutrophication and acidification. Increased flushing from storm events may accelerate nutrient loss from wetlands, disturb settled sediment and bring in nutrients.

21.6 Protecting fresh water habitats

Many of Scotland's fresh water habitats are protected for their conservation interests through designation. Eight of Scotland's rivers are designated as Sites of Special Scientific Interest (SSSIs) for their riverine habitats, with another four notified for the presence of freshwater pearl mussels (*Margaritifera margaritifera*) (Scotland has a sizeable proportion of the European population) and invertebrates of conservation importance. Other river stretches have protected populations of otters, gorge invertebrates or have been designated because of their geological importance. There are some 147 lochs designated for their standing water habitat, and some 284 wetlands designated for their swamp, fen and mires. A number of these sites, such as the Tweed are further protected under European legislation as Special Areas of Conservation (SACs) or Special Protection Areas (SPAs). Some are very extensive – the peatlands of Caithness and Sutherland represent one of the largest designated sites in the UK, covering some 140,000ha, whilst the Tay reedbeds represent 6% of the total UK area for this habitat. Others are much smaller and often fragmented, such as the many small fens that make up the Border Mires.

Plate 21.1 Reedbeds at Port Allen on the River Tay near Errol. © SNH Images

The condition of these protected sites is monitored through the SCM scheme led by SNH. Data from the most recent survey in 2009 showed that 75% of fresh water and 64% of wetland features were in favourable or unfavourable recovering condition (SNH, 2009). The main reasons for poor condition were invasive species, lack of remedial management and, occasionally, water quality.

Fresh water and wetlands form one of the five Ecosystem Groups in the Scottish Biodiversity Strategy, and include nine of the UKBAP priority habitats: lowland fens; reed beds; lowland raised bogs; rivers; ponds; oligotrophic and dystrophic lakes; mesotrophic lakes; eutrophic standing waters; and coastal and floodplain grazing marsh. Of these, the latest assessment (Mackey and Mudge, 2010) recorded that 40% were declining, 20% had no trend, with 20% increasing and 20% fluctuating (probably stable). Five habitats, which were assessed in 2005, were re-assessed in 2008, but given small numbers, little or no change is evident between these two assessments.

Although the data are limited, the 2007 Countryside Survey suggests that Scotland's ponds are in better condition than their English counterparts, and have increased in number in recent years (Williams *et al.*, 2010).

The monitoring of water bodies for the WFD has produced the first Scotland-wide picture of the way they have been modified by human impacts, for example, for hydro-electricity, for flood prevention, for water supply, for irrigation. The building of weirs and sluices, flood banks and irrigation ditches, the drainage of wetlands and the canalisation of streams have changed flow regimes, water level fluctuations, the frequency of inundation, the course and even the very existence of some rivers and wetlands. Weirs and sluices for water-mills or abstraction intakes form barriers to fish migration, especially salmon, lampreys and eels.

21.7 Conclusions

Lochs, rivers and a wide range of other wetland habitats provide vital ecosystem services. Over recent decades, new environmental legislation and improvements in practices and management have reduced air, land and water pollution, allowing wildlife to re-colonise parts of Scotland that had become degraded by industrialisation, intensive agriculture, development and dereliction.

The overall picture of 56% of rivers and 66% of lochs meeting at least good ecological status is better than in many other industrialised countries. A programme of measures is now in place to improve this further through river basin management plans. Fish diversity is being restored in the catchments and estuaries of the Forth and Clyde, otters are returning to many parts of Scotland, and habitat restoration schemes are being promoted to great effect.

However, many pressures still threaten the health of our fresh waters and wetlands, and SEPA (2010) estimate that some 43% of water bodies are still being adversely impacted by human activities. Of these, the most widespread causes were: diffuse pollution from intensive agriculture and urban run-off; changes to flow regimes and water levels; structural alterations of banks, channels, lochs and river beds; and the presence of invasive non-native species. Some of these, especially those impacting flow regimes and river continuity, are the historic legacy of past drainage schemes, mill races and hydropower dams.

Although there are several monitoring schemes in place, the extent and number of sites, species and habitats is variable, and in some cases limited. Some of the data available from the monitoring networks are patchy, and more work is needed to determine the significant changes in habitat quality and extent, and in dependent species populations. Typically, lower taxa are very poorly represented in monitoring programmes, whilst small-scale fresh waters and wetlands are missing from many monitoring networks all together.

Above all though, our own well-being depends on the quality of the fresh water environment. In order to protect this vital resource, we need to appreciate and value the complete range of services provided by healthy, functioning ecosystems. This will require a coordinated approach to data collection and an integrated approach to sustainable catchment management. Together, these approaches need to respond to the key pressures threatening the quality of Scotland's fresh waters and wetlands, but at the same time we need to seize the opportunities to improve these habitats and to encourage more of the public use and enjoyment of our wonderful wetland environments. We have a made a good start, and the prospects ahead are encouraging. There remains a key requirement to ensure that we transfer our scientific knowledge into policies and ultimately into actions on the ground.

Acknowledgements

My thanks to SNH for the invitation to contribute to this conference and publication, and to staff in SNH and SEPA for invaluable discussions and support of this work. Particular thanks are due to Catriona Hendrie of SNH for her encouragement, advice and forbearance during the production of this paper, and to Iain Sime, Claire McSorley, Simon Foster, Des Thompson and anonymous reviewers for comments on earlier drafts.

References

Alveres, B., Clelland, Z., Johnstonova, A. and Comerford, E. (2007). *Insh Marshes – Its hydrology, multiple uses and economic value*. RSPB Scotland report.

Austin, G.E., Rehfisch, M.M. and Banks, A. (2007). Natural Heritage Trends: developing a Scottish Wintering Waterbird Indicator. *Scottish Natural Heritage Commissioned Report* No. 227.

Barnett, C., Hossell, J., Perry, M., Procter, C. and Hughes, G. (2006). *Patterns of climate change across Scotland: Technical Report.* SNIFFER Project CC03, Scotland & Northern Ireland Forum for Environmental Research.

Environment Agency and Scottish Government (2009). The river basin management plan for the Solway Tweed river basin district 2009-2015. http://www.sepa.org.uk/water/river_basin_planning.aspx

Evans, C.D., Chapman, P.J., Clark, J.M., Monteith, D.T. and Cresser, M.S. (2006).

Alternative explanations for rising dissolved organic carbon exports from organic soils. *Global Change Biology*, **12**, 2044-2053.

Ferguson, C.A., Carvalho, L., Scott, E.M., Bowman, A.W. and Kirika, A. (2008). Assessing ecological responses to environmental change using statistical models. *Journal of Applied Ecology*, **45**, 193-203.

Gosling, R. (2009). *Changes in flow variability in snow-influenced catchments in Scotland.* Unpublished SEPA Factsheet, 2009.

MacDonald, A.M. and O'Dochartaigh, B.E. (2005). *Baseline Scotland: an overview of available groundwater chemistry data for Scotland.* British Geological Survey (CR/05/239N) (Unpublished).

MacDonald, A.M., Robins, N.S., Ball, D.F. and O'Dochartaigh, B.E. (2005). An overview of Groundwater in Scotland. *Scottish Journal of Geology*, **41**, 3-11.

Mackey, E.C. and Mudge, G. (2010). *Scotland's Wildlife: An assessment of biodiversity in 2010.* Scottish Natural Heritage, Inverness.

Millennium Ecosystem Assessment (2005). *Millennium Ecosystem Assessment: Ecosystems and Human Well-being: synthesis.* Washington D.C., Island Press.

Moxley, J. (2009). *Trends in organic carbon in Scottish rivers and lochs.* Unpublished SEPA Factsheet.

Radford, A., Riddington, G., Anderson, J. and Gibson, H. (2004). The economic impact of game and coarse angling in Scotland. Research report prepared for Scottish Executive Environment and Rural Affairs Department.

Scottish Government (2009). The river basin management plan for the Scotland river basin district 2009-2015. http://www.sepa.org.uk/water/river_basin_planning.aspx

SEPA (1996). *State of the Environment Report 1996.* Scottish Environment Protection Agency, Stirling.

SEPA (2006). *State of Scotland's Environment 2006.* Scottish Environment Protection Agency, Stirling.

SEPA (2010). Trends in Scottish river quality. Website http://www.sepa.org.uk/science_and_research/data_and_reports/water/scottish_river_water_quality.aspx, accessed on 3 September 2010.

SNH (2008). The economic impact of Scotland's natural environment. *Scottish Natural Heritage, Commissioned Report* No. 304.

SNH (2009). Notified habitats in favourable condition. Part of the Scottish Biodiversity Indicator suite. Scottish Natural Heritage.

Smith, I.R. and Lyle, A.A. (1979). *Distribution of Freshwater in Great Britain.* Institute of Terrestrial Ecology, Cambridge.

SNIFFER (2006). An online handbook of climate trends across Scotland; http://climatetrendshandbook.sccip.org.uk/index.html, accessed 30 August 2010.

Soulsby, C., Malcolm, R. and Malcolm I. (2000). Groundwater in headwaters: hydrological and ecological significance. *Geological Society, London, Special Publications*, **182**, 19-34.

Kernan, M., Battarbee, R.W., Curtis, C.J., Monteith, D.T. and Shilland, E.M. (eds.) (2010). *United Kingdom Acid Waters Monitoring Network 20 year interpretative report. Recovery of lakes and streams in the UK from acid rain.* ECRC Research Report #141. Report to the Department for Environment, Food and Rural Affairs (Contract EPG 1/3/160)

United Nations Environment Programme (UNEP) (2005). 2nd edition, *Vital Water Graphics: An overview of the state of the World's fresh water and marine waters*, http://www.unep.org/dewa/vitalwater/index.html

Werritty, A., Spray, C., Ball, T. *et al.* (2010). Integrated catchment management: from rhetoric to reality in a Scottish HELP basin. BHS Third International Symposium, Newcastle, July 2010, Role of Hydrology in Managing Consequences of a Changing Global Environment.

Williams, P., Biggs, J., Crowe, A., *et al.* (2010). *Countryside Survey: Ponds Report from 2007.* Technical Report No. 7/07 Pond Conservation and NERC/Centre for Ecology & Hydrology. (CEH Project Number: C03259).

Worral, F. and Burt, T. (2007). Trends in DOC concentration in Great Britain. *Journal of Hydrology*, **346**, 81-92.

22 Whisky and Water: Why Both Matter

Julie Hesketh-Laird

Summary

1. Scotch Whisky is an iconic product. Sold in 200 countries worldwide, over 90 million cases were exported in 2008. The growth of the industry has helped shape Scotland's economy and culture. In turn, Scotch Whisky has been shaped by the Scottish landscape and environment. Scotch must, by law, have been produced in a distillery in Scotland, from water and malted barley, and matured in Scotland in oak casks for no less than three years. The character of each Scotch is therefore uniquely influenced by its local environment.
2. Protecting this environment, and investing to secure Scotch's long-term sustainability, is a top priority for Scotland's distillers.
3. This paper explores the importance of the natural environment to the sustainability of the industry and the importance of Scotch Whisky to the economy. The work of the industry to identify and respond to changes in our environment, not least those which may be caused by climate change, is examined. The industry's collective plans for step-change, the immediate challenges and long-term sustainability objectives are also explored.

22.1 Introduction

Whilst Scotch Whisky is synonymous with Scotland's landscape, equally, the industry is part and parcel of our economic landscape too. Whisky has been made successfully in Scotland for over 500 years. This paper reflects on why that matters today and how distillers are responding to changes in the natural environment.

'Scotch Whisky' is defined in UK law and is protected at European Union and World Trade Organisation level as a recognised 'Geographical Indication' (GI). A product with a GI status is identifiable as a product originating in a region or locality in a particular country. For a GI product, its reputation for quality or authenticity is

Hesketh-Laird, J. (2011). Whisky and Water: Why Both Matter – *The Changing Nature of Scotland*, eds. S.J. Marrs, S. Foster, C. Hendrie, E.C. Mackey, D.B.A. Thompson. TSO Scotland, Edinburgh, pp 237-248.

intimately linked to its geographical origin. This legal protection is vitally important as it protects Scotch Whisky from unfair competition and underpins Scotch Whisky's reputation for high quality.

There are five legally defined types of Scotch Whisky (Single Malt; Blended Malt; Blended; Blended Grain and Single Grain). The two basic types of Scotch Whisky, from which all blends are made, are Single Malt and Single Grain.

'Single Malt Scotch Whisky' is produced from water and malted barley at a single distillery by batch distillation in pot stills. A 'Single Grain Scotch Whisky' is distilled at a single distillery but which, in addition to water and malted barley, may also be produced from whole grains of other malted or unmalted cereals. 'Blended Malt Scotch Whisky' is a blend of two or more Single Malt Scotch Whiskies from different distilleries, and a 'Blended Grain Scotch Whisky' is a blend of two or more Single Grain Scotch Whiskies from different distilleries. 'Blended Scotch Whisky' is a combination of one or more Single Malt Scotch Whiskies with one or more Single Grain Scotch Whiskies.

Figure 22.1 shows the Malt Whisky production process. In the distilling process, the malted barley is milled and then warm water is added to convert the malt in the barley starch to sugar. This part of the process is known as mashing and the product of the mashing process is a sugary liquid called worts. Yeast is then added to ferment the worts to produce a liquid containing about 8% alcohol. This is then distilled twice in distinctive copper pot stills to produce a final spirit strength of nearly 70% alcohol. The new make spirit is then transferred into casks for maturation. Grain distillation differs in that a variety of cereals may be used for the process (including maize and wheat) and the actual distillation process itself is undertaken in a Patent or Coffey still (a continuous distillation process), in contrast to the batch process for malt Scotch Whisky production. Figure 22.2 shows a cross-section through a Coffey still.

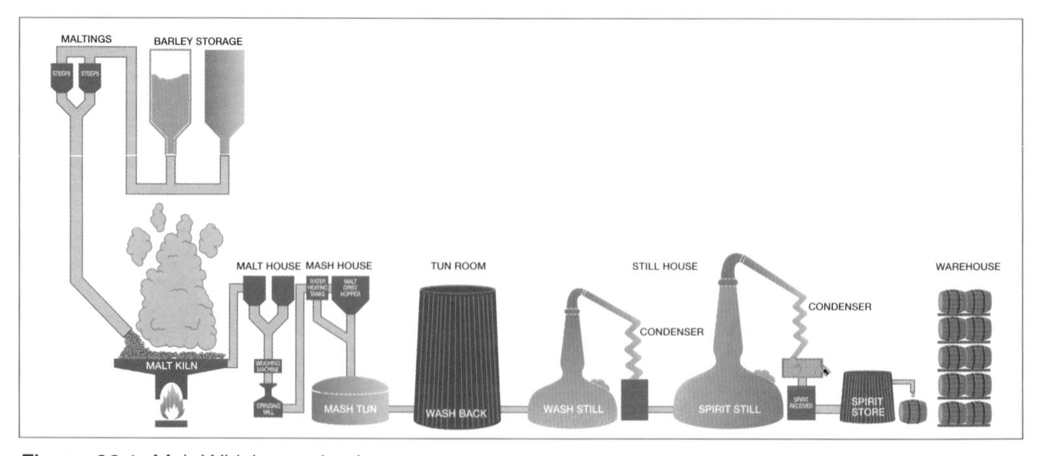

Figure 22.1 Malt Whisky production.

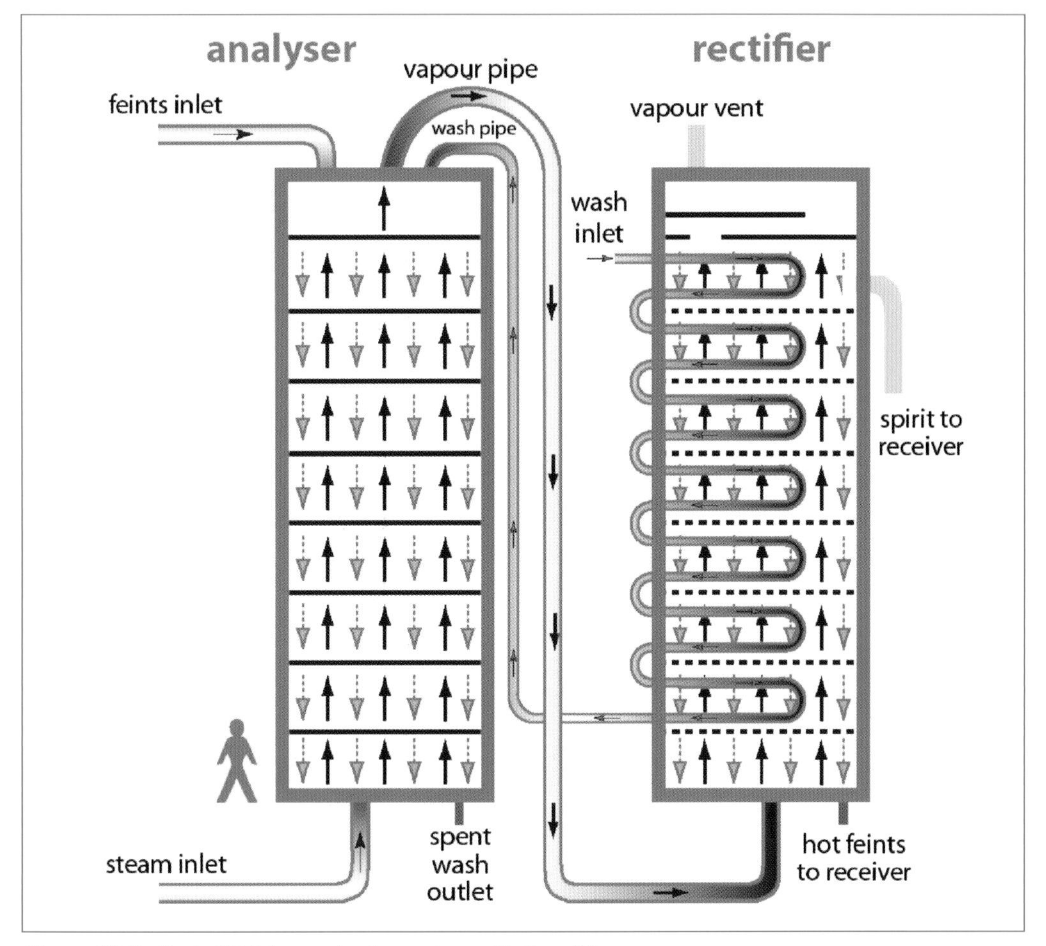

Figure 22.2 Grain Whisky production using a Coffey still.

22.2 Scotch Whisky and the economy

Scotch Whisky is Scotland's leading export and represents 20% of Scottish manufactured exports. By sending 90 million cases of Scotch worldwide, the industry contributed a massive £3.1 billion to the UK balance of trade in 2008 (SWA, 2008).

But that's only part of its impact. The industry adds huge value to the Scottish economy. One and a quarter million people visit a distillery every year. The spending contributed to the local, often rural, economies by these tourists is higher in comparison to many other visitor attractions.

The Scotch Whisky Association (SWA) estimated that for 2009, industry investment across its supply chain – from barley growers to glass manufacturers – was over £700 million a year, supporting 40,000 jobs. And, SWA estimates that over £500 million of new capital investment in distilling was announced in 2008-2009 to prepare for growth in emerging markets.

Markets for Scotch Whisky are worldwide and the perception of the quality production environment and raw materials is important to our overseas consumers. The reach of Scotch Whisky is vast, being enjoyed in over 200 markets globally. In 2008, the French consumed more Scotch than Cognac and represented the leading marketplace, ahead of the USA and Spain. Figure 22.3 shows key global markets for 2008. Whilst 2009 was a tougher trading year for Scotch, emerging markets like China, Brazil and India represent large untapped potential, and as the industry and its trade association tackles the removal of tariffs (import duties, often only targeted at imported spirits), the industry would expect these markets to grow and industry investment has been in anticipation of that longer-term growth.

But even that doesn't tell the whole story. The industry contributes to the rest of the Scottish economy, from farmers through to hauliers and glass manufacturers. Their fortunes too, depend on our success. Whisky matters to our economy and to the many communities that depend on a thriving industry. It also matters to our environment.

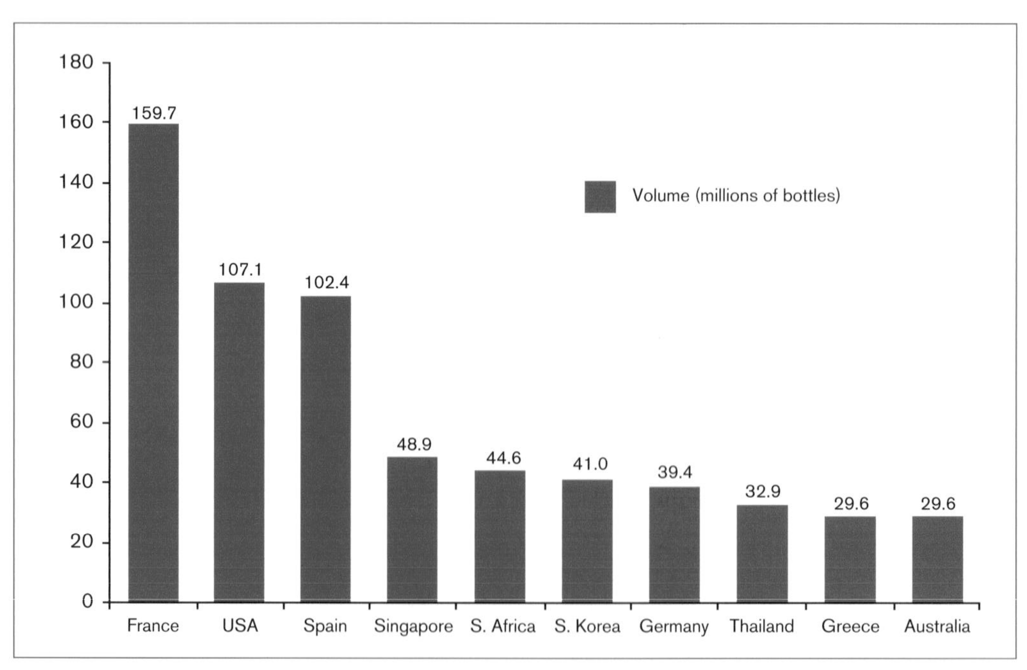

Figure 22.3 Scotch Whisky exports 2008 (Source: SWA 2009).

22.3 Scotch Whisky Environmental Strategy

In June 2009, the SWA launched an ambitious Environmental Strategy setting out our long-term direction (SWA, 2009a). Our goals were collective – developed by the industry for the industry, under the auspices of the Scotch Whisky Association.

Individually distillers have great 'green' stories to tell. This initiative harnessed their commitment. Tough targets up to 2050 were based on the sector's biggest areas of impact, identified through a Life Cycle Analysis (SWA, 2009b), conducted by the Scotch Whisky Research Institute (SWRI) in Edinburgh, the industry's scientific centre of excellence. It is, to our knowledge, the only comprehensive assessment of a whole sector's environmental impact and the most forward looking of any sectoral environmental strategy within the food and drink sector.

One aim of the environmental strategy was to reduce fossil fuel use by 80%. This would save over 750,000 tonnes of carbon dioxide a year – equivalent to removing 235,000 cars from Scotland's roads. But the industry is going further and also focussing on water management; packaging materials and waste; sustainable casks and working in partnership with our supply chain.

These are areas where distillers can make a real difference. The sector can invest, collaborate and innovate but we must, importantly, work with Government and regulators to ensure a competitive regulatory landscape for production. Here we have created an opportunity to promote within the industry and beyond the idea that responsible environmental management and profitability can go hand in hand.

On water, the industry is committed to engaging actively with relevant authorities in the development of Scotland's River Basin Management Plans (RBMPs). These plans, led by the Scottish Environmental Protection Agency (SEPA), ensure that public sector bodies, businesses and individuals work together to protect the water environment and address significant impacts by coordinating all aspects of water management to 2015, when they will be reviewed and updated. The plans are being produced as one of the requirements of the European Union's Water Framework Directive and similar plans are being put in place across Europe. The Scotch Whisky industry's priority is to ensure that a sustainable and good quality water supply is maintained and the SWA is engaging through SEPA's various consultative committees to ensure that distillers interests are recognised.

Let us consider the industry's structure. One hundred and eight distilleries in 2008 were licensed to produce Scotch – seven grain distilleries which continuously distil grain whisky from cereals, like wheat and barley and 101 malt distilleries which operate batch distillation of malted barley in copper stills. In 2008, SWA members at their six grain distilleries produced around 300 million litres of new make spirit and at their 79 malt distilleries, 225 million litres (SWA, 2008).

This number is growing, with five new malt distilleries opened since 2005, 18 re-opened over the last decade, and a further seven malt distilleries currently at different stages of planning.

It almost goes without saying that distilleries were historically situated in locations with abundant and good quality water – as well as at sites far away from the tax man. These locations have remained unchanged for over a century. Almost half of our malt distilleries are clustered around the River Spey and many of the largest in the industry sit on, or near the coast for dilution of effluent discharge.

22.4 Water use in the industry

Distillers use a variety of water sources. Surface water from rivers, lochs and canals, as well as ground water sources through borehole abstractions are used for malt distilling. Whereas mains water offers an additional but constant supply for grain distilling and packaging operations.

SWA's lifecycle analysis (SWA, 2009b) estimated that the industry uses around 62 million tonnes of water a year. That figure includes malting inputs from commercial maltsters and companies malting in-house. The vast majority of water use, over 90%, is borrowed from the environment and returned unaltered (save a temperature increase) as we use it for cooling water – that is to condense the spirit coming off the stills.

During the production process, water is also used to steep grains – when grains are immersed in water three times with an air rest in between to increase the moisture content of the cereal from 12% to around 45% in order to trigger germination. Water is used for mashing and the production of wort – the sugary liquid extracted after mashing the grains with water. It is used for reducing spirit strength prior to storing in casks and also to reduce the strength of the final spirit to the legal minimum of 40% alcohol before bottling. Figure 22.4 shows where in the Scotch Whisky production process water is used.

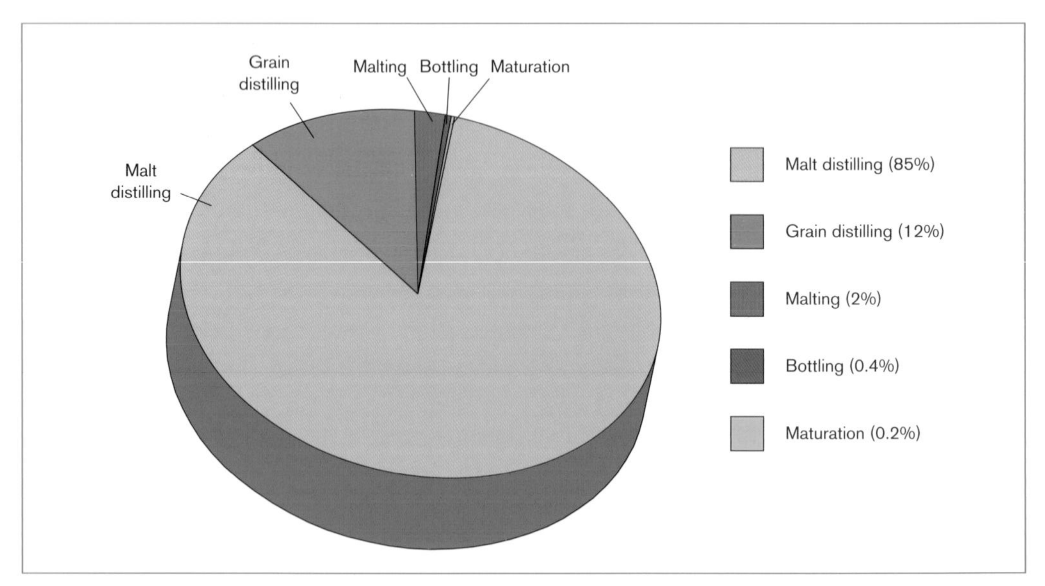

Figure 22.4 Water use in the Scotch Whisky industry 2006.

Of all those varied uses of water in the industry, by far the majority of water used is in malt distilling. This is because malt distilleries use water to condense spirit coming from the stills, in contrast to grain distilleries which are configured so as not to require cooling water inputs, instead relying on carefully balancing the temperatures of inputs and outputs. The vast majority of water used at malt distilleries is returned as cooling water. The character of the water that goes into the product directly is essential to a distiller's success.

22.5 The influence of water on Scotch Whisky

The recipe for Scotch is simple. By law, it can only contain cereals, water and yeast; all natural products that rely on the environment for their quality. It must be distilled and matured in oak casks in Scotland for a minimum of three years. With so few ingredients, each component will have a marked effect on the qualities of the Scotch Whisky produced.

Distillers of course argue about what makes their whisky special. For many, water is the most important single factor and a good source of soft water is essential to a distillery. Other influences like the size and shape of the still and the cask used for maturation also make their mark. With a growing number of distilleries in Scotland and with the expertise of company blenders, the industry produces a remarkable range of products. The environment in which Scotch Whisky is made is proven to have a subtle but important impact on the qualities and taste of the final dram. Both the environment's impact on the industry, and the industry's impact on the environment, are critical to distillers.

The SWRI is doing a lot of work in this area. Its research has confirmed, for example, that the geographical source of process water has an impact on Scotch Whisky's sensory characteristics (Wilson, 2008). Process waters with a greater humic content were found to produce spirit with sweeter, cleaner sensory characteristics. Waters with a lower humic content produced heavier characteristics such as sulphury, meaty aromas. Surprisingly perhaps, SWRI found that peaty waters don't give rise to peaty characteristics in the spirit – peaty, smoky aromas are associated exclusively from the burning of peat during kilning of the barley and not from any phenolic compounds in process water.

Wilson's work at the SWRI also looked at the quality requirements of reducing water – water used to reduce the strength of cask strength matured Scotch Whisky to the required bottling strength (40% minimum). Water at least of potable standard is used to protect human health. But in order to ensure that no aesthetic impairments are caused by the reducing water, filtration is often required. Water with high iron content, for example, is unsuitable for reducing as together with the

Plate 22.21 Deanston distillery. Originally a cotton mill this eighteenth century building is situated on the banks of the River Teith in Perthshire and uses the power of the water to generate electricity from its own turbines as well as during the distilling process. © Scotch Whisky Association

tannins in Scotch, it can produce coloured complexes, which aren't harmful, but can alter the colour of the final product. Hard water is undesirable too as again it might lead to calcium precipitation in the bottle. Distillers frequently demineralise reducing water before use to meet the consumers' expectations of how the whisky should look in the bottle.

Given the strong influence that water supplies have on location, raw material availability and spirit quality, the industry has long recognised the need to act sustainably. Sustainability and the long-term view is natural to distillers – it is a long-term business. What distillers make in 2009 will not, by law, be Scotch Whisky until the starter's gun has fired at the London Olympics in 2012. And it is unlikely to be bottled and on shelves until two Olympics after that.

Taking that long-term view, distillers are investing heavily in environmental stewardship to mitigate their impacts. They are constantly risk-assessing potential impacts and looking at how a changing environment might affect the industry.

22.6 Climate impacts on the industry

Distillers need high quality, plentiful cereal supplies and farmers require plentiful water to grow the cereals required. In 2008, the industry used over 470,000 tonnes of malted barley and over 530,000 tonnes of other cereals, mostly wheat. By far the vast majority of that million tonnes plus of cereals was procured from Scotland and Northumbria. That is how we want it to be.

Whilst climate predictions for barley growing in Scotland are largely positive with potentially a longer, warmer and drier growing season, there is a higher risk of more intense rainfall, more wind and more storms.

The industry is already investing collectively in a number of climate change related projects, such as the development of drought resistant barley varieties. A £2 million five-year LINK project entitled 'Green Grain' (Genetic Reduction in Energy Use and Emissions of Nitrogen Through Cereal Production (Anon., 2009)) aims to decrease the overall footprint of distillers by minimising the environmental impact of growing cereals, without compromising yield. The project is collaboratively funded by partners from the private and public sectors (SWRI, Agricultural Development and Advisory Service, FOSS, Wessex Grain, Syngenta, Green Spirit Fuels, Nottingham University, Home Grown Cereals Authority, Grampian County Foods as well as the UK and Scottish Governments). Fundamental to this project is finding low nitrogen cereal varieties which require less fertiliser nitrogen, which will reduce water eutrophication and the general energy burden. Our aim is to reduce fertiliser requirements by 50%.

22.7 Scotch Whisky industry mitigation initiatives

Over the last two years, in excess of £500 million has been invested in operational infrastructure for the future. Companies were more cautious with new investment in 2009; but they have not gone back on decisions taken in the board rooms in 2007 and 2008. And 20% of this investment has gone into sustainability measures. We want to make more whisky using less energy and with a reduced environmental impact. Further details of industry investment and initiatives to meet our voluntary targets are set out on the SWA's website (SWA, 2009c).

Diageo's recently completed £40 million investment in the 10 million litre capacity Roseisle distillery on the Moray coast was closely watched by the whole whisky community. The opportunity to build a distillery on this scale, from scratch is a rare one, and Diageo placed environmental sustainability at the heart of their design.

The site has been built with an overall objective for an energy and water neutral operation and an overall Biological Oxygen Demand (BOD) reduction. Diageo is meeting its water recovery objectives largely by recovery from the distillery and malting co-product streams. Their water recovery plant takes pot ale, spent lees and steeping water from the process and separates the liquids from solid residues and balance flows to ensure an even load flows to the recovery plant.

Effluent is then fed to an anaerobic digester to produce methane for steam raising. Aerobic treatment removes the remaining BOD and nitrogen and membrane filtration separates the solids from the final treated water. This has allowed the company to recover 95% of the distillery's water demand. Recovered water is then sent to Burghead maltings to re-use in the steeping water for their grain. Water aside, the site recovers a staggering 85% of its energy demand to boot. The icing on the cake is that the build has achieved Building Research Establishment Environmental Assessment Method (BREEAM) standard by virtue of its sustainable construction materials, natural ventilation, heating, lighting and sustainable urban drainage system.

Such first rate achievements require significant investment by companies but before bricks can be laid, they also require a fair and clear operational framework within which to make their investment decisions. Each environmental success story belies a detailed engagement with planners, regulators (such as Scotland's Environmental and Rural Services (SEARS)) partners, feasibility studies and rigorous analysis of the many and varied rules and regulations that apply to the Scotch Whisky industry.

Whilst the industry's relationship with its regulators has not always been as positive as they are at the time of writing, over the past four to five years, we have built a strong partnership with SEPA in particular, around the way Scotland will manage its water supplies. This is based on a major investment from the industry in training new SEPA recruits and exposing to them the detailed realities of our processes and challenges through site visits and presentations. This programme has been complemented by a continued dialogue with SEPA's management team who have worked hard on this relationship too.

We won't always agree with each other but we welcome the visible change in SEPA's relationship with our regulated businesses away from a policing role towards an enabling one, and a regulator that actively manages its relationships with key business customers. We now need to harness that growing understanding to ensure that EU and Scottish Government policies create a supportive business environment.

We have actively engaged in the RBMP process to date through the National Advisory Group (NAG) and local groups. The Scottish Government and SEPA are to be congratulated for leading Scotland's thinking, engaging stakeholders so comprehensively and delivering RBMPs for Scotland. Through the process, the NAG has delivered the theory on which SEPA can base hard decisions around allocating water supplies to users.

We wish to lay down a marker at this stage. Significant additional thought is now needed to ensure that requirements on users of the water environment are cost-effective, proportionate and justifiable in view of the environmental benefits they seek to achieve. Here, I am not referring to annual fees and charges from regulators. Whilst it is essential that distillers have adequate notice of planned regulatory charges of these to plan budgets, it is most important that only proportionate and cost-effective engineering and technical solutions to environmental problems be required by regulators to achieve policy decisions. We will be looking to the Scottish Government to clarify mechanisms for testing the cost-effectiveness of measures required by the Water Framework Directive.

22.8 Conclusions

The Scotch Whisky industry and its suppliers have key roles to play in maintaining Scottish fresh water and wetland habitats. We have a responsibility to ensure that our activities do not contribute to any acceleration in changes to these resources and habitats. But we also have a clear responsibility too for delivering long-term sustainable economic growth for Scotland and continuing our major contribution to the Scottish economy.

We've been pleased at the partnership that we have seen emerge between distillers and our supply chains, regulators, governments and environmental stakeholders as our Environmental Strategy evolved.

We recognise, though, the need to go further as we move into the delivery phase of our ambition. Our biggest common challenge is that we all better understand each others respective priorities and operating environments to ensure that the timing of policy decisions allows investment at an acceptable pace.

References

Anon. (2009). GREEN GRAIN. http://www.bertini-stirtloe.com/projects/green_grain.html, accessed on 3 December 2009.

SWA (2008). Scotch at a Glance 2008. SWA, Edinburgh.

SWA (2009a). Scotch Whisky Industry Environmental Strategy. SWA, Edinburgh.

SWA (2009b). The Lifecycle Assessment of Scotch Whisky. http://www.scotch-whisky.org.uk/swa/files/LifeCycleAssessment.pdf, accessed on 3 December 2009.

SWA (2009c). Website Publications Page. http://www.scotch-whisky.org.uk/swa/106.html, accessed on 3 December 2009.

Wilson, C. (2008). *The Role of Water Composition on Malt Spirit Quality*. PhD Thesis. Heriot-Watt University.

23 Restoration of Scotland's Rivers: Some Challenges Ahead

David J. Gilvear

Summary

1. River ecosystem restoration is one of the most challenging of all attempts to restore ecosystem functions in Scotland. The need for this can arise from natural as well as human influenced changes in river flow volume and course/flood plain morphology, as well as the growing prevalence of invasive non-native species.
2. The restoration work can involve catchment-scale activities transcending many land ownership boundaries, and draws on engineering, hydromorphological and ecological practices. This chapter provides examples of such restoration activities.
3. Several decades may pass before the benefits of river restoration actions emerge. Looking ahead, we will need to see more resourcing of participatory fora comprising land owners, land and river managers, government agencies, NGOs and the wider public, to develop restoration activities. There may be a greater reliance on volunteers to monitor the outcome of these.

23.1 Introduction

Aquatic ecosystems consist of four components: water quantity; water quality; the physical habitat, and species. Substantial deterioration in any one of these can lead to a reduction in ecological status of the ecosystem (see Spray, Chapter 22). Despite water quality improvements in Scotland, the Scottish Environment Protection Agency (SEPA) statistics for 2008 suggest that 28% of rivers still suffer from pollution, 27% have excess water abstraction and 34% have hydromorphological alterations (Scottish Government, 2009).

Gilvear, D.J. (2011). Restoration of Scotland's rivers: some challenges ahead – *The Changing Nature of Scotland*, eds. S.J. Marrs, S. Foster, C. Hendrie, E.C. Mackey, D.B.A. Thompson. TSO Scotland, Edinburgh, pp 249-256.

Climate change presents formidable challenges for fresh water conservation. There are impacts on hydrology with increased high rainfall events and ensuing flash floods. The Flood Risk Management (Scotland) Act 2009 forms a framework to assess and manage flood risks based on the European Communities Floods Directive. The Act aims to reduce the negative impacts of flooding on human health, the environment, the economy and cultural heritage; it aligns flood basin management with the river basin designations under the Water Environment and Water Services (Scotland) Act 2003. Gilvear and Black (1999) showed that even small changes in flood regimes in the Rivers Tay and Earn can have a significant impact on the stability of the flood embankment. Accordingly, higher flows during the winter may lead to more unstable channels resulting in shifts in channel position, increased bank erosion and debris transportation, and channel incision. While these processes are natural, the socioeconomic impacts can be considerable, affecting land users as well as roads, railways, bridges and houses.

The growth of renewable energy developments has also given rise to significant changes in river flow (Gilvear, 1994). The advent of the The Renewables Obligation (Scotland) Order 2007 (under the Electricity Act 1989) has seen an increase in the number of river run hydro-electric schemes, which during dry weather can divert much of the water from riverbeds. Wind turbines may also lead to heightened concentrations of dissolved organic carbon in catchment waters (Grieve and Gilvear, 2008; Waldron *et al.*, 2009), with important ecological implications for fresh water ecosystems.

Against this backdrop of change, I provide examples of some recent restoration activities.

23.2 Alterations to flow

Man made changes to water flow date back centuries – Shaw (1984, cited in Gilvear, 1994) reports that water was diverted to run water mills in the twelfth century. Centres of population are located far from the wettest parts of Scotland, which means that water must be transported across large distances to provide domestic water (which is often stored in reservoirs). Most major rivers in the north and west of Scotland have hydro-electric schemes in place. The flow of water downstream from these is considerably altered from the natural state, which can have a detrimental effect on the wildlife. Hanley and Black (2006), in an assessment of the Tummel hydro-electric scheme, reported that seven of the eight reservoirs and many of the associated rivers would be assessed as no more than moderate under the Water Framework Directive (WFD) due to the impact of these schemes. Mitigating management, such as installing improved fish passes and optimising compensation flows directly below the dam, can be developed to reduce the impacts.

23.3 Morphological change in rivers

Greater confidence in engineering defences and the needs of a growing population have resulted in housing and agriculture developments on land that naturally floods. To accommodate this, rivers that pass through settlements tend to be retained in culverts or have concrete lined banks. In lowland agricultural areas, a river can be a single straightened near-trapezoid channel behind embankments to protect the farmland from inundation. Straightened banks mean that there is no reduction in velocity or energy dissipation as the water passes downstream; indeed the design of some banks will result in an increase in energy when compared to a more natural heterogeneous structure. Increased flood events as a result of climate change (see Spray, Chapter 21) mean that greater effort will need to go into managing these areas.

23.4 Invasive non-native species

We have many non-native fresh water species in Scotland (see Boon and Bean, 2010). Those which are invasive can have significant detrimental impacts on biodiversity (for international context, see McNeely *et al.*, 2001).

Table 23.1 lists the main invasive fresh water species recorded in Scotland. The River and Fisheries Trust for Scotland (RAFTS, 2011) identifies a further 15 species for which there are few records in Scotland (or are already present in England and Wales, and may become invasive). Once established invasive species can be difficult to eradicate and the associated costs can be considerable. The removal of Azolla (*Azolla filiculoides*) from Airthrey Loch in the grounds of the University of Stirling costs in the region of £20,000 per annum for a relatively small local scale problem. The three main riparian non-native species – giant hogweed (*Heracleum mantegazzianum*), Japanese knotweed (*Fallopia japonica*) and Himalayan balsam (*Impatiens glandulifera*) all die back in winter, resulting in an increased risk of bank erosion during flooding events. The parasitic worm, *Gyrodactylus salaris*, which decimated wild Atlantic salmon (*Salmo salar*) populations in Norway, has cost over 500 million euro in the 25 years since it was introduced in Europe (Bakke *et al.*, 2004). Whilst not present in Scotland, a code of practice is in place to ensure this remains the case (SEERAD and DEFRA, 2002).

A key factor in the successful management of non-native invasives is to increase public awareness so that early interventions are carried out before the species become established (see Bremner and Park, 2007).

Table 23.1 Main invasive species associated with Scotland's fresh waters

Species	Distribution	Impact
	Plants of River Margins	
Giant hogweed *Heracleum mantegazzianum*	Widespread	Dense stands can exclude native species. The plant dies back in winter, resulting in an increased risk of bank erosion. Can cause recurring painful skin blisters.
Japanese knotweed *Fallopia japonica*	Widespread	Dense stands can exclude native species. The plant dies back in winter, resulting in an increased risk of bank erosion. Can cause structural damage and impede water flow.
Himalayan balsam *Impatiens glandulifera*	Widespread	Dense stands can exclude native plants and the attractive flowers may preferentially attract pollinators. The plant is annual, so there is an increased risk of bank erosion in the winter.
	Submerged Plants (in part or fully)	
Canadian pondweed *Elodea canadensis*	Widespread, especially in Lowlands	Can outcompete native species and may impede boat traffic if stands are dense.
Nuttall's pondweed *Elodea nutallii*	Mainly central belt	See above. May be under-recorded due to its similarity to Canadian pondweed.
Curly waterweed *Lagarosiphon major*	Some records in central belt and southern Highlands	Can outcompete native species through vigorous growth and by making the water more alkali. May impede boat traffic.
Australian swamp stonecrop *Crassula helmsii*	Sporadic records throughout Scotland	Forms dense emergent rafts that shade out other plants, restrict water flow and cause deoxygenation.
	Floating Plants	
Water fern *Azolla filiculoides*	Central belt	Dense growth on the water surface can restrict light to water plants. Decaying plant material can result in deoxygenation. May impede water flow.
	Invertebrates	
North American signal crayfish *Pacifastacus leniusculus*	Sporadic records throughout Scotland	Displaces the native white-clawed crayfish (*Austropotamobius pallipes*). Can exclude fish species and cause disruption to breeding sites.
	Vertebrates	
American mink *Mustela vison*	Throughout Scotland, except the northern Highlands	Voracious predator of birds, aquatic mammals and fish.
Minnows *Phoxinus phoxinus*	Throughout much of Scotland	Although native to England and Wales when introduced to Scotland this species outcompetes native salmonids.
Ruffe *Gymnocephalus cernuus*	Central belt – especially Loch Lomond	This species has had a disastrous impact on endemic and endangered powan (*Corengonus clupeoides*).

23.5 River ecosystem restoration case studies

Several organisations have been advocating natural flood management in recent years, notably RSPB and WWF (Johnstonova, 2009; Johnson, 2009). Projects have been set up to demonstrate natural flood management and to explore the extent to which these can result in reducing flood peaks. Stirling Council recently commissioned a study to assess the extent to which natural flood management on the River Allan can help mitigate flooding problems in the area; a similar investigation is underway on the Eddleston Water in the Borders. This work requires the cooperation of landowners, and is improved through collaborative dialogues between affected communities (Howgate and Kenyon, 2009).

At the landscape level, woody debris in headwater tributaries and floodplain forest, and especially woodland vegetation over some of the hillslopes, can potentially attenuate floods. Some models predict an increase of between 15 and 71% in floodwater storage due to floodplain forest (Thomas and Nisbet, 2007). In reality we actually need to wait decades before we can be clearer about management responses, in order to monitor the consequences of large floods and the effects of a variety of management regimes in place.

Plate 23.1 The river Clyde at Carstairs, showing meanders and the evolution of oxbows. © P & A Macdonald/SNH

River ecosystem restoration work can involve single species. The European beaver (*Castor fiber*) was widely distributed in Scotland until the early sixteenth century (Kitchener and Conroy, 1996). In 2009, beavers were released into the wild at Knapdale Forest, Argyll, as part of a trial under SNH's *Species Action Framework* (Scottish Natural Heritage, 2007; Gaywood *et al.*, 2008).

Some restoration measures can have much wider benefits, though there is some debate about the nature of these. Pakeman (2011), for instance, summarises some work on river margins and questions the full range of traditionally accepted benefits. On the other hand, the attenuation of the flow regime via natural flood management not only results in flood mitigation but may support small scale hydro-electric schemes. Planting of woodland on floodplains for biofuels could help attenuate floods. Even the reintroduction of the beaver may have wider benefits, as beaver ponds may help attenuate floods and process nutrient rich agricultural runoff.

23.6 Some trends in river restoration

Gilvear and Casas-Mulet (2008) chart the development of river restoration projects in Scotland. Since the 1990s these have steadily increased in number, with the focus shifting from fisheries related activities to nature conservation. During 2006-2009, fish and fisheries projects (35%) were still the most dominant driver for restoration, with nature conservation second (22%; at least half of these focussed on features notified under the EU Habitats Directive 92/43/EEC). Of all the projects identified, 36% had multiple drivers. As Gilvear and Casas-Mulet (2008) note, some benefits of these restoration activities will not be realised for at least 20 years.

23.7 Looking ahead

Whilst there has been growth in catchment scale restoration projects over the past two decades, most are still undertaken at the 'reach' scale. There is important potential for the River Basin Management Planning process (Natural Scotland, 2009) to provide a framework for the delivery of river restoration at the catchment scale. However, there are decadal delays between implementation and benefits. Roni *et al.* (2008) note an apparent failure, at the global scale, of stream restoration projects because of inappropriate temporal and spatial scale monitoring, and a failure to learn lessons from past projects (partly a failure of inadequate monitoring). A standardised monitoring approach for river restoration should be developed for Scotland and built into the costs of restoration – so that lessons can be learnt and management practices adapted accordingly.

In times of economic recession we may need to deploy volunteers to undertake more of the monitoring. Clearly, we need to monitor at the catchment scale, and for this to be successful we need buy in from land owners, land managers and users. This will require resource investment in participatory fora and a significant effort so that people work together.

Acknowledgements

I thank Sue Marrs, Simon Foster, Des Thompson, Phil Boon and an anonymous referee for comments on an earlier draft.

References

Bakke, T.A., Harris, P.D., Hansen, H., Cable, J. and Hansen, L.P. (2004). Susceptibility of Baltic and East Atlantic salmon *Salmo salar* stocks to *Gyrodactylus salaris* (Monogenea). *Diseases of Aquatic Organisms*, **58**, 171-177.

Boon, P.J. and Bean, C.W. (2010). Fresh water non-native species – prevention, control or eradication? In *Species Management: Challenges and Solutions for the 21st Century*, ed. by J.M Baxter and C.A. Galbraith. TSO Scotland, Edinburgh. pp 229-246.

Bremner, A. and Park, K. (2007). Public attitudes to the management of invasive non-native species in Scotland. *Biological Conservation*, **193**, 306-314.

Gaywood, M., Batty, D. and Galbraith, C. (2008). Reintroducing the European beaver in Britain. *British Wildlife*, **19**, 381-391.

Gilvear, D.J. (1994). River flow regulation. In *The Fresh Waters of Scotland. A National Resource of International Significance*, ed. by P.S. Maitland, P.J. Boon and D.S. McLusky. pp 463-487.

Gilvear, D.J. and Black, A. (1999). Flood induced embankment failures on the River Tay: implications of climatically induced hydrological change in Scotland. *Hydrological Sciences Journal*, **44**, 345-362.

Gilvear, D.J. and Casas-Mulet, R. (2008). *River Restoration at the Catchment Scale in Scotland.* Centre for River EcoSystem Science, University of Stirling, Stirling. SEPA Commissioned Report.

Grieve, I. and Gilvear D.J. (2008). Effects of windfarm construction on concentrations of dissolved organic carbon and suspended solids concentrations from peat catchments at Braes of Doune, Scotland. *Mires and Peat*, **4**, 1-11.

Hanley, N. and Black, A.R. (2006). Cost-benefit analysis and the Water Framework Directive in Scotland. *Integrated Environmental Assessment and Management*, **2**, 156-165.

Howgate, O.R. and Kenyon, W. (2009). Community cooperation with natural flood management: a case study in the Scottish Borders. *Area*, **41**, 329-340.

Johnson, R. (2009). *Flood Planner. A manual for the natural management of river floods.* WWF Scotland, Dunkeld, Scotland.

Johnstonova, A. (2009). *Meeting the challenges of implementing the Flood Risk Management (Scotland) Act 2009.* RSPB Scotland, Edinburgh.

Kitchener, A.C. and Conroy, J.W.H. (1996). History of the beaver in Scotland and the case for its reintroduction. *British Wildlife*, **7**, 156-161.

McNeely, J.A., Mooney, H.A., Neville, L.E., Schei, P. and Waage, J.K. (eds.) (2001). *A Global Strategy on Invasive Alien Species.* International Union for Conservation of Nature and Natural Resources, Gland.

Natural Scotland (2009). *The river basin management plan for Scotland river basin district 2009-2015.* Scottish Government, Edinburgh.

Pakeman, R.J. (ed.)(2011). *Biodiversity and farming. A summary of research outputs from the Scottish Government's 'Environment – land use and rural stewardship' research programme.* Macaulay Land Use Research Institute, Aberdeen.

River and Fisheries Trust for Scotland (RAFTS) (2011). www.invasivespecies scotland.org.uk

Roni, P., Hanson, K. and Beechie, T. (2008). Global review of the physical and biological effectiveness of stream habitat rehabilitation techniques. *River Research and Applications*, **18**, 461-479.

Scottish Government (2009). The River Basin Management Plan for the Scotland River Basin District 2009-2015. http://www.sepa.org.uk/water/river_basin_ planning.aspx

Scottish Natural Heritage (2007). *A Five Year Species Action Framework: Making a difference for Scotland's species.* SNH, Perth.

SEERAD and DEFRA (2002). Code of Practice to Avoid the Introduction of *Gyrodactylus salaris* to GB.

Shaw, J. (1984). *Water Power in Scotland.* John Donald Publishers, Edinburgh.

Thomas, H. and Nisbet, T.R. (2007). An assessment of the impact of floodplain woodland on flood flows. *Water and Environment Journal*, **21**, 114-126.

Waldron S., Flowers H., Arlaud, C., Bryant, C. and McFarlane, S. (2009). The significance of organic carbon and nutrient export from peatland-dominated landscapes subject to disturbance, a stoichiometric perspective. *Biogeosciences*, **6**, 363-374.

24 The Dumfries and Galloway Catchment Management Initiative

Alastair McNeill and Paul Sutherland

Summary

1. The Dumfries and Galloway Catchment Management Initiative was set up in 2000 as a precursor to the then forthcoming Water Framework Directive. The Initiative was innovative and linked the relatively new concept of catchment management planning to habitats and species through Local Biodiversity Action Plans.
2. Working in partnership with land managers and a range of stakeholders the Initiative has secured funding in excess of £600,000 to support and deliver a range of projects, from developing footpaths to controlling invasive species, and encouraging environmental best practice across Dumfries and Galloway.

24.1 Introduction and background

The Dumfries and Galloway Catchment Management Initiative began as a Scottish Environment Protection Agency (SEPA) led pilot project in 2000. It aimed to deliver the objectives contained within the wetland section of the Dumfries and Galloway Local Biodiversity Action Plan (Anon., 1999) and was seen as a precursor to the then forthcoming EU Water Framework Directive (WFD) (Anon., 2000). At that time the concept of catchment management planning was fairly new and the Initiative was perceived as a novel project for SEPA, as it addressed habitat and species issues in addition to water quality and quantity. This led to the Initiative being jointly funded with Scottish Natural Heritage (SNH) from 2003 through to 2010.

The Initiative spans Dumfries and Galloway in south west Scotland. The region is mostly rural and comprises of 6,426km^2 lying between the Southern Uplands in

McNeill, A. and Sutherland, P. (2011). The Dumfries and Galloway Catchment Management Initiative – *The Changing Nature of Scotland*, eds. S.J. Marrs, S. Foster, C. Hendrie, E.C. Mackey, D.B.A. Thompson. TSO Scotland, Edinburgh, pp 257-262.

the north and the Solway Firth to the south (Figure 24.1). There are 13 river catchments ranging from the Border Esk in the east to the River Luce in the west draining the Southern Uplands into the Solway Firth.

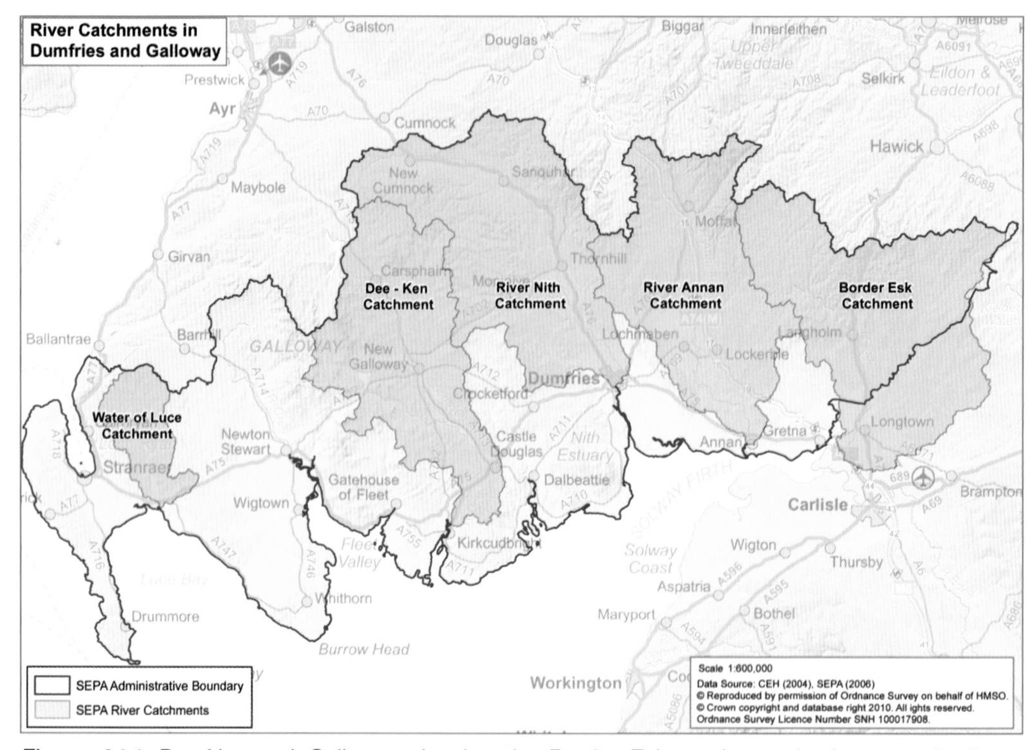

Figure 24.1 Dumfries and Galloway showing the Border Esk catchment in the east, the Luce catchment in the west and the area's three largest catchments, the Nith, the Annan and the Dee-Ken.

The Initiative's first aim was to develop catchment management plans for the region's three largest river catchments, the Annan, Dee-Ken and the Nith. Its second aim was to use the plans to develop and deliver conservation projects that conserve and enhance the ecological quality of the river and its surrounding habitats. The Initiative embraces the principles of ecosystem services and recognises that rivers are integral to land use management and provide a range of diverse activities and services. People are central to this process and the Initiative ensured that land managers and stakeholders had the opportunity to learn about and contribute to the catchment management planning process. Catchment management planning groups or partnerships were established for each of the three rivers. Membership was voluntary and open to all interested people and stakeholders. These groups have played an essential role in gaining the support of local people and land managers without whom it would have been impossible to produce the catchment management plans and implement the wide range of successful projects we have delivered to date.

24.2 Catchment management plans

Catchment management plans provide baseline information for a river system and its environs against which future comparisons can be drawn. Information relating to water quality, water quantity and biodiversity as well as topics such as forestry, farming, industrial activities, urban development and tourism are brought together in a single plan. Key issues for action were detailed in the plans.

The first management plan developed was the River Annan Coordination Plan, 2002 (SEPA, 2002). The Annan catchment was first choice for a plan because a stakeholder partnership, established in the mid 1990s to address environmental issues arising from major road construction projects (McNeill, 1996; McNeill and Olley, 1998), had already worked collectively towards improving the ecological quality of the catchment. In 2004 the Dee-Ken catchment management plan (SEPA, 2004) was published, followed by a plan for Dumfries and Galloway's largest river catchment, the Nith in 2006 (SEPA, 2006).

24.3 Addressing key issues

From the outset, partners intimated that the Initiative should not become a 'talking shop' and that its success would be measured by the projects it delivered to address the key issues identified in the plans. The Initiative recognised that continued partnership working beyond the catchment management planning stage would be essential in terms of tackling issues and that different parties may become involved to help facilitate different projects. Whilst the Initiative took the lead during the development of the catchment management plans, it did not need to take the lead in delivering projects. The Initiative discovered that it worked best as a facilitator, bringing stakeholders together to develop ideas and to apply for grants to raise funds for individual projects. The responsibility for project delivery was left to land managers, stakeholders and Non Governmental Organisations (NGOs) who possessed the relevant skills and experience to undertake the work required.

Following the publication of catchment management plans for the rivers Annan, Dee-Ken and Nith, the Initiative has developed many partnership projects that have delivered ecological improvements within these catchments. To provide a flavour of the types of issues the Initiative has addressed some examples are presented below.

24.3.1 Annandale Way

This project established footpaths and signs adjacent to the River Annan and its tributaries allowing public access between the coastal town of Annan and the rural hinterland. Supported by a grant from Dumfries and Galloway Council and Heritage Lottery Funding (Anon., 2009) over 88km of walks were completed in 2009.

24.3.2 Invasive non-native species project

Japanese knotweed (*Polygonum cuspidatum*), giant hogweed (*Heracleum mantegazzianum*) and Himalayan balsam (*Impatiens glandulifera*) have aggressively colonised many catchments in Dumfries and Galloway. In 2007, the Initiative undertook a project to map the extent of these species in the Annan and Nith catchments and produced a best practice leaflet for distribution to landowners, land managers and members of the public. Phase II of this project began in 2010 in partnership with the Annan and Nith District Salmon Fisheries Boards and Solway Heritage, a local environmental charity. A catchment wide approach is being taken to control these species and the project has employed an invasive non-native species project officer for the Annan and Nith catchments. The project aims not for complete eradication but to vastly reduce their extent and to build the knowledge, skills and experience necessary for landowners and managers to continue controlling what remains at the end of the five-year project period.

24.3.3 North American signal crayfish working group

The Dee-Ken catchment management plan identified North American signal crayfish (*Pacifastacus leniusculus*) as a significant issue and in 2006 the Initiative established a working group to highlight the legal issues, licensing issues and the responsibilities of agencies. The working group has since evolved to assist in the management of a trial crayfish trapping and research project. The trial, financed by the Scottish Government, gathered valuable information and removed over a million crayfish from the loch during 2009. A case is being prepared in 2010 to undertake a further and more extensive three year project.

24.3.4 Working towards best practice

Working towards best practice was a two phase project. Phase I of this project provided open days aimed at encouraging farmers within the Dee-Ken catchment to adopt best environmental management practices for farmland birds, hedgerows, wetlands and sustainable farm drainage systems (McNeill, 2000). Phase II took things a step further by providing funding for the Farming and Wildlife Advisory Group (FWAG) to undertake biodiversity audits of farms. A wetland and wildlife best practice leaflet was also produced and distributed to every farm in the catchment. The project was awarded the 'Caring for the Environment' LEADER + Rural award in 2007.

24.3.5 Whitesands interpretation project

The River Nith flows through Dumfries at an area known as the Whitesands. This urban reach of river is ecologically rich but contamination by litter has created a negative public image. To enhance public awareness of the river's wildlife value, a project began in 2008 in partnership with a local community group, the River Nith Society, and was funded by Dumfries and Galloway Council, SEPA and SNH. The project culminated in the erection of interpretation boards around the Whitesands explaining the ecological value of the river.

24.4 Conclusions and future activities

Catchment management plans are not unique to Dumfries and Galloway but developing such plans as a precursor to the WFD's river basin management process and linking them to strategic regional plans such as the Local Biodiversity Action Plan was innovative. The catchment management plans have provided baseline information on watercourses, which in turn has informed the WFD process and the development of the Solway Tweed River Basin Management Plan. Over the next few years, environmental issues identified within the Solway Tweed River Basin Management Plan and the Local Biodiversity Action Plan will require action - the Initiative is uniquely placed to deliver this action at a local level, involving local people with the support of stakeholders and NGOs.

Since the Initiative was launched in 2000 it has helped to secure in excess of £600,000 to support and deliver projects across Dumfries and Galloway. However, as the UK attempts to recover from recession, public sector funding is likely to be reduced in forthcoming years and this will be a critical factor to the ongoing and long term success of the Initiative.

References

Anon. (1999). *Dumfries & Galloway Local Biodiversity Action Plan.* Dumfries & Galloway Local Biodiversity Partnership.

Anon. (2000). Directive 2000/60/EC of the European Parliament *Establishing a framework for the community action in the field of water policy.* European Union.

Anon. (2009). Annandale Way. Sulwath Connections (Heritage Lottery Funded).

McNeill, A. (1996). Road Construction and River Pollution in South-West Scotland. *Journal of the Chartered Institution of Water and Environmental Management*, **10**, 174-182.

McNeill, A. (2000). Natural Remedy (Urban Drainage). *Surveyor*, **20 April,** 12-15.

McNeill, A. and Olley, S. (1998). The Effects of Motorway Runoff on Watercourses in South-West Scotland. *Journal of the chartered Institution of Water and Environmental Management*, **12**, 433-439.

SEPA and Environment Agency (2009). Draft Solway Tweed River Basin Management Plan for the Solway Tweed River Basin District.

SEPA (2002). *The Annan Catchment Co-ordination Plan.*

SEPA (2004). *The Dee-Ken Catchment Management Plan.*

SEPA (2006). *The River Nith Catchment Management Plan* (Incorporating the Lochar Water).

The Changing
Nature of Scotland

Lowlands

Lowlands

The lowlands are perhaps one of the most accessible ecosystems in Scotland. For many people these are the doorstep to nature, and what most people probably think of as 'countryside'. From familiar scenes of fields and hedgerows to the less familiar (certainly in Scotland) of lowland fens, support a vast array of biodiversity. These are amongst our most modified of habitats. Centuries of farming has moulded and shaped vast tracts of the lowlands, which has in turn altered the species composition. But these still remain areas which are, or can be, important for nature.

Some key events for agriculture in Scotland since 1970

1975	Government White paper *Food from Our Own Resources* urged the expansion of agriculture
1977	*Nature Conservation and Agriculture* is the Nature Conservancy Council's first published policy paper
1979	Government White paper *Farming and the Nation* touched on nature conservation issues
1986	Agriculture Act introduced ESAs (Environmentally Sensitive Areas), with first tranche announced in 1987
1987	The Government proposed to spend more money on the agricultural environment through its 'Farming and Rural Development' package
1988	Voluntary 'set-aside' schemes to reduce agricultural surpluses announced
1992	Common Agricultural Policy (CAP) reforms introduced compulsory set-aside in exchange for area-based payments
1993	Stubble burning became illegal
1996	Countryside Premium Scheme extended to Scotland replacing Habitat Scheme, introduced to provide support for creating or managing specific habitats for a period of 10 or 20 years
1997	UK Government committed to greenhouse gas emissions being 20% less than 1990s levels – by 2010
1998	RSPBs 'Land for Life' campaign highlighted the plight of many farmland birds

ble field with wild flowers. Bankfoot, Tayside.
NH Images

1999	Devolution – Responsibility for agriculture devolved to the new Scottish Parliament and Executive
2001	Outbreak of foot and mouth disease in the UK
2001	Control of Pollution (Silage, Slurry and Agricultural Fuel Oil) (Scotland) Regulation
2001	A Forward Strategy for Scottish Agriculture stated that high environmental standards in farming are vitally important, introducing concept of whole farm support and land management contracts
2002	Prevention of Environmental Pollution from Agricultural Activity (PEPFAA) code published
2002	Custodians of Change – Agriculture and Environment Working Group report concluded that priority environmental issues for Scottish Agriculture were diffuse pollution to water; biodiversity and habitat protection; landscape change
2005	Single Farm Payment (SFP) introduced as part of package of CAP reform, which decoupled payments from activity. Compliance with Statutory Management Requirements (SMRs) (Cross Compliance) and with Good Agricultural and Environmental Conditions (GAEC) standards required as condition of funding
2007	Set aside payments incorporated into SFP with compulsory set aside requirement reduced to zero percent in 2008
2011	Scotland's first Land Use Strategy laid in Parliament on 17 March

Whilst certainly the largest areas of lowland habitats exist in the southern areas of Scotland, northern and western Scotland have extensive areas, perhaps the most spectacular being machair in the Western Isles. Lowlands exist in their own right and provide a range of important habitats, and of course provide much of our food from numerous farms.

In this section, we have four chapters which focus on farming, changes in biodiversity and how we can target efforts to secure the conservation of lowland species in the future. Jonathan Hall begins by looking at the changing nature of farming (Chapter 25). Over the years farming has gone through many changes; recent times have seen the effects of mechanisation and the drive for cheaper and more widely available crops. Farming remains a heavily subsidised area but it has proved resilient and has evolved through the ages. There is an increasing acknowledgement across the sector that farming does not only exist to put food on our table, but delivers benefits to everyone.

The decline of farmland birds has been highlighted for several years and it is concerning how little we understand the reasons for the declines. Scotland's biodiversity indicator, which covers farmland birds, illustrates that since 1994 the trends for 27 farmland species have shown some improvement. Pastoral and wetland species such as lapwing (*Vanellus vanellus*) and kestrel (*Falco tinnunculus*) have shown large declines, whereas some of the generalist species such as goldfinch (*Carduelis carduelis*) and song thrush (*Turdus philomelos*) have shown increases.

Jeremy Wilsons' chapter (26) provides compelling evidence that progressive intensification of agricultural production has pervasive and severe effects on wildlife across a wide range of taxonomic groups. In several cases, the cause of species decline has been clearly identified: e.g. corncrake (*Crex crex*), skylark (*Alauda arvensis*) and grey partridge (*Perdix perdix*). Indeed some areas such as the north-west of Scotland are still rich in biodiversity. No area has escaped the effects of declines, however, and in many cases we still urgently need research to inform conservation action. Where agri-environment interventions are well-founded, with clear objectives and targeted the results can be spectacular. Climate change impacts present daunting new challenges in managing the countryside, as will the demand for new crops such as bio-fuels.

In Chapter 27, Davy McCracken and Andrew Midgley cover the difficult topic of how are we going to deal with biodiversity declines. They suggest that identifying the areas important for nature (High Nature Value Farmland) is a step in the right direction. However, many of the areas which are important also have a dwindling number of active farmers. We may have to think about altering support systems if we are to keep these areas economically active and important for wildlife.

Finally, Emma Teuten presents a new approach to bird conservation targeting which has already had good results in England. The method is testimony to 'simple is best'. The Bird Conservation Targeting Project working with others, including SNH, RSPB and Scottish Government, has identified a list of species which could benefit from a targeted approach. The project has another important aspect – it encourages volunteers to submit records. Hopefully, over time and working with farmers and land managers, we will start to see the benefits of targeted conservation work.

The Lowlands are often forgotten about, or taken for granted. The chapters in this section serve as an important reminder of why they are integral to Scotland. They also remind us that there are some real challenges ahead if we are to hold onto some of our farmland nature.

25 The Changing Nature of Scottish Farming

Jonathan Hall

Summary

1. Farming is a critical activity for Scotland and has shaped many of the landscapes that we can see today.
2. Eighty-five percent of land in Scotland is under some form of agricultural management and farming supports a large number and range of businesses from the food sector to hauliers.
3. Farming delivers a range of commodities such as cattle, sheep, wheat and barley. Farming is not however, just about producing food and more often there is a wider rural development benefit from farming which has to be recognised. Policies are being developed which reflect these benefits but are also about providing areas for people to go, supporting wildlife and managing habitats.
4. Increasingly farmers are undertaking some form of business diversification in order to remain viable. The activities are wide-ranging and can include providing tourist accommodation, pony trekking and farm shops.
5. There are currently over 20 policies which relate to agriculture. Not all of them are clear and some conflict with each other. Some, such as the Water Framework Directive, are not specifically designed for agriculture, but they can have a significant impact on farming practises. It is important to make policies easy to understand as well as looking at the benefits that will be delivered.

25.1 Introduction

Farming has been a principal land-use throughout Scotland for centuries and over this time we have seen several changes to the methods and types of farming. Prior to the industrialised era in the nineteenth century farming was largely an activity undertaken by many people with a limited range of crops and livestock on offer. The

Hall, J. (2011). The Changing Nature of Scottish Farming – *The Changing Nature of Scotland*, eds. S.J. Marrs, S. Foster, C. Hendrie, E.C. Mackey, D.B.A. Thompson. TSO Scotland, Edinburgh, pp 269-280.

advent of mechanisation resulted in fewer people employed in farming and field size was increased to accommodate machinery. After the Second World War the UK government farming policy was aimed at ensuring the UK was self-sufficient. There was an increased emphasis on production, which led to the use of a number of chemical pesticides and herbicides to improve yields. From the 1960s there was another period of change when it became obvious that some of the chemicals being used and methods operated were having a detrimental affect on our wildlife. Thus began the change of farming to what we see today as an industry that acknowledges its role as a provider of goods and services as well as the guardian of the unique biodiversity that occupies our farmland. Farmland covers approximately 5.6 million hectares (about 85%) of Scotland's land area.

There is growing support for farming having a more prominent rural development delivery role, and we can expect farming to deliver for society on a number of levels:

- Clear contribution to sustainable economic growth;
- Secure supplies of safe, high quality and locally produced food;
- Managed countryside with enhanced environmental quality and safeguarded landscapes;
- Support for vibrant rural communities and rural opportunities; and
- Support for industries which are dependent on farming.

In return, it is reasonable for the farming sector to seek the following from society:

- Thriving (profitable) farm businesses – output prices that equate to the costs of production;
- Provision of direct support to reflect the value/cost of existing public benefits of farming activities;
- Reward for the delivery of additional non-market goods; and
- Investment in the capacity/capability of agricultural production and all the associated co-products.

In this paper I explore these issues, and argue that we need to see key changes across the farming and rural policy sectors in order to sustain our environment more effectively in the future.

25.2 Scottish agriculture 'PLC'

As an industry, Scottish agriculture supports over 22,000 farm businesses. These vary from small enterprises comprising one or two individuals to larger ones, employing in excess of 100 people. In 2009 around 67,000 people were directly employed in agriculture in Scotland (Anon., 2010a) – this represents around 8% of the rural workforce and makes agriculture the third largest employer in rural Scotland, after the service industries and public sector. The type of farming is varied and reflects the evolution of farming practices across Scotland over the centuries. In the south, farming is predominantly dairy and arable, whilst further north the farming practices are more livestock dominated. Over the past few years there has been an increase in the numbers of specialist farms (e.g. specialist beef) which have developed in response to the needs of customers.

In economic terms several factors set farming apart from other industries. As an industry farming tends to be heavily 'borrowed', around £1.4 billion in 2009 (Anon., 2010a), resulting in a mixed investment picture. Farms and farmers are highly affected by the volatility in market prices. Changes to the cost of feedstock and fertilisers can have significant impacts on the profits realised at the end of a year. Over the years the industry has become increasingly support dependent. Systems such as Single Farm Payments (SFP) and the Less Favoured Area Support Scheme (LFASS) have been relied on by farms and farmers as a means of supporting their businesses through the global economic uncertainties that have been faced.

There are other issues arising in farming, including the ever increasing bureaucratic burdens and regulatory costs. In addition, in an attempt to address the age profile of farmers and attract new entrants into farming, initiatives by organisations such as the Tenant Farming Forum (Cook and Grieve, 2009), have been introduced. Disease and its effects on farming often make the headlines (foot and mouth, *Bovine Spongiform Encephalopathy* (BSE) etc.) increasing the public awareness of animal diseases on farms. This often has knock-on effects to the economy, people do not want to buy a product that is linked with disease. It is important to remember that whilst these may capture the public attention they have a tendency to label entire portions of the industry as 'diseased' and detract from the fact that animal disease is potentially economically crippling to farms. Often the diseases are not widespread, they are contained and they do not detract from the high quality products Scottish farmers produce. The ever increasing cost to deal with diseases on livestock means that farmers are not only battling with the survival of their stock but also with their livelihoods.

Arable farming does not escape the issues of disease. Every year we see new diseases and pests that are resistant to chemicals or the previous methods of control, which means that new disease and pest resistant strains of crops are required. In the UK consumers look for products which have not been genetically modified and are produced with a low environmental and economic cost. This means that farmers increasingly have to rely on innovative methods of control for diseases. With predicted climate change it is likely that further new diseases and pests, which previously were restricted to other areas, may start to appear.

Increasingly, and possibly as a result of some of the issues outlined above, farmers have undertaken some form of business diversification to provide extra income. The activities are wide-ranging and can include providing tourist accommodation, pony trekking and farm shops. The Farm Management Handbook

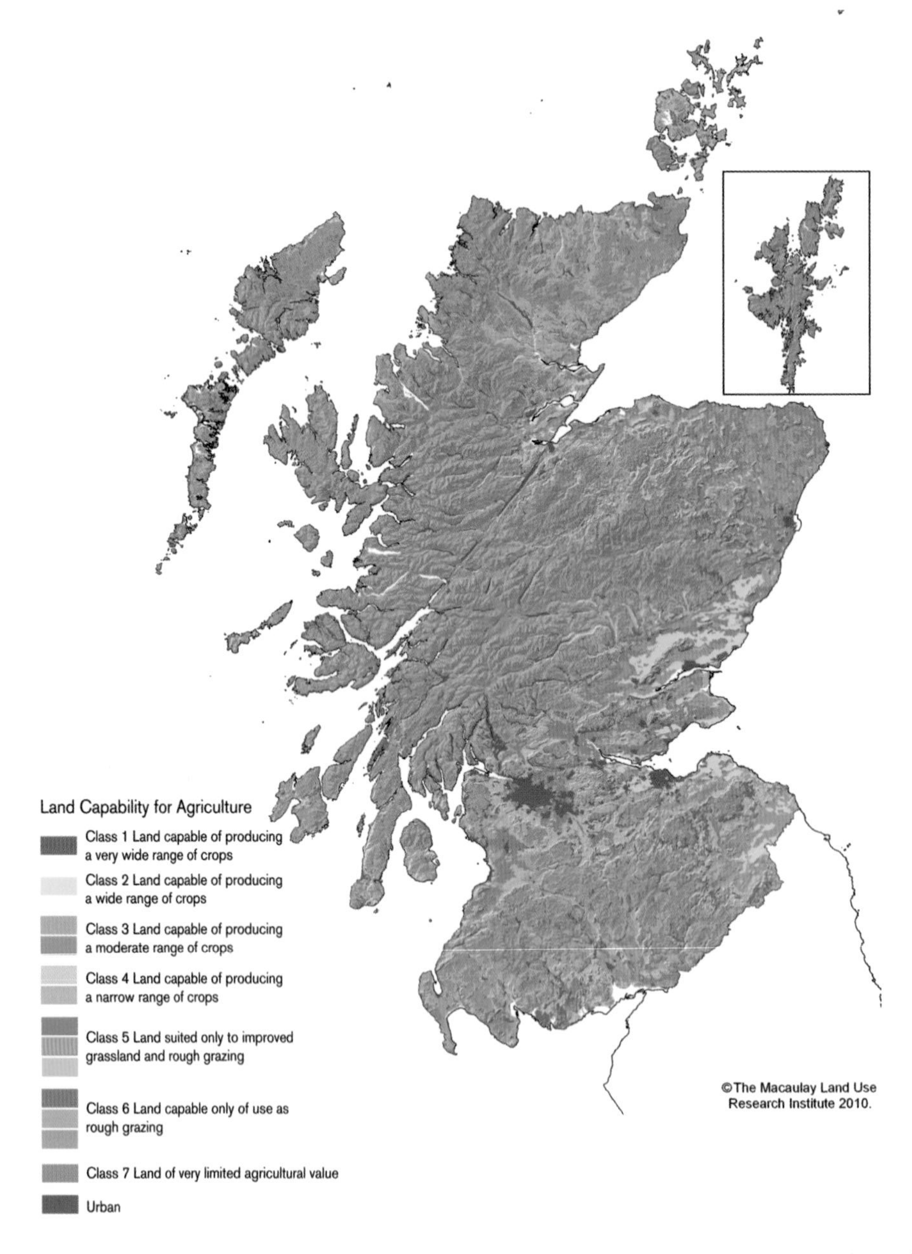

Figure 25.1 Land capability for agriculture in Scotland. The areas in purple are classed as less suitable for farming. Macaulay Institute (2002).

2009/10 (McBain and Curry, 2009) estimated that around 50% of farms in the UK supplement traditional incomes through farm diversification. Government agricultural strategies recognise the need for farm businesses, where appropriate, to seek opportunities for sustainable diversification.

The Scottish Government's Farm Accounts Survey for Scotland (Anon., 2010b), estimates that the average Farm Business Income decreased by £2,200 from £40,900 in 2007/08 to £38,700 in 2008/09. The largest decreases in income were for Specialist Cereal and General Cropping farms and mainly due to a large rise in the cost inputs, particularly for fertiliser and fuel. Specialist Cereal farms also experienced a reduction in the value of cereal output.

Approximately 85% of Scotland's agricultural land is classed as being less-favoured (Anon., 2010a). Less-Favoured Areas (LFA) in Scotland are marked by poor soils and low agricultural income, and they receive support through the LFASS. There is a close correlation between LFA and the land capability classification developed by the Macaulay Institute (Figure 25.1) (Wright *et al.*, 2006). The land capability classification is based upon intrinsic biophysical limitation of the land, that is limitations that cannot be removed or ameliorated by reasonable management, and therefore act as constraints to use (Brown *et al.*, 2008). The land-use capability system was adapted for agriculture in the UK by the pioneering work of Bibby and Mackney (1969). In the future the proportion of land classed as being less-favoured is likely to alter as a result of predicted climate change. Brown *et al.* (2008) suggest that their scenario-based analysis of future land capability has indicated that predicted climate change is likely to substantially modify the current range of options for land use in Scotland, and evidence from recent change suggests that this may indeed already be occurring. Furthermore they suggest that land-use options in the east and south of the country are likely to increase, while in most western districts they will remain constrained. The potential expansion in areas of 'prime' land would be mainly at the expense of the lower-graded land. This is likely to alter the types of farming that we see across Scotland and change the land-use and may result in a re-evaluation of less-favoured areas.

25.3 Scottish farming's contribution to people, the economy and the environment

The contribution from farming to Scotland's people, our economy and environment is wide-ranging. For the most part it is driven by the fact that Scottish farming delivers a range of commodities (beef, lamb, milk, barley etc.). Increasingly the importance of farms and farming to deliver a range of other benefits such as providing areas for recreation, education and support important habitats and species is being recognised.

25.3.1 Scottish farming commodities

The goods produced by farming (the commodities), are the mainstay of farming. Without the demand for the goods produced by farmers farming would not exist. They broadly fit into the following nine categories:

Farming Type	Scotland's key farming facts
Beef cattle	Scotland has almost 30% of the UK herd of breeding cattle and 4% of the EU herd.
Sheep	Scotland has 20% of the UK breeding flock. The UK has the largest sheep flock in the EU – over a quarter of the total EU flock.
Dairy farms	In 2008 there were 192,000 dairy cows. 1.132 million litres of milk were produced worth more than £302 million.
Pigs	In 2007 58,000 tonnes of pig meat was produced worth £60 million.
Poultry	In 2007 931 million eggs were produced worth £30 million.
Cereals	In 2008 454,000 hectares of cereals were grown in Scotland, accounting for 12% of the UK cereal area.
Potatoes	In 2008 just over 29,000 hectares of potatoes were grown producing over 1.28 million tonnes.
Oilseed rape	In 2008 33,000 hectares of oilseed rape were grown producing over 115,000 tonnes.
Fruit and vegetables	In 2007 2,400 tonnes of raspberries and 1,300 tonnes of strawberries were produced. Field vegetables such as carrots are grown on the very best land.

Source NFUS, 2010.

Since 2001 there has been a decline in the numbers of sheep, cattle and pigs (Figure 25.2). It is still, in 2010, too early to say what the effects will be on the habitats, biodiversity and the economy of such a decline, particularly in the numbers of sheep in some of the rural areas of Scotland. The reasons for the decline are not clear but poor market prices and changes to the subsidies paid to farmers through the Common Agricultural Policy (CAP) may have affected the numbers of sheep, pigs and cattle on Scottish farms.

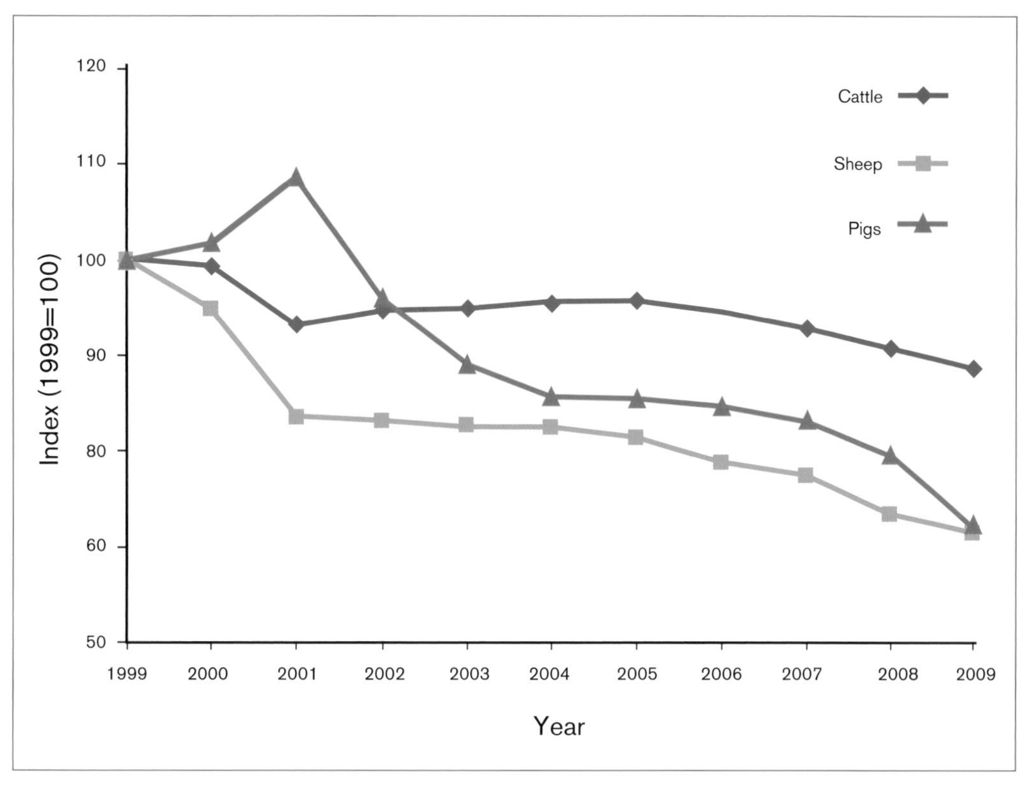

Figure 25.2 Livestock Indices, ten year trends relative to 1999. The graph shows the trends for cattle sheep and pigs in Scotland. (Source: Farm Accounts Survey, Scottish Government, Rural and Environment Research Analysis Directorate).

25.3.2 Public and rural development benefits of Scottish farms

The commodities described above are an essential part of Scottish farms. Increasingly though the contribution is not just commodity driven; other outputs from farming are prominent in terms of public rural development benefit. Whilst in the past the intensification of farming practices led to the decline of a range of species and habitats, in the twenty first century it is acknowledged that farming has a responsibility to create, and manage, a range of habitats that are used by species, many of which are of conservation concern (e.g. Wilson, Chapter 26; McCracken and Midgely, Chapter 27).

The contribution from farming is not just about the creation and management of biodiversity, habitats, landscape and cultural heritage. Farms also provide opportunities for access and recreation. Several farms participate in green ventures offering a range of opportunities for people to enjoy and learn about the outdoors. For example, in addition to creating these opportunities several farms in Scotland participate in the Care Farming initiative. Care Farming is a partnership which promotes mental and physical health through giving people the opportunity to spend time working on the land. Those who can benefit include people with learning difficulties, work-related stress, mental health issues, drug and alcohol problems or employability challenges. Care Farming participants can work on traditional farms or in forestry, horticulture and other land management activities. Care Farming combines care of the land with care of people and there is evidence that it can deliver great personal, social and economic benefits for everyone involved (Care Farming Scotland, 2009).

25.4 Valuing Scotland's farming

Valuing Scotland's farming is not a straightforward exercise. Data on the total business income from farming (see Anon., 2010b) only present part of the picture. If you move away from the view of Scottish agriculture as a business in the strictest economic terms it becomes more difficult to value the contribution of Scotland's farms. Farms and farmers increasingly have to deal with a declining market return for their products together with an increasing cost of production. This cost to price squeeze is reducing the return that farmers can obtain from their products. In the future it is likely that there will be less financial support in the form of subsidies for the actual products and more support for wider rural development benefits. This is already reflected by shifts in policy direction from production support and to wider rural development benefits. There are likely to be further changes to the current systems of farming support to make sure that the subsidies are providing public benefits whilst ensuring production objectives are met.

25.5 Scottish farming's pivotal role

Agriculture might not dominate Scotland's economy – in 2008 it was approximately 0.8% Gross Value Added (GVA) (Anon., 2010a) – it does however play a pivotal role. Farms and farming influence and support a large number of businesses. The produce from farms are essential for food processing and the food and drink sector. These areas rely on the high quality produce from Scotland's farmers. The Scotch whisky industry is perhaps one of the most iconic products from Scotland and this relies heavily on high quality barley and other cereals from Scottish farmers (see Hesketh-Laird, Chapter 22). Farming also supports other businesses such as hauliers, vets and tractor dealerships. These are essential for farms and farmers to help maintain their high standards and continue to be as efficient as possible. Farming is also highly significant for land and water management. Scottish farming yields high quality produce and provides a unique social infrastructure, but are we making the most of this?

25.6 The current policy framework

There are at least 20 different policies directly related to agriculture. As Figure 25.3 shows they do not all work together to deliver the same outputs from agriculture, some are intended to deliver improvements in environmental quality (e.g. the Water Framework Directive) and others are based on improving production outputs (e.g. Single Farm Payments). Indeed there are several policies which place conflicting demands and expectations on farmers as a result of their implementation. These policies can also mean that farming is less driven around market forces and more

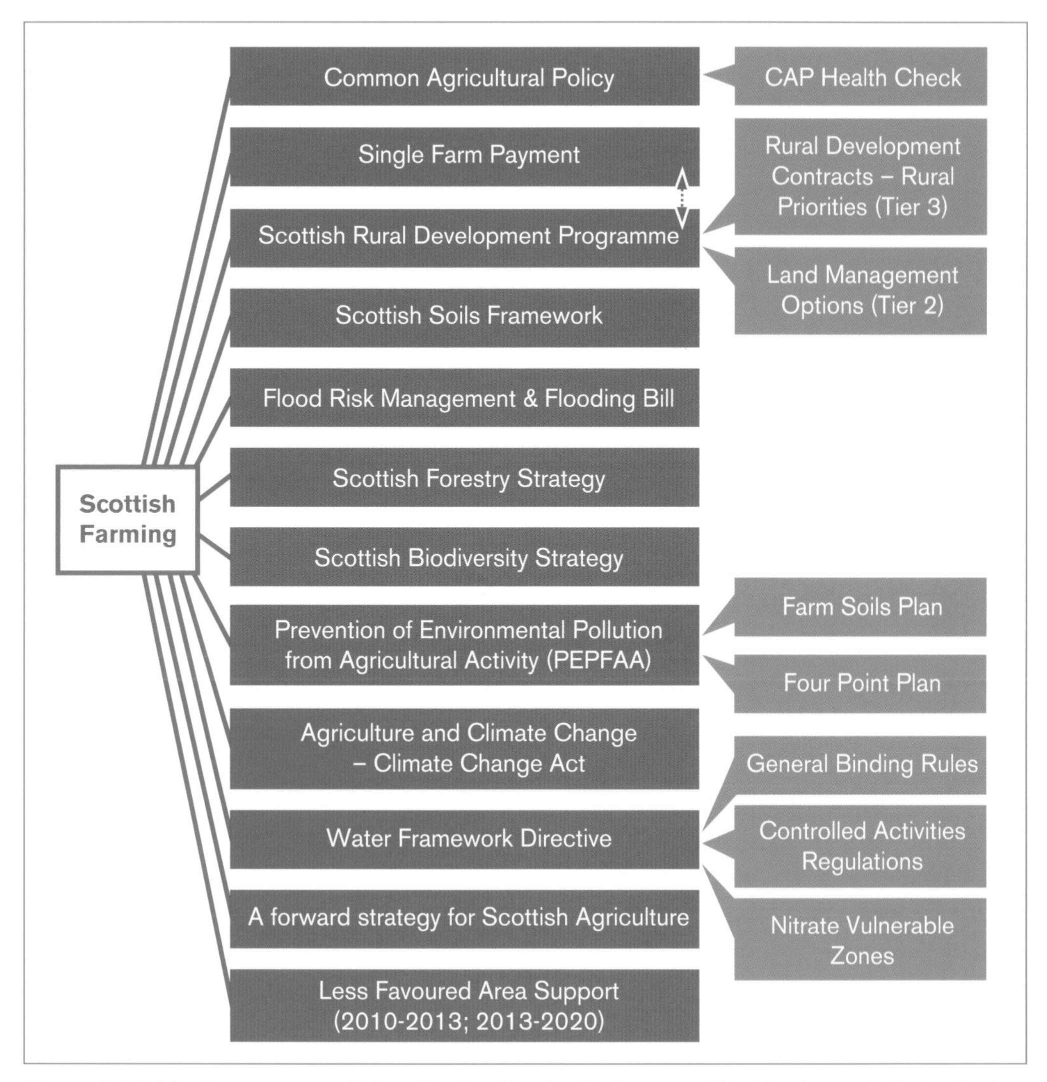

Figure 25.3 The key current policies affecting Scotland's farmers. The blue boxes indicate the key current policies, as not all policies have an environmental focus the green boxes refer to the part of the policy which relates to the environment. This is not a complete list of all policies and is shown as an indication of the complexities facing farmers.

influenced as a result of changing policies which may not necessarily be linked with the market.

The policies are generally not straightforward or easy to understand; indeed they may at times be viewed as contradictory and complex. These policies influence the farmer's activities so a lack of understanding from the farmer or the agencies, will lead to misunderstandings, confusion and a likely failure in the overall aims.

The drivers for change need to be clearly defined. For instance, farms play an important part in soil and water management. Water management provides an example of the complexity of the problems faced, with several different policies requiring different activities and actions from farmers, farms and agencies. The issues relating to the policies and the targets set have not always been communicated clearly to farmers and farming.

Predicted climate change is a growing and significant issue, farmers clearly have a role to play in mitigation and adaptation of the effects through, for example improving habitat connectivity. However, currently the issues surrounding climate change are not viewed by many farmers as a key part of their work. The policies which are in place to try and address the issues are difficult to understand and are not engaging farmers at the correct level. The issue of complexity of policies needs to be worked on by all of the agencies in conjunction with farms and farmers. By communicating with farmers at the correct level – instead of discussing targets, mitigation and emissions and aiming to deliver policies which help farms become more efficient, it is far more likely that the aims of the policies will be met.

The current policy framework does not achieve all of its aims because of contradictions. Currently it is difficult to maximise production and at the same time improve the environment. Determining where these trade-offs exist can only be done by policy makers.

25.7 Scottish agriculture and society

25.7.1 What should Scottish agriculture deliver to society?

Farming has to, and does, contribute meaningfully to society. Farming is an important component of sustainable economic growth. Currently some aspects of farming are well placed to deliver this aim such as some types of organic farming, but there are other areas of farming which could contribute more sustainable economic growth, particularly the highly intensive arable farms. However it has to be remembered that farming is essential for society as a means of securing supplies of safe, high quality locally produced food. Farmers also manage large areas of the countryside and can safeguard landscapes. Farming is well placed to support vibrant rural communities and provide opportunities for access, amenity and recreation.

25.7.2 *What should society deliver to Scottish agriculture?*

It is only fair to look at the other side of the coin in terms of what can be delivered from society to agriculture. The increasing quest for cheaper output prices from consumers can place a huge burden on farms and farmers. A crucial aim is for farms to be regarded as thriving (profitable) businesses where priced outputs at least equate to the cost of production.

With the increasing emphasis on the delivery of rural development benefits, farming needs direct support to reflect the value and cost of these.

It is important that there is sufficient and appropriate investment in improving the capacity/capability of agricultural production and all of the associated co-products. The ultimate aim is to have society back the systems of support for farming.

25.8 Changing the policy regime to deliver

It could be argued that some of the current systems of support provide farmers with little incentive to maintain farming activity. It is important that this is changed; support should be more aligned to activity and not merely on historical payment systems. Policies should reflect the changing emphasis from production orientated mechanisms to those that deliver public benefits, whilst showing that the production elements are still considered. This will be a very fine balancing act and will probably mean that support systems, which vary according to area, will need to be developed to reflect the differing levels of public benefits achievable throughout Scotland. It may be necessary to consider base payments with additional rewards for delivery of more than the basics, in a revised policy regime. Another important change would be to shift the emphasis from good environmental condition to management and paying farmers for the process rather than the result. This is likely to have a greater by-in from the farming community and with less animosity as a result of having to deliver conflicting aims. Finally any change to the policy regimes will have to include investment to improve the viability of farming and ultimately to reduce the levels of support that are currently needed.

25.9 The future for Scottish farming

There are a range of highly influential policy drivers that will affect farms and farming in the future. We are in a period of large-scale change for farming policy at both a national and European level with revisions to SRDP and the current reform of the CAP. In addition, with the predicted effects of climate change it is important that farming is seen as a way to assist in efforts for mitigation of and adaptation to the effects.

Scottish agriculture ultimately affects the changing nature of Scotland. Scottish agriculture and rural policies are inextricably linked. It is predominantly about rural land use, this is however changing as the need to deliver public goods comes more to the fore. It is about driving forward Scotland's rural economy as well as delivering good environmental management. We must be careful to place the correct levels of emphasis on both areas. Farming needs to be economically viable and environmentally aware. Ultimately if we manage the changes facing Scottish farming these can have a positive impact on the changing nature of Scotland.

Acknowledgements

I am grateful to Simon Foster and an anonymous referee for improving the manuscript. The comments and concerns in this paper are personal, and should not be read as the official policy of the National Farming Union of Scotland or SNH.

References

Anon. (2010a). *Agriculture Facts and Figures (2010).* The Scottish Government Rural and Environment Research and Analysis Directorate, Edinburgh.

Anon. (2010b). *Farm Income Estimates 2009.* The Scottish Government, Edinburgh.

Bibby, J.S. and Mackney, D. (1969). Land-use capability classification. *Technical Monograph No. 1: Soil surveys of England and Wales and Scotland.* Rothamsted Experimental Station, Harpenden.

Brown, I., Towers, W., Rivington, M. and Black, H.I.J. (2008). Influence of climate change on agricultural land-use potential: adapting and updating the land capability system for Scotland. *Climate Research*, **37**, 43-57.

Care Farming Scotland (2009). http://www.carefarmingscotland.org.uk/, accessed on 10 June 2010.

Cook, P. and Grieve, J. (2009). *Getting new talent into the industry: A guide to methods for a phased entry into farming.* Tenant Farming Forum. Scotland.

McBain, C. and Curry, J. (2009). *The Farm Management Handbook 2009/10.* The Scottish Agricultural College.

NFUS (National Farming Union of Scotland) (2010). Scotland's Farming Facts, http://www.nfus.org.uk/farming-facts/what-we-produce, accessed on 11 June 2010.

Wright, I.A., Birnie, R.V.B., Malcolm, A., Towers, W. and McKeen, M. (2006). *The potential use of the Land Capability for Agriculture Classification for determining support to disadvantaged areas of Scotland.* The Macaulay Institute, Aberdeen.

26 Bird Conservation and Lowland Agriculture

Jeremy D. Wilson

Summary

1. Agriculture is a dominant land use in the UK and Scotland. Intensification of lowland agriculture since the Second World War has caused biodiversity loss across many taxonomic groups. A few species – especially those able to exploit crop plants as food – have benefited.
2. The reasons for declines of bird species on lowland farmland are now well understood, and provide robust evidence for development of bird conservation measures in agri-environment schemes and on set-aside land.
3. These measures have reversed national population declines where they have been targeted at a high proportion of the species' population (notably, in Scotland, corncrake (*Crex crex*)), but have yet to be deployed at a sufficient scale to reverse the declines of widespread species, such as lapwing (*Vanellus vanellus*). In Scotland, the decline of the corn bunting (*Emberiza calandra*) is now so severe that it should be considered an immediate priority for targeted agri-environment measures.
4. Climate change and food security concerns may increase pressure on biodiversity in lowland agricultural systems. Research is needed to find solutions to integrating food production, climate change adaptation and biodiversity conservation. Agri-environment schemes provide a solid foundation on which to build.
5. Some farming and crofting systems in Scotland, such as the machair of the Hebrides, support a rich biodiversity of international importance. Changes to farm subsidies to maintain these high nature value agricultural systems and practices would be hugely beneficial.

Wilson, J.D. (2011). Bird Conservation and Lowland Agriculture – *The Changing Nature of Scotland*, eds. S.J. Marrs, S. Foster, C. Hendrie, E.C. Mackey, D.B.A. Thompson. TSO Scotland, Edinburgh, pp 281-298.

26.1 Introduction

Farming dominates the lowland landscapes of the United Kingdom (UK) and Scotland. From the ploughing campaigns of the Second World War to the UK's accession to the European Economic Community and its Common Agricultural Policy (CAP) in 1973, to the present day, intensification of production has been a dominant theme of UK agriculture, supported by Government policy and investment in underpinning science and technology (Shrubb, 2003).

Agricultural intensification is about increasing the efficiency with which primary production is directed to the human food chain and, to the extent that this is achieved, wild nature is bound to suffer (Krebs *et al.*, 1999). Damaging effects of agricultural intensification on biodiversity first came to public attention in the 1950s and 1960s when early generations of pesticides, notably organochlorines such as DDT, aldrin and dieldrin, proved to have persistent toxic effects throughout the food chain (Carson, 1963). This resulted in catastrophic population declines of raptors such as sparrowhawks (*Accipiter nisus*) and peregrines (*Falco peregrinus*) (Newton, 1986). Subsequent generations of pesticides have allowed these populations to recover but nonetheless agricultural intensification continues in other forms.

This paper reviews the impacts of agricultural change on biodiversity in lowland agricultural systems, with a particular focus on bird populations. It discusses the strengths and weaknesses of various forms of agri-environmental management that have sought to mitigate biodiversity losses in intensive farming systems – and looks ahead to the challenges that bird conservation in lowland agricultural landscapes is likely to face in the future.

26.2 Agricultural intensification

26.2.1 Arable cropping

In arable systems, the main elements of intensification have comprised:

- Increases in agrochemical use (pesticides and inorganic fertilisers) which reduce the abundance and diversity of a wide range of arable plants and invertebrates (Wilson *et al.*, 1999; Robinson and Sutherland, 2002);
- Development of autumn sown cereal varieties which permit earlier sowing and harvesting and reduce or eliminate the winter and spring fallow period with its stubble seed resources for granivorous birds and subsequent nesting opportunities for species such as skylarks (*Alauda arvensis*) and lapwings (*Vanellus vanellus*) (Wilson *et al.*, 1997; Hancock and Wilson, 2003; Sheldon *et al.*, 2007);

- Increasingly powerful and efficient agricultural machinery allowing cleaner harvesting, reducing availability of waste crop and weed seed after harvest, and permitting rapid, synchronous completion of crop operations, thus reducing both spatial and temporal diversity in the landscape; and
- Introduction of large-scale growing of 'new' arable crops such as oilseed rape for fodder and fuel and, most recently, bioenergy crops such as *Miscanthus* (elephant grass).

26.2.2 Grassland

By the mid-1980s around 97% of Britain's lowland grasslands had been subject to some form of agricultural improvement (Fuller, 1987), including cultivation and conversion to arable production, re-seeding with a limited mix of competitive fodder grass species, drainage and increasing application of inorganic fertilisers. Agriculturally improved grasslands support much reduced plant and invertebrate communities (Wilson *et al.*, 1999). Higher stocking rates or more frequent harvesting as forage grasses then have additional impacts on breeding birds by increasing nest destruction rates for many ground-nesting species, including breeding waders, corncrakes (*Crex crex*) and songbirds such as skylarks, meadow pipits (*Anthus pratensis*), whinchats (*Saxicola rubetra*) and corn buntings (*Emberiza calandra*) (e.g. Beintema and Müskens, 1987; Green, 1996; Donald, 2004; Müller *et al.*, 2005; Wilson *et al.*, 2007a).

26.2.3 Landscape-scale change

The effects of agricultural intensification at the field and farm-scale have become increasingly evident as change to agricultural landscapes. The most obvious of these has been the increasing polarisation of agricultural land use, with specialised arable enterprises growing simplified, grass-free rotations (often dominated by winter wheat and oilseed rape) in the warmer, drier conditions of the south and east of Britain, and pure grassland enterprises based on grass silages or imported feeds for livestock further to the north and west. Mixed farms with a diversity of crops, grassland and livestock have become scarcer, though they still characterise some Scottish lowland landscapes.

Until the 1980s, increasingly powerful agricultural machinery, strong production incentives and grant-aid encouraged removal of habitat features such as hedgerows, trees and ponds to allow for increased field sizes. Although neglect and dereliction of such habitats continues in arable systems where hedgerows no longer serve any stock-proofing function, net loss of these features has been slowed and in some cases reversed in more recent years, encouraged by agri-environment funding.

Lastly, it is also important to consider the agricultural and ecological relationships between lowland agriculture and upland grazing systems from a bird conservation perspective. Upland breeding birds such as black grouse (*Tetrao tetrix*), golden plover (*Pluvialis apricaria*), curlew (*Numenius arquata*), skylark, ring ouzel (*Turdus torquatus*) and twite (*Carduelis flavirostris*) are amongst the species which commute from moorland nesting habitats to feed on soil invertebrates or seeds and on improved agricultural ground below the enclosure line (Burfield, 2002; Robson and Percival, 2002; Pearce-Higgins and Yalden, 2003; Wilkinson and Wilson, 2010). Equally, a variety of upland breeding birds, including lapwing, golden plover, curlew, skylark, twite and snow bunting (*Plectrophenax nivalis*) winter in lowland agricultural habitats (Hancock and Wilson, 2003; Wilson *et al.*, 2009). Agricultural change on enclosed farmland can thus have important impacts on bird populations breeding elsewhere.

26.3 Agricultural intensification and biodiversity change

26.3.1 Losses

Evidence of biodiversity loss in the face of agricultural intensification is now widespread across taxonomic groups. For example, in *The New Atlas of the British & Irish Flora*, Preston *et al.* (2002) found a preponderance of declines amongst the arable flora and grassland plant species associated with low nutrient requirements. Of the six factors identified as having had the most profound influence on plant population trends, five are aspects of agricultural intensification. Amongst fungi, Spooner and Roberts (2005) noted that agricultural improvement of grasslands can reduce communities of waxcap (*Hygrocybe spp.*) fungi from a species richness measured at over 20 (and occasionally over 30) species, to none. Long-term declines of many butterflies (Asher *et al.*, 2001), moths (Woiwod and Harrington, 1994), bees (Goulson *et al.*, 2008) and cereal-field arthropod populations (Ewald and Aebsicher, 1999) can also be attributed to agricultural intensification, as can losses of amphibians, reptiles and some mammals (Harris *et al.*, 1995).

26.3.2 Gains

Evidence of biodiversity gain as a result of agricultural intensification is markedly scarcer than that of loss. Gains tend to be associated with species which either consume the crop product being grown or benefit from the high nutrient levels associated with agricultural environments. For example, some competitive plant species associated with high nutrient requirements have increased in agricultural environments (Preston *et al.*, 2002). Equally, bird species which are direct consumers of growing crops or crop wastes have benefitted. For example, the spread of oilseed rape growing has permitted a major increase in woodpigeon (*Columba palumbus*) populations (Inglis *et al.*, 1997), and may have helped compensate for the loss of weed seeds as nestling food for linnets (*Carduelis cannabina*) (Moorcroft *et al.*, 2006). Furthermore several species of wintering geese have benefitted from the availability of increased quantities of protein-rich grass or autumn-sown cereal (Gill *et al.*, 1997).

26.3.3 The effects of agricultural intensification on bird populations

With a few exceptions such as those described above, the impacts of agricultural intensification in causing declines of bird populations have been severe. The declines are unusually well documented, especially in Britain, where high quality population trend data collated by the British Trust for Ornithology (BTO) revealed the generality of farmland bird population declines between the 1960s and 1980s (Marchant *et al.*, 1990), such declines have continued to the present day in England (Figure 26.1). Associations between population declines and measures of lowland agricultural intensification have been demonstrated nationally in England and Wales (Chamberlain

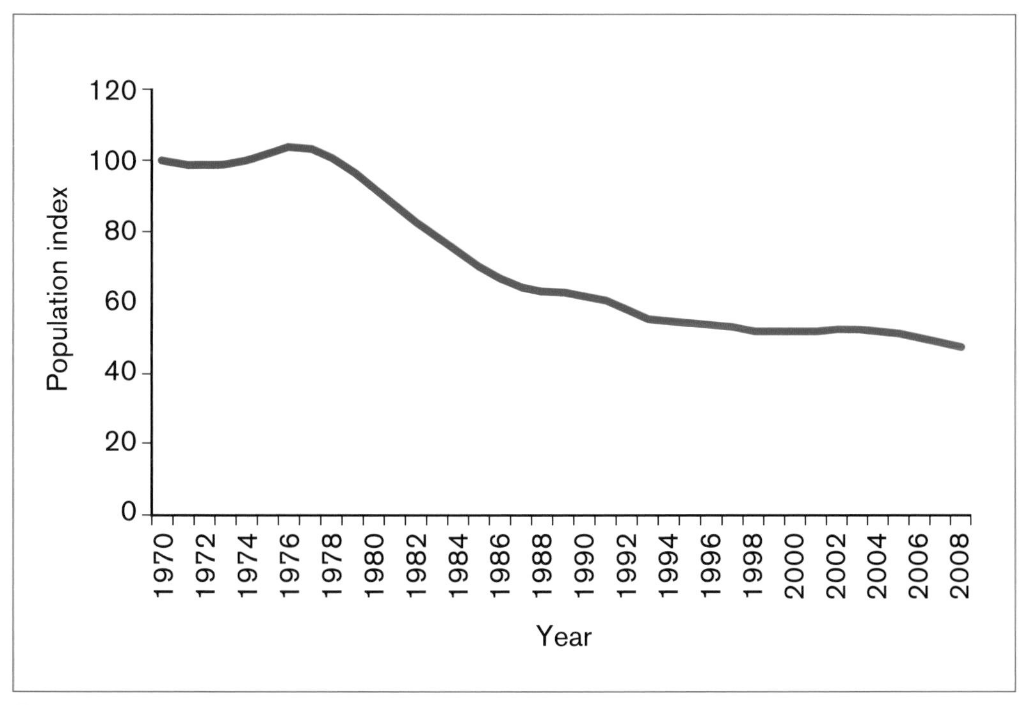

Figure 26.1 Defra Public Service Agreement composite farmland bird indicator for England and Wales, 1970-2008. Data available from www.defra.gov.uk and derived from trends for 19 species (corn bunting, goldfinch, greenfinch, grey partridge, jackdaw, kestrel, lapwing, linnet, reed bunting, rook, skylark, starling, stock dove, tree sparrow, turtle dove, whitethroat, woodpigeon, yellowhammer, yellow wagtail).

et al., 2000), Scotland (Benton *et al.*, 2002), and across Europe (Donald *et al.*, 2006). In England, a composite indicator of the population trend of 19 lowland farmland bird species is now the basis for a Government Public Service Agreement target to halt and reverse population declines, which were most severe from the late 1970s to the early 1990s, but have continued more slowly into this century (Figure 26.1).

Plate 26.1 Corn bunting. With a population reduced to around 700 breeding territories in Scotland and still declining, this species needs urgent, targeted intervention through agri-environment schemes. Recent studies in eastern Scotland show that such intervention can be effective, but that the scale of implementation is currently insufficient. © Andy Hay (rspb-images.com)

In Scotland, long-term population data have always been sparser, but breeding range changes between the two national breeding bird atlases in 1968-1972 (Sharrock, 1976) and 1988-1991 (Gibbons *et al.*, 1993) suggest severe declines of species such as grey partridge (*Perdix perdix*), lapwing, corncrake, tree sparrow

(*Passer montanus*), yellowhammer (*Emberiza citrinella*) and corn bunting which had also shown declines elsewhere in the UK. More recently, however, construction of a similar composite indicator of population trends for lowland farmland species suggests that, since 1994, net declines in Scotland have halted and show a modest recovery for the included species (Figure 26.2). However, it is important to remember that this indicator excludes species such as grey partridge, tree sparrow and corn bunting which are too scarce for their trends to be measured reliably as part of an indicator that is based primarily on the relatively small sample of Scottish Breeding Bird Survey plots (n = 330 in Scotland; n = 2,516 in England; Risely *et al.* (2009)). This may present a more positive impression of trends than would be the case if the indicator was able to measure the trends of these scarcer species, as it does in England.

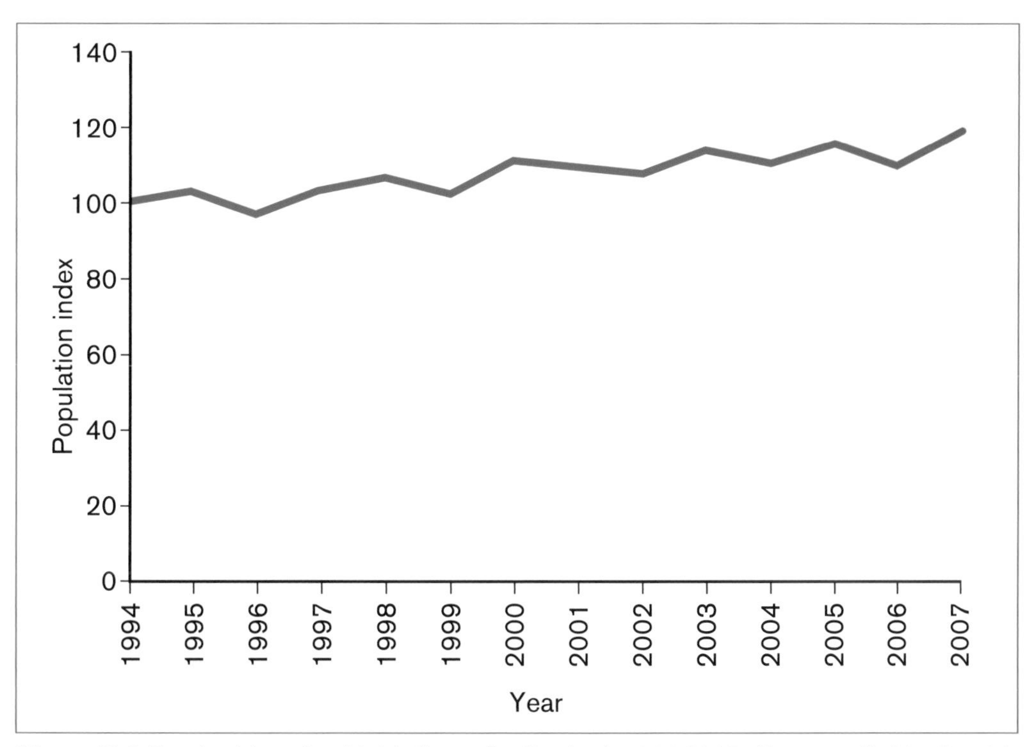

Figure 26.2 Farmland breeding bird indicator for Scotland, 1994-2007. Data supplied by Scottish Natural Heritage, and derived from trends for 26 species (swallow, blackbird, blue tit, buzzard, crow, chaffinch, corncrake, dunnock, goldfinch, greenfinch, great tit, jackdaw, kestrel, lapwing, linnet, oystercatcher, pied wagtail, reed bunting, rook, sedge warbler, skylark, song thrush, starling, whitethroat, woodpigeon, yellowhammer).

Broad-scale associations between population trends and measures of agricultural change have been complemented by many more detailed studies. The long-term studies of the Game & Wildlife Conservation Trust on the grey partridge were amongst the first of their kind, and showed the combined roles of increasing pesticide use in reducing food availability for chicks, loss of nesting cover along field edges, and predation of adult birds in driving population declines through reduced reproductive success and survival (Potts, 1986). Today, similar diagnostic studies have been carried out on many other species, and these illustrate the range of mechanisms through which agricultural intensification has driven population change across diverse bird life-histories (Newton, 2004; Wilson *et al.*, 2009) (Table 26.1).

Table 26.1 Summary of main agricultural causes of population change for some lowland farmland bird species (from Wilson *et al.*, 2009).

Species	Main agricultural causes of population change
Grey partridge	Decline caused by indirect effects of pesticides on chick survival through reduction in insect populations, and effects of changing hedgerow management on availability of nesting habitat.
Corncrake	Long-term decline caused mainly by destruction of nests and young by early and repeated cutting of forage grasses. Conservation measures to delay cutting and provide cover throughout the breeding season have led to population recovery in the core range in Scotland.
Lapwing	Declines caused by the combined effects on availability of nesting opportunities and nest success of grassland intensification, loss of spring cropping, and loss of mixed farming.
Woodpigeon	Earlier decline driven by loss of clover-based leys as a winter food source, but with subsequent increase allowed by growth in oilseed rape acreages providing an alternative winter food source.
Skylark	Decline caused by loss of nesting and foraging opportunities in dense, autumn-sown crops coupled with high rates of nest loss in intensive grass silage systems.
Chough	Causes of long-term population fluctuations not fully understood, but both intensification and abandonment of grazing management of coastal grasslands leads to declines, through reductions in abundance and availability of soil invertebrates and, in turn, the effects of this on survival, especially of first-year birds.
Corn bunting	Decline caused by effects of herbicide use, efficient harvesting, and loss of spring-cropping on availability of weedy, grain-rich over-winter stubbles, combined with impacts of arable and grassland intensification on invertebrate chick foods. These effects are compounded by the impacts of earlier cereal harvesting and repeated silage cutting on nest success.

26.4 Agri-environment management – the 'greening' of the Common Agricultural Policy

26.4.1 Surpluses and set-aside

During the 1980s, public and policy concern over rising food surpluses in the European Union prompted, through several mechanisms, a slowing of the 'engine of destruction' (Marren, 2002) of agricultural intensification. Compulsory set-aside was introduced in 1992 to tackle cereal surpluses and over the years to 2007 resulted in between 5% and 18% of arable ground being taken out of production in any one year. Though designed as a production control mechanism, the potential wildlife benefits of the fallowing of several hundred thousand hectares of arable ground were quickly recognised (Wilson and Fuller, 1992) and subsequent modification to management regulations ensured that much biodiversity benefit was gained from this land, including for foraging and ground-nesting birds (Sotherton, 1998; Henderson and Evans, 2000; Donald, 2004).

26.4.2 Organic farming

At the same time, there was rapid growth in public demand and policy support for the development of organic farming. Although driven by perceived nutritional and food safety benefits, one of the strongest evidence bases for the value of organic production methods is knowledge of the biodiversity benefits that can accrue. These benefits stem especially from withdrawal of many agrochemicals, adoption of more diverse crop rotations and sympathetic non-crop habitat management (e.g. strict limits on the timing of hedge-cutting operations). Two recent reviews find strong evidence that organic farms support a greater abundance and diversity of wildlife across a wide range of taxonomic groups than their 'conventionally' managed counterparts (Bengtsson *et al.*, 2005; Hole *et al.*, 2005).

26.4.3 Agri-environment schemes

From a biodiversity perspective, the most important form of this 'greening' of subsidy support stemmed from the 1986 Agriculture Act. As a result of the Act, subsidy support for farmers was introduced to adopt agricultural practices that would safeguard and enhance parts of the country of particularly high landscape, wildlife or historic value. The Environmentally Sensitive Area (ESA) Scheme was born and, through many successor schemes, agri-environment payments and management have been with us ever since and are now available without geographical restriction across all agriculturally managed land in the UK. In Scotland, Rural Development Contracts, available under Scotland's Rural Development Programme, draw together environmental management support for farmland, moorland and forestry.

The management content of agri-environment schemes, at least as far as bird conservation objectives are concerned, has been informed by the strong and growing knowledge base of the mechanistic links between agricultural and bird population change (Table 26.1). Where agri-environment management targeted at the recovery of a given species population is based on (i) a thorough diagnosis of the reasons for population decline, (ii) prior testing of remedial management from biological, practical and economic perspectives, and (iii) targeted deployment of the tested measures to benefit a sufficiently high proportion of the species' population then the results can be spectacular (Evans and Green, 2007). In the UK, national population recoveries of cirl buntings (*Emberiza cirlus*), stone curlews (*Burhinus oedicnemus*) and corncrakes have all been achieved through Agri-environment management following these principles (Peach *et al.*, 2001; Brown and Grice, 2005; O'Brien *et al.*, 2006). Without it, all three species would probably by now be extinct as breeding birds in the UK.

Of course such successes are not universal. Kleijn and Sutherland (2003) criticised agri-environment implementation across Europe both for its (often) weak evidence base and the frequent lack of good evaluation studies to test the efficacy of individual management measures and their scheme-wide implementation. Since then such studies have burgeoned (e.g. Lye *et al.*, 2009) with increasing evidence across a wide range of taxonomic groups that well-designed agri-environment management can be at least locally beneficial. However, it is important to remember that successful reversal of the population trends of corncrakes, stone curlews and cirl buntings in the UK has come about because well-resourced and well-targeted management has been directed at a very high proportion of the remaining populations of the species concerned. Each had been reduced to a population of just a few hundred pairs (at best) at the time at which conservation management began in earnest. Many of the species whose populations continue to decline as a consequence of agricultural intensification, including UK Biodiversity Action Plan priority species such as lapwing, grey partridge, skylark, yellowhammer and corn bunting, remain more widespread and with remaining UK populations numbered in tens or hundreds of thousands of pairs. The reach of agri-environment management will need to extend to benefit the majority of the populations of these species if their declines are to be reversed. As yet, there is no clear evidence of this, but the recent signs of partial recovery of populations of tree sparrows both in England and Scotland are intriguing in this respect and merit more detailed analysis to test the extent to which they can be ascribed to successful agri-environment management.

26.5 Future challenges

Driven by growth in human population and economic aspiration, globalisation of food markets and climate change, security of food and energy supply is now seen as one of this century's greatest global challenges (Royal Society, 2009). The impact of these global drivers on the extent, nature and intensity of agricultural land use in the UK are difficult to predict. It remains unclear whether we will witness large-scale agricultural land use changes like the widespread planting of bioenergy crops such as short-rotation coppice or *Miscanthus*, or new generations of genetically modified (GM) crops. At present our understanding of the biodiversity impacts of such changes remains scant. For example, although one of the largest-scale field experiments ever undertaken showed strong evidence of deleterious impacts of the husbandry of GM herbicide tolerant crops on seed food supplies of granivorous birds (Gibbons *et al.*, 2006), the influence on biodiversity of new generations of GM crops will depend entirely on the traits chosen for modification and the associated impact on crop husbandry. However, there is a growing consensus that any second 'green revolution' must be a sustainable intensification, achieved without further adverse environmental impacts (Firbank, 2009; Royal Society, 2009) and, wherever possible, reversing previous losses. Achieving this will necessitate successful integration of food production with the delivery of other ecosystem goods and services such as bioenergy, carbon storage, soil function and biodiversity conservation (Firbank, 2005; Robertson and Swinton, 2005).

Our growing understanding of the relationship between agricultural intensification and biodiversity loss and some of the management solutions that have been explored through agri-environment schemes, management of set-aside land and in organic farming systems, all provide a solid knowledge base on which to build. However, new research will need to examine the extent to which existing management for biodiversity conservation on lowland farms conflicts or is consistent with the delivery of other ecosystem services (Bradbury *et al.*, 2010). Some co-benefits certainly exist. For example, conservation tillage can deliver biodiversity, soil health and carbon benefits (Holland, 2004). The creation of small-scale wetland features for water and pollution management purposes can deliver biodiversity benefits (Bradbury and Kirby, 2006). Existing agri-environment management may 'soften' agricultural landscape matrices and assist species' responses to climate change by increasing functional connectivity between semi-natural habitat patches (Donald and Evans, 2006), although this proposition needs more thorough testing (Hodgson *et al.*, 2009). Given that trade-offs between food production and delivery of environmental goods and services are inevitable, research will need to understand at what spatial gain these trade-offs are best made (Wilson *et al.*, 2010). Some degree of restoration of ecological heterogeneity in intensive agricultural systems by making time and space for the life cycles of wild nature is likely to be needed across all spatial scales from the field to the landscape (Benton *et al.*, 2003; Tscharntke *et al.*, 2005).

Lowland agricultural systems in Scotland are well placed to meet the challenges of managing the joint needs of food production and biodiversity conservation. We have seen (Figures 26.1 and 26.2) that since the mid-1990s, population trends of

Plate 26.2 Lapwing. The machair of the Western Isles supports one of the most important assemblages of breeding waders in Europe. This assemblage includes lapwing, redshank, snipe, ringed plover and dunlin – the epitome of a High Nature Value farming system. © Lorne Gill/SNH

some farmland birds in Scotland have tended to be more positive than those in England. This may partly reflect that lowland agriculture in Scotland has not experienced the same levels of agricultural intensification as further south, and thus that agri-environment and set-aside management have had more traction in slowing and even reversing biodiversity losses. However, there is no room for complacency. The effects of the withdrawal of compulsory set-aside in late 2007 remain to be seen (any impact on farmland bird population trends will become evident when indicators are updated to 2009), and some individual species continue to show severe declines. Perhaps most notable amongst these is the corn bunting which continues to decline in its remaining population strongholds in eastern Scotland and on the Western Isles (Wilson *et al.*, 2007b; Watson *et al.*, 2009). Recent monitoring of population responses to agri-environment management in north-east Scotland shows that existing schemes have the capacity to slow or even reverse declines (Perkins *et al.*, 2008), but a higher proportion of the population needs to be targeted by management than is currently the case. With 2010 designated the International Year of Biodiversity, a commitment on the part of Scottish Government to reverse the national decline of corn buntings through agri-environment management would be a welcome step.

Lastly, it is also important to recognise that Scotland continues to support low-intensity, high nature value (HNV) farming systems that are of international importance for the biodiversity that depends upon them (Bignal and McCracken,

1996; McCracken and Midgely, Chapter 27). The rich biodiversity supported by the crofting agriculture of the Western Isles machair, including a bird community with over 15,000 breeding pairs of six wader species (Fuller *et al.*, 2010), corncrakes (O'Brien *et al.*, 2006), twite (Wilkinson and Wilson, 2010) and corn buntings (Wilson *et al.*, 2007b), as well as very high densities of skylarks, meadow pipits, starlings (*Sturnus vulgaris*) and wheatears (*Oenanthe oenanthe*) is just one case in point. Such HNV farming systems are economically marginal; farmers and crofters face pressures to intensify production on the one hand or abandon it on the other. Agri-environment schemes have a critical role to play in maintaining such systems. The evolution of farm subsidy from income support or compensation for agricultural disadvantage, to providing active and positive support to maintain the agricultural systems and practices that support such rich and internationally important biodiversity would be hugely beneficial (Swales and Moxey, 2008). Current discussions on the future of the Common Agricultural Policy beyond 2013 provide the platform to consider how such evolution could begin.

Acknowledgements

I thank Des Thompson, Sue Marrs and Ed Mackey for the invitation to speak at the SNH-SEARS conference '*The Changing Nature of Scotland*', and Andy Douse, Katrina Marsden, Allan Perkins, Vicki Swales and Des Thompson for helpful comments on drafts of the manuscript.

References

Asher, J., Warren, M., Fox, R. *et al.* (2001). *The Millennium Atlas of Butterflies in Britain and Ireland.* Oxford University Press, Oxford.

Beintema, A.J. and Müskens, J.D.M. (1987). Nesting success of birds breeding in Dutch agricultural grasslands. *Journal of Applied Ecology*, **24**, 743-758.

Bengtsson, J., Ahnstrom, J. and Weibull, A.C. (2005). The effects of organic agriculture on biodiversity and abundance: a meta-analysis. *Journal of Applied Ecology*, **42**, 261-269.

Benton, T.G., Bryant, D.M., Cole, L. and Crick, H.Q.P. (2002). Linking agricultural practice to insect and bird populations: a historical study over three decades. *Journal of Applied Ecology*, **39**, 673-687.

Benton, T.G., Vickery, J.A. and Wilson, J.D. (2003). Farmland biodiversity: is habitat heterogeneity the key? *Trends in Ecology and Evolution*, **18**, 182-188.

Bignal, E.M. and McCracken, D.I. (1996). Low-intensity farming systems in the conservation of the countryside. *Journal of Applied Ecology*, **33**, 413-424.

Bradbury, R.B. and Kirby, W.B. (2006). Farmland birds and resource protection in the UK: cross-cutting solutions for multifunctional farming? *Biological Conservation*, **129**, 530-542.

Bradbury, R.B., Stoate, C., Tallowitz, J.K.B. (2010). Lowland farmland bird conservation in the context of wider ecosystem service delivery. *Journal of Applied Ecology*, **47**, 986-993.

Brown, A. and Grice, P. (2005). *Birds in England.* T. & A.D. Poyser, London.

Burfield, I.J. (2002). *The breeding ecology and conservation of the ring ouzel (Turdus torquatus) in Britain.* PhD. University of Cambridge.

Carson, R. (1963). *Silent Spring.* Hamish Hamilton, London.

Chamberlain, D.E., Fuller, R.J., Bunce, R.G.H., Duckworth, J.C. and Shrubb, M. (2000). Changes in the abundance of farmland birds in relation to the timing of agricultural intensification in England and Wales. *Journal of Applied Ecology*, **37**, 771-778.

Donald, P.F. (2004). *The Skylark.* T. and A.D. Poyser, London.

Donald, P.F. and Evans, A.D. (2006). Habitat connectivity and matrix restoration: the wider implications of agri-environment schemes. *Journal of Applied Ecology*, **43**, 209-218.

Donald, P.F., Sanderson, F.J., Burfield, I.J. and van Bommel, F.P.J. (2006). Further evidence of continent-wide impacts of agricultural intensification on European farmland birds. *Agriculture, Ecosystems & Environment*, **116**, 189-196.

Evans, A.D. and Green, R.E. (2007). An example of a two-tiered agri-environment scheme designed to to deliver effectively the ecological requirements of both localised and widespread bird species in England. *Journal of Ornithology*, **148**, S279-S286.

Ewald, J.A. and Aebsicher, N.J. (1999). *Pesticide Use, Avian Food Resources and Bird Densities in Sussex.* JNCC Report 296. Joint Nature Conservation Committee, Peterborough.

Firbank, L.G. (2005). Striking a new balance between agricultural production and biodiversity. *Annals of Applied Biology*, **146**, 163-175.

Firbank, L.G. (2009). It's not enough to develop agriculture that minimizes environmental impact. *International Journal of Agriculture & Sustainability*, **7**, 1-2.

Fuller, R.J., Humphreys, E.M., Wilson, J.D., Hoccom. D. and Calladine, J.C. (2010). Changes in breeding wader populations of the machair of the Western Isles, Scotland, between 2000 and 2007. *Bird Study*, **57**, 121-124.

Fuller, R.M. (1987). The changing extent and nature conservation interest of lowland grasslands in England and Wales: a review of grassland surveys 1930-1984. *Biological Conservation*, **40**, 281-300.

Gibbons, D.W., Reid, J.B. and Chapman, R.A. (1993). *The New Atlas of Breeding Birds in Britain and Ireland: 1988-1991*. T. & A.D. Poyser, London.

Gibbons, D.W., Bohan, D.A., Rothery, P. *et al.* (2006). Weed seed resources for birds in fields with contrasting conventional and genetically modified herbicide-tolerant crops. *Proceedings of the Royal Society of London B*, **273**, 1921-1928.

Gill, J.A., Watkinson, A.R. and Sutherland, W.J. (1997). Cause of the redistribution of pink-footed geese (*Anser brachyrhynhcus*) in Britain. *Ibis*, **139**, 497-503.

Goulson, D., Lye, G.C. and Darvill, B. (2008). Decline and conservation of bumble bees. *Annual Review of Entomology*, **53**, 191-208.

Green, R.E. (1996). Factors affecting the population density of the corncrake (*Crex crex*) in Britain and Ireland. *Journal of Applied Ecology*, **33**, 237-248.

Hancock, M.H. and Wilson, J.D. (2003). Winter habitat associations of seed-eating passerines on Scottish farmland. *Bird Study*, **50**, 116-130.

Harris, S., Morris, P., Wray, S. and Yalden, D. (1995). *A Review of British Mammals: Population Estimates and Conservation Status of British Mammals other than Cetaceans*. Joint Nature Conservation Committee, Peterborough.

Henderson, I.G. and Evans, A.D. (2000). Responses of farmland birds to set-aside and its management. In *Ecology and Conservation of Lowland Farmland Birds*, ed. by N.J. Aebsicher, A.D. Evans, P.V. Grice & J.A. Vickery. British Ornithologists' Union, Tring. pp 69-76.

Hodgson, J.A., Thomas, C.D., Wintle, B.A. and Moilanen, A. (2009). Climate change, connectivity and conservation decision-making: back-to-basics. *Journal of Applied Ecology*, **46**, 964-969.

Hole, D.G., Perkins, A.J., Wilson, J.D. *et al.* (2005). Does organic farming benefit biodiversity? *Biological Conservation*, **122**, 113-130.

Holland, J.M. (2004). The environmental consequences of adopting conservation tillage in Europe: reviewing the evidence. *Agriculture, Ecosystems & Environment*, **103**, 1-25.

Inglis, I.R., Isaacson, A.J., Smith, G.C., Haynes, P.J. and Thearle, R.J.P. (1997). The effect on the woodpigeon (*Columba palumbus*) of the introduction of oilseed rape into Britain. *Agriculture, Ecosystems and Environment*, **61**, 113-121.

Kleijn, D. and Sutherland, W.J. (2003). How effective are European agri-environment schemes in conserving and promoting biodiversity? *Journal of Applied Ecology*, **40**, 947-969.

Krebs, J.R., Wilson, J.D., Bradbury, R.B. and Siriwardena, G.M. (1999). The second Silent Spring? *Nature*, **400**, 611-612.

Lye, G., Park, K., Osborne, J., Holland J. and Goulson, D. (2009). Assessing the value of Rural Stewardship schemes for providing foraging resources and nesting habitat for bumblebee queens. *Biological Conservation*, **142**, 2023-2032.

Marchant, J.H., Hudson, R., Carter, S.P. and Whittington, P. (1990). *Population Trends in British Breeding Birds.* British Trust for Ornithology, Tring.

Marren, P. (2002). *Nature Conservation.* Collins, London.

Moorcroft, D., Wilson J.D. and Bradbury, R.B. (2006). The diet of nestling linnets (*Carduelis cannabina*) on lowland farmland before and after agricultural intensification. *Bird Study*, **53**, 156-162.

Müller, M., Spaar, R., Schifferli, L. and Jenni, L. (2005). Effects of changes in farming of subalpine meadows on a grassland bird, the whinchat (*Saxicola rubetra*). *Journal of Ornithology*, **146**, 14-23.

Newton, I. (1986). *The Sparrowhawk.* T. & A.D. Poyser, Calton.

Newton, I. (2004). The recent declines of farmland bird populations in Britain: an appraisal of causal factors and conservation actions. *Ibis*, **146**, 579-600.

O'Brien, M., Green, R.E. and Wilson, J. (2006). Partial recovery of the population of corncrake (*Crex crex*) in Britain 1993-2004. *Bird Study*, **53**, 213-224.

Peach, W.J., Lovett, L.J., Wotton, S.R. and Jeffs, C. (2001). Countryside Stewardship delivers cirl buntings in Devon, UK. *Biological Conservation*, **101**, 361-373.

Pearce-Higgins, J.W. and Yalden, D.W. (2003). Variation in the use of pasture by breeding European golden plovers (*Pluvialis apricaria*) in relation to prey availability. *Ibis*, **145**, 365-381.

Perkins, A.J., Maggs, H.E., Wilson, J.D., Watson, A. and Smout, C. (2008). Targeted management intervention reduces rate of population decline of corn buntings (*Emberiza calandra*) in eastern Scotland. *Bird Study*, **55**, 52-58.

Potts, G.R. (1986). *The Partridge: Pesticides, Predation and Conservation.* Collins, London.

Preston, C.D., Pearman, D.A. , Dines, T.D. (2002). *The New Atlas of the British and Irish Flora.* Oxford University Press, Oxford.

Risely, K., Noble, D.G. and Baillie, S.R. (2009). *The Breeding Bird Survey 2008.* BTO Research Report 537. British Trust for Ornithology, Thetford.

Robertson, G.P. and Swinton, S.M. (2005). Reconciling agricultural productivity and environmental integrity: a grand challenge for agriculture. *Frontiers in Ecology & Environment*, **3**, 38-46.

Robinson, R.A. and Sutherland, W.J. (2002). Post-war changes in arable farming and biodiversity in Great Britain. *Journal of Applied Ecology*, **39**, 157-176.

Robson, G. and Percival, S.M. (2002). The use of marginal farmland by curlew *Numenius arquata* breeding on upland moors. *Aspects of Applied Biology*, **67**, 75-84.

Royal Society (2009). *Reaping the Benefits: Science and the Sustainable Intensification of Global Agriculture.* The Royal Society, London.

Sharrock, J.T.R. (1976). *The Atlas of Breeding Birds in Britain and Ireland.* British Trust for Ornithology, Tring.

Sheldon, R.D., Chaney, K. and Tyler, G.A. (2007). Factors affecting nest survival of northern lapwings (*Vanellus vanellus*) in arable farmland: an agri-environment scheme prescription can enhance nest survival. *Bird Study*, **54**, 168-175.

Shrubb, M. (2003). *Birds, Scythes and Combines: A History of Birds and Agricultural Change.* Cambridge University Press, Cambridge.

Sotherton, N.W. (1998). Land use changes and the decline of farmland wildlife: an appraisal of the set-aside approach. *Biological Conservation*, **83**, 259-268.

Spooner, B. and Roberts, P. (2005). *Fungi.* Collins, London.

Swales, V. and Moxey, A. (2008). *Targeting CAP support at High Nature Value Farming and Crofting Systems.* Report to RSPB.

Tscharntke, T., Klein, A.M., Kruess, A., Steffan-Dewenter, I. and Thies, C. (2005). Landscape perspectives on agricultural intensification and biodiversity: ecosystem service management. *Ecology Letters*, **8**, 857-874.

Watson, A., Perkins, A.J., Maggs, H.E. and Wilson, J.D. (2009). Decline of corn bunting (*Emberiza calandra*) on east Scottish study areas in 1989-2007. *Bird Study*, **56**, 213-220.

Wilkinson, N.I. and Wilson, J.D. (2010). Breeding ecology of Twite (*Carduelis flavirostris*) in a crofting landscape. *Bird Study*, **57**, 142-155.

Wilson, J.D. and Fuller, R.J. (1992). Set-aside: potential and management for wildlife conservation. *Ecos*, **13**, 24-29.

Wilson, J.D., Evans, J., Browne, S.J. and King, J.R. (1997). Territory distribution and breeding success of skylarks (*Alauda arvensis*) on organic and intensive farmland in southern England. *Journal of Applied Ecology*, **34**, 1462-1478.

Wilson, J.D., Morris, A.J., Arroyo, B.E., Clark, S.C. and Bradbury, R.B. (1999). A review of the abundance and diversity of invertebrate and plant foods of granivorous birds in northern Europe in relation to agricultural change. *Agriculture, Ecosystems and Environment*, **75**, 13-30.

Wilson, J., Anderson, G., Perkins, A., Wilkinson, N. and Maggs, H. (2007a). Adapting agri-environment management to multiple drivers of decline of corn buntings (*Emberiza calandra*) across their UK range. *Aspects of Applied Biology*, **81**, 191-198.

Wilson, J.D., Boyle, J., Jackson, D.B., Lowe, B. and Wilkinson, N.I. (2007b). Effects of cereal harvesting on a recent population decline of corn buntings (*Emberiza calandra)* on the Western Isles of Scotland. *Bird Study*, **54**, 362-370.

Wilson, J.D., Evans, A.D. and Grice, P.V. (2009). *Bird Conservation and Agriculture*. Cambridge University Press, Cambridge.

Wilson, J.D., Evans, A.D. and Grice, P.V. (2010). Bird conservation and agriculture: a pivotal moment? *Ibis*, **152**, 176-179.

Woiwod, I.P. and Harrington, R. (1994). Flying in the face of change: the Rothamsted Insect Survey. In *Long-Term Experiments in Agricultural and Ecological Sciences*, ed. by R.A. Leigh and A.E. Johnston. CABI Publishing, Wallingford. pp 321-342.

27 Halting Farmland Biodiversity Declines: A Way Forward

Davy McCracken and Andrew Midgley

Summary

1. Halting biodiversity loss on farmland by 2010 in Scotland, as in the rest of the EU, will not be achieved. Although the condition of many habitats has improved, particularly within designated areas, and there have been population increases of some species of high nature conservation concern, these have been offset by a continuing decline in the quality of habitats and status of species in much of Scotland's wider countryside.
2. Landscape simplification and the associated habitat degradation is the key driver of farmland biodiversity decline. It is clear that this cannot be addressed effectively at the scale required solely by using agri-environment schemes within the current Scottish Rural Development Programme (SRDP). Encouraging all farmers to achieve a minimum level of appropriate habitat diversity and/or management at the farm scale in order to qualify for their single farm payment could help address landscape simplification.
3. Without further changes to the way that agricultural support is targeted then Scotland's farmland biodiversity is likely to continue to decline. Any future policy change in the structure of agricultural funding to increase farmland biodiversity and other environmental goals will however, require a robust evidence base to inform that change.

27.1 Overview

The aim of this chapter is to highlight the need to address farmland biodiversity declines in Scotland by considering:

McCracken, D. and Midgley, A. (2011). Halting Farmland Biodiversity Declines: A Way Forward – *The Changing Nature of Scotland*, eds. S.J. Marrs, S. Foster, C. Hendrie, E.C. Mackey, D.B.A. Thompson. TSO Scotland, Edinburgh, pp 299-314.

- the wider context of issues affecting farmland biodiversity across Europe and the main approaches taken to date to address declines;
- how farmland biodiversity in Scotland has fared to date and what the major policy-orientated challenges are for the future; and
- how farmland biodiversity concerns could be better targeted and existing budgets for biodiversity measures on farms made to go further.

27.2 The wider European context

Europe's countryside and cultural landscapes have been shaped by farming over centuries. Farmland, including arable land and permanent grassland, is one of the dominant land covers in Europe, covering over 45% (173 million hectares) of the European Union 27 member states (EU-27). It has been estimated that 50% of all species in Europe depend on agricultural habitats (Kristensen, 2003). Consequently, some of the most critical conservation issues today relate to changes to traditional farming practices on habitats such as hay meadows, lowland wet grasslands, heathlands, chalk and dry grasslands, blanket bogs, moorlands and arable land. The majority of these habitats have been created and need to be maintained by farming. In most cases taking the land out of agricultural production is not the appropriate choice for biodiversity conservation, and instead it is vital to ensure that the intensity of agricultural management is appropriate (Bignal and McCracken, 1996).

European agriculture is still very diverse, ranging from large specialised commercial holdings to part-time farming using mainly traditional practices. Agricultural modernisation and intensification over the last 60 years has had significant impacts on the biodiversity value of Europe's farmland. The mechanisation of agriculture has resulted in the elimination of many landscape elements such as hedgerows, the drainage of wetlands and the ploughing up of semi-natural grasslands. Species richness and habitat diversity has also declined due to related factors such as increased pesticide and fertiliser use, the simplification of crop rotations, increases in livestock grazing densities and changes to the timing of grazing, cutting and cropping practices. This development of intensively-managed agricultural land has affected all agricultural sectors and has occurred across most of the lowland areas of Europe, but has been especially dominant in the north and west (Henle *et al.*, 2008).

There are, however, still areas of Europe where soil, climatic, economic and policy constraints have meant that it was not possible to intensify the farming practices to the same extent. Such areas not only generally contain more of a patchwork of semi-natural and natural habitats but also the farmland is more varied and subject to a greater range of management intensities. This leads to the farmland and associated habitats containing a higher biodiversity value than in the areas where intensification has occurred. What is termed High Nature Value (HNV) farmland still occurs in association with traditional cropping systems in southern Europe and in association with the use of machair for cropping by crofters in Scotland. However, in general the majority of Europe's remaining HNV farmland is now largely associated with livestock grazing systems on semi-natural habitats in the mountains and other remote areas of Europe (McCracken *et al.*, 2005).

27.3 Addressing agricultural biodiversity concerns

27.3.1 Nature conservation policies

The main policy instruments for site protection at European Union (EU) level are the Birds and Habitats & Species Directives (79/409/EEC, 92/43/EEC) and the associated EU-wide network of representative protected sites (Natura 2000 Network). A large proportion of the Natura 2000 network is on farmland, which can generally be assumed to be of a high nature value. Out of the 198 habitat types listed in Annex 1 of the Habitats & Species Directive, 65 are threatened by agricultural intensification, whilst 26 grazed pasture habitats and six mown grassland habitats are threatened by the abandonment of pastoral management practices (Ostermann, 1998). For example, across the EU-27, targeted habitats that depend on extensive farming, cover about 15% of the terrestrial part of Natura 2000 sites. Measures taken for the conservation of habitats within these sites have the potential to make a considerable contribution to the goals of maintaining HNV farming if implemented effectively and at a sufficient scale (EEA, 2009). However, the HNV farming concept also emphasises that biodiversity conservation goals in Europe will not be met by only protecting particular habitats or species, or designating certain areas for their management. There is also a need to maintain low-intensity agricultural land uses that favour the dynamics of natural processes and create opportunities for biodiversity to flourish across large, contiguous areas of land. Such large-scale maintenance is recognised as necessary in order to provide a vital complement to conservation objectives within the Natura 2000 network (EEA, 2009).

27.3.2 Halting biodiversity loss by 2010

The Convention on Biological Diversity (CBD) was signed in Rio de Janeiro in 1992 (UN, 1992). In 2002, the CBD Conference of Parties adopted the goal of achieving a significant reduction of the current rate of biodiversity loss at the global, regional and national level by 2010. The European Union Member States, went further and in 2002 declared their own goal of halting the loss of biodiversity by 2010. Although there are no specific CBD objectives related to agricultural biodiversity, in

Europe agriculture and agricultural biodiversity are considered to be important components of the 2010 target (Zdanowicz *et al.*, 2005).

In 2006, the European Environment Agency (EEA) also highlighted that progress towards achieving the EU's commitment to halt biodiversity loss on farmland in Europe by 2010 was unlikely to be reached without additional integrated policy efforts (EEA, 2006). Across Europe at that time, HNV farming systems were under threat from intensification and abandonment of farm management practices, resulting in a subsequent loss in farmland biodiversity. Conversely, already intensified farms had generally not made the large-scale changes to their farming systems which were considered necessary to reverse the loss of habitat diversity at the landscape level and produce the conditions required to allow farmland biodiversity to recover.

Plate 27.1 Machair is a unique farmed habitat, and a good example of High Nature Value Farmland. It is one of the rarest habitats in Europe found only in the north of Britain and Ireland. © SNH Images

In recognition of this, in 2006 the European Commission's *Biodiversity Communication* highlighted that their strategy for halting biodiversity loss on farmland by 2010 and beyond would put a greater emphasis on:

- action for Europe's most important habitats and species through proposing, designating, protecting and managing effectively the Natura 2000 network of protected areas; and
- complementing Natura 2000 and the conservation of threatened species through also encouraging agri-environment actions favourable to biodiversity on land outwith protected areas (CEC, 2006).

Although the *Biodiversity Communication* placed an emphasis on taking action to address farmland biodiversity concerns (through, for example, optimising the use of agri-environment schemes and preventing intensification or abandonment of HNV farming systems), the main thrust was on encouraging Member States to use existing policy and support mechanisms to help achieve this.

27.3.3 Changes to agricultural support mechanisms

The Common Agriculture Policy (CAP) and associated national agricultural policies have been the main drivers behind the land use and farming practice changes which have impacted on Europe's farmland biodiversity. The CAP initially aimed to increase productivity and provide more food at a lower cost for EU countries, while also achieving a fair standard of living for farmers. This was achieved through stabilisation of markets (through a single market with common prices) and a more autonomous approach with less reliance on imports and preference given to member states as well as free movement of goods (Young *et al.*, 2005). However, by the 1980s, the CAP and its market and structural support policies were held responsible for increasing habitat degradation, overproduction of food products, intensification of farming practices, and the concentration of production from fewer, more specialised farms (Bignal *et al.*, 2001).

In the early 1980s the CAP experienced the first of a succession of changes in emphasis. Measures were introduced to control surplus production and also to provide compensation to farmers for loss of income as a result of their adopting environmentally sensitive forms of farming. The subsequent 1992 CAP reform further recognised the environmental role of farming by increasing the availability of agri-environmental schemes across the EU. In 1998, the Agenda 2000 (CEC, 1999) reform took these further and introduced a set of minimum environmental requirements which are applied to all farmland subject to CAP support payments (i.e. what is known as environmental cross-compliance), as well as the opportunity for farmers to obtain support (under the Rural Development Regulation) for additional activities other than farming *per se*.

The review of the CAP in 2003 removed the focus on production and increased the focus on environmental concerns. Consequently, since 2005 most financial support provided to farmers is no longer dependent on them growing specific areas of crops or retaining a certain number of animals. Instead, farmers receive a Single Farm Payment (which in the former EU-15 is largely based on their historic level of CAP support), provided they undertake to comply with a suite of EU Directives (including the Birds and Habitats & Species Directives) and keep their land in good agricultural and environmental condition. In addition, the majority of farmers have seen the level of their Single Farm Payment decrease to allow Member States to fund an increase in the amount of funding available via rural development measures (McCracken and Klockenbring, 2007).

The most recent reform of the CAP in 2005 represented a radical change in the system of farm support provided within the EU. This largely reflected two of the demands from environmental organisations, namely the removal of the need for farmers to have a particular area of crops or number of animals in order to qualify for CAP support and mandatory environmental cross-compliance for all sectors supported by direct payments. The retention of a focus on agri-environment schemes in the rural development measures was good in principle. However, the reforms have, to date, done little to address the question as to whether or not the programmes themselves have been effective in achieving their biodiversity objectives. The ecological complexity of farmland and the fact that no two farms are the same has been difficult to address. As has making clear the distinction between HNV farming and the more impoverished systems of management and production associated with intensively managed areas (Bignal and McCracken, 2000).

27.4 How has farmland biodiversity in Scotland fared to date?

Tracking trends in farmland biodiversity is difficult given that data for only a few groups (e.g. birds, butterflies) are collected on an annual basis, while data on the occurrence and condition of many habitats is collected over longer time intervals. In addition, in many cases it is difficult to separate out habitats or species which are wholly farmland-specific. Nevertheless, an impression can still be gained by considering what is known about the condition of sites designated specifically for their nature conservation importance, and how particular populations of Biodiversity Action Plan priority farmland species have changed over the years. Away from designated sites the potential ecological health can be gauged using the results of periodic Countryside Surveys and a consideration of population trends across broader farmland species groups. Detailed information on the current status of farmland biodiversity in Scotland can be obtained from a range of sources, such as Norton *et al.* (2009), McCracken and Midgley (2010), Mackey and Mudge (2010) and Wilson (Chapter 26).

27.4.1 Status of designated sites and protected species of high nature conservation concern

Focussed work on protected sites has improved the condition of several habitats associated with agricultural management. Data from SNH's Site Condition Monitoring programme suggests that 45% of notified grassland habitat features, 54% of lowland habitat features and 64% of wetland habitat features were in either favourable or unfavourable recovering condition in 2009. This represents an improvement compared to 2006, when only 38%, 33% and 57% of those three habitat features, respectively, were assessed to be in either favourable, or

Plate 27.2 Corncrake numbers in Scotland have increased in recent years. Farmers and conservationists have worked together to manage cropping regimes and areas to improve the valuable cover these secretive migrant birds need to breed in the summer. © SNH Images

unfavourable recovering condition (McCracken and Midgley, 2010). These increases are largely due to management measures which have been put in place to improve the condition of previously unfavourable sites (Mackey and Mudge, 2010). In addition, actions targeted on particular species of high nature conservation concern have resulted in population increases. For example, the corncrake (*Crex crex*) has benefited from a combination of targeted management on designated sites and corncrake-specific agri-environment measures applied in the wider countryside (O'Brien *et al.*, 2006), with the result that the populations in Scotland increased by 181% between 1994 to 2008 (SNH, 2010).

27.4.2 Status of habitats and species in the wider countryside

Such gains have, however, been offset by a continuing decline in the quality of much of Scotland's wider countryside (that is farmland falling outwith designated sites). The 2007 Countryside Survey (Norton *et al.*, 2009) highlighted that the length of managed hedges in Scotland decreased by 7% between 1998 and 2007 and only one third of managed hedges were in good structural condition in 2007 (though with signs of improving condition between 1998 and 2007). However, only 6% of managed hedges on arable land were in both good structural condition and had appropriately managed margins in Scotland in 2007. In addition, plant species richness in hedgerow margins decreased by 22% between 1998 and 2007, including declines in food plants of birds and butterflies (Norton *et al.*, 2009).

Trends in terrestrial breeding birds in Scotland are recorded primarily through the Breeding Bird Survey run by the British Trust for Ornithology (Risely *et al.*, 2009). Since 1994 to the most recent estimate of the farmland bird index in 2008, farmland birds in Scotland showed an overall increase of 26% (SNH, 2010). It must, however, be remembered that farmland bird populations across the UK are known to have declined significantly between the 1970s and 1980s and it is likely that Scottish farmland birds underwent similar declines during that period. In addition, the Breeding Bird Survey is based on a relatively small sample of plots and farmland bird species which have declined severely, such as grey partridge (*Perdix perdix*), tree sparrow (*Passer montanus*) and corn bunting (*Emberiza calandra*) are not captured by that survey. The farmland bird index trend in Scotland has to be seen in this context and the rise between 1994 and 2008 may simply reflect some bottoming out at relatively low population levels for some species. Although as Wilson (Chapter 26) highlights a combination of agri-environment measures and set-aside may have genuinely resulted in a rise in populations of some species, such as yellowhammer (*Emberiza citrinella*), during that period.

27.5 What are the major challenges for the future?

There are a number of key policy-oriented challenges which have contributed to the failure to fully address farmland biodiversity declines in Scotland to date. All of these are of relevance across the EU but in Scotland many of the policies required to address these challenges need to be developed and/or implemented.

27.5.1 Biodiversity remains a low political priority

All Member States have agri-environment schemes built into their Rural Development Programmes (RDP) and government departments/agencies charged with developing and overseeing these schemes. Generally, in most, if not all, Member States, addressing farmland biodiversity concerns is not a high government-wide policy priority and may be overshadowed by other concerns such as health, security or the state of the economy. This also means that the amount of funds directed towards agri-environment schemes is limited and insufficient to address the scale of the actions required. For example, although over 70% of the total £1.6 billion budget for the current 2007-2013 Scottish Rural Development Programme (SRDP) has been allocated to measures for improving the environment and the countryside, once the budgets required for Less Favoured Area Support Scheme and woodland management/creation are taken into account this leaves just over £40 million per year available for spending on agri-environment measures, many of which are focused on other environmental concerns, such as pollution mitigation measures, rather than specifically on actions for farmland biodiversity (McCracken and Midgley, 2010). Indeed, Scotland has allocated a much lower proportion of its overall anticipated RDP spend to agri-environment measures *per se* when compared to other Member States such as Austria, England, Denmark, Finland and Sweden (Farmer *et al.*, 2008).

27.5.2 Ensuring farmer engagement

The reduction of the historic level of market support measures and direct subsidy payments (Pillar 1 of the CAP) and the use of the funds to provide the budget for RDPs (Pillar 2 of the CAP), means that most farmers need to engage with the RDP funded under Pillar 2 if they do not want their overall payment levels to decrease. However, RDPs contain a wide range of activities, and farmers therefore do not necessarily have to look specifically to biodiversity options within agri-environment schemes in order to try and recoup the funds. For example, Table 27.1 shows the top ten SRDP Rural Priority options to which the most amount of funding had been committed after the first five rounds of applications across Scotland. Of the overall amount of funding committed to these, less than 50% concerned options specifically involving some form of actions with direct or, in the case of the woodland creation options, potentially indirect anticipated biodiversity benefits. Even when the overall total amount of funds committed across all 126 options available within the SRDP is taken into account, the commitment to options with a direct or potentially indirect biodiversity benefit still only amounts to just over 50% of the total commitment across the lifetime of the SRDP (McCracken and Midgley, 2010).

Table 27.1 The top ten Scottish Rural Development Programme (SRDP) Rural Priority options approved from the first five Rural Priority Advisory Committee rounds (Scottish Government, 2010).

Ranking based on funds committed	Option description	Cases with option	Total amount of funds committed
1	Restructuring agricultural businesses	384	£27,888,619
2	Hedgerows - three years for biodiversity benefits	639	£12,849,233
3	Open grazed or wet grassland for wildlife	740	£12,177,236
4	Diversification outwith agriculture	99	£10,772,188
5	Woodland creation - native woodland planting	216	£6,986,988
6	Development/Creation of micro-enterprises	35	£6,026,888
7	Manure/slurry storage and treatment - manure storage	128	£5,976,960
8	Mown grassland for wildlife	442	£5,620,018
9	Community services and facilities	25	£5,008,120
10	Woodland creation - mixed conifer/broadleaved woodland	78	£3,777,159
	Total amount of funds committed to these top 10 options:		**£97,083,409**
	Total amount of funds committed to options ranked 2, 3, 5, 8 and 10:		£41,410,634
	Overall total amount of funds committed to all 126 available options:		£157,375,157
	Overall total amount of funds committed to all options with a biodiversity focus:		£81,732,714

27.5.3 The scale of the funding challenge

A recent study for the UK Land Use Policy Group estimated the scale of future environmental land management activity necessary to meet current policy objectives and how much it might cost to deliver the management required at a UK and national level (Cao *et al.*, 2009). The analyses suggested that biodiversity, climate change and resource protection will account for the greatest land area needing management under future agri-environment scheme options. The study estimated that the total cost of meeting publicly defined environmental objectives in Scotland would be just under £450 million per year, with over £250 million per year estimated as being required to address biodiversity concerns effectively. This is more than five times the funding currently available from the agri-environment allocations within Scotland. The level of funding is hardly surprising bearing in mind that most of the environmental services required by wider society (including the management of carbon, water, biodiversity and landscapes) are currently unrewarded by conventional markets. It is interesting to note, however, that the total estimated cost of meeting environmental management objectives is still less than the total Scottish current spend on CAP Pillars 1 and 2 combined.

27.6 A way forward

Scottish farmers, their farming systems and individual farming practices are needed to maintain and improve conditions for habitats and species of farmland biodiversity concern (Hall, Chapter 25). However, as a recent report for the Scottish Government highlighted, the land-use drivers which currently impact most on land managers are CAP-based policy instruments, such as the Less Favoured Areas Support Scheme, the Single Farm Payment and Agri-Environment Measures. The latter two support mechanisms are expected to continue in some form after 2013 (when the next rural development programming period starts), and hence are expected to continue to be major drivers of agricultural land use decisions in Scotland until at least 2019 (Miller *et al.*, 2009).

27.6.1 Achieving effective targeting of biodiversity actions

The current SRDP provides the opportunity for farmers and land-managers to make collaborative applications and more applicants could be encouraged to make use of this avenue to address biodiversity concerns at an appropriate scale on the ground. Farmland biodiversity concerns cover a wide range of habitats and species. To date much of the effort of agri-environment schemes has been focused on actions aimed at particular habitats or species, largely driven by the Biodiversity

Action Plan process. In addition, most current agri-environment actions are targeted at the level of an individual field (or part of a field) or at best at the level of an individual farm. But there is little or no consideration of what is being done on neighbouring farms when considering what actions to develop on any one farm. Farmland biodiversity is influenced by what is happening in its immediate surroundings and what is happening at the farm and wider landscape scale (Donald and Evans, 2006). Hence trying to address farmland biodiversity concerns through influencing the management of only part of one farm is generally not going to be sufficient enough of a change to make a big enough difference on the ground (Kleijn and Sutherland, 2003).

27.6.2 Making the existing budget go further

Landscape simplification and the associated habitat degradation is the key driver of farmland biodiversity declines (Benton *et al.*, 2003; Hendrickx *et al.*, 2007). It is also clear from Section 27.5 above that these issues cannot be addressed in Scotland at the scale required solely by using the current agri-environment schemes available within the SRDP. The amount of funding available is too limited and unlikely to increase within the foreseeable future. Landscape simplification could be addressed and the available limited Pillar 2 funds used more effectively if all farmers were required to do more in order to qualify for Pillar 1 support. In this way, the onus could be put on all farmers to achieve a minimum level of appropriate habitat diversity and/or management at the farm scale in order to qualify for Pillar 1 support and become eligible for Pillar 2 funding for additional specific agri-environment actions.

McCracken and Klockenbring (2007) suggested that basic cross-compliance requirements could be strengthened, and made more consistent across Europe. For example, by putting emphasis on achieving greater protection for watercourses by stipulating a 5m minimum distance from ditches, streams and waterbodies where no ploughing, fertiliser or pesticides were allowed. Also giving greater protection to existing features and boundary habitats of biodiversity value (such as trees and hedgerows) by ensuring that they are maintained in good condition and/or establishing buffer zones around such features. In addition McCracken and Klockenbring (2007) suggested making it mandatory for farms to be required to have, or to establish, at least 7% of the farm's utilised agricultural area as Ecological Priority Areas, following a similar approach to that taken in Switzerland (Herzog *et al.*, 2005). The 5m buffer zones alongside watercourses could qualify towards this proportion, as could habitats of greater biodiversity potential (for example species rich grassland) and areas of pastures, meadows and annual and permanent crops under more

Plate 27.3 Stream and buffer strip near Milnathort, Perthshire. © Lorne Gill/SNH

extensive management on the farm. Such an approach would potentially increase (at no extra cost) the habitat heterogeneity, and hence general biodiversity value, of the more intensified farmland and could increase the probability of more targeted agri-environment actions achieving their biodiversity goals. It could also mean that not only farms with existing HNV would be able to benefit from the types of habitats already forming part of the on-farm resource but also that funds could become available to implement additional HNV farming-specific support measures. It would, however, be down to all those involved in policy formulation to consider whether such suggestions could be an acceptable way forward.

27.7 Conclusions

In Scotland, as elsewhere in Europe, concern about farmland biodiversity declines has raised questions not only about how biodiversity actions on farmland can be better targeted but also about how this can be best achieved and funded. There is therefore a need for a fundamental rethink as to how actions to benefit biodiversity on farmland are targeted and supported. However, in addition to any payments for environmental enhancement, there is also an associated need for efficient and effective regulation to ensure that Scotland's biodiversity is not degraded through agricultural production. Hence, any changes to cross-compliance conditions will only be effective drivers of positive land-use change if these are backed up by appropriate monitoring and enforcement of those conditions. Any future change in the structure of the funding for achieving farmland biodiversity goals will, however, require a robust evidence base to inform that policy change and ensure that the desired biodiversity outcomes can be achieved by the changes being implemented.

References

Benton, T.G., Vickery, J.A. and Wilson, J.D. (2003). Farmland biodiversity: is habitat heterogeneity the key? *Trends in Ecology and Evolution*, **18**, 182-188.

Bignal, E.M. and McCracken, D.I. (1996). Low-intensity farming systems in the conservation of the countryside. *Journal of Applied Ecology*, **33**, 413-424.

Bignal, E. and McCracken, D.I. (2000). The nature conservation value of European traditional farming systems. *Environmental Reviews*, **8**, 149-171.

Bignal, E., Jones, G. and McCracken, D. (2001). Comment: Future directions in agriculture policy and nature conservation. *British Wildlife*, **13**, 16-20.

Cao, Y., Elliott, J., McCracken, D.I. *et al.* (2009). *Estimating the scale of future environmental land management requirements for the UK.* A report for the UK Land Use Policy Group (LUPG). ADAS UK Ltd and Scottish Agricultural College.

CEC (1999). Europe's *Agenda 2000: strengthening and widening the European Union.* Commission of the European Communities, Brussels.

CEC (2006). *Communication from the Commission. Halting the loss of biodiversity by 2010 and beyond: Sustaining ecosystem services for human well–being.* Commission of the European Communities, Brussels.

EEA (2006). *Progress towards halting the loss of biodiversity by 2010.* European Environment Agency, Copenhagen.

EEA (2009). *Distribution and targeting of the CAP budget from a biodiversity perspective.* Technical Report 12/2009. European Environment Agency, Copenhagen.

Donald, P.F. and Evans, A.D. (2006). Habitat connectivity and matrix restoration: the wider implications of agri-environment schemes. *Journal of Applied Ecology*, **43**, 209-218.

Farmer, M., Cooper, T., Swales, V. and Silcock, P. (2008). *Funding for farmland biodiversity in the EU: gaining evidence for the EU budget review.* A report for the RSPB by Institute for European Environmental Policy and Cumulus Consultants.

Hendrickx F., Maelfait J.P., Van Wingerden W. *et al.* (2007). How landscape structure, land-use intensity and habitat diversity affect components of total arthropod diversity in agricultural landscapes. *Journal of Applied Ecology*, **44**, 340-351.

Henle, K., Alard, A., Clitherow, J. *et al.* (2008). Identifying and managing the conflicts between agriculture and biodiversity conservation in Europe:- a review. *Agriculture, Ecosystems & Environment*, **124**, 60-71.

Herzog, F., Dreier, S., Hofer, G. *et al.* (2005). Effect of ecological compensation areas on floristic and breeding bird diversity in Swiss agricultural landscapes. *Agriculture, Ecosystems & Environment*, **108**, 189-204.

Kleijn, D. and Sutherland, W.J. (2003). How effective are European agri-environment schemes in conserving and promoting biodiversity? *Journal of Applied Ecology*, **40,** 947–969.

Kristensen P. (2003). *EEA core set of indicators: revised version April 2003.* Technical report. European Environment Agency, Copenhagen.

Mackey, E.C. and Mudge, G. (2010). *Scotland's Wildlife: An assessment of biodiversity in 2010.* Scottish Natural Heritage, Inverness.

McCracken, D. and Klockenbring, C. (2007). Overview of the selection of biodiversity technical measures. *MEACAP: Impact of Environmental Agreements on the CAP* Project WP5 Final Report. 90 pp DG Research Specific Targeted Research Project SSPE-CT-2004-503604.

McCracken, D., Klockenbring, C., Zdanowicz, A. and Baldock, D. (2005). Agricultural biodiversity: issue to be aware of within MEACAP. *MEACAP: Impact of Environmental Agreements on the CAP* Project WP5 Background Document. 24 pp DG Research Specific Targeted Research Project SSPE-CT-2004-503604.

McCracken, D.I. and Midgley, A. (2010). How well is farmland biodiversity being maintained? In: Skerratt, S., Hall, C., Lamprinopoulou, C. *et al.*, *Rural Scotland in Focus*, 70-79. Scottish Agricultural College, Edinburgh.

Miller, D., Schwarz, G., Sutherland, L.A. *et al.* (2009). *Changing land use in rural Scotland: drivers and decision makers. Rural Land Use study Project 1.* Scottish Government Social Research, Edinburgh.

Norton, L.R., Murphy, J., Reynolds, B., Marks, S. and Mackey, E.C. (2009). *Countryside Survey: Scotland Results from 2007.* NERC/Centre for Ecology & Hydrology, The Scottish Government, Scottish Natural Heritage.

O'Brien, M., Green, R.E. and Wilson, J.D. (2006). Partial recovery of the population of corncrakes *Crex crex* in Britain, 1993-2004. *Bird Study*, **53**, 213-224.

Ostermann, O.P. (1998). The need for management of nature conservation sites designated under Natura 2000. *Journal of Applied Ecology*, **35**, 968-973.

Risely, K., Noble, D.G. and Baillie, S.R. (2009). The Breeding Bird Survey 2008. *BTO Research Report* 537. British Trust for Ornithology, Thetford.

Scottish Government (2010). Scottish Rural Development Programme – Rural Priorities Statistics. www.scotland.gov.uk/Topics/farmingrural/SRDP/RuralPriorities/RuralPrioritiesStats/DataOption, accessed on 11 January 2010.

SNH (2010). *Scotland's Biodiversity State Indicators: Abundance of Terrestrial Breeding Birds.* http://www.snh.gov.uk/docs/B536405.pdf, accessed on 11 January 2010.

UN (1992). *Convention on Biological Diversity.* United Nations, Rio de Janeiro. http://www.biodiv.org/doc/legal/cbd-en.pdf.

Young, J., Watt, A., Nowicki, P. *et al.* (2005). Towards sustainable land use: identifying and managing the conflicts between human activities and biodiversity conservation in Europe. *Biodiversity & Conservation*, **14**, 1641-1661.

Zdanowicz, A., Miller, C. and Baldock, D. (2005). The Convention on Biodiversity and its potential implications for the agricultural sector in Europe. *MEACAP: Impact of Environmental Agreements on the CAP* Project WP5 Background Document. DG Research Specific Targeted Research Project SSPE-CT-2004-503604.

28 The Bird Conservation Targeting Project

Emma L. Teuten

Summary

1. Distribution maps for a suite of scarce and declining breeding bird species are produced and updated annually.
2. These maps are used by the government conservation agencies to guide funding of agri-environment and woodland grant schemes.
3. The project encourages and highlights the importance of sharing of biological data.

28.1 Overview

Many birds are rapidly declining in both range and population (Eaton *et al.*, 2009), including species such as the tree sparrow (*Passer montanus*), lapwing (*Vanellus vanellus*) and curlew (*Numenius arquata*). In an ideal world we could help the chances of all species by improving their habitats. However, when resources are limited, the most practical solution is to target conservation to the areas that will best benefit nature. So how do we know which areas to target?

Rising to meet the challenge for scarce and declining birds is the Bird Conservation Targeting Project (BCTP), an ambitious partnership between bird conservation organisations and government agencies. In Scotland, the project produces breeding distribution maps for 30 scarce and declining birds that are likely to benefit from improvements to their breeding habitats. The maps can be used to guide the prescription of land management advice based on the species already breeding in an area, or for allocating funding towards sites known to be important for birds.

The project was initiated in England in 2004, with the aim of filling the knowledge gap left since the completion of the last breeding-bird Atlas in 1991 (Gibbons *et al.*, 1993). Subsequently, BCTP maps have been used to guide the spending of hundreds of millions of pounds in agri-environment and woodland grant schemes in

Teuten, E.L. (2011). The Bird Conservation Targeting Project – *The Changing Nature of Scotland*, eds. S.J. Marrs, S. Foster, C. Hendrie, E.C. Mackey, D.B.A. Thompson. TSO Scotland, Edinburgh, pp 315-320.

England, Wales and Northern Ireland (for example, see Phillips *et al.*, 2010). In April 2009, the first Scottish distribution maps were produced for a suite of scarce and declining target species, listed in Table 28.1.

Table 28.1 Species targeted by the Bird Conservation Targeting Project (BCTP) in Scotland.

Common name	Common name	Common name
barn owl	lapwing [b]	snipe [b]
black grouse	lesser redpoll	spotted flycatcher
capercaillie	long-eared owl	tree pipit
chough	marsh tit	tree sparrow [a]
corn bunting	nightjar	twite
corncrake	redshank [b]	whinchat
curlew [b]	redstart	willow tit
grasshopper warbler	reed bunting [a]	wood warbler
grey partridge	ring ouzel	yellow wagtail
hawfinch	Scottish crossbill	yellowhammer [a]

[a] Included in the seed-eating bird assemblage
[b] Included in the farmland wader assemblage

28.2 Map production

28.2.1 Data collation

To ensure the maps have the most extensive coverage possible, data are collected from a large range of sources. These include coordinated national surveys, for example Breeding Bird Survey (BBS), county bird clubs, local record centres, BirdTrack, and the National Biodiversity Network (NBN). In 2010, the first records from the 2007-11 Bird Atlas (coordinated by the British Trust for Ornithology (BTO), Birdwatch Ireland and the Scottish Ornithologists' Club), will be incorporated into BCTP maps. Since the Atlas covers all species present throughout the whole of the UK, inclusion of Atlas data will increase the robustness and geographical coverage of the BCTP target maps.

Examples of BCTP map outputs are shown for Scottish crossbill (*Loxia scotica*) in Figures 28.1 and 28.2. Each map covers a five-year window, and is updated annually. Maps and data are provided to the project partners annually, and are available to others on request.

Figure 28.1 National breeding distribution map for Scottish crossbill (2003-08). Data are mapped at 2km resolution, with 2km buffers.

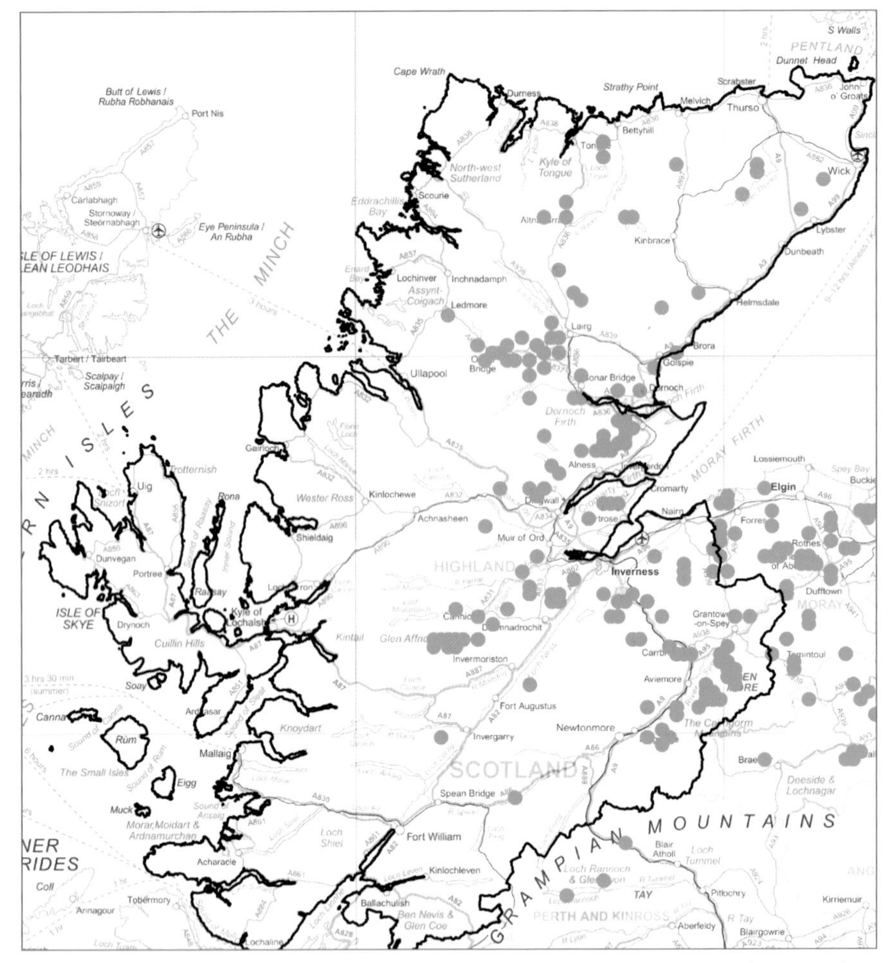

Figure 28.2 Regional (Highland) breeding distribution map for Scottish crossbill (2003-08). Data are mapped at 2km resolution, with 2km buffers.

28.2.2 Production of tailored outputs

Tailored outputs have been developed for incorporation into existing systems. For example, assemblage maps that show hotspots for species with similar habitat requirements are used by Natural England to guide funding of the Higher Level Stewardship agri-environment scheme (Phillips *et al.*, 2010). By targeting areas with multiple scarce and declining species that have similar habitat requirements, the benefits of conservation management are more cost-effective. In Scotland, we are developing outputs in partnership with Scottish Natural Heritage (SNH), to support the implementation of the Scotland Rural Development Programme (SRDP). Species assemblage maps specific to existing SRDP Rural Development contract packages are being prepared. These include assemblages of 'seed-eating birds' and 'farmland waders'. Figure 28.3 illustrates the distribution of seed-eating bird assemblage in north east Scotland. In this example, the assemblage comprises of a suite of birds that include common species (linnet (*Carduelis cannabina*), house sparrow (*Passer domesticus*) and skylark (*Alauda arvensis*)), as well as target species (reed bunting (*Emberiza schoeniclus*), tree sparrow and yellowhammer (*Emberiza citrinella*); Table 28.1).

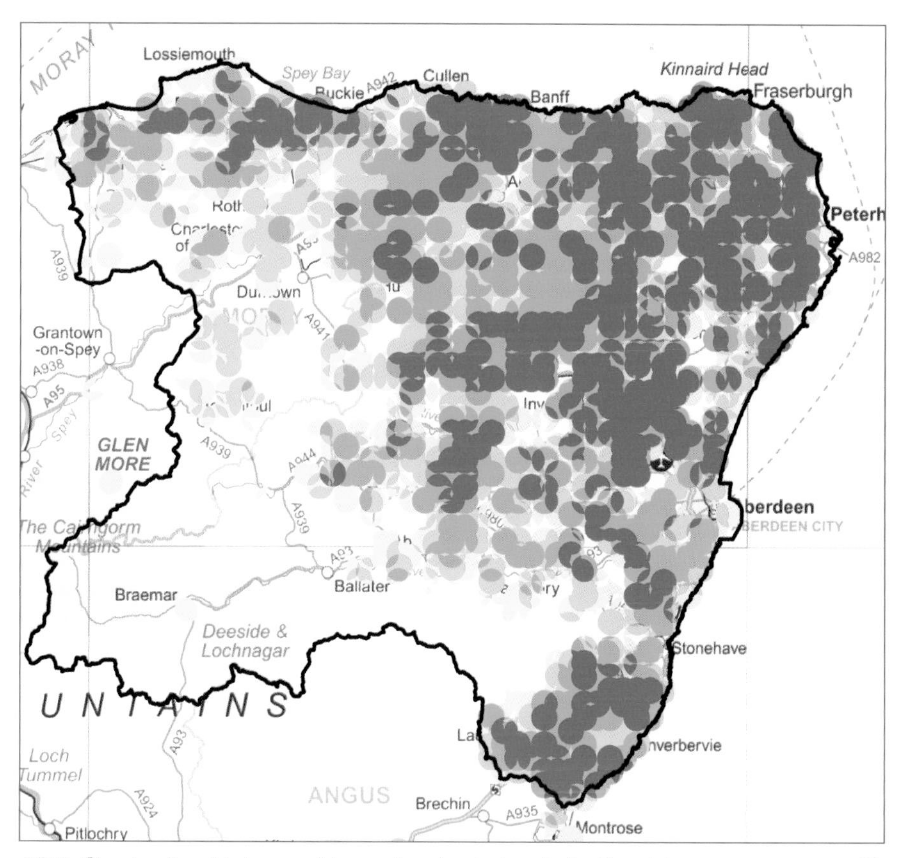

Figure 28.3 Seed-eating bird assemblage, showing hotspots for linnet, house sparrow, reed bunting, skylark, tree sparrow and yellowhammer. This assemblage suite is specific to an existing SRDP Rural Development Contract (RDC) package. The colour gradient is red where the greatest diversity of the species in the assemblage is present. While data for linnet, house sparrow and skylark were not collected by the BCTP in 2008, excellent coverage by the northeast Scotland Breeding Bird Atlas 2002-06 (SOC-Grampian, 2010) allowed the production of this map.

28.2.3 Encouraging local biological recording

The BCTP quickly converts data into tangible outputs. For example, within a year of the submission of a record to a local bird recorder, BirdTrack, or to a local record centre, it can be incorporated into BCTP maps. Relatively rapid record processing means that every year new target areas appear on BCTP maps. These quickly feed through to the government agencies, to be used to guide agri-environment resources. Thus, bird conservation benefit from surveys is maximised. Schemes that quickly put data to use also help empower individuals, and encourage involvement in biological recording.

28.3 Conclusion

The success of the BCTP relies heavily on our ability to access nationwide breeding bird records. Ideally, the maps will show the location of every known breeding site for our target species. The better our access to high-quality datasets, the more accurate the resulting maps will be at targeting conservation effort in the most effective places. This project demonstrates the importance of sharing data for conservation purposes. Recording observations in centralised databases such as the NBN and BirdTrack is encouraged.

Acknowledgements

The BCTP is supported by a partnership between BTO, Centre for Environmental Data and Recording, Countryside Council for Wales, Department of Agriculture and Rural Development, Forestry Commission England, Forestry Commission Wales, Forest Service, Natural England, Northern Ireland Environment Agency, Royal Society for the Protection of Birds (RSPB), and SNH.

The maps are based on Ordnance Survey material with the permission of Ordnance Survey on behalf of the Controller of Her Majesty's Stationery Office

References

Eaton, M.A., Brown, A.F., Noble D.G. *et al.* (2009). Birds of Conservation Concern 3: the population status of birds in the United Kingdom, Channel Islands and the Isle of Man. *British Birds*, **102**, 296-341.

Gibbons, D.W., Reid, J.B. and Chapman, R.A. (1993). *The New Atlas of Breeding Birds in Britain and Ireland: 1988–1991*. T. & A.D. Poyser, London.

Phillips, J., Winspear, R., Fisher, S. and Noble, D. (2010) Targeting Agri-Environment Scheme Delivery for Farmland Birds in England. *Lowland Farmland Birds III: delivering solutions in an uncertain world (British Ornithological Union Conference Proceedings), http://www.bou.org.uk/bouproc.net/ifb3/phillips-etal.pdf.*

Scottish Ornithologists' Club – Grampian branch, 25 January 2010, *north east Scotland Breeding Bird Atlas 2002-2006*; http://www.wildlifeweb.co.uk/atlas/. Accessed on 16 March 2010.

The Changing Nature of Scotland

Woodlands

Woodlands

Scotland is a deforested country, and for many environmentalists visiting here for the first time the absence of woodland is striking. With around 17% of the land covered by trees, Scotland falls far short of the relative woodland extent of many other European countries.

Some key events for woodland nature in Scotland since 1970

1970	Native Pinewood Discussion Group formed
1972	The Woodland Trust established
1977	The Nature Conservation Review is published
1977	Native Pinewood Grant introduced
1980	Loch a' Mhuilinn, Scotland's most northerly oak wood, becomes a National Nature Reserve (NNR)
1985	*Broadleaves in Britain* published by the Forestry Commission, signalling an expansion of broad-leaved, native and semi-natural woods
1985	Broadleaved Woodland Grant Scheme introduced
1988	Scottish Community Woodland Group formed, which later became Scottish Native Woods
1988	Farm Woodland Scheme established to encourage tree-planting on surplus farmland
1989	Reforesting Scotland formed
1990	RSPB purchased Abernethy Forest (declared an NNR in 1982, and classified as a Special Protection Area (SPA) in 1990)
1991	Forestry Commission reorganised into Forest Authority and Forest Enterprise, with the latter responsible for managing the State's forests
1992	Highland Birchwoods established, a partnership between SNH, Forestry Commission and The Highland Council
1993	The Woodland Trust purchase (711ha) Ledmore and Migdale Woods

e lungwort, a lichen growing on an oak tree at
nish National Nature Reserve. Western Scotland
ome to internationally important communities of
odland lichens. © Lorne Gill/SNH

1994	Millennium Forest for Scotland Trust created
1995	The Wildwood Group started and in 1996 purchased Carrifran with assistance from donors and SNH
1996	Borders Forest Trust formed
1996	Montane Scrub Action Group established
1998	EU Life funded Wet Woods Restoration Project began improving the condition of five wet woods in Scotland
2000	Scotland's first Forestry Strategy is published by the Forestry Commission
2002	The five year EU Life funded *Capercaillie Life Project* begins
2006	Trees for Life begin the process of purchasing the 4,000ha Dundreggan Estate in Glenmoriston, concluding in 2008
2006	Second Scottish Forestry Strategy launched
2009	The National Forest Estate Strategic Plan 2009-2013 published
2009	Scottish Government's Rationale for Woodland Expansion published
2011	Scottish Forestry Strategy progress indicators published

In the first of three chapters in this part of the book, Bob McIntosh, Chief Executive of the Forestry Commission, details the composition and cover of woodland in Scotland (Chapter 29). Government owned woodland comprises a third of the national resource, and more than 90% of it is coniferous. The much smaller amount of private woodland is also dominated by conifers, though 30% of private woods are broadleaf. The most prevalent trees across broadleaf Scotland are birch (*Betula spp.*) (almost 80,000 hectares comprise birch forest) with the second species – oak (*Quercus spp.*) – covering just over a quarter of that area. Whilst a further 60,000 hectares of woodland is mixed broadleaf, these areas are small compared with the stands of conifers. Sitka spruce (*Picea sitchensis*) forest exceeds half a million hectares, with Scots pine (*Pinus sylvestris*) covering just over a quarter of this area. By setting out the various government policies guiding woodland management in Scotland, McIntosh unravels a complex and ambitious framework. Economic, social and political forces have changed over recent decades, presenting significant challenges for managers working with a resource that can itself take many decades to mature, or at least become economically viable.

Chris Quine and David Edwards (Chapter 30) present a compelling case for the many ecosystem services provided by wood. They detail the provisioning, regulating and cultural services afforded by woodlands, and look ahead to how these might change. With the current target for woodland expansion in Scotland aiming for 25% cover by 2050 we need critical thinking on the costs and benefits of achieving this. The authors provide important pointers, and ask us to think of wood as a 'fifth' element of nature, rather than simply as a commodity.

In the final chapter, Philip Ashmole argues persuasively in favour of grass-roots restoration of woodland (Chapter 31). Born out of his first hand experience of research – and galvanising people and organisations into restoring our native woodland cover – this chapter is both insightful and provocative. The clear chronology of initiatives and projects reveals how just a few individuals and projects have transformed the prospects for ecological restoration in Scotland. At Beinn Eighe, Creag Meagaidh, Glen Affric and on Rum the seeds were sown for a groundswell movement to revitalise our woods. Concluding with a succinct summary of the re-creation of Carrifran Wildwood, Ashmole bluntly sets out some of the key steps we need to take in order to, in his words, 'take pride in the state of the land of Scotland as we pass it to the next generation'.

Taken together, these chapters reveal a genuine desire amongst foresters, conservationists and researchers to see sweeping improvements in the quality and integrity of Scotland's landscape, with woodlands restored to their natural place in the landscape. The economic and climatic changes ahead will doubtless shape the nature and pace of woodland expansion. However, if the chapters here leave one important message, it is that just a few people and organisations propelled by a desire to restore native woodland, can make a real and lasting difference.

29 The Extent, Nature and Distribution of Scotland's Woodlands

Bob McIntosh

Summary

1. This paper describes the current status of Scotland's woodlands in terms of their extent, nature and distribution. Woodlands cover 17% of Scotland's land area with approximately 450,00ha being Government owned.
2. Whilst forestry policies are the main drivers in determining how our woodlands are managed, other policies are important in determining the direction and provide a focus on the rationale behind woodland expansion policy. The key current Scottish Government policy drivers affecting forestry policy and strategy are the Scottish Government's Climate Change Delivery Plan; Renewables Action Plan; and 'Equally Well', the Ministerial taskforce on health inequalities.
3. The key forestry and natural heritage challenges for the future are to provide woodlands which can achieve multiple objectives for nature, the economy and Scotland's people.

29.1 Introduction

The landscape of Scotland has undergone many changes since the retreat of the last ice sheet some 10,000 years ago, but perhaps the most dramatic change has been the large reduction in the extent of our native forests. Our understanding of the nature and extent of these forests is incomplete, but it is very likely that some 6,000 years ago, woodland covered the majority of the land surface of Scotland (Tipping, 2003). The composition was mainly broadleaved trees in the south (and at lower elevations elsewhere) and mainly pine and birch forests in the higher elevations of central and north Scotland. The relatively rapid decline in woodland cover since that time, largely

McIntosh, B. (2011). The Extent, Nature and Distribution of Scotland's Woodlands – *The Changing Nature of Scotland*, eds. S.J. Marrs, S. Foster, C. Hendrie, E.C. Mackey, D.B.A. Thompson. TSO Scotland, Edinburgh, pp 327-340.

as a result of climate change and human interference, reduced Scotland's woodland cover to around 4% of the land area by the 1700s. Woodland cover remained at this level until the twentieth century when a large reforestation programme began. This programme was prompted by a concern, after the First World War, that the UK lacked the strategic timber reserve to serve the country's needs in the event of another war. This programme is continuing, though the policy drivers have been periodically reviewed and revised, leading to changing expectations around the purpose and nature of the new forests being created.

This paper describes the current status of woodlands in Scotland in terms of their extent, nature and location. It also reviews the current policy drivers, and considers the likely nature and extent of woodlands in the future.

29.2 Current extent and nature

29.2.1 The national inventory

The Forestry Commission carries out periodic inventories of woodlands within Great Britain with the next one planned to begin in 2010. The last inventory of Scotland's woodlands took place during the late 1990s (Forestry Commission, 2002). The inventory used as its basis the land cover map created during the Land Cover of Scotland project in 1988 (Macaulay Institute, 1993). Two separate surveys were carried out:

- The main woodland survey covering woodlands of 2ha or more; and
- A survey of woodlands and trees (less than 2ha), covering small woods, groups of trees, linear features (for example hedgerows, shelter belts) and individual trees.

The data presented here are largely based on the results of the last inventory.

29.2.2 Woodland area, type and ownership

Table 29.1 shows the current woodland area, type and ownership based on the latest Government statistics (Forestry Commission, 2009). There are currently some 1.33 million ha of woodland in Scotland, covering 17% of the land area. Of this, about 450,000ha (34%) is Government owned, and administered by Forestry Commission Scotland. The remaining 880,000ha (66%) is owned and managed by private landowners, local authorities, non-governmental organisations and others.

Scotland's woodland area is largely (79%) coniferous in nature with only 21% consisting of mainly broadleaved species. The Government estate is predominantly (94%) coniferous woodland. This reflects the relatively recent origins and the impact of the post war policy of planting fast-growing conifer species such as sitka spruce (*Picea sitchensis*) on upland site types. The non-government estate has 70% conifer and 30% broadleaf, reflecting its greater age, the traditions of some of the privately owned estates and the varying management objectives among the non-government owners.

Table 29.1 Woodland area, type and ownership

Ownership	Area		Conifer		Broadleaf	
	Thousand ha	%	Area	%	Area	%
Government	450	34	425	94	25	6
Other	880	66	620	70	260	30
TOTAL	1330	100	1045	79	285	21

29.2.3 Species composition

Table 29.2 shows the area of woodland by main species or species group. The total figures differ from those in Table 29.1 because of the exclusion of coppice, felled awaiting replanting and integral open space, all of which are included in Table 29.1.

Sitka spruce, a native of North America, accounts for 58% of the area of the conifer species. This reflects its suitability to Scottish climatic conditions, its ability to grow on soil types not suited to native species and its value to the timber processing sector.

The pines represent the next largest conifer species group, accounting for some 29% of the total area of conifer, with just over half consisting of the native Scots pine (*Pinus sylvestris*). The remainder largely consists of lodgepole pine (*Pinus contorta*) and Corsican pine (*Pinus nigra*). The former was generally planted on infertile organic soils, while the latter is generally restricted to littoral soils in coastal areas.

The broadleaved woodland is generally dominated by birch (*Betula spp.*) and mixed broadleaves. In general, broadleaved woodlands, other than birch, are located on relatively fertile sites at lower elevations throughout Scotland. The majority of the birch is in remnant semi-natural birchwoods scattered throughout the uplands in the north and west of the country.

Table 29.2 Woodland area by principal species

Category	Species/Groups	Area (thousand ha)	% of Category
Conifers	Scots pine	136	15
	Other pines	128	14
	Sitka spruce	528	58
	Larch	65	7
	Other conifers	51	6
	Mixed conifers	8	1
	TOTAL	916	
Broadleaves	Oak	21	10
	Beech	10	5
	Sycamore	11	5
	Ash	5	2
	Birch	78	38
	Elm	1	-
	Other broadleaves	19	9
	Mixed broadleaves	62	30
	TOTAL	207	

Source: Forestry Commission, 2002

29.2.4 Native species and native woodlands

The majority of the conifer area is comprised of introduced species, mainly originating in North America. The native Scots pine accounts for only 15% of the conifer area and 12% of the total woodland area. Native broadleaved species are more widely represented with oak (*Quercus spp.*), ash (*Fraxinus excelsior*) and birch accounting for some 50% of the broadleaved woodland and 9% of the total woodland area.

Determining the area of native woodlands in Scotland is hampered by definitional issues and by the lack of a comprehensive survey. This is being addressed by a new native woodland survey which is being carried out by Forestry Commission Scotland, due to be completed in 2013. Taking native woodlands to be woods which are largely made up of native trees and shrubs, then it is clear that the definition covers both semi-natural woods that have never been cleared and new woodlands planted with native species, regardless of whether the objective is to create a productive woodland or to re-create a native woodland structure and species composition. Table 29.3 shows a recent estimate of the extent of native woodlands types in Scotland and the area that can be described as being semi-natural. These figures suggest that around 30% of woodlands in Scotland can be described as being native woodlands, while 13% can also be described as being semi-natural.

Table 29.3 Estimated areas of native woodland types in Scotland.

Woodland type	Estimated area (K thousand ha)	
	Total	Semi-natural
Upland birchwoods	90	74
Upland oakwoods	50	35
Native pinewoods	181	31
Upland mixed ashwoods	21	14
Wet woodlands	21	14
Lowland mixed broadleaved	28	10
TOTAL	391	178

Source: Forestry Commission Scotland, 2006

29.2.5 Location

Table 29.4 shows the distribution of woodlands in relation to the Scottish Government's accessibility zonation (Scottish Government, 2007). The majority of woodlands are located in the 'remote rural' and 'very remote rural' zones. This is a reflection of past forestry policies which identified the uplands as the prime area for the reforestation programme so as to avoid land which had good agricultural prospects and in order to create economic activity in the remoter parts of the country. As a consequence, there tends to be an inverse relationship between population density and woodland area, with the highest woodland cover being in areas of lowest population density.

Table 29.4 The location of Scotland's forests by Scottish Government accessibility zonation

Zone	% of land area	% of population	% of total forest area within zone	% of zone which is forest
Urban	1.5	69	0.5	5
Accessible rural	23	21	20	15
Remote rural	23	6	36	27
Very remote rural	53	4	44	14

29.3 Current policy

29.3.1 Forestry policy

The Scottish Government's forestry policy priorities are set out in the Scottish Forestry Strategy (Forestry Commission Scotland, 2006). The policies are embedded within two key principles. Firstly, the creation and development of woodlands and related activities should take place within the context of an integrated approach to land use. Secondly, woodlands should be managed in accordance with the principles of sustainable forest management and should deliver an appropriate mix of economic, social and environmental outputs.

The government's interest in woodlands looks beyond the trees themselves to the related outcomes and considers the ultimate aim of forestry policy being the delivery of three key outcomes:

- Improved health and well-being of people and their communities;
- Competitive and innovative businesses contributing to the growth of the Scottish economy; and
- High quality, robust and adaptable environment.

In short, the Scottish Government would like to see more trees and woodlands, forming part of an integrated pattern of land use; more social, economic and environmental benefits arising from Scotland's woodlands and more people benefiting from these outputs.

29.3.2 Other related policies

While forestry policy is the main driver of direction, the multi-purpose nature of forestry brings it increasingly within the scope of other key government policies. Of particular current relevance to the forestry sector are:

- The Scottish Government's Climate Change Delivery Plan (Scottish Government, 2009a), which identified the forestry sector as a key player in helping to deliver net greenhouse gas emission reductions through carbon sequestration and through substitution of wood for fossil fuels and more carbon intensive building materials;
- The Scottish Government's Renewables Action Plan (Scottish Government, 2009b) which identified biomass as a component of an ambitious target for renewable energy production in Scotland, with particular reference to the role of biomass in heat production; and
- Equally Well, the report of the Ministerial taskforce on health inequalities (Scottish Government, 2008a) which identified the need for a cross-government approach to health care and the need to provide appropriate physical environments that promote healthy lifestyles.

29.3.3 Woodland expansion policies

The Scottish Forestry Strategy envisages woodland cover growing from its current level (17% of the land area) to 25% by the second half of this century. This requires the creation of a further 650,00ha of woodland at a rate of around 10,000ha per year. This aspiration is supported by the Climate Change Delivery Plan which requires the creation of 10,000ha to 15,000ha of woodland per year. The case for an expansion of Scotland's woodland area is set out in the Scottish Government's Rationale for Woodland Expansion (Scottish Government, 2008b) which lists the following key benefits expected to arise from an increased woodland area:

- **Helping to tackle greenhouse gas emissions.** Carbon sequestration, timber and fuel production;
- **Restoring lost habitats and adapting to climate change.** Forest habitat networks and new native woodlands;
- **Helping to manage ecosystem services.** Sustainable flood management, and protection of soil and water resources;
- **Underpinning a sustainable forest products industry.** Consistent and reliable timber supply for timber processing and wood fuel investments;
- **Supporting rural development.** Supporting local businesses and farm diversification;
- **Providing community benefits.** Provision of welcoming and well-managed woodlands in and around communities and where health and community need is greatest; and
- **Enhancing urban areas and improving landscapes.** Improving derelict, underused and neglected land, improving degraded or unsightly environments and diversifying farmed landscapes.

Plate 29.1 Mixed woodland by Loch Ard in the Trossachs. © Forestry Commission

It is anticipated that these benefits will be met through the development of four main types of woodland. Firstly, there is a desire to increase the area of native woodlands particularly where these would contribute to the development of key habitat networks and/or the development of riparian woodlands. Secondly, there is a requirement for more, well-designed productive woodlands (both conifer and broadleaf). These woodlands are expected to make a significant contribution to carbon sequestration as well as ensuring the development of a long term, sustained yield of raw material. Thirdly, the role of woodlands in contributing to urban regeneration is being increasingly recognised and this is providing the impetus for creation of new woodlands close to communities. These woodlands are expected to provide opportunities for recreation and community involvement as well as contributing to landscape and biodiversity enhancement. Finally, there remains an important role for small woodlands of mixed species which help to increase the diversity of farmed landscapes.

In addition to these woodland types, there is growing interest in the development of woodlands where the main objective is production of wood fibre for use as a fuel in renewable energy production. Short rotation coppice of willow (*Salix*) species is already being undertaken in Scotland on a limited scale and interest is increasing in growing conifers and broadleaved species on a 12 to 15 year cycle.

29.4 Key forestry and natural heritage challenges

29.4.1 Woodland expansion

Achievement of the Scottish Government's aspirations will involve approximately 650,000ha of land being converted from its current use to woodland over the next 60 or so years. This will result in a major land use change affecting some 8% of Scotland's land area and has the potential to generate conflict with other land use interests. The aim must be to achieve this expansion within the context of a consensus over the future of Scotland's rural areas. To achieve this, a framework will be required which enables land managers and public policy interests to work together to achieve the optimum use of Scotland's land resource. Key to this must be the concept of integration and the need to achieve a number of different outcomes from the same area of land wherever possible. The recent announcement by the Scottish Government of an intention to produce a land use strategy provides an opportunity to consider how best to align public policy and public regulatory and incentive schemes with land managers' objectives to encourage the development of a land use pattern which delivers a diverse, resilient, low carbon rural economy; a high quality, robust and adaptable environment; and confident, vibrant rural communities. The production of regionally based Indicative Forestry Strategies, such as The Scottish Borders Woodland Strategy (Scottish Borders Council, 2005) which gives spatial expression to the themes contained within the Scottish Forestry Strategy has helped in the quest for a consensus on woodland expansion priorities and may provide a suitable model on which to base the development of a land use strategy for Scotland.

29.4.2 Forest structure

Many of Scotland's woodlands are relatively young, having been established within the last 100 years as single age, single species plantations on upland, relatively infertile, site types. As these plantations mature, and felling and restocking programmes begin to take place, the opportunity exists to redesign these woodlands and to introduce more species and structural diversity. This process is well underway in both public and private forests. The development of forest design plans is a key process in the management of forests and in the planning of future species composition and structure. The production of such plans is normal practice within Forestry Commission Scotland forests and grant aid is available to other woodland owners to encourage a similar approach and to offset the cost of production of these plans.

In taking forward the process of forest design there is a need to clarify the vision for the future structural and species diversity of our woodlands. The experience of managing conifer plantations in upland Scotland is relatively recently obtained and questions remain about the appropriateness of different silvicultural systems and the number and juxtaposition of different species that are required to create forests which are robust, diverse and adaptable enough to meet the needs of future generations (Humphrey *et al.*, 2006). While some pointers can be gleaned from examination of forest structures across Europe, the extent to which these models are applicable to Scottish conditions is questionable and the development of bespoke silvicultural systems which are appropriate for Scottish conditions remains a priority. For instance, the relatively high wind speeds encountered in the Scottish uplands result in an increased risk of windblow and therefore a need to carefully consider the impact of thinning and of rotation length on stand stability. In areas of particularly high windthrow risk the choice of silvicultural system may be very limited.

29.4.3 Woodland deer populations

Whilst major developments have been made in the management of woodland deer populations, it remains the case that the impacts of deer on woodlands are significant in many situations. Browsing by deer is perhaps the biggest single factor limiting the development of greater species diversity within Scotland's woodlands. Natural regeneration of tree species may be severely impacted and managers may choose to plant a more limited range of species because of the high cost of protection of species more vulnerable to deer browsing. In general, most woodland deer populations are probably under-culled, if population reduction is the aim, and there is some way to go before it can be said that woodland deer densities are being maintained at levels appropriate to the achievement of woodland management objectives. The spread of the sika deer (*Cervus nippon*) is of particular concern. Introduced into Scotland in the latter part of the nineteenth century, this species is spreading steadily and is now present in woodlands throughout most of the north and west of Scotland and in some parts of central and southern Scotland. As well as causing additional management cost there is the complexity of hybridisation between sika and the native red deer (*Cervus elaphus*) which threatens the genetic integrity of the latter.

29.4.4 Priority species and habitats

Scotland's woodlands and the species associated with them, have suffered over the years from fragmentation of habitat and negative influences such as over-grazing. The process of reversing these trends has begun through action to create new native woodlands and to enhance the status of key woodland species within both native woodlands and productive, non-native woodlands. Through the

Biodiversity Action Plan process, targets have been set for increasing the area of the native woodland types (Sing and Patterson, 2008). This involves the creation of new native woodlands, action to improve the condition of existing native woodlands and restoration of native woodlands on sites where the former native woodlands were replaced with introduced species. These are referred to as Plantations on Ancient Woodland Sites (PAWS) and the Scottish Forestry Strategy envisages that, by the second half of this century, restoration will be well under way on the most worthwhile 70% of sites with remnant native woodland communities maintained or enhanced on the remainder.

Particular challenges remain, including dealing with invasive non-native species such as *Rhododendron ponticum*. Removal of this species is technically possible but very expensive and work is underway in Argyll, the main problem area, to quantify the size of the problem and the likely cost of treatment. The conservation and enhancement of woodland grouse – black grouse (*Tetrao tetrix*) and capercaillie (*Tetrao urogallus*), populations also remains challenging. The influence of climate change on the status of these populations is relatively poorly understood but may over-ride the benefits of the targeted habitat improvement and predator control work which is being carried out in many areas of woodland. There is much to learn too, about the best ways to design forest structure and species composition, and adapt forest management techniques, to favour conservation and enhancement of other woodland species such as the red squirrel (*Sciurus vulgaris*) and the pearl-bordered fritillary butterfly (*Bolaria euphrosyne*). Conservation of the red squirrel requires action to improve their habitat while limiting the scope for expansion of the grey squirrel (*Sciurus carolinensis*) through habitat manipulation and targeted control measures.

29.4.5 Climate change

The predicted changes in Scotland's climate as a result of global warming may affect the suitability and growth of some tree species in current use. Indications are that in parts of east Scotland it is highly likely that increased drought stress will render some of the traditional species like sitka spruce unsuitable. Climate change guidelines are currently being developed by the Forestry Commission and will be published during 2010. These guidelines will encourage forest managers to carefully consider species choice when establishing or regenerating woodlands and to move towards a greater degree of species diversity.

The impact of climate change on pests and diseases is difficult to predict, but indications are that an increase in temperature will assist the spread and development of many pest species. For instance, in Scotland we have already seen the impacts of pests and diseases such as sudden oak death (*Phytophthora ramorum*) and red band needle blight (*Dothistroma septosporum*), two relatively new problems, the increasing occurrence of which may be linked to climate change. Factors such as increased drought stress will increase the susceptibility of some tree species to attack. There is a need to develop policies and practices to prevent, mitigate or adapt to the impact of these pests as we learn more about their response to climate change.

29.4.6 Monitoring and research

A comprehensive programme of research is undertaken by the Forestry Commission. Much of the fundamental work on techniques for establishing and managing woodlands has been done and the attention is now focussed on increasing productivity, adding value to forest products, understanding the consequences of climate change and developing the knowledge that is needed to ensure that environmental improvement and community related activities are effectively targeted. Research is required to help understand the biodiversity implications of different management systems and practices so that the future development of Scotland's forest ecosystems is guided by a strong evidence base. With little long term experience to draw on in this country, decisions are sometimes made on the basis of intuition, incomplete evidence and questionable comparisons with other countries.

Understanding the implications of climate change is a key research priority. It is important to quantify the carbon footprint of different forest types and management regimes on different sites to inform the development of relevant policy and ensure that woodlands and forestry contribute effectively to climate change mitigation and adaptation. Of particular importance in this area is the need for better understanding of the life cycles and impacts of pest species and diseases.

29.5 Conclusions

Over the past hundred years the area of woodland in Scotland has increased significantly and a further increase is planned. This represents one of the most significant land use changes that this country has experienced. At the same time, society's expectations about the nature and purpose of woodlands have evolved. Current forestry policy is firmly rooted in the concepts of multiple use and sustainability, with a resultant requirement to transform or restructure the single species, even aged plantations created in previous decades.

Woodlands are not an end in themselves but are a means to an end. To secure public support for further afforestation and for the use of public funds to support forest management, woodland owners and managers must ensure that woodlands deliver outcomes which are socially and politically relevant. This includes the production of raw material for industry and appropriate levels of environmental enhancement and community benefit. There is a need too, for woodlands and woodland based activities to be seen as part of an integrated approach to land use which seeks to optimise the use of our scarce land resource. This will require careful consideration of where new woodlands should be located and may sometimes lead to a need to remove forest from land which, with the benefit of hindsight, would be better used for other purposes. The creation of mature and diverse woodlands takes time but the end product can be worth the wait. Careful planning of the nature and location of new woodlands, and of the structure of existing woodlands, will provide Scotland with a resource which will sustain a thriving industry, increase Scotland's biodiversity and contribute to an increase in the health and well-being for all the people of Scotland.

References

Forestry Commission (2002). *National Inventory of Woodland and Trees – Scotland.* Forestry Commission, Edinburgh.

Forestry Commission (2006). *The Scottish Forestry Strategy.* Forestry Commission, Edinburgh.

Forestry Commission (2009). *Forestry Statistics, 2009 – A compendium of statistics about woodland forest and primary wood processing in the United Kingdom.* Forestry Commission, Edinburgh.

Humphrey, J., Quine, C. and Watts, K. (2006). The influence of forest and woodland management on biodiversity in Scotland: recent findings and future prospects. In *Farming, Forestry and the Natural Heritage: Towards a More Integrated Future*, ed. by R. Davison and C.A. Galbraith. The Stationery Office, Edinburgh. pp 59-75.

Macaulay Land Use Research Institute (1993). *The Land Cover of Scotland, 1988.* Final report.

Scottish Borders Council (2005). *The Scottish Borders Woodland Strategy.* Scottish Borders Council, St Boswells.

Scottish Government (2007). *Rural Scotland Key Facts 2007: People and Communities, Services and Lifestyle, Economy and Enterprise.* Scottish Government, Edinburgh.

Scottish Government (2008a). *Equally Well Implementation Plan.* Scottish Government, Edinburgh.

Scottish Government (2008b). *The Scottish Government's Rationale for Woodland Expansion.* Forestry Commission, Edinburgh.

Scottish Government (2009a). *Climate Change Delivery Plan.* Scottish Government, Edinburgh.

Scottish Government (2009b). *Renewables Action Plan.* Scottish Government, Edinburgh.

Sing, L. and Patterson, G. (2008). *Native Woodland Targets and Forest habitat networks in Scotland.* Forestry Commission, Edinburgh.

Tipping, R. (2003). Living in the Past: Woods and People in Pre-History to 1000 BC. In *People and Woods in Scotland*, ed. by T. C. Smout. University Press, Edinburgh. pp 14-39.

30 Why do Woodlands Matter to Scotland? The Source of the Fifth Element and More

Christopher P. Quine and David Edwards

Summary

1. Trees, woodlands and wood inspire strong emotions in many people and some writers have suggested that wood as a material should be regarded as a fifth element.
2. The production of wood/timber is often perceived as the main contribution of woodlands, and has been the focus of considerable past management. In more recent years the practice of forestry has evolved to incorporate improved scientific knowledge and the need for woodlands to meet multiple objectives. Sustainable forest management aspires to balance objectives and the needs of today with those of the future. There is growing interest in the potential for woodlands and forests to help society in Scotland mitigate and adapt to climate change.
3. There is increasing interest in the concept of 'ecosystem services' as a means of identifying and valuing the contribution of natural environments to human well-being and quality of life. Biodiversity and nutrient cycles underpin the provision of ecosystem services that contribute to human well-being. Provisioning services provide materials of value, regulating services create equable environments, and cultural services represent a broader range of societal benefits.
4. The multiple benefits provided by Scotland's woodlands are described within the framework of ecosystem services. Although the valuation and monitoring of ecosystem services requires development, it is clear that woodlands provide a range of services. Scotland's woodlands are an important source of the fifth element (wood) but also contribute to life and livelihoods in many other ways.

Quine, C.P. and Edwards, D. (2011). Why do Woodlands Matter to Scotland? The Source of the Fifth Element and More – *The Changing Nature of Scotland*, eds. S.J. Marrs, S. Foster, C. Hendrie, E.C. Mackey, D.B.A. Thompson. TSO Scotland, Edinburgh, pp 341-354.

'[Trees] ...Nothing can compete with these larger-than-life organisms for signalling the changes in the natural world.' (Roger Deakin)

30.1 Introduction

In this chapter, we use the framework of ecosystem services to explore why woodlands matter and how they contribute to the lives and livelihoods of people in Scotland. Woodlands, trees, and wood as a material inspire strong emotions. Roger Deakin, in his book *Wildwood: a journey through trees* highlighted how some writers consider wood to be so fundamental to life that it should be regarded as a fifth element (Deakin, 2007). In fact, the philosophical tradition from which such a concept originated does not recognise earth, wind, fire and water as the preceding four elements but rather wood as one of a set of energy flows. Nevertheless, the elemental nature of woodlands and what they provide to society creates wide interest and respect. Woodlands are self-evidently a source of wood, and for millennia have been used by humans to meet a range of needs including shelter and food. However, such values did not prevent the widespread loss of woodland cover in Scotland, to the extent that at the start of the twentieth century only 5% of Scotland remained wooded. Concerns over the lack of timber led to a large scale afforestation programme, designed to maximise production of wood. However, as in many other countries (Seymour and Hunter Jr., 1999), forestry practice in Scotland evolved in the latter half of the twentieth century to once again provide a range of societal needs.

The term sustainable forest management has emerged from policy discussions initiated within the Convention on Biological Diversity. It has been defined as –

> *The stewardship and use of forests and forest lands in a way, and at a rate, that maintains their biodiversity, productivity, regeneration capacity, vitality and their potential to fulfil, now and in the future, relevant ecological, economic and social functions, at local, national and global levels, and that does not cause damage to other ecosystems*
>
> Helsinki Declaration 1993 (MCPFE, 1993).

A number of process controls and incentives have emerged to support the aims of sustainable forest management. These include the UK Forestry Standard (Anon., 2004) that describes appropriate characteristics and is underpinned with detailed guidance; voluntary certification schemes such as those of the Forestry Stewardship Council and Pan European Forest Certification to give customer assurance of sustainable production (Bills, 2001); and targeted grant aid so that new woodland is established in suitable locations with appropriate specifications.

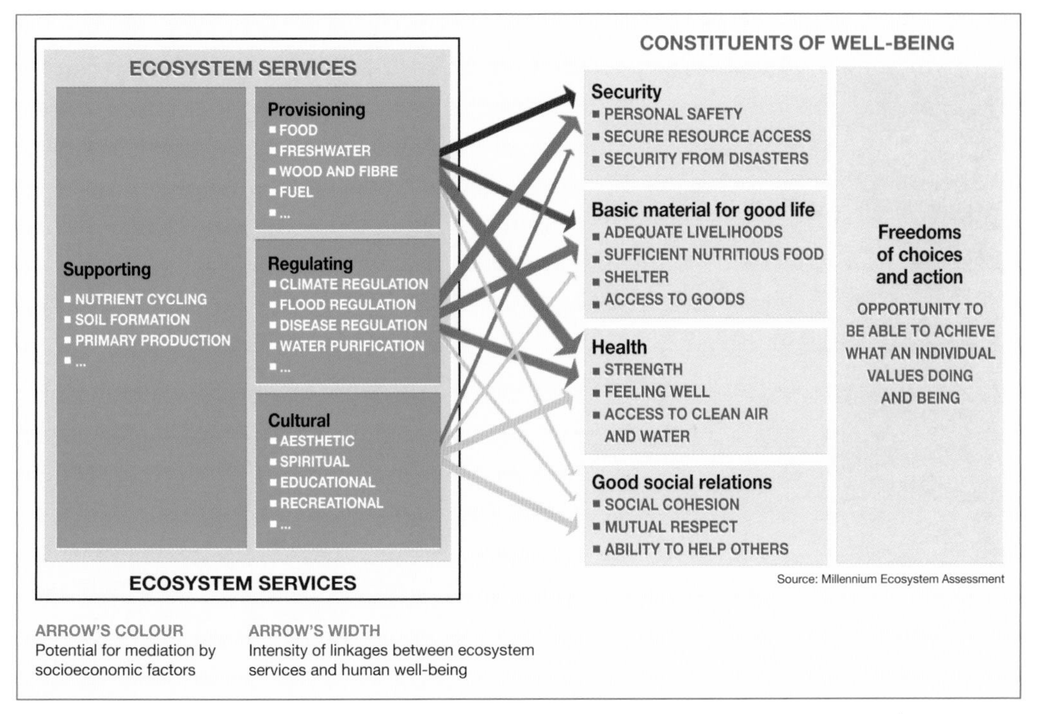

Figure 30.1 The complex linkages between ecosystem services and human well being (Extract from MEA – World Research Institute, 2003).

Policy and guidance has also been developed to control deforestation for other uses such as renewable energy developments. Management of public forests has demonstrated the evolution of best practice (McIntosh, Chapter 29). There are new demands for forests and woodlands to contribute to mitigation of and adaptation to climate change (Read *et al.*, 2009).

There is growing interest in the concepts of ecosystem services, their linkage to human well-being, and their valuation as a means of guiding and supporting natural resource management. Services are a familiar concept in today's society – with nations renowned for their service industry, notions of service culture, and indeed services provided by companies to consumers, and local councils to householders. Ecosystem services are perhaps less familiar. Ecosystem services are the benefits people obtain from ecosystems. These include provisioning services such as food and water; regulating services such as flood and disease control; cultural services such as spiritual, recreational, and cultural benefits; and supporting services, such as nutrient cycling, that maintain the conditions for life on Earth (World Research Institute, 2003). The *Millennium Ecosystem Assessment* (World Research Institute, 2003) provided a framework linking the drivers of change, the underpinning resource of biodiversity, the services that ecosystems provide, and the constituents of human well-being (Figure 30.1). A number of regional or country-specific assessments are now being conducted and, for the UK, will be completed in 2011. These seek to define what society obtains from natural environments, and how such services might be valued in a way that ensures their perpetuation. In a global assessment, over 100 services were identified from woodlands (Shvidenko *et al.*, 2003). In this chapter we use the ecosystem services framework, and findings from the *Forestry for People* study (Edwards *et al.*, 2009) to explore how woodlands matter to Scotland.

30.2 Scotland's woodlands – the underpinning resource

30.2.1 Extent and character

Trees are long-lived organisms. The woodland cover of today and its character reflect how policy (including incentive and control), management (past and current objectives of numerous owners), and bioclimatic factors and constraints have interacted over decades and centuries. In 2009, 17% of Scotland's land area was covered in trees, compared with 37% in the European Union and 44% in Europe; and a global average of 30% (Forestry Commission, 2009a). The woodland in Scotland comprises just over one million ha conifer and 300,000ha broadleaf trees. Much of the woodland has been established (or re-established) during the twentieth century and all woodland has been modified to some extent by human activities. Only 65,000ha to 89,000ha are regarded as ancient semi-natural woodland (FAO, 2006) and only 133,000ha semi-natural. The extent and condition of native woodland is being assessed by the Native Woodland Survey of Scotland, which began in 2009 and is due to be completed in 2013.

30.2.2 Biodiversity

Although much is known about the plant and bird communities of Scotland's woods, the underpinning biodiversity of Scotland's woodlands is not well defined. Biodiversity is thought to be modest when compared to sub-tropical and tropical ecosystems, and also in comparison to temperate continental woodlands. Biodiversity reflects constraints of post-glacial colonisation, restricted range of environmental conditions, and the influence of the marginal maritime position on range. The sustained loss of woodland cover has been reflected in the loss of woodland species in the last 1,000 years. Nevertheless, Scotland's woodlands reflect often locally unique ecosystems of the temperate/boreal forest boundary.

The UK Biodiversity Action Plan recognises two broad woodland habitats (broadleaved, mixed and yew woodland and coniferous woodland) and eight priority habitat types of which two (upland birch woodland and native pine woods) are only found in Scotland and four others (upland oak woodlands, wet woodlands, upland mixed ash woodland, wood pasture and parkland) are prominent. Atlantic oakwoods are valued for their bryophyte and lichen communities (Malcolm *et al.*, 2005), whilst native pinewoods provide some unique assemblages at the temperate/boreal forest margin (Humphrey, 2006).

The large scale afforestation in the mid twentieth century of upland areas was seen as a threat to some internationally important ecosystems (Stroud *et al.*, 1988), and a number of open habitat communities and specialists were affected. However, the new woodland habitats that have emerged are home to an increasing number and diversity of species and are not the ecological deserts initially characterised (Humphrey *et al.*, 2003; Quine and Humphrey, 2009). There is scope for improving their contribution to biodiversity through choice of stand structures (Quine *et al.*, 2007), landscape arrangements (Humphrey *et al.*, 2009), and retention of particular habitats and microhabitats (Humphrey, 2005). There has also been targeted removal of forest to restore important native woodland (Thompson *et al.*, 2003), peatland and heathland habitats (Patterson and Anderson, 2000; Humphrey *et al.*, 2006).

30.3 Ecosystem services of woodlands

30.3.1 Provisioning services of woodlands – materials for well-being

Woodlands provide amongst other things sources of solid wood, fibre and fuel. This provision was the main driver behind the expansion of woodland area that took place in Scotland in the twentieth century; timber shortages were acute after the first and second World Wars and this led to the demand and action to provide a strategic timber reserve.

It has been estimated that every week, some 4,000 lorry loads of harvested wood are transported to processing mills in Scotland for conversion into timber for house building, fencing material, high-quality papers and other products (Scottish Forest Industries Cluster, 2004; Davies, 2009). The value of the timber industry to Scotland's economy in 2007/08 was estimated to be £460 million (Edwards *et al.*, 2008; Edwards *et al.*, 2009). The UK is the fourth largest (by value) importer of wood and wood products after USA, China and Japan (Forestry Commission, 2009a) and only a fifth of consumption is met by domestic production. Country level statistics are not available but self-sufficiency in wood and wood products in Scotland is probably higher than elsewhere in the UK, with some estimates that approximately three-quarters of consumption are home-grown. The main timber imports in 2002 were from European neighbours of Sweden, Latvia, Finland, Russia and Estonia (Thomson, 2004).

In Scotland wood as a source of fuel is currently of less importance than in other countries (but see regulating section below) and a public survey (Forestry Commission, 2009b) found that only 5% of respondents reported using wood as a fuel in their home.

The total employment in the Scottish forestry sector is around 13,200 full time equivalent jobs (that is direct, indirect and induced; excluding imported timber); direct employment equates to around 12,000 jobs. In addition, total employment due to spending by visitors to forests is around 17,900 full time equivalent jobs (Edwards *et al.*, 2008).

It might be thought that Scotland would not have a strong tradition of gathering other woodland products given the low woodland cover. However, recent surveys have found a surprisingly large use of wild plant materials and fungi, or Non-Timber Forest Products (NTFPs). A public survey in 2006 estimated that 13% of the Scottish population had gathered NTFPs from woodlands in Scotland on one or more of their woodland visits (Edwards *et al.*, 2009). Interviews with approximately 40 collectors (Emery *et al.*, 2006) found that over 200 NTFPs had been obtained from 173 vascular plant and fungal species, many providing multiple products. Emery *et al.* (2006) proposed 'That a vast majority of the collection is for household use suggests the deeply personal nature of this connection. Indeed, some gatherers consider the activity fundamental to their personal identity as human beings, as Scots, as members of their family, or as individuals.'

30.3.2 Regulating services of woodlands – security of well-being

The reality and threat of climate change is creating concern for the security of society across the globe. Action is required to mitigate and adapt to change from global to local scales (Read *et al.*, 2009). Globally between 2000 and 2005 it was estimated that deforestation was occurring at the rate of 13 million hectares per year (FAO, 2006). This represents approximately 18% of global anthropogenic carbon emissions and requires international action to tackle. The UK together, and Scotland alone, seek to influence practice by promoting sustainable forest management, and forest landscape restoration. Climate change projections for Scotland suggest wetter winters and more intense rainfall events (Ray, 2008).

Woodlands can help climate change mitigation and adaptation in a range of ways by sequestering and storing carbon (Broadmeadow and Matthews, 2003), and by providing substitutes for fossil fuels and for materials such as concrete and steel with higher carbon emissions. Rapid growth rates in Scotland along with other parts of temperate Europe mean that the accumulation of biomass is high for the latitude (for example net primary production of 12 to 25 cubic metres per hectare per year versus two to six for continental Europe and North America). Fast-growing plantations, such as sitka spruce (*Picea sitchensis*), can become carbon sinks in ten years (Black *et al.*, 2009). Increased use of wood in the construction industry can cut greenhouse gas emissions by 40 to 80% per building. Wood can be burnt directly as a source of energy, or used in bio-refining to provide biogas or liquid fuels (Suttie *et al.*, 2009).

Such benefits are becoming more widely understood and in a 2009 survey (Forestry Commission, 2009b) – around four-fifths of adult respondents agreed that 'trees are good because they remove carbon dioxide from the atmosphere and store it in wood'. Scottish woodlands, including their soils, are a valuable store of carbon and management of the whole ecosystem is important to protect this.

Sequestration of carbon by woodland can contribute to regulation of the global climate, but woodland can also provide local regulation. This includes shelter and shade for urban populations (Handley and Gill, 2009) and for livestock in rural areas (Gardiner *et al.*, 2006).

Trees and woodland are influential over aspects of the water cycle. Flood control can be aided by the presence of trees on floodplains which can delay and reduce the size of the flood peak (Thomas and Nisbet, 2007). Debris dams formed from fallen trees and branches can reduce water velocity, increase channel width and water depth; promote overbank flows and increase water storage; however, woody debris can cause blockages in engineering structures. Scotland has lost much of its riparian woodland but restoration is now of growing interest (see Ashmole, Chapter 31) as is reinstatement of a range of fluvial processes, including those provided by European beavers (*Castor fiber*). In a similar way, trees can aid landslip prevention and slope stabilisation by anchoring soil layers, and delaying extreme wetting of soils.

Very large expanses of forest can influence regional climate, particularly precipitation patterns. Trees, depending on a range of factors, have the ability to use more water than most other types of vegetation (Nisbet, 2005). Studies in the UK have found that between 25% and 45% of annual rainfall is typically lost by interception from conifer woodlands, compared with 10% to 25% for broadleaf woodlands (Calder *et al.*, 2003). These percentages remain remarkably constant over a wide range of total rainfall. Transpiration rates, on the other hand, vary little between coniferous and broadleaf woodland. Annual transpiration rates are within a relatively narrow range of 300mm to 350mm (Roberts, 1983). Overall, woodland cover is thought to have little effect on water yield from catchments in the uplands, but may have a substantial effect in lowland areas with lower rainfall, particularly on freely draining soils (Nisbet, 2005).

30.3.3 Cultural services of woodlands – health and well-being

Obesity and heart disease are major health problems in Scotland. In addition, over the next 30 years, the World Health Organisation (WHO) considers that mental well-being and stress will be major health challenges. There is growing interest in the contribution that woodlands can make to such health issues by providing places for exercise, restorative environments, and by removing pollutants and noise.

Many people already enjoy the benefits of spending time in woodlands. The total number of visits per year to woodlands by Scottish adults has varied between around 68 million (2005/06) and 37 million (2006/07), with weather thought to contribute to the variation. Woodlands can provide an environment suitable for a range of activities (Figure 30.2), many of which involve physical exercise. Around three percent of Scottish adults exercise for at least 30 minutes on five or more days per week in woodlands. The non-market value of woodland recreation is estimated to be between £44 million and £76 million per year (Edwards *et al.*, 2008, 2009).

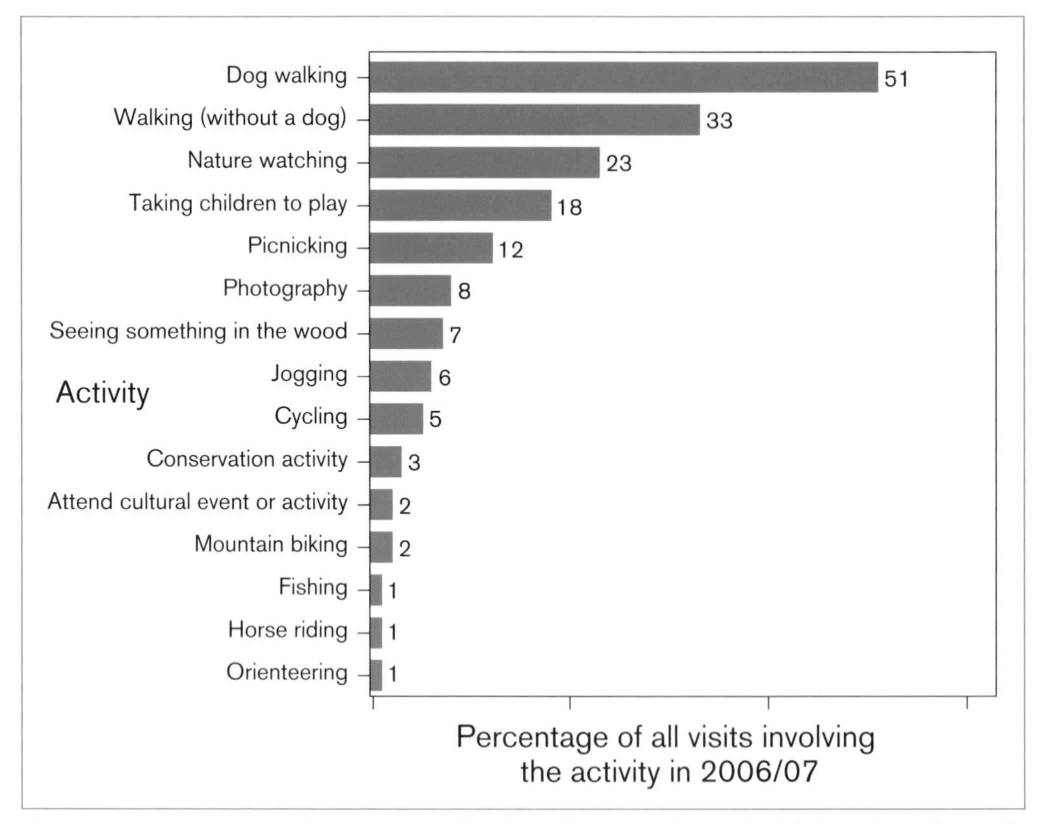

Figure 30.2 Percentage of the type of woodland visits by people in Scotland (Edwards *et al.*, 2008).

In addition to providing a place for exercise, woodlands are often associated with tranquillity and the opportunity to experience restorative environments. Around 82% of Scottish adults agree (or strongly agree) that woodlands are places to reduce stress and anxiety (Edwards *et al.*, 2009). Nearly half (47%) of Scottish adults who had visited woodlands in the previous 12 months reported that they felt healthier when spending time there. Perceived benefits included physical health through exercise; mental health through relaxation, stress relief and improved mood; and social health and well-being through meeting other people (including family or friends) whilst in woodlands. The annual value of health benefits of Scottish woodlands is estimated to be between £10 million and £111 million at 2007/08 prices (Edwards *et al.*, 2009).

However, the benefits of the woodland experience are not equally distributed nor are they universally appreciated. The proportion of the adult population who had visited woodland and the average number of visits per adult is lower (half in 2005/06) for people living in an area which is considered part of the most deprived 15% of the Scottish population (Edwards *et al.*, 2009). When asked how often they would like to visit woodland and the outdoors in the next 12 months, 23% of respondents said they would like to visit several times a month or several times a week, but almost the same proportion (25%) reported that they do not want to visit in the next 12 months. The main reason that 65% of respondents stated for not visiting woodlands was that they are not interested in going (Forestry Commission, 2009b). There is clearly scope for increasing the proportion of the population for whom woodlands matter.

There is evidence that early experiences of outdoor activities are influential in sustaining interest and activities in later life (Ward Thompson *et al.*, 2004). Provision of education in an outdoor setting has distinct advantages, and this has led to the development of the Forest School concept with a variety of structured activities (O'Brien and Murray, 2007). There are also opportunities to incorporate visits to woodlands as part of standard curricula and the Forestry Commission in Scotland already works with an estimated 20% of schools (Edwards *et al.*, 2008). This means that every year on average 24% of Scottish children visit a woodland as part of a nursery or school trip, totalling around 510,000 visits. The educational opportunities are not restricted to schooling. A public opinion survey of UK adults (Forestry Commission, 2009b) found that 7% of respondents said they or their family had been involved within the last 12 months in a school visit (3%), a guided walk or talk (2%), an event at a woodland visitor centre (3%) or another learning event (1%).

Trees and woodlands can also provide more direct health benefits by filtering pollution. Trees trap dust particles and absorb sulphur dioxide and ozone. Net pollution absorption by woodland was estimated to have reduced the number of deaths brought forward by air pollution by between 59-88 deaths and between 40-62 hospital admissions (Willis *et al.*, 2003).

30.3.4 Cultural services of woodlands – social relations

There is an increasing forest culture in Scotland and Smout (2003) has suggested that a phase of reconciliation is taking place in which people are re-establishing links with and affinity for woodlands. The Non Timber Forest Product survey by Emery *et al.* (2006) found a substantial proportion of the population accessed woodlands for resources. In addition, woodlands provide settings for a range of social activities, although a minority are not positive (for example dumping, arson, vandalism).

People becoming involved in the management of woodlands can help sustain active and supportive communities (Lawrence *et al.*, 2009). There are around 138 community woodland groups in Scotland, with approximately 13,500 members. The groups manage around 250 woodlands covering 1.4% of the woodland area in Scotland. However, only 44% of the area of this woodland is community owned, and around 50% of income to community woodland groups is from grants by public bodies (Edwards *et al.*, 2008). Only 12% of income to community woodlands is from the sale of forest products and other goods and services.

The extent to which woodlands support community engagement and development is also reflected in the extent of volunteering. In 2006/07, around 7,500 volunteers undertook forest-related work in Scotland, representing a total of 47,500 volunteer days. Around 25% of effort related to community woodland groups, and a further 47% to a range of non-governmental organisations (Edwards *et al.*, 2008). There have also been developments in the use of nature-based settings for teaching offenders and school children new skills and building self-esteem (O'Brien *et al.*, 2008).

The contribution of woodlands to culture and landscape can be more controversial. Trees and woodlands provide some of the iconic and defining landscapes of Scotland (for example, images of Caledonian pinewoods). However, the large scale afforestation of the twentieth century has been responsible for substantial landscape change that attracted adverse comment. There are estimated to be 1,418 scheduled ancient monuments located within Scottish forests, 150 recorded Heritage Trees and at least 1,000 recorded Ancient Trees in Scotland. The lack of annual cultivation makes woodlands a more benign environment than arable for the survival of a range of archaeological structures. The presence of trees and woodland is thought to have an economic value, reflected in the prices of housing in developments with and without trees. Around 557,000 people in Scotland have visible woodland within 1km of their homes and the economic value of woodland views from homes and on journeys by commuters in Scotland has been estimated to be between around £21 million and £90 million per year at 2007/08 prices. In addition the economic value (GVA) of visitor spending attributed to woodlands, where woodland was the primary reason for the visit, is around £209 million at 2007/08 prices (Edwards *et al.*, 2008).

30.4 The challenges for future woodland management

This paper highlights that not only do Scotland's woodlands provide wood (the fifth element) but they are also associated with a range of other ecosystem services that make a major contribution to society. These contributions range from the obvious (timber production and associated employment) to the inspirational (the sense of place that woodlands provide). So woodlands really do matter. There may be conjecture over the extent to which they do matter. The evidence base is patchy and there remains substantial uncertainty over how best to quantify and value many of the ecosystem services, in particular the ones relating to the cultural aspects. There are undoubtedly technical challenges in quantifying the extent and location of these services, not least in isolating the contribution of woodlands from other land uses within particular areas (integrated landscapes, catchments). Some consider that attempts to place monetary values on ecosystem services is impossible or conceptually flawed, while others consider it a means of achieving more equitable distribution of benefits. This is likely to be an active area of research and debate for a number of years.

Should there be more woodland to improve the supply of ecosystem services that benefit the people of Scotland? Recent policy statements have proposed forest expansion to achieve 25% woodland cover in Scotland, not least to achieve carbon sequestration and help with commitments to mitigate climate change. There is public support for further tree planting; for example, the public opinion survey (Forestry Commission, 2009b) found that around 79% of respondents agreed there was at least one benefit of forestry worth supporting with public money, with the benefits 'to provide places for wildlife to live' and 'to help tackle climate change' often seen as the most important. Careful attention to technical constraints, and to the values of other habitats, will be necessary to get the best net contribution from forest expansion, rather than just the increase of some services at the expense of others.

Can the management of woodland be modified to enhance the provision of ecosystem services that benefit the people of Scotland? The choice of woodland type and its location ultimately constrains the mix of ecosystem services that will be available. The management of woodlands may seek to produce a range of services or focus on one. To this end the practice of forestry has evolved in recent years to incorporate new knowledge and ways to achieve multiple objectives, so that producing a range of ecosystem goods and services is possible. There remain challenges in establishing the right mix of incentive, control and market such that woodlands continue to matter and be valued by Scotland's people. It remains to be seen whether it is as the fifth element (and more) or if it is the ability to fix another element, carbon, that ensure woodlands matter most to Scotland in the future.

Acknowledgements

Thanks to colleagues at Forest Research, and particularly all those involved in sponsoring and conducting the *Forestry for People* study.

References

Anon. (2004). *The UK Forestry Standard* (2nd edition). Edinburgh and Belfast, Forestry Commission GB and Forest Service Northern Ireland.

Bills, D. (2001). The UK Government and certification. *International Forestry Review*, **3**, 323-326.

Black, K., Byrne, K.A., Mencuccini, M. *et al.* (2009). Carbon stock and stock changes across a Sitka spruce chronosequence on surface-water gley soils. *Forestry*, **82**, 255-272.

Broadmeadow, M. and Matthews, R. (2003). Forests, carbon and climate change. *Forestry Commission Information Note* 48. Forestry Commission, Edinburgh.

Calder, I.R., Reid, I., Nisbet, T.R. and Green, J.C. (2003). Impact of lowland forests in England on water resources – application of the HYLUC model. *Water Resources Research*, **39**, 1319-1328.

Carey, P.D., Wallis, S., Chamberlain, P.M. *et al.* (2008). In *Woodlands: Broadleaved, Mixed and Yew Woodlands; and Coniferous Woodland. Countryside Survey: UK Results from 2007*. NERC/Centre for Ecology & Hydrology, Chapter 6.

Davies, I. (2009). *Sustainable construction timber – sourcing and specifying local timber*. Forestry Commission Scotland, Edinburgh.

Deakin, R. (2007). *Wildwood: a journey through trees*, Hamish Hamilton.

Edwards, D., Morris J., O'Brien E.A. *et al.* (2008). The economic and social contribution of forestry for people in Scotland. *Research Note* 102, Forest Research, Edinburgh.

Edwards, D., Elliott, A., Hislop, M. *et al.* (2009). *A valuation of the economic and social contribution of forestry for people in Scotland.* Forestry Commission Research Report. Forestry Commission Scotland, Edinburgh.

Emery, M., Martin, S. and Dyke, A. (2006). *Wild harvests from Scottish woodlands: social, cultural and economic values of contemporary non-timber forest products.* Forestry Commission, Edinburgh.

FAO (2006). *Global Forest Resources Assessment 2005.* Forests and Agriculture Organisation, Rome.

Forestry Commission (2009a). *Forestry Statistics 2009*. Forestry Commission, Edinburgh.

Forestry Commission (2009b). *Public opinion of forestry, 2009, UK.* Forestry Commission, Edinburgh.

Gardiner, B.A., Palmer, H. and Hislop, A.M. (2006). The principles of using wood for shelter. *Information Note* 81, Forestry Commission, Edinburgh.

Handley, J.F. and Gill, S.E. (2009). In *Combating climate change – a role for UK forests. An assessment of the potential of UK's trees and woodlands to mitigate and adapt to climate change*, ed. by D.J. Read, P.H. Freer-Smith, J.I.L. Morison *et al.* TSO, London.

Humphrey, J.W. (2005). Benefits to biodiversity from developing old-growth conditions in British upland spruce plantations: a review and recommendations. *Forestry*, **78**, 33-53.

Humphrey, J.W. (2006). Ecology and management of native pinewoods: overview of special issue. *Forestry*, **79**, 245-247.

Humphrey, J.W., Ferris, R. and Quine, C.P. (eds) (2003). *Biodiversity in Britain's planted forests. Results from the Forestry Commission's biodiversity assessment project.* Forestry Commission, Edinburgh.

Humphrey, J.W., Ray, D., Brown, T. *et al.* (2009). Using focal species modelling to evaluate the impact of land use change on forest and other habitat networks in western oceanic landscapes. *Forestry*, **82**, 119-134.

Humphrey, J.W., Quine, C.P. and Watts, K. (2006). The influence of forest and woodland management on biodiversity in Scotland: recent findings and future prospects. In *Farming, Forestry and the Natural Heritage: Towards a More Integrated Approach*, ed. by R. Davison and C.A. Galbraith. The Natural Heritage of Scotland 14. TSO, Edinburgh, pp 59–75.

Lawrence, A., Anglezarke, B., Frost, B., Nolan, P. and Owen, R. (2009). What does community forestry mean in a devolved Great Britain. *International Forestry Review*, **11**, 281-297.

Malcolm, D.C., Cochrane, P., Cottrell, J. and Chamberlain, D.E. (eds) (2005). Botanical Society of Scotland Atlantic Oakwoods Symposium. *Botanical Journal of Scotland*, **57**, (1-2) Special Issue.

MCPFE (1993). *Helsinki Declaration – Resolution H1 General Guidelines for the Sustainable Management of Forests in Europe.* The second Ministerial Conference on the Protection of Forest in Europe., Helsinki, Finland.

Nisbet, T.R. (2005). Water use by trees. *Information Note* 65, Forestry Commission, Edinburgh.

O'Brien, L. and Murray, R. (2007). Forest School and its impacts on young children: case studies in Britain. *Urban Forestry and Urban Greening*, **6**, 249-265.

O'Brien, L., Townsend, M. and Ebden, M. (2008). *Environmental volunteering – motivations, barriers and benefits.* Report to the Scottish Forestry Trust and Forestry Commission.

Patterson, G.S. and Anderson, A.R. (2000). Forests and peatland habitats. *Guideline Note* No.1. Forestry Commission, Edinburgh.

Quine, C.P. and Humphrey, J.W. (2009). Plantations of exotic tree species in Britain: irrelevant for biodiversity or novel habitat for native species? *Biodiversity and Conservation*, **19**, 1503-1512.

Quine, C.P., Fuller R.J., Smith K.W. and Grice, P.V. (2007). Stand management: a threat or opportunity for birds in British woodland? *Ibis*, **149**, 161-174.

Ray, D. (2008). Impacts of climate change on forests in Scotland – a preliminary synopsis of spatial modelling research. *Forestry Commission Research Note* 001. Forestry Commission, Edinburgh.

Read, D.J., Freer-Smith, P.H., Morison, J.I.L. *et al.* (2009). *Combating climate change – a role for UK forests.* TSO, London.

Roberts, J.M. (1983). Forest transpiration: a conservative hydrological process? *Journal of Hydrology*, **66**, 133-141.

Seymour, R.S. and Hunter Jr, M.L. (1999). Principles of ecological forestry. In *Maintaining biodiversity in forested ecosystems*, ed. by M.L. Hunter Jr. Cambridge University Press, Cambridge, pp 22-61.

Scottish Forest Industries Cluster (2004). *Scotland's Forest Industries.* Scottish Enterprise, Edinburgh.

Shvidenko, A., Barber, C.V. and Persson, R. (2003). Forest and Woodland Systems. Chapter 21 in *Millennium Ecosystem Assessment*, Island Press.

Smout, T.C. (ed.) (2003). *People and woods in Scotland.* Edinburgh University Press, Edinburgh.

Stroud, D.A., Reed, T.M., Pienkowski, M.W. and Lindsay, R.A. (1988). *Birds, bogs and Forestry.* Nature Conservancy Council, Peterborough.

Suttie, E., Taylor, G., Livesay, K. and Tickell, F. (2009). Potential of forest products and substitution for fossil fuels to contribute to mitigation. In *Combating climate change – a role for UK forests. An assessment of the potential of UK's trees and woodlands to mitigate and adapt to climate change*, ed. by D.J. Read, P.H. Freer-Smith, J.I.L. Morison *et al.* TSO, London.

Thomas, H. and Nisbet T.R. (2007). An assessment of the impact of floodplain woodland on flood flows. *Water and Environment Journal*, **17**, 65-85.

Thomson, M. (2004). International markets in wood products. *Information Note* 60, Forestry Commission, Edinburgh.

Thompson, R., Humphrey, J.W., Harmer, R. and Ferris, R. (2003). *Restoration of native woodland on ancient woodland sites.* Forest Practice Guide, Forestry Commission, Edinburgh.

Ward Thompson, C., Aspinall, P., Bell, S. *et al.* (2004). *Open space and social inclusion: local woodland use in central Scotland.* Forestry Commission, Edinburgh.

Willis, K.G., Garrod, G., Scarpa, R. *et al.* (2003). *The social and environmental benefits of forests in Great Britain.* Forestry Commission, Edinburgh.

World Research Institute (2003). *Ecosystems and Human Well-Being: A Framework for Assessment* (Millennium Ecosystem Assessment). Island Press, Washington DC.

31 Grass-roots Contributions to Woodland Restoration in the Scottish Uplands

Philip Ashmole

Summary

1. In the middle of the twentieth century Scotland's native wildlife and habitats were in a poor state. The last 25 years have seen an increase in recognition of the problems and in determination to repair some of the damage.
2. International initiatives helped to raise awareness of biodiversity issues. In Scotland, individuals and environmental activist groups played a major role in highlighting past losses and in leading the way towards ecological restoration.
3. The need for restorative action was recognised among staff of government agencies and led to changes in land management and provision of support for the grass-roots.
4. Native woodland initiatives in the south of Scotland, such as the Carrifran Wildwood project, exemplify different approaches to ecological restoration.
5. Simpler support mechanisms and stronger leadership for environmental protection would encourage the grass-roots activity through which members of the public work with official bodies and Non-Governmental Organisations to preserve and enhance their natural heritage.

31.1 The Scottish environment at its nadir

In some respects, the 1950s-1970s represented a low point in the state of the Scottish environment. The extent and quality of many natural habitats suffered under the impact of human activity. The range and abundance of species within some groups – for instance predatory mammals, farmland birds, raptors and some

Ashmole, P. (2011). Grass-roots Contributions to Woodland Restoration in the Scottish Uplands – *The Changing Nature of Scotland*, eds. S.J. Marrs, S. Foster, C. Hendrie, E.C. Mackey, D.B.A. Thompson. TSO Scotland, Edinburgh, pp 355-372.

butterflies and moths – declined (Ratcliffe, 1977; Ratcliffe and Thompson, 1988; Usher, 2002). Native woodland had contracted to a tiny fraction of its extent compared to 6,000 years ago (Smout *et al.*, 2005) (see Figure 31.1). Grazing of the uplands by unfenced livestock and recent management of sheep (*Ovis aries*), red grouse (*Lagopus lagopus scoticus*) and red deer (*Cervus elaphus*) created artificial vegetation patterns. This also decimated populations of vulnerable trees such as

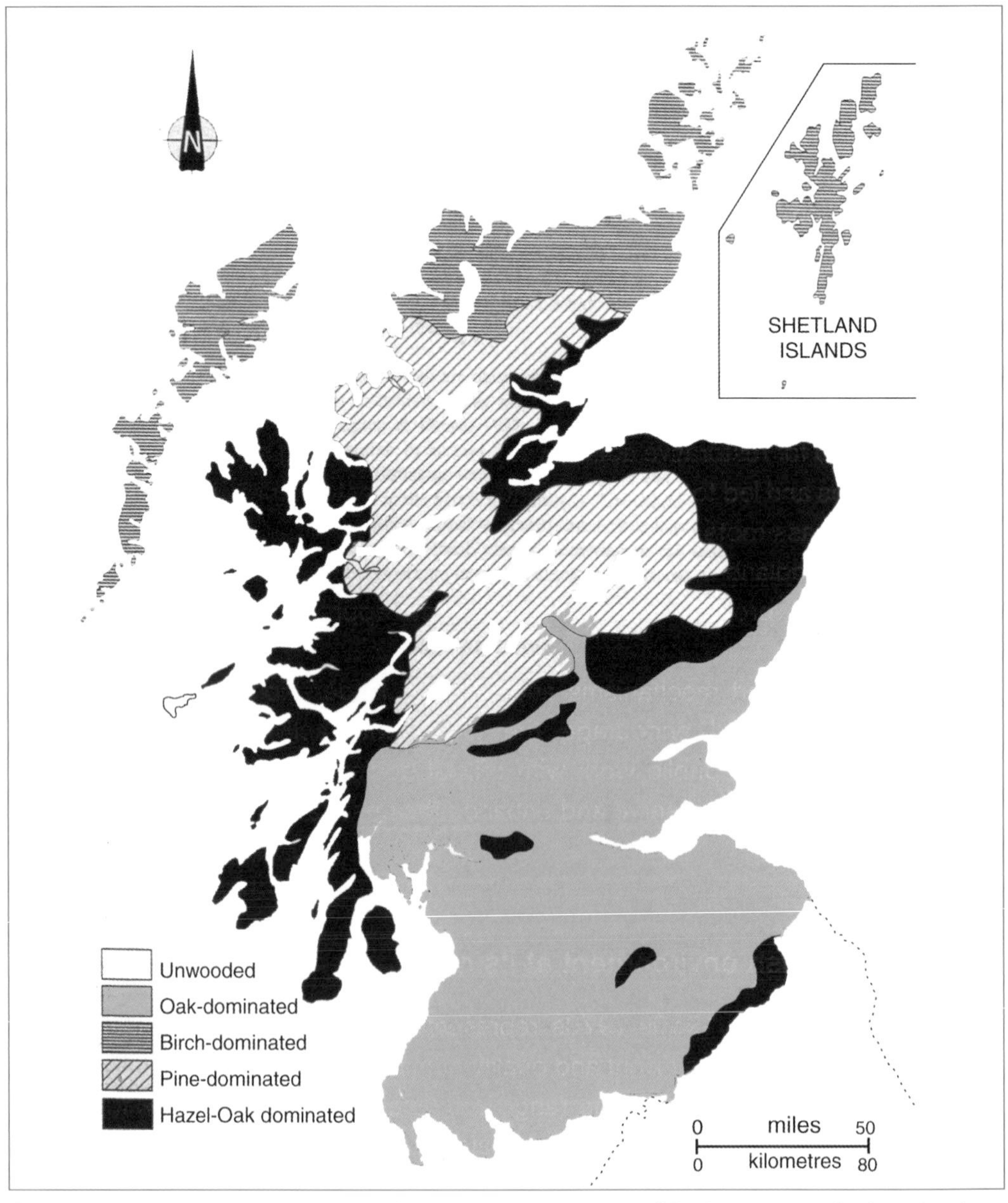

Figure 31. 1 Major woodland types in Scotland 6,000 years ago (Tipping, 1994, edited version from Ashmole and Ashmole, 2009, p16).

aspen (*Populus tremula*) (Worrell, 1995), shrubs such as juniper (*Juniperus communis*) and dwarf birch (*Betula nana*) (Hester, 1995), and removed elements of the native fauna from large parts of the uplands (Lovegrove, 2007). Intensification of agriculture led to drainage of wetlands, removal of hedgerows and extensive use of herbicides. Water pollution was widespread, and DDT and other pesticides caused severe declines in some animal species at high trophic levels (Newton, 1997).

The role of humans in the denudation of upland Scotland over the past six millennia has been much discussed (Tipping, 1994; Smout *et al.*, 2005; Ashmole, 2006). The native woodland model of the Macaulay Institute (Towers *et al.*, 2004) and analysis of tree lines by Hale *et al.* (1998) both suggest that while some areas are at present too wet and cold for the development of native woodland, large parts of the Scottish uplands could still support woodland given appropriate control of herbivores. Fenton (2008) argued that woodland loss was caused largely by natural processes, especially deterioration of soil condition, whereas other ecologists consider that human activities are heavily implicated. They argue that in the absence of domestic stock, natural predation would ensure lower numbers and a patchier distribution of wild herbivores, and that more native woodland would have survived (Bennett, 2009; Stolzenburg, 2008).

31.2 Changing attitudes and support

The second half of the twentieth century saw accelerating change in attitudes towards the Scottish environment. The degraded state of much of the uplands was brought to public attention by Fraser Darling (Darling, 1949), while a decade later a landmark review of native pinewoods (Steven and Carlisle, 1959) raised consciousness of their small size and much restricted range. In a 1985 symposium, *Trees and Wildlife in the Scottish Uplands* (Jenkins, 1986) A.A. Rowan mentioned an awakening recognition by the Forestry Commission (FC) of the importance of broadleaves in upland forests, while G.F. Peterken emphasised the tiny proportion of the area of Scotland that carried woodland dominated by native broadleaf trees and shrubs or native pinewoods. (A later review by MacKenzie and Callander (1995) indicated that little more than 1.7% of the land area of Scotland carried woodland of natural origin.) At the same symposium Keith Kirby signalled the importance of conservation management at the landscape scale and pointed out – in words that should be etched in the minds of ministers and administrators today – that 'nature conservation is a proper constraint on the productive use of land, and not an 'optional extra'. The consciousness of loss was also reflected in literary works such as *Woodland that was not*, a poetic lament by Jim Crumley (1993) on the barrenness of a Highland glen.

31.3 The growth of afforestation

Although the gradual deforestation of the Scottish uplands was a source of sadness to ecologists, it was mainly the sudden conifer afforestation following the Second World War that stimulated public concern for natural habitats and biodiversity in Scotland during the 1980s and early 1990s. Feelings ran high in the Southern Uplands, where many individuals and at least one group, the Campaign for the Future of the Border Hills, publicly deplored the drastic changes caused by conifer planting in traditional denuded landscapes. In the far north, the impact of plantation forestry on the Flow Country of Caithness and Sutherland, mainly in the period 1979-1987, catalysed a wave of protest. The Nature Conservancy Council (NCC) showed its concern at the loss of peatland habitats (Stroud *et al.*, 1987; Nature Conservancy Council, 1998) and the Royal Society for the Protection of Birds (RSPB) highlighted the threat to open country birds (Bainbridge *et al.*, 1987).

The afforestation resulted from a combination of low land values, government policies and tax incentives. Conifer plantations were established over about 9% of the total land area of Scotland between 1940 and 1980 (Rowan, 1986) and many native woods were cleared or under-planted with conifers. Planting was largely of exotic species, with spruce dominating in the south and west. Native species, which formed nearly all the woodlands in the Highlands at the start of the twentieth century, had declined to less than two thirds of the woodland area by the end of the Second World War and to only one third by the mid 1980s. In the lowlands the change was even more extreme, with native species reduced to one tenth of total woodland area (MacKenzie and Callander, 1995, 1996).

The afforestation caused drastic alterations in the landscape and significant losses of open habitats and associated native wildlife. Although it has now been shown that diversity in some taxonomic groups can eventually become comparable in plantations of exotic conifers and in native oak and Scots pine woodlands (Quine and Humphrey, 2010) the short rotation and low diversity in plantations normally creates unnatural habitats lacking many of the niches (such as decaying prone trunks, and deep bark crevices and holes in ancient trees) utilised by more specialised native species.

31.4 Sites of Special Scientific Interest (SSSIs)

By the 1980s the designation of Sites of Special Scientific Interest (SSSIs) and the landmark *Nature Conservation Review* by Derek Ratcliffe (1977) had provided a foundation for conservation of natural habitats in the UK. The stated aim of the review was to select a series of sites forming a network such that 'each site represents a significant fragment of the much-depleted resource of wild nature now remaining in this country'. However, the protection available under the SSSI and National Nature Reserve (NNR) designations often proved inadequate to prevent damage to the sites, and many areas of ecological importance were left unprotected. Despite some good news, the fortunes of some groups of wildlife species remained at a low ebb during the latter part of the twentieth century (Fleming *et al.*, 1997).

31.5 The emergence of 'ecological restoration'

During this period, however, there was increasing emphasis on ecological restoration, the repair of damaged ecosystems, a concept that developed most explicitly in the United States during the 1980s (Jordan, 1993). In Scotland, early initiatives included the 1951 purchase by the Nature Conservancy of Beinn Eighe, Britain's first NNR, where attention focused on conservation and expansion of the remnant native pinewoods (Johnston and Balharry, 2001). In 1957 Rum was acquired as an NNR and Jo Eggeling and Peter Wormell set about establishing native woodland on the island (Wormell, 1977; Planterose, 1990). In 1985 Creag Meagaidh was purchased for the nation and ecological restoration was set in motion by Dick Balharry and Peter Duncan, mainly by culling red deer (Ramsay, 1997).

Although these were government initiatives, they depended largely on leadership by individuals within the relevant organisations. In the 1980s pioneer environmental activists in the Highlands started serious attempts to raise public awareness of the unsatisfactory state of upland Scotland and to start 'grass-roots' remedial action. Leading the way towards ecological restoration were a handful of visionary people.

The Native Pinewood Discussion Group was formed by Rawdon Goodier in 1970 and in 1978 broadened its remit and its name to include all native woodland. In 1988 Alan Drever founded the Scottish Community Woodland Campaign and this later became Scottish Native Woods, which exists to rescue, restore and expand Scotland's native woodlands. Recently, in cooperation with the Highland Aspen Group, it has played a major role in promoting the restoration of aspen populations. Bernard Planterose began planting trees on Isle Martin, near Ullapool, in the early 1980s, when working for the RSPB. In the late 1980s David Mardon, ploughing a lonely furrow within the National Trust for Scotland (NTS), but with backing from the NCC, initiated attempts to restore montane willow scrub at Ben Lawers NNR by building exclosures (Mardon, 1991 and *pers comm.*). In 1996 David Mardon and Diana Gilbert made key contributions to a conference on montane scrub habitats in Scotland (Gilbert *et al.*, 1997) and joined others in launching the Montane Scrub Action Group, an informal partnership of professionals supported by their organisations, which aimed to raise awareness of montane scrub and promote its restoration (Scott, 2005).

31.6 'Trees for Life' and 'Reforesting Scotland'

In the mid 1980s Trees for Life (TFL) began work – under the dedicated leadership of Alan Watson Featherstone – on restoration of native pinewoods on land owned by the Forestry Commission in Glen Affric, where some forest regeneration measures had already been taken. The Forestry Commission, initially hesitant in its support, quickly saw the potential benefits of partnerships with grass-roots groups. TFL developed an ambitious vision of a natural wild forest extending to about 1,500km^2 in the north-central Highlands (Watson, 1992). In 2006 it purchased the 4,000 hectare estate of Dundreggan in Glen Moriston and started restoration of diverse native vegetation types.

Reforesting Scotland was a group initiative with its roots in the inspiring journal, *The Tree Planters Guide to the Galaxy*, launched in 1989. Key players included Bernard and Emma Planterose, Ron Greer, Martin Howard, Donald McPhillimy and Andy Wightman. Subsequently, Reforesting Scotland has worked effectively to promote the connections between people and woodlands. In 1993 the group organised a study tour on which 31 delegates from Scotland, representing a wide range of land use organisations, visited farms and rural industries in western Norway. They were impressed with the healthy rural culture and the involvement of individuals in management of their local landscape. The same year saw a significant step towards increasing this kind of involvement in Scotland, with the purchase by the Assynt Crofters Trust of the North Assynt Estate. This was followed by other buy-outs and by the *Land Reform (Scotland) Act 2003*, which fundamentally altered the relationship between landowners, local people and the general public (Lawrence *et al.*, 2009).

31.7 The CBD and National Lottery – key catalysts

In 1992 the Convention on Biological Diversity (CBD) was signed at the Earth Summit in Rio de Janeiro, calling for national strategies to conserve, protect and enhance biological diversity. Two years later the UK government responded with the UK Biodiversity Action Plan (BAP), which focused on broad habitats and species of special concern. The UK plan led to the development of local BAPs, and in the best instances, such as that for Dumfries and Galloway (Norman, 2009) the expertise of a large number of people was brought to bear. The Earth Summit raised awareness of biodiversity issues among members of the public and thus contributed to the pressure for restoration of natural habitats.

The establishment of the National Lottery in late 1994 provided new opportunities for environmentalists. A group including Simon Pepper of WWF Scotland and John Hunt of RSPB responded with the inspired idea of the Millennium Forest for

Scotland Trust (MFST). This was an umbrella organisation designed to enable relatively small native woodland projects to gain funding from the Millennium Commission. MFST led to the establishment of 80 woodland projects, resulting in the creation or improvement of some 20,000ha of native woodland (MFST, 2001). Although MFST was constrained by the bureaucracy of the Millennium Commission it enabled determined groups of enthusiasts throughout Scotland to create new native woodlands. However, MFST had a short active life and this was followed by a period when native woodland restoration seemed to rank low among the priorities of the National Lottery.

31.8 Government support for native woodlands

The 1980s saw a significant change in the attitude of the forestry establishment towards native woodlands and this was reflected in their publications and funding arrangements. The FC published a policy document on broadleaved woodland (Forestry Commission, 1985) and later also the landmark Bulletin 112, *Creating New Native Woodlands* (Rodwell and Patterson, 1994), while reports from SNH and FC highlighted the need for forest habitat networks (Peterken *et al.*, 1995). Financial incentives were put in place, initially for native pinewoods and in 1989 for all types of native woodland under the Woodland Grant Scheme (WGS).

SNH and the FC also began to focus on the relationships between people and woodlands and on the benefits that woodlands can provide (Quine, Chapter 30). In particular the FC provided funding to landowners under WGS and its successor the Scottish Forestry Grants Scheme (SFGS), as well as through Locational Premium schemes. Furthermore, over 100 native woodland projects were undertaken on the FC estate (Peterken and Stevenson, 2004). Many of the larger projects such as Glen Affric, the Sunart oakwoods and the Cree Valley owed much to both the energy of grass-roots activists and volunteers within community-based organisations, and to sources of funding to which they had access.

There was also increasing awareness of the ecological importance of Plantations on Ancient Woodland Sites (PAWS) where under-planting with exotic species had seriously modified the natural habitat. Removal of non-native trees from native pinewoods on FC land was initiated in 1992 and techniques were developed for converting PAWS back into native pinewoods or deciduous woodlands, with the aim of restoring much of their original diversity (Pryor *et al.*, 2002; Thompson *et al.*, 2003).

31.9 Recent initiatives

In recent years there have been a number of major native woodland initiatives by NGOs, including the National Trust for Scotland's treeline planting on the

Tarmachan range near Loch Tay, the Woodland Trust work at Glen Finglas in the Trossachs and the RSPB management of Abernethy Forest on Speyside. Other projects have been funded through the Scottish Forestry Alliance, which combines the 'people power' of the RSPB and the Woodland Trust with the resources of the Forestry Commission and the financial backing of a major oil company (BP) to establish native woodlands in many parts of Scotland (Humphrey *et al.*, 2005).

The end of the twentieth century saw increasing public support for the reinstatement of species native to Scotland. The European Union deserves credit for imposing a duty on member states to study the desirability of reintroducing lost native species, implying a responsibility for damage to wildlife caused by our activities. Reinstatement of European beaver (*Castor fiber*) and Eurasian lynx (*Lynx lynx*) is especially relevant to native woodland restoration, since beaver activity creates complex partly wooded wetland habitats that were presumably once widespread in the UK but are now almost entirely absent (Gurnell, 1998), while lynx prey on roe deer (*Capreolus capreolus*), which inhibit both natural regeneration and the establishment of native woodland (Hetherington and Gorman, 2007).

Grass-roots initiatives have played a significant role in the reinstatement of European beaver in Scotland. Hugh Chalmers organised a study tour to Brittany in 1996, with participants including academics and staff from a wide range of organisations including SNH, and the Scottish Beaver Network was established to promote the return of the beaver. An official project was eventually undertaken and has achieved initial success, although the cost has been greeted with some incredulity by conservationists in continental Europe.

31.10 Action for native woodlands in and near the Borders

The first annual gathering of Reforesting Scotland in 1992 was an inspiring occasion, but since its focus was largely on the pinewoods of the Highlands, an initiative for the broadleaved woodlands of the Southern Uplands seemed overdue. The *Restoring Borders Woodland* conference, organised by Peeblesshire Environment Concern with support from SNH, was held in 1993. Contributors documented the historical loss of native forests and discussed various approaches to restoration (Ashmole, 1994).

This conference saw the first mention in public of the idea that a grass-roots group could reinstate the original native vegetation in an entire upland valley. The vision of a 'Wildwood' was inspired by the discovery that in the denuded valley of Gameshope, in the west of the Scottish Borders, a tiny and largely coniferised woodland remnant on a precipitous slope retained many of the tree and shrub species that would have been present in the fully developed post-glacial woodland. This suggested that large-scale restoration of diverse broadleaved woodland in the area would be ecologically appropriate. At that time, however, there was no obvious prospect of obtaining the requisite funding.

The establishment of the National Lottery in 1994 stimulated extraordinary grass-roots activity in the Borders relating to native woodlands. This was orchestrated by the late Tim Stead, who in 1987 had founded an early example of community-owned woodland, at Wooplaw near Lauder. With support from SNH, a bid was submitted to the Millennium Forest for Scotland Trust. It comprised eight projects – including 'Borders Wildwood' – relating to native woodlands and relevant economic activities. The bid was approved in autumn 1995 and the group became the founding Board of Trustees of The Borders Forest Trust (BFT) in January 1996.

In the subsequent 15 years, BFT has played a pivotal role in promoting woodland habitat networks and establishing native woodland in the Scottish borderlands, working closely with community groups, landowners, NGOs, local authorities and government agencies (McGhee, 2010; Scottish Borders Council, 2005). BFT is actively developing its vision for restoration of the ancient Ettrick Forest (Kohn, 2003) and now owns two large properties in Dumfriesshire, both purchased by public subscription.

31.11 Carrifran Wildwood: a grass-roots ecological restoration initiative

The Wildwood Group was formed by members of Peeblesshire Environment Concern in autumn 1995 and became a devolved element within BFT. A mission statement was soon developed, so as to ensure that donors and everyone having contact with the project had a clear understanding of the objective, and to prevent – as far as possible – deviation from the basic vision during the centuries required for full restoration of the Wildwood ecosystem:

> *'The Wildwood project aims to re-create, in the Southern Uplands of Scotland, an extensive tract of mainly forested wilderness with most of the rich diversity of native species present in the area before human activities became dominant. The woodland will not be exploited commercially and the impact of humans will be carefully managed. Access will be open to all, and it is hoped that the Wildwood will be used throughout the next millennium as an inspiration and an educational resource.'*

In 1996 the Wildwood Group approached the new owner of Capplegill Farm in Moffatdale, eastern Dumfriesshire, with a view to purchasing Carrifran valley. This was a distinct catchment forming the eastern part of the farm and extending to 665ha, with a large range in altitude. The asking price was very high, but the group eventually secured a two-year option to purchase at a much lower figure. This was still well above the agricultural valuation of the land, rendering it impossible for SNH to help fund the purchase. However, members of the public responded with extraordinary generosity to an appeal for funds, demonstrating the depth of feeling about native woodlands in the minds of many people. Donors, including more than 600 Founders who gave £250, £500 or more, contributed four fifths of the required sum of ~£400,000. The rest of the funds came from charitable trusts.

Grass-roots groups need to foster their credibility if they are to gain official support. In November 1997 the Wildwood Group organised a meeting on native woodland restoration in southern Scotland. It was held at the Royal Botanic Garden Edinburgh under the banners of BFT and the Biodiversity Unit of the University of Edinburgh, and was attended by 180 delegates (Newton and Ashmole, 1998). The immediate purpose was to ensure that when work started at Carrifran it would be on the basis of the best available scientific evidence and practical expertise. Many of the matters discussed had much wider relevance; these included interpretation of the pollen record, the importance of genetic considerations when sourcing planting stock and the restoration of montane scrub and treeline.

During 1998 more than 20 members of the Wildwood Group participated in development of the planting plan for Carrifran, and in the following year a full Environmental Statement was produced by the group to support a WGS application for establishment of broadleaved native woodland over nearly half of the site. As a result of consultation, planting near features of archaeological interest was avoided. SNH were involved, since the valley was within the Moffat Hills SSSI and was soon to become a Special Area of Conservation (SAC). The proposed planting posed no risk to the montane plants that formed the basis of the designations and whilst SNH did not object to the plan they did specify avoiding planting on wet flushes and alongside most watercourses. The group challenged the latter point, since the great majority of ancient woodland remnants in the area concerned are 'long, skinny stands often along riverbanks and terraces' (Badenoch, 1994), but the stipulation stood.

SNH provided support for a Project Officer throughout the decade following purchase and the FC also endorsed the planting plan, which was compatible with their guidance on creating new native woodlands (Rodwell and Patterson, 1994). Carrifran was purchased on 1st January 2000 and MFST agreed to pay for fencing, interpretation and a small car park. Major support also came from the David Stevenson Trust, which paid for all the trees, grown in local commercial nurseries and back gardens from seed collected by volunteers. A decade after the purchase of Carrifran, nearly half a million trees have been planted and some 300ha of native woodland are under establishment. Many wildlife species – most noticeably

Plate 31.1 Volunteer planters near treeline, Carrifran, March 2008. © Philip Ashmole

Plate 31.2 Planted birches and alders, Carrifran. © Philip Ashmole

songbirds – are now re-colonising the lower part of the valley. Carrifran also has a good population of black grouse (*Tetrao tetrix*), some of them displaying at the highest altitude lek known in Scotland (Ashmole and Ashmole, 2009).

It was always the intention to restore natural habitats over the whole range of altitude offered by the site, from 160m in Moffatdale to just below the summit of White Coomb (821m). The upper margin of the main planting was between 450m and 600m, but a plan for limited planting between 600m and 750m in the hanging valley of Firth Hope was subsequently approved by SNH after a vegetation survey had been carried out (Chalmers and Ashmole, 2007). This proposal was extensively discussed with the FC but grant aid was not forthcoming for high level planting, so the work was done using volunteers and independent funding, which conferred greater flexibility. Most of the 12,500 trees and shrubs were planted by volunteers during high altitude camps between February and April in 2007-2010. Planting at about 550m near the western ridge of Carrifran was carried out in 2009 using one of the first grants approved under the Scotland Rural Development Programme (SRDP).

A recent review of environmental volunteering in Britain implied that volunteers are relatively passive participants (O'Brien *et al.*, 2008). In the Wildwood project, however, volunteers have played a central role. They have been instigators and drivers of the project and have been involved in developing the initial idea, planning, negotiating, fundraising, collecting (and sometimes propagating) seeds and cuttings, planting over 60,000 trees, surveying wildlife and undertaking over 100 monthly checks of the 12km perimeter fence. In such an ambitious project, however, professional input has also been essential.

31.12 Woodland initiatives in southwest Scotland

In the late 1990s the core grass-roots activity in the west of the Southern Uplands concentrated around Southwest Community Woodlands Trust (SCWT). MFST provided initial support, but the strong emphasis in the group on the secondary objective of MFST – 're-establishing social, cultural and economic links between communities and their local woodlands' – rather than on establishing and managing native woodlands, together with frustrations over bureaucracy, led to a troubled relationship. More recently, SCWT found financial support from other sources. In 2008 funds from Awards for All and local benefactors enabled the purchase of Taliesin, a woodland site at the foot of Screel Hill near Castle Douglas where 2,000 trees have been planted by SCWT members. Taliesin has now become a permanent countryside centre running craft workshops, festivals and educational initiatives, including provision of training in low impact technologies leading to employment opportunities.

In the far southwest, the Cree Valley Community Woodlands Trust (CVCWT) followed a different course. It formed in 1999 as a partnership of many organisations after public consultation and a feasibility study by a firm of property consultants. It had a vision of establishing a forest habitat network (incorporating a mosaic of native broadleaf woodlands and other habitats) from 'source to sea' in the catchment of the River Cree, linking a variety of woodland sites under different ownership. In 2009 CVCWT expanded its territory to include another 600ha of FC land along tributaries of the High Cree in a project associated with activity by the Galloway Fisheries Trust. CVCWT has developed strong involvement of volunteers and input by community organisations.

CVCWT also works in close and supportive partnership with FCS (Forestry Commission Scotland) in the Galloway Forest Park. In Galloway fragments of scrub remain at high altitudes and isolated bushes survive on islands in remote lochs (Murgatroyd, 2005). These relicts from centuries of grazing and burning throw light on the original forest of the area and thus underpin the Galloway Forest Park component of the Scotland-wide 'Action for Mountain Woodlands' project, organised by the Montane Scrub Action Group and funded by HLF with several partners. In Galloway, the work of community volunteers and activists in surveys and in the creation of a natural treeline demonstration site is informing and energising the creation of new 'woodland fringe habitat'. This habitat, which is of broadly native character and emulates natural treelines, will increasingly replace conifers at high elevation in the Galloway Forest Park (R. Soutar, *pers. comm.*).

31.13 Future nourishment of the grass-roots

What needs to be done to improve the natural environment of Scotland? Preceding sections of this paper have implied that conservation achievements often depend on key individuals and groups of activists, working either as volunteers or as employees within relevant organisations. Experience overseas also suggests that many major environmental initiatives – for instance John Muir's encouragement of President Theodore Roosevelt to establish National Parks in the USA, and the Green Belt Movement in Africa developed by Nobel Peace Prize winner Wangari Maathai – owe much to the vision of individuals, often with support from relevant authorities. 'Top-down' schemes emanating from governments are also important, but are often stimulated by grass-roots initiatives and changes in public opinion fostered by activists, rather than leading the way. Governments all over the world are recognising the value of community involvement, action and leadership in their forestry and woodland programmes. In Scotland the energy, enthusiasm and expertise of community groups should continue to add value to the work of agencies such as FCS and SNH.

The Millennium Forest for Scotland – a response to both public concern and the opportunity offered by the National Lottery – is a valuable example of an initiative that was sufficiently inspiring to stimulate individuals and grass-roots groups to devise a host of projects suitable for lottery funding. These were then able to gather additional support from private donors, a dispersed 'community of interest' and volunteers, as well as other public bodies. Subsequently, SNH and the FCS have given crucial funding to many groups, and wise advice and unstinting support has been provided by individual members of their staff.

In recent years, however, many people at the grass-roots level have become frustrated by the ever-increasing complexity of the processes needed to get conservation initiatives going in Scotland. Those who need to access public funds expend enormous amounts of time and energy trying to fight their way through the system and raising money for their own salaries. I suggest that a rigorous analysis of the environmental benefit gained by grant support would show that modest grants for simple projects awarded to individuals and small NGOs outperform – pound for pound – more elaborate (often partnership) schemes where procedural complexity favours large organisations and farm businesses that can obtain professional help, and where multiple objectives often lead to a lack of focus.

Moreover, I sense a significant rise in stress levels and lowered morale among front line staff in some government bodies, trying to support applicants as they struggle to master the complexity of continually changing regulations and funding arrangements. The implementation of the Scottish Rural Development Programme (SRDP) provides a good example, where although the desire for 'joined-up thinking' by government is understandable and the idea of a 'one-stop (online) shop' for rural funding is attractive on first sight, the complex procedures tend to disempower the people living and working on the land. In the case of the SRDP, the problem may be lessening as procedures become more familiar, and some simplification is apparently also under way, but lessons clearly need to be learned.

A more fundamental issue is whether SNH will be able to maintain – at a time of economic stringency and under long-term pressures imposed by impending global climate change and declining oil reserves – its ability to act as a champion for Scotland's people in opposing environmentally damaging development and supporting beneficial action. The 'balancing duty', by which SNH is required to take account of potential social and economic benefits when commenting on a development proposal, can be challenging, particularly outwith areas protected under the EU Birds and Habitats Directives.

The Scottish Government is committed to 'sustainable development' (SD), which should ensure that adequate weight is given to the need for long term protection of the superb natural environment that is one of Scotland's greatest assets. Unfortunately, however, it sometimes appears that 'while no policy document can now be written without some verbal genuflection to SD, when the levers of power are operated, it is often quietly forgotten' (Warren, 2009). It is important that the people of Scotland should remain excited about the welfare of their environment and feel that they can make a difference. The individuals who care most can generate strong grass-roots momentum for protection and restoration of the natural environment, by helping to explain and demonstrate its intrinsic – as well as its economic – value. But this momentum can only be maintained with support from government, as well as from the dedicated individuals within official bodies. Let us hope that in the years to come, the Scottish Government will work to ensure that both locally and internationally, SNH and the other agencies dealing with the environment, are seen as vibrant, credible, independent voices carrying the flag for the natural environment on behalf of citizens, supporting relevant NGOs and providing nourishment for the grass-roots. Only in this way can we hope to take pride in the state of the land of Scotland as we pass it to the next generation.

References

Ashmole, M. and Ashmole, P. (2009). *The Carrifran Wildwood Story: ecological restoration from the grass roots.* Borders Forest Trust, Jedburgh.

Ashmole, P. ed. (1994). *Restoring Borders Woodland.* Peeblesshire Environment Concern, Peebles.

Ashmole, P. (2006). The lost mountain woodland of Scotland and its restoration. *Scottish Forestry*, **60**, 9-22.

Badenoch, C. (1994). Woodland origins and the loss of native woodland in the Tweed valley. In *Restoring Borders Woodland*, ed. by P. Ashmole. Peeblesshire Environment Concern, Peebles.

Bainbridge, I.P., Housden, S.D., Minns, D. and Lance, A.N. (1987). Forestry in the Flows of Caithness and Sutherland. *Conservation Topic Paper*, No. **18**. Royal Society for the Protection of Birds, Sandy.

Bennett, K.D. (2009). Woodland decline in upland Scotland. *Plant Ecology & Diversity*, **2**, 91-93.

Chalmers, H., and Ashmole, P. (2007). Restoring the natural treeline at Carrifran. *Scrubbers' Bulletin*, **6**, 5-10.

Crumley, J. (1993). *Among Mountains.* Mainstream Publishing, Edinburgh & London.

Darling, F.F. (1949). History of the Scottish forests. Reprinted in *Tree Planters Guide to the Galaxy*, **7**, 25-27.

Fenton, J.H. (2008). A postulated natural origin for the open landscape of upland Scotland. *Plant Ecology & Diversity*, **1**, 115-127.

Fleming, L.V. Newton, A.C., Vickery, J.A. and Usher, M.B. (eds.) (1997). *Biodiversity in Scotland: Status, Trends and Initiatives.* The Stationery Office, Edinburgh.

Forestry Commission (1985). *The policy for broadleaved woodland.* Forestry Commission, Edinburgh.

Gilbert, D., Horsfield, D. and Thompson, D.B.A. eds. (1997). The ecology and restoration of montane and subalpine scrub habitats in Scotland. *Scottish Natural Heritage Review*, No. **83**.

Gurnell, A.M. (1998). The hydrogeomorphological effects of beaver dam-building activity. *Progress in Physical Geography*, **22**,167-189.

Hale, S.E., Quine, C.P. and Suárez, J.C. (1998). Climatic conditions associated with treelines of Scots pine and birch in Highland Scotland. *Scottish Forestry*, **52**, 70-76.

Hester, A.J. (1995). Scrub in the Scottish Uplands. *Scottish Natural Heritage Review*, No. **24**.

Hetherington, D.A. and Gorman, M.I. (2007). Using prey densities to estimate the potential size of reintroduced populations of Eurasian lynx. *Biological Conservation*, **137**, 37-44.

Humphrey, J.W., Gordon, P., Cowie, N. and Wilson, R. (2005). The contribution of the Scottish Forestry Alliance to the enhancement of woodland biodiversity in Scotland: a preliminary analysis. *Scottish Forestry*, **59**, 13-21.

Jenkins, D. ed. (1986). *Trees and Wildlife in the Scottish Uplands.* Institute of Terrestrial Ecology, Banchory.

Johnston, J.L. and Balharry, D. (2001). *Beinn Eighe: the mountain above the wood.* Birlinn, Edinburgh, for Scottish Natural Heritage.

Jordan, W.R. (1993). The re-entry of nature. *Reforesting Scotland*, **8**, 11-15.

Kohn, D. ed. (2003). *Restoring Borders Woodland: the vision and the task.* Occasional paper, Borders Forest Trust, Ancrum, Jedburgh.

Lawrence, A., Anglezarke, B., Frost, B., Nolan, P. and Owen, R. (2009). What does community forestry mean in a devolved Great Britain? *International Forestry Review*, **11**, 281-297.

Lovegrove, R. (2007). *Silent fields. The long decline of a nation's wildlife.* Oxford University Press, Oxford.

MacKenzie, N.A. and Callander, R.F. (1995). The Native Woodland Resource in the Scottish Highlands. *Forestry Commission Technical Paper*, **12**. Forestry Commission, Edinburgh.

MacKenzie, N.A. and Callander, R.F. (1996). The Native Woodland Resource in the Scottish Lowlands. *Forestry Commission Technical Paper*, **17**. Forestry Commission, Edinburgh.

Mardon, D. (1991). Montane willow scrub: gone today, gone forever? *Tree Planters Guide to the Galaxy*, **5**, 9-11.

McGhee, W. (2010). A year in the life of .... Borders Forest Trust. *Scottish Forestry*, **64**, 20-23.

Millennium Forest for Scotland Trust (2001). *Return of the Natives.* MFST, Glasgow.

Murgatroyd, I. (2005). Extreme botany. *Scottish Forestry*, **59**, 7-10.

Nature Conservancy Council (1988). *The Flow Country: the peatlands of Caithness.* NCC, Peterborough.

Newton, A.C., and Ashmole, P. eds. (1998). *Native woodland restoration in southern Scotland: principles and practice.* The University of Edinburgh and the Borders Forest Trust, Ancrum, Jedburgh.

Newton, I. (1997). *Population Ecology of Raptors.* T. & A.D. Poyser. Berkhamstead.

Norman, P. (2009). *Dumfries and Galloway Local Biodiversity Action Plan.* Dumfries and Galloway Council.

O'Brien, L., Townsend, M. and Ebden, M. (2008). *Environmental volunteering: motivations, barriers and benefits.* Report to the Scottish Forestry Trust and Forestry Commission. Forest Research, Alice Holt, Farnham.

Peterken, G.F., Baldock, D. and Hampson, A. (1995). A forest habitat network for Scotland. *Scottish Natural Heritage Review*, No. **44**.

Peterken, G. F. and Stevenson, W. (2004). *New dawn for native woodland restoration on the Forestry Commission estate in Scotland.* Forestry Commission Scotland, Edinburgh.

Planterose, B. (1990). An interview with Peter Wormell. *Tree Planters Guide to the Galaxy*, **2**, 2-4.

Pryor, S.N., Curtis, T.A. and Peterken G.F. (2002). *Restoring plantations on ancient woodland sites.* Woodland Trust, Grantham.

Quine, C.P. and Humphrey, J.W. (2010). Plantations of exotic tree species in Britain: irrelevant for biodiversity or novel habitat for native species? *Biodiversity & Conservation*, **19**, 1503-1512.

Ramsay, P. (1997). *Revival of the Land: Creag Meagaidh National Nature Reserve.* Scottish Natural Heritage.

Ratcliffe, D.A. ed. (1977). *A Nature Conservation Review.* 2 vols. Cambridge University Press, Cambridge.

Ratcliffe, D.A. and Thompson, D.B.A. (1988). The British uplands: their ecological character and international significance. In *Ecological change in the uplands*, ed. by M.B. Usher and D.B.A. Thompson. Blackwell, Oxford. pp 9-36.

Rodwell, J. and Patterson, G. (1994). Creating New Native Woodlands. *Forestry Commission Bulletin*, **112**.

Rowan, A.A. (1986). The nature of British upland forests in the 1980s. In *Trees and Wildlife in the Scottish Uplands*, ed. by D. Jenkins. Institute of Terrestrial Ecology, Huntingdon, UK.

Scott, M. (2005). Montane scrub – the challenge of the 'wee trees'. *British Wildlife*, **16**, 318-325.

Scottish Borders Council (2005). *Scottish Borders Woodland Strategy.*

Smout, T.C., MacDonald, A.R. and Watson, F. (2005). *A history of the Native Woodlands of Scotland, 1500-1920.* Edinburgh University Press, Edinburgh.

SNH (1993). *Sustainable Development and the Natural Heritage – the SNH approach.* Scottish Natural Heritage, Battleby.

Steven, H.M. and Carlisle, A. (1959). *The native pinewoods of Scotland.* Oliver and Boyd, Edinburgh.

Stolzenburg, W. (2008). *Where the Wild Things Were.* Bloomsbury, New York.

Stroud, D.A., Reed, T.M., Pienkowski, M.W. and Lindsay, R.A. (1987). *Birds, Bogs and Forestry.* Nature Conservancy Council, Peterborough.

Thompson, R., Humphrey, J., Harmer, R. and Ferris, R. (2003). *Restoration of native woodland on ancient woodland sites.* Practice Note. Forestry Commission, Edinburgh.

Tipping, R. (1994). The form and fate of Scotland's woodlands. *Proceedings of the Society of Antiquaries of Scotland*, **124**, 1-54.

Towers, W., Hall, J., Hester, A., Malcolm, A. and Stone, D. (2004). *The potential for native woodland in Scotland: the native woodland model.* Scottish Natural Heritage, Battleby.

Usher, M.B. (2002). Scotland's biodiversity: trends, changing perceptions and planning for action. In *The State of Scotland's Environment and Natural Heritage*, ed. by M.B. Usher, E.C. Mackey and J.C. Curran. The Stationery Office, Edinburgh. pp 257-269.

Warren, C. (2009). *Managing Scotland's Environment.* 2nd ed. Edinburgh University Press, Edinburgh.

Watson, A. (1992). The Trees for Life Project. *Tree Planters Guide to the Galaxy*, **7**, 3-6.

Wormell, P. (1977). Woodland insect population changes on the Isle of Rhum in relation to forest history and woodland restoration. *Scottish Forestry*, **31**, 13-36.

Worrell, R. (1995). European aspen (*Populus tremula* L.): a review with particular reference to Scotland. 1. Distribution, ecology and genetic variation. *Forestry*, **68**, 93-105.

The Changing Nature of Scotland

Uplands

Uplands

Around half of Scotland is upland in character. Blanket bog comprises fifty percent of this, and the rest is a mosaic of rough grassland, dwarf-shrub heath and a range of other mountain and moorland habitats. Many studies have quantified the cover of principal habitats, and several historical studies point to marked losses of natural habitat extent through deforestation, grazing and burning (e.g. Usher and Thompson, 1988; Bonn *et al.*, 2009; Britton *et al.*, 2009). In recent years, the evidence base points to one principal finding – an expansion by nearly 8% of acid grassland between 1998 and 2007 (Mackey & Mudge, 2010).

Some key events for nature in the uplands of Scotland since 1970

1982	Lurcher's Gully, Cairngorms Public Inquiry ruled against ski development expansion (further development proposal rejected in 1991)
1983	John Muir Trust formed to protect wilderness
1984	NCC purchased Creag Meagaidh SSSI to secure its natural heritage importance (created a NNR in 1986)
1985	Major publicity given to the Duich Moss SSSI, Islay conflict between 'conservation, peat, geese and islanders'
1986	NCC published *Nature Conservation and Afforestation*
1986	World Wilderness Conference called for Cairngorms to be designated a World Heritage Area (call repeated in 1987)
1987	NCC published *Birds, Bogs and Forestry*
1988	NCC published *The Flow Country*. Tax breaks on forestry schemes abolished
1991	Cairngorms Working Party formed (published report in 1992, making recommendations for protection and enhancement)
1994	Cairngorm Funicular Plan submitted, and Visitor Management Plan (with restricted access from development building) was agreed
1995	Cairngorms SAC proposal was submitted to the EC

n Harrier. © Laurie Campbell

1995	Mar Lodge Estate, Cairngorms purchased by the NTS, and Forsinard reserve, Sutherland purchased by RSPB
1997	*Birds of Prey and Red Grouse* (so-called Langholm report) published. Moorland Working Group formed to resolve raptor-grouse moor issues (became larger Moorland Forum in 2002)
1998	UK Upland Habitat Action Plan published
1999	Southern Upland Partnership formed
2000	Ben Nevis was acquired by the John Muir Trust
2002	International Year of Mountains (*Mountains of Northern Europe: conservation, management, people and nature*, published in 2005, reviews activities in support of this)
2003	Third national survey of golden eagles undertaken (previous ones in 1982, 1992)
2003	Cairngorms National Park is established
2007	European Structural Fund Programme for Lowlands and Uplands Scotland 2007–2013 launched
2007	Langholm Moor Demonstration Project launched
2008	Scotland's Moorland Forum launched its 'Uplands Solutions' project
2008	Royal Society of Edinburgh – Committee of Inquiry into the *Future of Scotland's Hills and Islands* proposed a new approach based on an explicit policy of achieving rural community viability
2009	*Farming Retreat from the Hills* – report by Rural Policy Centre SAC highlighted the dramatic fall in livestock numbers, particularly sheep since 1999 and outlined implications for biodiversity
2010	IUCN launches Commission of Inquiry on UK peatlands (to report in 2011)
2011	Scotland's first Land Use Strategy laid in Parliament on 17 March

Seven chapters reflect the breadth of research and knowledge on the changing nature of the uplands. Rob Brooker (Chapter 32) provides a comprehensive overview of the key drivers of change, notably nitrogen deposition, land-use, and to a still uncertain degree, climate. Indeed, Brooker comments that we still have only skeletal evidence of responses of habitats and species to climate, with the evident 'unresponsiveness' of the uplands meriting much closer examination. Grazing has clearly played an enormous role in shaping the landscape, and it will be fascinating to see how the uplands respond to declining numbers of grazing sheep.

James Pearce-Higgins (Chapter 33) looks at what we currently know, and perhaps more importantly what we do not know, about the effects of climate change on upland birds. Pearce-Higgins studied the ecology of the golden plover (*Pluvialis apricaria*) in the Peak District for his PhD. He found evidence of rising spring temperatures influencing the timing of available cranefly (*tipulid*) prey, which in turn had potential consequences for the timing of the plovers' hatch. Subsequently he has developed ideas regarding winter and/or summer temperature and precipitation influences on at least 12 species of birds in the Scottish Uplands, including the three arctic-alpine specialist breeders – ptarmigan, dotterel and snow bunting. It is arguable that increases in the amount of spring rainfall may have greater implications for some birds. For instance the indicator showing changes in upland birds has shown no overall change since 1994 (see Foster *et al.*, Chapter 2), this however, masks declines of some species, in particular two iconic upland birds the curlew (*Numenius arquata*) and golden plover. The late Jeff Watson provided a summary of some recent studies of golden eagles (*Aquila chrysaetos*) which point to marked effects on eagle productivity in parts of west Scotland (Watson, 2010). Importantly, Pearce-Higgins sets out in detail the consequences of such effects for how we manage protected areas. He makes a strong case for developing a robust monitoring framework which links the detection of changes to appropriate management responses – something, which will be difficult to achieve given constraints in resourcing. However, at least we are beginning to look ahead, and to think about how we need to respond to a different climate – if indeed we do need to.

By taking a look at the nature of some of the human influences on the changing upland landscape, Jamie Lindsay and Simon Thorp (Chapter 34) describe the complexities of managing this. They are primarily concerned with the distinctively cultural landscape of heather moorland, managed through muirburn, livestock control and predator management to maximise numbers of red grouse (*Lagopus lagopus scoticus*) shot. This chapter details how people and organisations work together to reconcile differences in approaches and to build on alliances of activities and views. They highlight the key importance of understanding the nature of human forces beyond simply being aware of the ecological complexities of the land and its nature.

Carrying on with this theme, Jayne Glass and colleagues (Chapter 35) have developed a new method for monitoring upland estate management. Their methods involve consensus building and the use of facilitators to tackle perceptions of problems and ways of addressing these. David Windle and colleagues (Chapter 38) describe another facet to working with people, this time working with volunteers to map and assess changes in hill tracks in north east Scotland. This is new work, which began in 2008, but developed research initiated by one of the most eminent ecologists still working in Scotland, Dr Adam Watson. The authors hope to extend their work across the Cairngorms National Park, to develop our understanding of how tracks change.

It is striking how scientific work in the uplands has moved from the basics of ecological investigations to much more integrated and inter-disciplinary approaches. In their overview of ecological change in the British Uplands, Usher and Thompson (1988) barely mention studies of political or organisational processes, because then there were few such studies. Now major research institutes and groups work closely with government bodies and NGOs to devise ways of tackling environmental issues, and endeavour to influence the policies, management practices and activities of key organisations with influence over the land.

But of course we still need solid ecological field studies. Gordon Rothero and colleagues (Chapter 37) describe a remarkable study of snowbed bryophytes in the highest reaches of the Cairngorms. Working in often harsh weather conditions, the authors have provided a very clear account of differences in the frequencies of some species between 1989 and 2007-08. One species, the starry saxifrage (*Saxifraga stellaris*), was not recorded in any of the snowbed plots in 1989, but by 2007 was present in 17 plots. A network of monitoring sites has now been established, and on-going work here will surely point the way to how plants respond to climate and other influences at one extreme of Britain.

Two of the founding fathers of British upland ecology, Dr Donald McVean and the late Dr Derek Ratcliffe, worked in the Scottish Highlands between 1956 and 1958 to devise a new classification and understanding of plant communities. Their seminal textbook (McVean and Ratcliffe, 1962) became a benchmark in our understanding of the diversity of plantlife in the uplands. Working for a PhD on upland vegetation Louise Ross has revisited some of the original McVean and Ratcliffe plots to see if there have been changes over the past 50 or so years. In Chapter 36, Ross and co-workers describe some of the early results. It would appear that the alpine heaths, grasslands and dwarf-shrub heaths have changed more than the peatland habitats – something which may surprise many ecologists. Some of the more generalist graminoids have increased in cover, whilst the cover of lichens, bryophytes, shrubs and forbs have declined. What has caused these shifts? Early analyses are pointing to the importance of increasing levels of nitrogen deposition and higher grazing pressures compared with the late 1950s, but possibly also warmer temperatures. This work underlines the importance of having robust ecological foundations on which to build our understanding of the nature of change.

References

Bonn, A., Allott, T., Hubacek, K. and Stewart, J. (eds.) (2009). *Drivers of Environmental Change in the Uplands.* Routledge, London.

Britton, A.J., Beale, C.M., Towers, W. and Hewison, R.L. (2009). Biodiversity gains and losses: Evidence for homogenisation of Scottish alpine vegetation. *Biological Conservation*, **142**, 1728-1739.

McVean, D. and Ratcliffe, D.A. (1962). *Plant Communities in the Scottish Highlands.* Monograph No. 1 of the Nature Conservancy. HMSO, London.

Usher, M.B. and Thompson, D.B.A. (eds.) (1988). *Ecological Change in the Uplands.* Blackwell Scientific, Oxford.

Watson, J. (2010). *The Golden Eagle.* Second Edition. A & C Black/Poyser, London.

32 The Changing Nature of Scotland's Uplands – an Interplay of Processes and Timescales

Rob Brooker

Summary

1. The historical context within which we attempt to manage current environmental change impacts in Scotland's uplands is important.
2. Environmental drivers impact on landscape and biodiversity patterns set by long-term interactions between people and the environment.
3. Key current environmental change drivers, in particular nitrogen deposition, land use change and, to some degree, climate change, are increasing the productivity of historically unproductive systems, enabling the encroachment of more competitive species and possibly driving the loss of characteristic upland species which are dependent on low system productivity.
4. Interestingly, the evidence base for responses in habitats and species to climate change, even at the highest altitudes, is skeletal. The 'unresponsiveness' of the uplands to climate change merits closer examination.
5. Finally, conservation benchmarks are discussed. In upland systems that have always been changing, occasionally quite rapidly, what do we take as our baseline or benchmark for management efforts?

32.1 Introduction

The obvious starting point when considering how the uplands and their biodiversity are responding to environmental change is to consider those environmental pressures that we know are of current importance, including changes in management, increasing nitrogen deposition loads, and climate change. However, it is perhaps useful sometimes to step back and to take a longer-term perspective.

Brooker, R. (2011). The Changing Nature of Scotland's Uplands – an Interplay of Processes and Timescales – *The Changing Nature of Scotland*, eds. S.J. Marrs, S. Foster, C. Hendrie, E.C. Mackey, D.B.A. Thompson. TSO Scotland, Edinburgh, pp 381-396.

Here, I consider some of the major events that have shaped the structure of the Scottish Uplands – both human and natural – and their impacts on biodiversity. I focus in particular on changes in vegetation and habitats, with some more limited discussion of their consequences for associated fauna, beginning at a point 15-12,000 years b.p. (before present). By taking this long-term perspective it becomes clear that the landscapes that we see today, and the patterns of biodiversity within them, are the result of on-going changes. In order to understand and interpret the impacts of some of the key current environmental drivers it is essential to understand this historical context.

However, this historical perspective also raises some difficult questions. Most obviously, if environments are continually fluctuating, and natural systems are always in a state of responsive flux, why should we be concerned about current change? Questions are also raised that are central to discussions concerning the future of the uplands. As set out elsewhere in this book (in particular see Lindsay and Thorp, Chapter 34), we need to define clear priorities and targets for management of the uplands. But, in systems that are continually changing and developing how do we set our benchmark?

It should be noted that in this chapter I take the usual and reasonable liberty of including under the upland heading most areas north and west of the highland boundary line (excluding of course the productive areas of crofting land and farm land in valley bottoms and on coastal fringes) as well as the higher altitude areas of the southern uplands and borders region. The British Uplands are characterised by an oceanic climate, with cooler, wetter and windier conditions in the north and west. Upland-type systems therefore are not only found in the uplands *sensu stricto*, and upland habitats in the south and east of Scotland occurring at 300m to 400m above sea level can be found at sea level in the north and west of Scotland.

32.2 Environmental change in the uplands – the historical context

Information throughout this section has been drawn largely from the following work: Fraser Darling and Morton Boyd (1964); Maclean (1993); and McKirdy *et al.* (2007).

About 12,000 years b.p. there was a notable warming of the climate. At the time Scotland was heavily glaciated. The glacier systems were not as thick or widespread as they had been at the peak of the ice a few thousand years earlier, but even so they covered a considerable extent of the country. Their melt-out started the current Holocene interglacial period, which is also referred to as the postglacial period.

The retreat of the ice led to the development of soils, and the colonisation of vegetation. Low temperatures and the initial absence of soils would mean that biological processes proceeded relatively slowly, but by 8,500 years b.p. much of the Scottish Uplands was covered by woodland. Pine-birch woodland (*Pinus sylvestris* and *Betula spp.*) covered the central upland area from Strathspey northwards, with birch-hazel woodland (*Betula spp.* and *Coryllus avellana*) in northern Sutherland and Caithness and hazel-oak woodland (*C. avellana* and *Quercus spp.*) at lower altitude and toward the coast. Oak, hazel and elm (*Ulmus spp.*) dominated in the south of Scotland. Mountain tops remained unwooded and probably covered by dwarf shrub vegetation similar to that found beyond the treeline in northern Scandinavia today. The transition zone between the two would have been filled by willow (*Salix spp.*) and birch scrub.

The relative paucity of vascular plant species in the Scottish uplands has been attributed to the isolation of Scottish mountain systems from the species-rich southern mountains such as the Alps (Polunin and Walters, 1985), which were centres of endemism and species retreat during the previous ice ages. Ice-free areas – nunataks – occurred on the mountain tops of Scotland, but it is neither clear whether these were continually ice-free, or whether they provided sufficient refugia for the retreat of Scottish alpine species. Although the post-glacial climate during the period of forest expansion was initially warmer, drier, and less variable than at present, roughly 6,500 years b.p. the climate became more variable and shifted to generally wetter and cooler conditions, leading to the expansion of peat areas and the replacement of upland woodland by wet heaths.

The first evidence of human habitation within Scotland comes from before 10,000 years b.p., but it is only at about 6,000 years b.p. that there is evidence of settled farming activity. Coastal systems and valley bottoms were widely occupied. Coastal systems had the benefit of ready access by sea, as well as comparatively easily-worked soils. However, there is also evidence of woodland clearance for upland pasture establishment, and there are even signs of crop production in the uplands during the Bronze Age. Despite poorer climatic conditions, particularly cooling during the late Bronze Age, farming activities continued to have an impact on the uplands. This occurred particularly through the process of transhumance – the movement of people and livestock from lowland or coastal systems to mountain valleys and pastures to make use of the short summer period of good grazing. Holl and Smith (2007) provide an interesting review of the legacy of transhumance for today's upland biodiversity. These hill pastures – and the settlements associated with them – were the Shielings. Continued use of the Shielings, including the grazing and dunging impact of associated animals, is likely to have modified the vegetation such that current vegetation in some areas still reflects these cultural practices. Woodland near to the Shielings was managed for fuel, and park-type woodland developed where grazers operated beneath an open woodland canopy.

Strath'an, for example, was an important route of migration from the Moray coastal plain to summer grazing areas within the Cairngorms, and the vegetation along the Strath, particularly in areas where the cattle halted overnight, remains detectably different in composition even today.

Gradually, lowland forests were cleared and more intensive farming expanded out from the coastal plain. Some of the woodland was burned during periods of war and some burned to improve the land for cultivation. Further expansion of farming into wooded areas was likely promoted by the extermination of large predators such as the wolf (*Canis lupus*), the last of which was supposedly killed around the mid 1700s. Hunting, in combination with woodland clearance, also led to the extinction of some key herbivores, including moose (*Alces alces*) (extinct by about 1300) and the wild ox, urus or auroch (*Bos taurus primigenius*), and changes in the habits of others. Perhaps most importantly red deer (*Cervus elaphus*) went from inhabiting open forested ground to surviving year-round in the afforested upland environments. This has had consequences both for the upland plant communities that are impacted by their grazing, for example limiting the regeneration of woodland following cessation of more intensive management such as cyclic burning, and also for the upland red deer themselves which, relative to those inhabiting woodland systems, have decreased body size, delayed puberty in the females, and comparatively low fertility (Staines *et al.*, 1995).

Following this piecemeal clearance of the woodlands, systematic exploitation for timber and charcoal began around the sixteenth century and accelerated following the collapse of the first Jacobite uprising of 1715. Following the 1745 rebellion much of the upland pasture land was turned over to grazing forage for sheep, and the Shielings in the valleys were emptied. The richer upland pastures developed during the Shieling system are likely to have been maintained in some places by sheep grazing, and comparatively productive in-by land can still be seen next to abandoned Shielings in the valley-bottoms. A final significant change in the management of the uplands was the rise of the shooting estates during the 1800s. Particularly in the eastern and southern uplands, the management regime for grouse moor – cyclic burning management – further promoted the extensive dominance of heather (*Calluna vulgaris*) (Figure 32.1), and limited the potential for woodland regeneration following any associated reductions in herbivore numbers (Figure 32.1). Extensive deer forests also developed, either above the areas of sheep grazing or grouse management in the east and south, or at lower levels in the north and western highlands, where the wetter climate limited the dominance of heather.

These examples demonstrate that the upland landscape as seen today is the result of human influence over thousands of years, which is itself overlain on and constrained by a landscape and ecology formed and still heavily influenced by the last glaciation.

Figure 32.1 Traditionally managed upland moorland system with rotational heather burning to enhance grouse numbers. Areas of recent monoculture plantation forestry, with some small sections of recent clear-felling (top left), can also be seen. © Rob Brooker

For example, on the Scottish mountain tops we have alpine systems which, although relatively poor in vascular plant species, are rich in bryophytes and mosses. The low system productivity in these areas, along with the grazing impacts of deer and sheep at lower altitudes, prevents the encroachment of dwarf shrubs or scrub. In terms of woodland, 'natural' upland woodland is highly fragmented due to management activities, although there are large areas of plantation resulting from twentieth century reforestation schemes (discussed in more detail below). The intervening areas are covered by moorland which is dependent, particularly in the south and east, on rotational burning (Figure 32.1) and some limited grazing to maintain its open nature. The upland landscape has clearly been continually developing under the influence of man, and in response to both economic and societal drivers, as well as 'natural' drivers such as species migration and shifts in climate.

32.3 Recent drivers of environmental change in the uplands

There are a number of more recent drivers of change ('recent' being taken here as operating from the mid-to-late 1940s onwards) which have caused and are causing considerable concern for those interested in conserving Scotland's upland biodiversity. I will briefly examine the effects of each, discussing how their impacts are related in part to the longer-term processes that have led to the structure of upland environments.

32.3.1 What changes have been detected?

Long-term data are particularly useful for detecting change in higher-altitude upland systems which contain many long-lived, slow-growing species in relatively unproductive conditions, and which are thus normally relatively slow to respond. Some monitoring data were collected intentionally, for example through the Environmental Change Network (ECN) sites, but perhaps some of the best information comes through serendipity. For example, recent work by Andrea Britton and colleagues (Britton *et al.*, 2009) has involved revisiting a widespread set of plots initially recorded in order to describe alpine vegetation in Scotland. The original recording work was undertaken by Birse and Robertson between 1963 and 1987, with most data being collected in the early 1970s (see Britton *et al.*, 2009 for details). Between 2004 and 2006 a targeted resurvey of these plots was undertaken and focussed on four areas with a high density of original plots: the Cairngorms, Mull, the Southern Uplands and the Northern Isles.

In brief, Britton *et al.* found a general increase in species richness over time across all sites, but that this was stronger for vascular plants and bryophytes than for lichens. The greatest changes were seen in the vegetation found in the immediate vicinity of springs, followed by snowbeds, with fellfield (open, wind-swept mountain-top) systems changing the least (Figure 32.2). Overall there was a general homogenisation of the composition of these communities, that is plant communities from these four quite strongly-contrasting mountain areas are becoming more similar. There are likely to be a number of interacting factors involved in driving such changes. For example homogenisation may be the result of the expansion of widespread generalist species in response to warming and nitrogen deposition. The unproductive nature of these upland systems makes many of the species growing in them sensitive to drivers that increase productivity such as higher temperatures or increased soil nutrient availability. The greatest decline in lichen diversity, for example, was seen in the Southern Uplands, which experience the highest nitrogen pollution load of all the areas surveyed. The sizable changes in snowbed systems, as well as the decline in cover and frequency of species with northern and alpine distributions, also indicate a climate impact.

In contrast to the increase in richness detected by Britton *et al.*, the recent analysis of Countryside Survey 2007 data (Carey *et al.*, 2008) from mountain, moor and heath habitats showed a 12% reduction in the mean species richness score in the dwarf shrub heath broad habitat, from an average of 20.3 to 17.8 plant species per plot, between 1990 and 2007. However, this habitat class includes more

Figure 32.2 Mountain top communities typical of those revisited by Britton *et al.* (2009) in order to assess long-term trends in vegetation in Scottish mountain-top systems. These include a) wind-clipped dwarf shrub heath, b) fellfield, c) *Sphagnum*-rich spring, and d) snow-bed communities. Photographs reproduced with permission of A. Britton, James Hutton Institute.

lower-altitude areas than that examined by Britton *et al.*: increasing productivity in high altitude systems can remove limits of vascular plant growth allowing more plant species overall to survive, while at lower altitudes it enables the expansion of relatively competitive plant species, with the potential for exclusion of those that are less competitive. Such an effect may be indicated by the increased cover of grass species relative to forbs detected by Countryside Survey between 1998 and 2007 in dwarf shrub heath habitats.

A further repeat survey in the uplands, by Louise Ross *et al.* (Chapter 36) in 2007 and 2008, re-examined habitats surveyed by McVean and Ratcliffe (1962). Ross *et al.*'s findings are similar to those of Britton *et al.* in that they indicate an increased dominance of generalist upland species. They also found that not all systems are changing to the same extent. As they state 'Alpine heaths, grasslands and dwarf-shrub heaths have undergone more change than ombrogenous and soligenous mires, which have retained more of their original character'.

Importantly, the findings of these surveys may be demonstrating in part the impacts of two key drivers of current significant concern for upland systems: nitrogen deposition and climate change.

32.3.2 Nitrogen deposition

Nitrogen deposition is clearly associated with human activity and in particular industrialisation. Some of the most obvious effects of nitrogen deposition in the UK can be seen in the northern Pennine regions to the east of Manchester (Lee and Caporn, 1998). High levels of nitrogen input are immediately detrimental to some upland species groups such as bryophytes and lichens. For example, negative impacts of nitrogen deposition on species richness have been found following experimental nitrogen addition to lichen-rich *Calluna* heath in the Cairngorms (Britton and Fisher, 2007). In particular it was the lichen species that declined, and this was likely to be due to the direct negative impacts of nitrogen on lichens, as the surrounding vegetation showed little apparent response (Britton *et al.*, 2008). However, nitrogen inputs can also operate through changes in the interactions between species. The moss *Racomitrium lanuginosum*, is the main bryophyte component of much of the high mountain moss heaths found particularly in the extensive high plateaux of the Cairngorms, the West Highlands and Ben Wyvis plateaux. As with lichens, high levels of nitrogen input are inimical to the moss, but have also been shown to increase competition from surrounding vascular plants, in particular stiff sedge (*Carex bigelowii*). Furthermore, high nitrogen inputs lead to grassier vegetation and this attracts herbivores, including sheep, deer, and mountain hares. Grazers both trample and chew the moss, and their dunging further enriches the soil which creates a negative feedback loop, the end result of which is the gradual loss of *Racomitrium* from these systems (Pearce *et al.*, 2003; Van der Wal *et al.*, 2003). This is particularly important when we consider that such heaths are habitat for upland species of high conservation concern such as the dotterel (*Charadrius morinellus*), which depend upon the moss-rich heaths both for nesting in, and also to provide food – much of it from tipulid larvae and adults – for developing chicks (Galbraith *et al.*, 1993).

32.3.3 Climate change

Certain long-term trends in vegetation have been attributed to climate change, for example increases across the UK in the ranges of native species with a wide, southerly European distribution, and decreases in species with a very northerly European distribution (Preston *et al.*, 2002). Changes detected at the UK level are mirrored in alpine systems across the world (Krajick, 2004). One aspect of alpine systems, making them of particular conservation concern, is that the upward expansion of lowland species leads to their increasing fragmentation and isolation. In Scotland this is likely to be exacerbated by the fragmenting effects of land management and the restriction of many species to limited areas free from intense grazing, for example the restriction of arctic-alpine plants to rock ledges on Ben Lawers, or of willow scrub to the cliff ledges of Corrie Fee in Glen Doll.

Once again long-term data are essential in detecting and understanding those changes that are occurring, and they can throw-up some surprising results. For example, a study of the decline of the ring ouzel (*Turdus torquatus*) in upland breeding sites across Britain (Beale *et al.*, 2006) found that territory occupancy was regulated by climatic drivers both in the UK and at the birds' wintering grounds in Morocco. Decreased summer rainfall is thought to be influencing the availability of, for example, berries and key insect foods in the autumn, whilst spring rainfall in Morocco appears to influence juniper berry production at the birds Moroccan over-wintering grounds.

What is perhaps a little surprising is that some systems seem relatively 'unresponsive'. As mentioned, fellfield systems seem little changed based on analysis of revisits to the Birse and Robertson plots (Britton *et al.*, 2009). Climate as a regulatory factor is quite complex, and in Scotland high wind speeds are particularly important. It is possible that high wind speeds are limiting the temperature or nitrogen-driven increases in system productivity and expansion of more competitive species, so helping to maintain the open nature and diversity of these systems. The role of high wind speeds is borne out in recent modelling work (Crabtree and Ellis, 2010) which concluded that in lichen-rich alpine heath a 20% increase in wind speed would offset the effects of projected increases in temperature by limiting the growth of neighbouring plants. Indeed the 'unresponsiveness' so far of many upland habitat and species in the face of climate change merits much closer scrutiny.

32.3.4 Change in land use practice

The examples given so far have focused very much on high upland systems such as fellfields, snowbeds, and high mountain moss heaths. In the lower altitude areas of

Scotland's uplands a different driver is having significant impacts on biodiversity and ecosystems – changes in land-use practice. Land-use changes are more influential at lower altitudes because, as we descend into the valleys, both the productivity of the systems and the intensity of agricultural use increase.

Important long-term data on land use change during the post-war period comes from sources such as the June Agricultural Census returns used, for example, by Fuller and Gough (1999), the National Countryside Monitoring Scheme (the NCMS; Mackey *et al.*, 1998), and the Red Deer Commission's annual counts of deer numbers from 1959 onward (Staines *et al.*, 1995).

A key change in the uplands identified by the NCMS was the decline in cover of heather moorland (18% reduction between the 1940s and 1970s) and concomitant reductions in unimproved grassland and mire by 9% and 8% respectively (Tudor and Mackey, 1995). Of these declines, 62% was attributed to conversion to plantation coniferous forest – promoted by the Forestry Act of 1945 which directed forest expansion into marginal upland areas. The greatest rates of loss of heather moorland were seen in regions outside of the Highlands and Islands (Tudor and Mackey, 1995), but were substantially lower in areas being actively managed for grouse shooting (Robertson *et al.*, 2001).

However, even on areas being managed for shooting, heather decline has continued. This may result from increases in both sheep and deer numbers in the post-war period, and hence over-grazing, which generally drives a change from dwarf shrub- to graminoid-dominated plant communities (Hudson, 1995). Red deer numbers, although showing some decline in the early 1960s, rose sharply in the late 1960s and early 1970s. This was particularly true in the eastern and central Highlands, although changes in deer management such as increased winter-time feeding may have more strongly driven over-grazing in some areas than increasing numbers of overall (Staines *et al.*, 1995). High sheep numbers were promoted until recently by production-linked agricultural incentive payments (Robertson *et al.*, 2001).

More recent changes (from the late 1990s onward) in grazing management and other land-use practices in upland systems have been succinctly summarised in a recent report (Renwick and Waterhouse, 2008). This report indicates that there have been considerable recent reductions in grazing livestock in upland areas – in some areas between 35% and 60% – with the decline in sheep numbers being much greater than that for cattle. One important impetus for this has been the decoupling of livestock numbers from farm payments since the introduction of the Single Farm Payment Scheme. Other drivers of this reduction in grazing are the lack of available labour leading to the more intensive management of flocks on in-by land. Notably, the cause of this decline in livestock numbers is complex, with a high degree of geographical variation across the Highlands and Islands.

Figure 32.3 Birch woodland at Muir of Dinnet, Deeside, Aberdeenshire. Birch woodland in this area has expanded rapidly following the cessation of farming. © Rob Brooker

What are the likely consequences of these more recent changes in grazing regime? As discussed above with respect to nitrogen deposition and *Racomitrium* heath, sheep grazing might interact with other drivers of change to cause a greater impact than when working in isolation. Reduction in sheep numbers might have direct beneficial consequences for some high altitude plant communities. Plants previously

Figure 32.4 Improved grazing areas at the margins of heather moorland in Glen Gairn, also showing evidence of shrub and woodland expansion on the hill slope to the top right of the picture. © Rob Brooker

restricted to cliff ledges – for example downy willow (*Salix lapponum*) – might be able to extend their current ranges, so long as current low population sizes do not prevent them from producing sufficient viable propagules. However, some other habitats might suffer, with species rich grazed grasslands being increasingly dominated by taller vegetation and the encroachment of dwarf shrubs. Although declining sheep numbers might be compensated to some extent by increasing deer grazing, the browsing habit of these animals is different and so changes in vegetation will occur.

At a wider landscape level grazing is one of the key processes that have structured and continue to maintain the upland landscape. The impacts of reduced grazing can clearly be seen, both in areas where reductions in grazing pressure are intentional, for example in the expansion of woodland in the Royal Society for the Protection of Birds (RSPB's) Abernethy Estate following intensive deer management, but also in the expansion of birch woodland and scrub following general decline in herbivore numbers (Figures 32.3 and 32.4). Woodland expansion can have important below-ground impacts. The presence of even individual trees can significantly alter the composition of the understorey vegetation by drying soils, and this is associated with concomitant changes in the soil community. A study of a wet heath site at the Allt á Mharcaidh catchment in the Cairngorms (Brooker *et al.*, 2008) demonstrated how the presence of isolated Scots pines is associated with significantly higher species richness in the associated soil mite community. Trees can also alter soil communities and processes by increasing nutrient availability and the rate of decomposition. Critically, this increased productivity and acceleration of soil processes can be associated with reduction in carbon storage in the organic horizon of upland soils (Mitchell *et al.*, 2007).

32.4 Discussion

Clearly in the Scottish Uplands we have a landscape that has developed over the past 12,000 years through a slow interaction between people and nature, but which is characterised by relatively unproductive environments where moderate grazing and harsh abiotic environmental conditions help restrict the expansion of more competitive species. We also have a number of more recent drivers such as nitrogen deposition and climate change that would directly act to increase system productivity. Other drivers may act in synergy to exacerbate these effects, for example declining sheep grazing, although not all systems will be equally susceptible to either these direct or synergistic impacts. Within this context considerable effort is being put into both understanding the causes of change in upland habitats and ecosystems, and in managing that change to enable the uplands to continue to deliver the goods and services that we have come to expect.

One of the problems we face, however, in assessing the impacts of current change is that we still have an imperfect understanding of what our upland systems contain, particularly with regard to the less studied groups such as lichens, soil organisms and invertebrates. A good example of this is the recent discovery of the collembolan springtail (*Bourletiella viridescens*), which was found at 880m on Creagan Dubh in the Cairngorms during August 2009 by Tim Ransom. It is the first record of this species in Scotland, but is it newly arrived or has it always been there? The number of long-term records such as the Birse and Robertson or McVean and Ratcliffe data are not huge, although monitoring efforts have expanded greatly in recent years, for example through Environmental Change Network (ECN) and the UK Countryside Survey. Furthermore the uplands are difficult areas to survey comprehensively, and we lack taxonomic skills for the difficult species groups, although some efforts are being made to address this (e.g. Britton, 2008).

Not only do we have an imperfect understanding as to what the uplands currently contain, taking a longer-term look at environmental change in the uplands raises some difficult issues with respect to determining what the uplands *should* contain, and what goods and services we should expect them to deliver. It is clear that change in the uplands – even relatively rapid change – is nothing new: strong societal pressures have historically driven some rapid changes. But in systems that have been continually changing and developing, how do we set our benchmark? If we were to take, for example, heather moorland, it has been argued that a 1940s benchmark for restoration is inadequate as drivers of the decline in moorland cover having been acting over a far longer time period, that is from pre-1700 onward (Davies, 2009). A logical progression of this argument, though, could be that a more 'natural' Scottish upland environment would have relatively low cover of heather moorland, as this is likely to have been the case prior to major deforestation of upland systems and the imposition of management through cyclic burning and grazing.

Even if we were to take an earlier (e.g. 1900) benchmark as a target for moorland restoration, given the current unique combination of environmental and social conditions, which differs in many ways from that of the 1900s (different climatic conditions, higher nitrogen loads, greater pressure from tourism, less available and more expensive labour) is it actually possible to achieve this goal? Also, given that many of our more detailed records of biodiversity reach back – at best – to the 1940s and 1950s, how can we assess whether we have achieved our 1900 target 'in the round', including the wide diversity of organisms that are an important part of the upland biodiversity resource but which previously have not been well studied and may even now be poorly understood?

The problem of adopting benchmarks based on previous conditions – a general one for conservation ecology (Willis and Birks, 2006) – prompts us to consider whether we should instead be thinking about conservation of the uplands in a flexible adaptive framework that has targets for service provision and species conservation, but which is not struggling to achieve some long-gone apparent state of Eden. This would necessitate an assessment of current management targets for upland habitats and species. Such an assessment obviously needs to be sensitive to the cultural and economic value of existing land use and associated tradition, and should also take account of the wide range of demands that are currently, and will be, placed upon upland systems along with the realistic possibility of achieving these targets given current environmental and societal pressures. However, it does not argue for a cessation of management, nor that management is unfocussed, but simply that the goal of management *might not be* stasis if we conclude that stasis is impossible.

Acknowledgements

I would particularly like to thank Andrea Britton, Alison Hester, Chris Ellis, James Pearce-Higgins and Davy McCracken for their help in producing the presentation given at the 2009 conference in Perth, and in the production of this chapter, along with Des Thompson and two anonymous referees whose comments helped greatly in improving my original text. I would also like to acknowledge funding from the Scottish Government Rural and Environment Research and Analysis Directorate (RERAD).

References

Beale, C.M., Burfield, I.J., Innes, I.M.W. *et al.* (2006). Climate change may account for the decline in British ring ouzels *Turdus torquatus*. *Journal of Animal Ecology*, **75**, 826-835.

Britton, A.J. and Fisher, J. (2007). Interactive effects of nitrogen deposition, fire and grazing on diversity and composition of low-alpine prostrate *Calluna vulgaris* heathland. *Journal of Applied Ecology*, **44**, 125-135.

Britton, A. (2008). *The Montane Heathland Lichen Guide.* Macaulay Institute, Aberdeen.

Britton, A.J., Helliwell, R.C., Fisher, J.M. and Gibbs, S. (2008). Interactive effects of nitrogen deposition and fire on plant and soil chemistry in alpine heathland. *Environmental Pollution*, **156**, 409-416.

Britton, A.J., Beale, C., Towers, W. and Hewison, R.L. (2009). Biodiversity gains and losses: evidence for homogenisation of Scottish alpine vegetation. *Biological Conservation*, **142**, 1728-1739.

Brooker, R.W., Osler, G. and Gollisch, J. (2008). Association of vegetation and soil mite assemblages with isolated Scots pine trees on a Scottish wet heath. *Landscape Ecology*, **23**, 861-871.

Carey, P.D., Wallis, S., Chamberlain, P.M. *et al.* (2008). *Countryside Survey: UK Results from 2007.* NERC/Centre for Ecology & Hydrology, Wallingford.

Crabtree, D. and Ellis, C.J. (2010). Species interaction and response to wind-speed alter the impact of projected temperature change in a montane ecosystem. *Journal of Vegetation Science*, **21**, 744-760.

Davies, A. (2009). Review of the historical environmental changes in the UK uplands relevant to management and policy. http://www.sbes.stir.ac.uk/people/davies/index.html, accessed July 2010.

Fraser Darling, F. and Morton Boyd, J. (1964). *The Highlands and Islands.* Collins, London.

Fuller, R.J. and Gough, S.J. (1999). Changes in sheep numbers in Britain: implications for bird populations. *Biological Conservation*, **91**, 73-89.

Galbraith, H., Murray, S., Duncan, K. *et al.* (1993). Diet and habitat use of the Dotterel *Charadrius morinellus* in Scotland. *Ibis*, **135**, 148-155.

Holl, K. and Smith, M. (2007). Scottish upland forests: History lessons for the future. *Forest Ecology and Management*, **249**, 45-53.

Hudson, P. J. (1995). Ecological trends and grouse management in upland Britain. In *Heaths and Moorland:Cultural Landscapes*, ed. by D.B.A. Thompson, A.J. Hester and M.B. Usher. HMSO, Edinburgh. pp 282-293.

Krajick, K. (2004). All downhill from here? *Science*, **303**, 1600-1602.

Lee, J.A. and Caporn, S.J.M. (1998). Ecological effects of atmospheric reactive nitrogen deposition on semi-natural terrestrial ecosystems. *New Phytologist*, **139**, 127-134.

Maclean, F. (1993). *Scotland: A Concise History (Revised Edition).* Thames and Hudson, London.

Mackey, E.C., Shewry, M.C. and Tudor, G. J. (1998). *Land cover change: Scotland from the 1940s to the 1980s.* HMSO, Edinburgh.

Mitchell, R.J., Campbell, C.D., Chapman, S. *et al.* (2007). The cascading effects of birch on heather moorland: a test for the top-down control of an ecosystem engineer. *Journal of Ecology*, **95**, 540-554.

McKirdy, A., Gordon, J. and Crofts, R. (2007). *Land of Mountain and Flood: The geology and landforms of Scotland.* SNH and Birlinn Limited, Edinburgh.

McVean, D.A. and Ratcliffe, D.N. (1962). *Plant Communities of the Scottish Highlands.* Monograph No. 1 of the Nature Conservancy. HMSO, London.

Pearce, I.S.K., Woodin, S. and van der Wal, R. (2003). Physiological and growth responses of the montane bryophyte *Racomitrium lanuginosum* to atmospheric nitrogen deposition. *New Phytologist*, **160**, 145-155.

Polunin, O. and Walters, M. (1985). *A Guide to the Vegetation of Britain and Europe.* Oxford University Press, Oxford.

Preston, C.D., Telfer, M.G., Arnold, H.R. and Rothery P. (2002). The changing flora of Britain. In *New Atlas of the British and Irish Flora*, ed. by C.D. Preston, D.A. Pearman and T.D. Dines. Oxford University Press, Oxford. pp 35-45.

Renwick, A. and Waterhouse, T. (2008). *Farming's Retreat from the Hills.* Scottish Agricultural College, Edinburgh.

Robertson, P.A., Park, K.J. and Barton, A.F. (2001). Loss of heather *Calluna vulgaris* moorland in the Scottish uplands: The role of red grouse *Lagopus lagopus scoticus* management. *Wildlife Biology*, **7**, 37-42.

Staines, B.W., Balharry, R. and Welch, D. (1995). The impact of red deer and their management on the natural heritage in the uplands. In *Heaths and Moorland: Cultural Landscapes*, ed. by D.B.A. Thompson, A.J. Hester and M.B. Usher. HMSO, Edinburgh. pp 294-308.

Tudor, G. and Mackey, E.C. (1995). Upland land cover change in post-war Scotland. In *Heaths and Moorland: Cultural Landscapes*, ed. by D.B.A. Thompson, A.J. Hester and M.B. Usher. HMSO, Edinburgh. pp 28-42.

Van der Wal, R., Pearce, I., Brooker, R. *et al.* (2003). Interplay between nitrogen deposition and grazing causes habitat degradation. *Ecology Letters*, **6**, 141-146.

Willis, K.J. and Birks, H.J.B. (2006). What is natural? The need for a long-term perspective in biodiversity conservation. *Science*, **314**, 1261-1265.

33 How Ecological Science Can Help Manage the Effects of Climate Change: A Case Study of Upland Birds

James W. Pearce-Higgins

Summary

1. Populations of upland birds are less-well monitored than many of their lowland counterparts, although there is evidence that more than ten species are experiencing population declines.
2. There is uncertainty over the causes of these declines, although there is evidence for some adverse impacts of recent climate change on a few species, as illustrated by the possible impacts of rising temperature upon golden plovers (*Pluvialis apricaria*), and populations of their cranefly (*Tipulidae*) prey. Others may be increasingly threatened by further changes in the climate, whereas some species may benefit.
3. There is considerable debate about how conservationists should respond to climate change. In relation to UK upland birds, I argue for the protection of large areas of semi-natural habitat, and the development of a framework to maximise the resilience of vulnerable populations.
4. This framework requires the establishment of long-term monitoring of a range of taxa; research to identify the primary mechanisms by which climate change will affect species; trials of potential adaptation management to counter those effects; and if successful, the wider implementation of such management.
5. Science is essential to guide the management of change, and monitoring and research should be given priority to reduce current uncertainties. However, given uncertainties over both future climate change impacts and the potential for effective adaptive management, policies should follow a 'no-regrets principle', providing biodiversity benefits both now and in the future.

Pearce-Higgins, J.W. (2011). How Ecological Science Can Help Manage the Effects of Climate Change: A Case Study of Upland Birds – *The Changing Nature of Scotland*, eds. S.J. Marrs, S. Foster, C. Hendrie, E.C. Mackey, D.B.A. Thompson. TSO Scotland, Edinburgh, pp 397-414.

33.1 Background

Climate change is predicted to result in significant increases in temperature for Scotland of the order of 1.5°C to 5.5°C for the summer and 1°C to 4°C for the winter by the 2080s, from the 1960 to 1990 baseline levels, according to a medium emissions scenario. Winter precipitation in Scotland may increase by up to 35% during the same interval, whilst summer rainfall may decline by up to 33% (UKCP09, 2009). There is evidence that some of these predictions are already being realised, with recent mean temperature increases from 1961 to 2004 in excess of 1°C during the spring and summer in Scotland, and a significant increase in winter precipitation during the same period by 58% (Barnett *et al.*, 2006).

These changes are widely regarded as threatening the existence of many UK bird species, particularly in the uplands where some species are at the southern edge of their global range (Huntley *et al.*, 2007). In the UK, these populations are concentrated in Scotland, where over 50% of upland habitats occur. In relation to birds, a number of high latitude breeding species occupy unenclosed upland moorland, grassland and blanket bog habitats (Pearce-Higgins *et al.*, 2009a), and are regarded as being particularly vulnerable to climate change in the UK, with northwards range contractions predicted (Huntley *et al.*, 2007). Indeed, recent population trends of rare northerly distributed birds covered by the Rare Breeding Birds Panel (a group who collect breeding data on the rarer species of birds breeding in the UK) show species are declining at least partly in response to climate change, whilst rare southern species are increasing in abundance, as climatic conditions ameliorate (Green *et al.*, 2008). More widely, recent trends of common species across Europe also reflect the predicted sensitivity of those species to climate change (Gregory *et al.*, 2009). However, neither study specifically covers UK upland birds.

33.2 Recent changes in upland bird populations

Despite considerable interest in upland birds, and a level of recording effort that probably exceeds that for most other taxa, populations of many UK upland birds remain poorly monitored, particularly in comparison to bird populations elsewhere. The national Breeding Bird Survey (BBS) does not currently provide a robust estimation of trends for many upland bird species. The coverage of two totemic and widespread upland bird species, red grouse (*Lagopus lagopus scoticus*) and golden plover (*Pluvialis apricaria*), averages 53 and 42 1km survey squares respectively in Scotland (Risely *et al.*, 2009), where the cut-off for trend estimation is 30. Populations of rarer species such as golden eagle (*Aquila chrysaetos*), hen harrier (*Circus cyaneus*), merlin (*Falco columbaris*), black grouse (*Tetrao tetrix*), dotterel

(*Charadrius morinellus*) and ring ouzel (*Turdus torquatus*) are monitored periodically by specific surveys. Repeat surveys have allowed recent population changes to be estimated for most, although differences in survey methods confounded estimates for some. There remain some species, however, for which there are no robust estimates of recent population change, or even abundance (Pearce-Higgins *et al.*, 2009a). Altogether, 63% of upland species appear to be declining in Scotland (Table 33.1).

These declines cannot be simply attributed to climate, as there have been considerable changes in the upland environment during the last few decades. The most widespread of these have been changes in large herbivore abundance, grouse moor management intensity and the expansion of commercial afforestation (reviewed in Pearce-Higgins *et al.*, 2009a). Changes in large herbivore abundance may affect species sensitive to vegetation structure, such as black grouse, golden plover and skylark (*Alauda arvensis*) (Calladine *et al.*, 2002; Pearce-Higgins and Grant, 2006). Over the longer term, grazing levels have a more gradual effect on moorland habitats leading to additional responses in upland birds (Thirgood *et al.*, 2000; Smith *et al.*, 2001; Pearce-Higgins and Grant, 2006) whilst large herbivores may also provide carrion for ravens (*Corvus corax*) and raptors. Large areas of the uplands are managed for red grouse through the rotational burning of heather and predator control. Whilst rotational burning affects species sensitive to vegetation structure, as outlined above, legal predator control is likely to enhance the productivity of many ground-nesting grouse and waders (Grant *et al.*, 1999; Summers *et al.*, 2004), resulting in higher densities on grouse moors (Tharme *et al.*, 2001). Conversely, illegal persecution of raptors limits their distribution (Whitfield *et al.*, 2004; Etheridge *et al.*, 1997). The conversion of upland areas to commercial forestry plantations has not only resulted in the direct loss of breeding habitat for a wide range of species, but declines in the abundance of species on neighbouring open ground (Marquiss *et al.*, 1978; Whitfield *et al.*, 2001; 2007; Buchanan *et al.*, 2003; Rebecca, 2006; Pearce-Higgins *et al.*, 2007; Hancock *et al.*, 2009). Recent population trends of many upland birds may be, at least qualitatively, linked to these changes in land-use (Pearce-Higgins *et al.*, 2009a), which need to be understood in order to examine any impacts of climate change.

Table 33.1 Summary of best assessments of recent trends in UK upland bird populations. Where multiple estimates are available, robust national trends were given priority over biased national trends or partial trends.

Species	UK population trend	Scottish population trend
Hen harrier	+39 % (1988/9 – 2004)[7]	+32 % (1988/9 – 2004)[7]
Golden eagle	+3 % (1992 – 2003)[8]	+3 % (1992 – 2003)[8]
Merlin	-13 % (1993/4 – 2008)[11]	-10 % (1993/4 – 2008) [11]
Peregrine	+14 % (1991 – 2002)[9]	-9 % (1991 – 2002)[9]
Red grouse	-10 %(1995 – 2007)[1]	-7 % (1995 – 2007)[1]
Ptarmigan	not available	not available
Black grouse	-22 % (1994/95 – 2005)[2]	-29 % (1994/95 – 2005)[2]
Dotterel	-23 % (1987/88 – 1999)[3]	-22 % (1987/88 – 1999)[3]
Golden plover	-8 % (1995 – 2007)[1]	-12 (1995 – 2007)[1]
Dunlin	Decline[6]	Decline[6]
Snipe	+35 % (1995 – 2007)[1]	+48 % (1995 – 2007)[1]
Whimbrel	- c. 50 %[10]	- c. 50 %[10]
Curlew	-38 % (1995 – 2007)[1]	-51 % (1995 – 2007)[1]
Greenshank	Increase[6]	Increase[6]
Skylark	-11 % (1995 – 2007)[1]	+3 % (1995 – 2007)[1]
Meadow pipit	-16 % (1995 – 2007)[1]	-25 % (1995 – 2007)[1]
Whinchat	-43 % (1995 – 2007)[1]	not available
Stonechat	+209 % (1995 – 2007)[1]	+259 % (1995 – 2007)[1]
Wheatear	-11 % (1995 – 2007)[1]	-14 % (1995 – 2007)[1]
Ring ouzel	-58 % (1989/91 – 1999)[4]	not available
Raven	+21 % (1995 – 2007)[1]	+67 % (1995 – 2007)[1]
Snow bunting	-33 % (1991 – 2005)[5]	-33 % (1991 – 2005)[5]

1 National trends from Breeding Bird Survey (Risely *et al.*, 2009). Note that a longer time series of trends from 1994-2008 are available for Scotland from SNH (2010), but as these are unsmoothed trends, and therefore not comparable with the UK BBS trends presented here, they are not included in the table.
2 From national survey (Sim *et al.*, 2008).
3 From 1987/88 to 1999 from national survey, although potential biases in site selection in 1987/88 mean this may not accurately reflect national trends (Whitfield, 2002).
4 Re-analysis of data from national survey to estimate minimum population change between Gibbons *et al.* (1993) and Wotton *et al.* (2002).
5 Reduction in Cairngorms stronghold from 1991 to 2005 (Marquiss, 2007).
6 Population change across non-random regions (Sim *et al.*, (2005).
7 From national survey (Sim *et al.*, 2007).
8 From national survey (Eaton *et al.*, 2007).
9 From national survey (Banks *et al.*, 2010).
10 Estimated change in Unst and Fetlar populations (Grant unpubl.).
11 From national survey (Ewing *et al.*, unpubl.).

33.3 The role of climate in driving upland bird populations

33.3.1 Overview

Several studies have examined the links between the productivity, survival or abundance of upland birds and climate (Table 33.2). Despite rising temperatures, and declining populations, it is noteworthy that where studied, the effects of temperature upon upland bird populations are largely positive. Thus, the subsequent breeding success of golden eagles is positively correlated with winter

Table 33.2 Known relationships between upland bird populations and weather. Relationships with weather summarised in relation to either temperature (T), including effects of snow or frost, or precipitation (P), during the winter (Wint) and summer (Sum). Symbols are defined as follows: + positive correlation; - negative correlation; ± quadratic correlation indicative of variable effects; 0 no effect. All relevant studies on a species are included, not just those from the UK uplands, and for species which only breed in the uplands, studies may indicate effects occurring on the wintering grounds, with each symbol representing the results of a particular study, or if a particular study examines multiple populations, individual populations.

	Wint T	Sum T	Wint P	Sum P	References
Golden eagle	+ + + 0	+ + 0	+ ± -	- - 0	Watson (1997); Watson *et al.* (2003)
Hen harrier		+-			Redpath *et al.* (2002)
Merlin		+		-	Fielding and Haworth (2003)
Red grouse		+ + ±		- -	Slagsvold (1975); Watson *et al.* (2000); Cattadori *et al.* (2005)
Ptarmigan		+ + +		- 0	Watson *et al.* (1998); (2000); Novoa *et al.* (2008)
Black grouse		+ -		- 0	Moss (1986); Zbinden and Salvioni (2003); Summers *et al.* (2004); Ludwig *et al.* (2006)
Golden plover	+ + 0	+ -			Yalden and Pearce-Higgins (1997); Pearce-Higgins and Yalden (2002); Piersma *et al.* (2005); Pearce-Higgins *et al.* (2010)
Dunlin		±			Beale *et al.* (2006b)
Curlew	+				Laursen (2005)
Skylark		±	+	-	Bradbury *et al.* (2003); Piha *et al.* (2007)
Ring ouzel		-		±	Beale *et al.* (2006a)
Snow bunting		+ +			Watson (1996); Hoset *et al.* (2004)

temperature, mediated through the abundance of live prey (Watson, 1997; Watson *et al.*, 2003), whilst there is direct or indirect evidence that the overwinter survival of a range of species is enhanced by milder winters. Golden plover (Yalden and Pearce-Higgins, 1997), and curlew (*Numenius arquata*) (Laursen, 2005) populations are negatively affected by low winter temperatures on lowland and coastal wintering areas, although the recent reduction in winter severity has reduced the importance of winter weather in driving recent population dynamics (Pearce-Higgins *et al.*, 2010). Breeding success is generally positively correlated with temperature (Table 33.2). Thus, the productivity or abundance of ground-nesting raptors (Redpath *et al.*, 2002; Fielding and Haworth, 2003), grouse (Slagsvold, 1975; Watson *et al.*, 1998, 2000; Novoa *et al.*, 2008), waders (Pearce-Higgins and Yalden, 2002) and some passerines (Watson, 1996; Bradbury *et al.*, 2003; Hoset *et al.*, 2004) is generally enhanced by warm weather. Whilst there is little evidence for consistent effects of winter rainfall upon bird survival rates, high spring and summer rainfall is detrimental to the productivity of most species, including raptors (Watson *et al.*, 2003, Fielding and Haworth, 2003) and grouse (Summers *et al.*, 2004).

33.3.2 Golden plovers: a case study

Predictions for increasing summer and winter temperature, and less summer precipitation, might be expected to result in improved survival and productivity rates in upland bird populations. However, a more detailed examination of the golden plover, illustrates why this may not be the case. Golden plovers are found towards the southern edge of their global breeding range in Scotland, and as a result future predicted climate change may place populations under increasing threat (Huntley *et al.*, 2007), despite positive effects of temperature upon over-winter survival (Piersma *et al.*, 2005) and chick growth rates and survival (Pearce-Higgins and Yalden, 2002). Studies in the Peak District have shown that during the breeding season, golden plovers feed mainly on adult and larval craneflies. Breeding adults commute to take advantage of high larval densities on in-bye fields (Pearce-Higgins and Yalden, 2003), and foraging chicks feed on both emerged adults and larvae on the peatland breeding territories (Pearce-Higgins and Yalden, 2004). The emergence of the small number of cranefly species common across such habitats are heavily synchronised to particular periods, with one of the most dominant craneflies (*Tipula subnodicornis)* emerging during May and June (Coulson, 1959, 1962; Pearce-Higgins and Yalden, 2004). The timing of hatching of first clutches roughly coincides with this period, as emerged adult craneflies provide an important food source for chicks, and determine their growth and survival rates (Pearce-Higgins and Yalden, 2004).

As observed in other species (Dunn, 2004), there is a strong correlation between spring temperature and golden plover egg laying dates (Pearce-Higgins *et al.*, 2005), which has resulted in recent advances in the timing of golden plover breeding (Moss *et al.*, 2005). This does not yet appear to have resulted in a mismatch in food availability, as the relationship between the timing of the peak in cranefly emergence and May temperature has a similar slope to that for golden plover breeding phenology and temperature. Future projected differences in the degree of warming during early spring (March and April) and late spring (May) may result in a phenological mismatch if the relationship between temperature and phenology remain constant (Pearce-Higgins *et al.*, 2005). Recent fluctuations in golden plover abundance do not, however, appear related to phenological mismatch during the preceding breeding season (Pearce-Higgins *et al.*, 2010).

There is stronger evidence for climate impacting on the abundance of cranefly, through effects operating on the early larval instars, which are vulnerable to

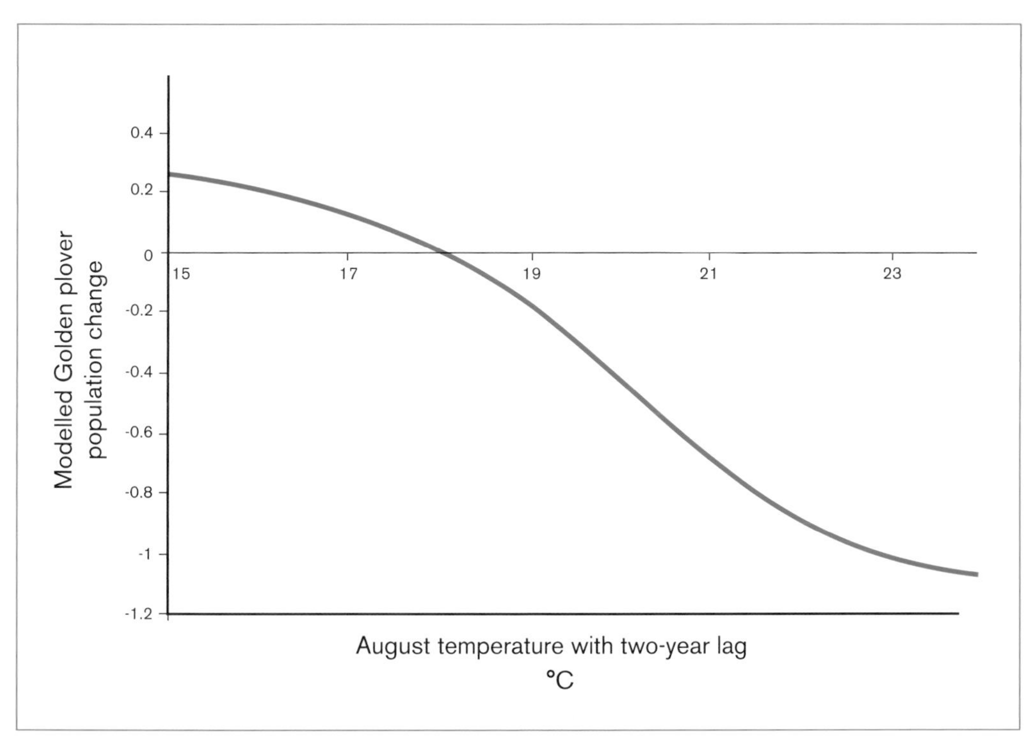

Figure 33.1 Modelled change in golden plover population [ln(n/n-1)] at Snake Summit in the Peak District (53°26'N 1°52'W) as a function of August temperature two-years previously. Relationship based upon the known relationship between August temperature and subsequent cranefly abundance (Pearce-Higgins *et al.*, 2010), cranefly abundance and golden plover productivity (Pearce-Higgins and Yalden, 2004; Pearce-Higgins *et al.*, 2005) and golden plover productivity and subsequent population change (Pearce-Higgins *et al.*, 2010).

desiccation (Coulson, 1962). After the emergence of *T. subnodicornis*, the laid eggs reside in the surface of the peat for a month, and then hatch in July, when they grow through three larval instars to over-winter as a fourth instar larvae, before pupating in May (Coulson, 1962). The magnitude of the peak of cranefly emergence in any one year is strongly negatively correlated with the previous August temperature (Pearce-Higgins *et al.*, 2010). This suggests that during a hot dry summer, the drying out of the peat surface results in a high mortality of young larvae. The Peak District studies showed a link between cranefly abundance and golden plover chick growth and overall productivity; fluctuations in the abundance of golden plovers are negatively correlated with August temperature with a two-year lag (Figure 33.1). These results are likely to have wide generality to other upland birds, as craneflies are important for a wide range of species, particularly other waders (Buchanan *et al.*, 2006). Similar effects may also affect populations of other key prey taxa, and urgently require focused further research.

33.3.3 Other drivers of change

Although food availability is a key driver of avian population dynamics, climate may affect bird populations through a wide-variety of mechanisms (Mustin *et al.*, 2007). For example, the incidence of *Trichostrongylus tenuis* infection in red grouse is related to summer temperature and rainfall, with increasingly negative effects for red grouse in warm wet summers, which may counteract beneficial effects of increasing temperature upon chick survival (Cattadori *et al.*, 2005). The expansion of cold-intolerant species into the uplands, such as stonechat (*Saxicola torquatus*), as a result of climate warming may be detrimental to more 'upland' species as a result of competition, although at present this is conjecture (e.g. von dem Bussche *et al.*, 2008). Upland birds are also likely to be sensitive to changes in predation rates as a result of climate-related changes in predator abundance, or changes in habitat.

33.4 Managing the effects of climate change

Having identified the potential for such changes, and mechanisms by which they may operate, the question remains whether there is anything that can be done to reduce the severity of future climate impacts upon vulnerable species. Although there are a number of components to a successful conservation strategy in the face of a changing climate (Green and Pearce-Higgins, 2010), I focus on two here; the management of species' range shifts, and of individual populations and sites. I do not discuss specifically the importance of minimising the severity of other pressures on vulnerable populations and species, but take this as an essential component of any effective conservation strategy (Hodgson *et al.*, 2009).

33.4.1 The management of species' range shifts

Climate change is predicted to cause latitudinal and altitudinal range shifts through the colonisation of new locations that become climatically suitable and loss from locations that become climatically unsuitable. However, there is considerable debate about the extent to which species will achieve their potential distribution, according to climatic suitability, or whether their distribution will be constrained by an ability to colonise climatically suitable locations, particularly given the anticipated speed of future climate change. In order to be colonised, future sites must contain suitable habitat and be sufficiently connected to the current range. These principles have received considerable interest in recent years, and it is argued that conservationists should promote both the existence of suitable habitat for a species in areas that it is likely to colonise as a result of predicted climate change, and the functional connectivity of that habitat to existing populations (Opdam and Wascher, 2004; Huntley *et al.*, 2007). However, currently the role of landscape connectivity to facilitate species range movements remains largely untested (Bailey, 2007) and there is an urgent need to account for such uncertainty in current decision making (Burgman *et al.*, 2005). Because of this uncertainty, current conservation strategies should maximise the area under protection, and target areas of high endemism and high environmental heterogeneity for protection (Hogdson *et al.*, 2009) to maximise the benefits now and increase the resilience of populations and species to climate change. Whilst action to improve connectivity may be important to manage range expansion for some species, in the absence of robust models to design networks for individual species, generic networks of habitat are most likely to favour generalist species (Dolman *et al.*, 2007).

The Scottish uplands exemplify landscapes with high environmental heterogeneity, given the variations in climate, altitude, soil, vegetation and management. In such environments, the protection of large and heterogeneous areas of habitat may be necessary to facilitate any altitudinal shifts in range as a result of climate change, whilst providing a range of micro-climates which may act as *refugia* for range-contracting species. As upland birds are relatively mobile compared to other taxa promoting landscape connectivity, as opposed to simply maximising the area of habitats and size of populations, may be a less important principle. One possible exception to this are grouse (Warren and Baines, 2002) which may benefit from landscape connectivity, although in Scotland, this will be to maximise the resilience of existing meta-populations rather than enable the colonisation of new areas as they become climatically suitable. Of course, upland areas may become increasingly colonised by 'lowland' species as a result of climate amelioration, as evidenced by increases in snipe (*Gallinago gallinago*) and stonechat populations in the uplands (Sim *et al.*, 2005), whilst linnet (*Carduelis cannabina*) and reed bunting (*Emberiza schoeniclus*) are already beginning to follow (Pearce-Higgins *et al.*, 2006). The extent to which habitats must be connected in order to be colonised warrants further investigation, perhaps using bird ringing data (Paradis *et al.*, 1998), or analysing patterns of colonisation.

33.4.2 Management of individual populations and sites

The protection and maintenance of sites will remain essential to future conservation management in a changing climate, particularly for species restricted to natural or semi-natural habitats (Green and Pearce-Higgins, 2010). However, if climate change projections are accurate, then populations at sites located close to the anticipated edge of their range, may ultimately be lost. Here, I propose a framework to support the conservation of such vulnerable populations, based on previous examples of successful conservation (Peach *et al.*, 2001; O'Brien *et al.*, 2006; Wilson *et al.*, 2009). These required monitoring to detect the initial problem, research to identify the causes of decline, and solution testing to trial appropriate conservation action, before putting into place extensive conservation action to reverse declines. These principles can be applied to climate change adaptation (Figure 33.2).

Firstly, there must be robust monitoring of species populations across their geographical range, which is only in place for some upland birds. Currently there is no regular monitoring of montane species (e.g. ptarmigan (*Lagopus mutus*) and snow bunting (*Plectrophenax nivalis*)), arguably the most sensitive upland birds to climate change, whilst it is questionable for many others whether the monitoring would be sufficiently sensitive to identify change at the range margins. Monitoring should not be restricted to birds, but also target keystone species at lower trophic levels, taking advantage of existing altitudinal and latitudinal gradients to increase the range of climatic conditions examined. As illustrated by the example of craneflies, such data may act as an early warning of potential future problems. Secondly, research should identify the primary mechanism(s) by which climate change will affect a particular species. To maximise resource efficiency, such research should focus on particular model species which act as indicators for a wider range of species. Work on golden plovers has highlighted the potential sensitivity of other cranefly specialists (Buchanan *et al.*, 2006) to future climate change. Thirdly such knowledge can be used to assess the potential for adaptation management to be initiated. For example, the primary mechanism by which golden plovers are sensitive to climate change is through the desiccation of early larval instars of craneflies during hot summers. Using this knowledge highlights the potential for desiccation risk to be reduced by raising water levels. As large areas of the uplands have been drained (Holden *et al.*, 2007), there is the potential to achieve this through a programme of drain blocking. Although there is uncertainty regarding the extent to which such management results in changes in the water table away from the drains, and the potential magnitude of any response by craneflies to changes in water

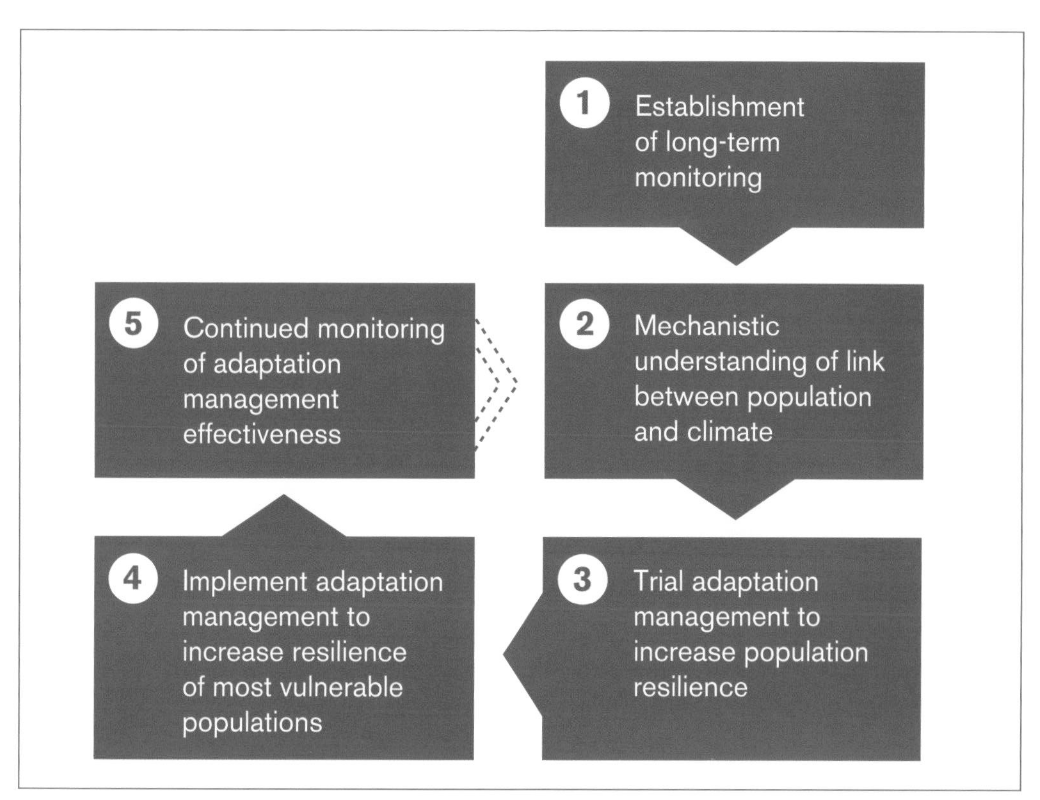

Figure 33.2 Schematic diagram outlining a potential approach to site-based adaptation management. If adaptation management becomes ineffective, it may be necessary to go from five to two (hence the dotted line). Alternatively, such a point may indicate that the limit to successful climate adaptation has been reached.

levels, these issues are open to scientific investigation. If successful, such management could then, fourthly, be implemented more widely to prevent or counter the decline of vulnerable populations. Fifthly, this implementation should be monitored to ensure that it remains effective. If there is evidence that the efficacy of adaptation management is reduced, it may be possible to return to research, to identify additional mechanisms of climate impacts and trial further potential solutions. Alternatively, the degree of climate change may eventually exceed the limit for successful management, when it may be necessary to cease management to maximise efficient use of conservation resources and, for example, target other vulnerable populations.

Even at this point, the protection of populations will not have been in vain, as the protection and conservation action would have maximised the number of offspring produced for subsequent dispersal and colonisation of other sites. Additionally, the protection of natural and semi-natural habitats associated with the protection of trailing edge populations provides areas for colonisation by individuals at the expanding range margins.

33.5 Conclusions

Science is essential to underpin the successful management of species populations in response to climate change, and there is much to be learned from existing conservation action. Firstly, it is important to reduce the severity of non-climate related pressures upon populations, such as those associated with increasing generalist predator populations and habitat change. There is an increasing knowledge base of land use and its effects on upland birds. More recently the impacts of additional pressures, such as the expansion of wind farms, also need to be considered and accounted for (Bright *et al.*, 2008; Pearce-Higgins *et al.*, 2009b). Secondly, the quality and extent of protected areas should be maximised, particularly where there is high environmental heterogeneity, such as in the uplands. There may be some benefit to maximising the connectivity of such habitats, although there is considerable uncertainty associated with the overall benefits from this strategy. Thirdly, site-based adaptation management may increase the resilience of individual sites and populations to climate change. This will be particularly important to maintain trailing edge populations. In Scotland, the long-term persistence of a number of upland species may depend upon our ability to do this successfully. Site-based adaptation requires an understanding of the mechanisms underpinning climate change impacts and robust monitoring to be established, which is currently not in place for most upland taxa.

We are currently at the start of significant predicted climate change and the future effectiveness of conservation adaptation strategies remain largely untested. Whilst urgent efforts should be made to reduce this uncertainty, it should also be acknowledged by policymakers and factored into decision-making according to a 'no-regrets' principle. Policies should ideally benefit existing biodiversity and the anticipated future biodiversity. The resilience of current conservation action to future climate change should be maximised and such action should be based upon best available ecological knowledge. There is much for ecologists to do to better inform adaptation policy and management, but there is also considerable potential for existing knowledge to be pulled together to inform decisions (Pearce-Higgins and Gill, 2010). Where adaptation management is implemented following the principles outlined above, monitoring should be put in place to allow for changes in response to this.

Acknowledgements

I am grateful to SNH for the invitation to submit this manuscript and to Richard Bradbury and Jeremy Wilson for comments on an earlier draft. Additional helpful comments were provided by Des Thompson and an anonymous referee.

References

Bailey, S. (2007). Increasing connectivity in fragmented landscapes: An investigation of evidence for biodiversity gain in woodlands. *Forest Ecology and Management*, **238**, 7-23.

Banks, A.N., Coombes, R., Crick, H.Q.P. *et al.* (2010). The breeding status of Peregrine Falcons *Falco peregrinus* in the UK and Isle of Man in 2002. *Bird Study*, **57**, 421-436.

Barnett, C., Hossell, J., Perry, M., Procter, C. and Hughes, G. (2006). *Patterns of climate change across Scotland: Technical Report.* SNIFFER Project CC03.

Beale, C.M., Burfield, I.J., Sim, I.M.W. *et al.* (2006a). Climate change may account for the decline in British ring ouzels *Turdus torquatus*. *Journal of Animal Ecology*, **75**, 826-835.

Beale, C.M., Dodd, S. and Pearce-Higgins, J.W. (2006b). Wader recruitment indices suggest Dunlin nesting success is temperature-dependent. *Ibis*, **148**, 405-410.

Bradbury, R.B., Wilson, J.D., Moorcroft, D., Morris, A.J and Perkins, A.J. (2003). Habitat and weather are weak correlates of nestling condition and growth rates of four UK farmland passerines. *Ibis*, **145**, 295-306.

Bright, J., Langston, R., Bullman, R. *et al.* (2008). Map of bird sensitivities to wind farms in Scotland: A tool to aid planning and conservation. *Biological Conservation*, **141**, 2342-2356.

Buchanan, G.M., Pearce-Higgins, J.W., Wotton, S.R., Grant, M.C. and Whitfield, D.P. (2003). Correlates of the change in Ring Ouzel Turdus torquatus abundance in Scotland from 1988-91 to 1999. *Bird Study*, **50**, 97-105.

Buchanan, G.M., Grant, M.C., Sanderson, R.A. and Pearce-Higgins, J.W. (2006). The contribution of invertebrate taxa to moorland bird diets and the potential implications of land-use management. *Ibis*, **148**, 615-628.

Burgman, M.A., Lindenmayer, D.B. and Elith, J. (2005). Managing landscapes for conservation under uncertainty. *Ecology*, **86**, 2007–2017.

Calladine, J., Baines, D. and Warren, P. (2002). Effects of reduced grazing on population density and breeding success of Black Grouse in northern England. *Journal of Applied Ecology*, **39**, 772-780.

Cattadori, I.M., Haydon, D.T. and Hudson, P.J. (2005). Parasites and climate synchronize red grouse populations. *Nature*, **433**, 737-741.

Coulson, J.C. (1959). Observations on the Tipulidae (Diptera) of the Moor House Nature Reserve, Westmoreland. *Transactions of the Royal Entomological Society, London*, **111**, 157-174.

Coulson, J.C. (1962). The biology of *Tipulia subnodicornis* Zetterstedt, with comparative observations on *Tipula paludosa* Meigen. *Journal of Animal Ecology*, **31**, 1-21.

Dolman, P.W., Hinsley, S.A., Bellamy, P.E. and Watts, K. (2007). Woodland birds in patchy landscapes: the evidence base for strategic networks. *Ibis*, **149 s2**, 146-160.

Dunn, P. (2004). Breeding dates and reproductive performance. *Advances in Ecological Research*, **35**, 69-87.

Eaton, M.A., Dillon, I.A., Stirling-Aird, P.K. and Whitfield, D.P. (2007). Status of golden eagle *Aquila chrysaetos* in Britain in 2003. *Bird Study*, **54**, 212-220.

Etheridge, B., Summers, R.W. and Green, R.E. (1997). The effects of illegal killing and destruction of nests by humans on the population dynamics of the hen harrier *Circus cyaneus* in Scotland. *Journal of Applied Ecology*, **34**, 1081-1105.

Fielding, A.H. and Haworth, P.F. (2003). Recovery of the South Pennine merlin (*Falco columbaris*) population. *In Birds of Prey in a Changing Environment*, ed. by D.B.A. Thompson, S.M. Redpath, A.H. Fielding, M. Marquiss, and C.A. Galbraith. The Stationery Office, Edinburgh. pp 201-208.

Gibbons, D.W., Reid, J.B. and Chapman, R.A. (1993). *The New Atlas of Breeding Birds in Britain and Ireland (1988-1991).* London. Poyser.

Grant, M.C., Orsman, C., Easton, J., Lodge, C., Smith, M., Thompson, G., Rodwell, S. and Moore, N. (1999). Breeding success and causes of breeding failure of curlew *Numenius arquata* in Northern Ireland. *Journal of Applied Ecology*, **36**, 59-74.

Green, R.E., Collingham, Y.C., Willis, S.G. *et al.* (2008). Performance of climate envelope models in retrodicting recent changes in bird population size from observed climate change. *Biology Letters*, **4**, 599-602.

Green, R.E. and Pearce-Higgins, J. (2010). Species management in the face of a changing climate. In *Species management: Challenges and Solutions for the 21st Century*, ed. by J.M. Baxter and C.A. Galbraith. The Stationery Office, Edinburgh. pp 517-536.

Gregory, R.D., Willis, S.G., Jiguet, F. *et al.* (2009). An indicator of the impact of climate change on European bird populations. *PloS ONE*, 4:e4678.

Hancock, M.C., Grant, M.C. and Wilson, J.D. (2009). Associations between distance to forest and spatial and temporal variation in abundance of key peatland breeding bird species. *Bird Study*, **56**, 53-64.

Hodgson, J.A., Thomas, C.D., Wintle, B.A. and Moilanen, A. (2009). Climate change, connectivity and conservation decision making: back to basics. *Journal of Applied Ecology*, **46**, 964-969.

Holden, J., Shotbolt, L., Bonn, A. *et al.* (2007). Environmental change in moorland landscapes. *Earth-science reviews*, **82**, 75-100.

Hoset, K.S., Espmark, Y., Moksnes, A. *et al.* (2004). Effect of ambient temperature on food provisioning and reproductive success in snow buntings *Plectrophenax nivalis* in the high arctic. *Ardea*, **92**, 239-246.

Huntley, B., Green, R.E., Collingham, Y.C. and Willis, S.G. (2007). *A climatic atlas of European breeding birds.* Durham University, The RSPB and Lynx Edicions, Barcelona.

Laursen, K. (2005). Curlews in the Wadden Sea – Effects of shooting protection in Denmark. *Wadden Sea Ecosystem*, **20**, 172-183.

Ludwig, G.X., Alatalo, R.V., Helle, P., *et al.* (2006). Short and long-term population dynamical consequences of asymmetric climate change in black grouse. *Proceedings of the Royal Society London, Series B*, **273**, 2009-2016.

Marquiss, M. (2007). Snow bunting. In *The Birds of Scotland*, ed. by R. Forrester and I. Andrews. pp 1473-1477.

Marquiss, M., Newton, I. and Ratcliffe, D.A. (1978). The decline of the raven *Corvus corax* in relation to afforestation southern Scotland and northern England. *Journal of Applied Ecology*, **15**, 129-144.

Moss, D., Joys, A.C., Clark, J.A. *et al.* (2005). Timing of breeding of moorland birds. BTO Research Report No. 362.

Mustin, K., Sutherland, W.J. and Gill, J.A. (2007). The complexity of predicting climate-induced ecological impacts. *Climate Research*, **35**, 165-175.

Novoa, C., Besnard, A., Brenot, J.F. and Ellison, L.N. (2008). Effect of weather on the reproductive rate of Rock Ptarmigan *Lagopus muta* in the eastern Pyrenees. *Ibis*, **150**, 270-278.

O'Brien, M., Green, R.E. and Wilson, J. (2006). Partial recovery of the population of Corncrakes *Crex crex* in Britain. *Bird Study*, **53**, 213-224.

Opdam, P. and Wascher, D. (2004). Climate change meets habitat fragmentation: linking landscape and biogeographical scale levels in research and conservation. *Biological Conservation*, **117**, 285-297.

Paradis, E., Baillie, S.R., Sutherland, W.J. and Gregory, R.D. (1998). Patterns of natal and breeding dispersal in birds. *Journal of Animal Ecology*, **67**, 518-536.

Peach, W.J., Lovett, L.J., Wotton, S.R. and Jeffs, C. (2001). Countryside stewardship delivers cirl buntings (*Emberiza cirlus*) in Devon, UK. *Biological Conservation*, **101**, 361-373.

Pearce-Higgins, J.W. and Gill, J.A. (2010). Unravelling the mechanisms linking climate change, agriculture and avian population declines. *Ibis*, **152**, 439-442.

Pearce-Higgins, J.W., Beale, C.M., Wilson, J. and Bonn, A. (2006). *Analysis of moorland breeding bird distribution and change in the Peak District.* Moors for the Future Report No. 11.

Pearce-Higgins, J.W., Dennis, P., Whittingham, M.J. and Yalden, D.W. (2010). Impacts of climate on prey abundance account for fluctuations in a population of a northern wader at the southern edge of its range. *Global Change Biology*, **16**, 12-23.

Pearce-Higgins, J.W. and Grant, M.C. (2006). Relationships between bird abundance and the composition and structure of moorland vegetation. *Bird Study*, **53**, 112-125.

Pearce-Higgins, J.W., Grant, M.C., Beale, C.M., Buchanan, G.M. and Sim, I.M.W. (2009a). International importance and drivers of change of upland bird populations. In *Drivers of Environmental Change in Uplands*, ed. by A. Bonn, T. Allot, K. Hubacek, J. Stewart. Routledge, London and New York. pp 209-227.

Pearce-Higgins, J.W. and Grant, M.C., Robinson M.C., and Haysom S.L. (2007). The role of forest maturation in causing the decline of Black Grouse *Tetrao tetrix*. *Ibis*, **149**, 143–155.

Pearce-Higgins, J.W., Stephen, L., Langston, R.H.W., Bainbridge, I.P. and Bullman, R. (2009b). The distribution of breeding birds around upland wind farms. *Journal of Applied Ecology*, **46**, 1323-1331.

Pearce-Higgins, J.W. and Yalden, D.W. (2002). Variation in the growth and survival of Golden Plover *Pluvialis apricaria* chicks. *Ibis*, **144**, 200-209.

Pearce-Higgins, J.W. and Yalden, D.W. (2003). Variation in the use of pasture by breeding European Golden Plovers *Pluvialis apricaria* in relation to prey availability. *Ibis*, **145**, 365-381.

Pearce-Higgins, J.W. and Yalden, D.W. (2004). Habitat selection, diet, arthropod availability and growth of a moorland wader: the ecology of European Golden Plover *Pluvialis apricaria* chicks. *Ibis*, **146**, 335-346.

Pearce-Higgins, J.W., Yalden, D.W. and Whittingham, M.J. (2005). Warmer springs advance the breeding phenology of golden plovers *Pluvialis apricaria* and their prey (*Tipulidae*). *Oecologia*, **143**, 470-476.

Piersma, T., Rogers, K.G., Boyd, H., Bunskoeke E.J. and Jukema, J. (2005). Demography of Eurasian Golden Plovers *Pluvialis apricaria* staging in The Netherlands, 1949-2000. *Ardea*, **93**, 49-64.

Piha, M., Linden, A., Pakkala, T. and Tiainen, J. (2007). Linking weather and habitat to population dynamics of a migratory farmland songbird. *Ann. Zool. Fennica*, **44**, 20-34.

Rebecca, G.W. (2006). *The breeding ecology of the Merlin* (Falco columbarius aesalon)*, with particular reference to north-east Scotland and land use change.* PhD thesis. Open University.

Redpath, S.M., Arroyo, B.E., Etheridge, B. *et al.* (2002). Temperature and hen harrier productivity: from local mechanisms to geographical patterns. *Ecography*, **25**, 533-540.

Risely, K., Noble, D.G. and Baillie, S.R. (2009). The Breeding Bird Survey 2008. *BTO Research Report* 537.

Sim, I.M.W., Gregory, R.D., Hancock, M.H. and Brown, A.F. (2005). Recent changes in the abundance of British upland breeding birds. *Bird Study*, **52**, 261-275.

Sim, I.M.W., Dillon, I.A., Eaton, M.A. *et al.* (2007). Status of the Hen Harrier *Circus cyaneus* in the UK and Isle of Man in 2004, and a comparison with the 1988/89 and 1998 surveys. *Bird Study*, **54**, 256-267.

Sim, I.M.W., Eaton, M.A., Setchfield, R.P., Warren, P.K. and Lindley, P. (2008). Abundance of male Black Grouse *Tetrao tetrix* in Britain in 2005, and change since 1995-96. *Bird Study*, **55**, 304-313.

Smith, A.A., Redpath, S.M., Campbell, S.T. and Thirgood, S.J. (2001). Meadow pipits, red grouse and the habitat characteristics of managed grouse moors. *Journal of Applied Ecology*, **38**, 390-400.

SNH (2010). *Biodiversity indicator.* http://www.snh.gov.uk/docs/B536405.pdf, accessed on 15 July 2010.

Slagsvold, T. (1975). Production of young by the willow grouse Lagopus lagopus (L.) in Norway in relation to temperature. *Norwegian Journal Zoology*, **23**, 269-275.

Summers, R.W., Green, R.E., Proctor, R. *et al.* (2004). An experimental study of the effects of predation on the breeding productivity of capercaillie and black grouse. *Journal of Applied Ecology*, **41**, 513-525.

Tharme, A.P., Green, R.E., Baines, D., Bainbridge, I.P., O'Brien, M. (2001). The effect of management for red grouse shooting on the population density of breeding birds on heather dominated moorland. *Journal of Applied Ecology*, **38**, 439-457.

Thirgood S.J., Redpath, S., Rothery, P., Newton, I. and Hudson, P. (2000). Habitat loss and raptor predation: disentangling long and short term causes of red grouse declines. *Proceedings of the Royal Society London, Series B*, **267**, 651-656.

UKCP09 (2009). *UK Climate Projections.* http://ukcp09.defra.gov.uk/, accessed on 11 December 2009.

von dem Bussche, J., Spaar, R., Schmid, H. and Schröder, B. (2008). Modelling the recent and potential future spatial distribution of the ring ouzel (*Turdus torquatus*) and blackbird (*T. merula*) in Switzerland. *Journal of Ornithology*, **149**, 529-544.

Warren, P.K. and Baines, D. (2002). Dispersal, survival and causes of mortality in black grouse *Tetrao tetrix* in northern England. *Wildlife Biology*, **8**, 91-97.

Watson, A., Moss, R. and Rothery, P. (2000). Weather and synchrony in 10-year population cycles of rock ptarmigan and red grouse in Scotland. *Ecology*, **81**, 2126-2136.

Watson, A., Moss, R. and Rae, S. (1998). Population dynamics of Scottish rock ptarmigan cycles. *Ecology*, **79**,1174–1192.

Watson, A. (1996). Scottish snow bunting *Plectrophenax nivalis* breeding and climate. *Ornis Fennica*, **73**, 137-140.

Watson, J. (1997). *The Golden Eagle.* T & AD Poyser, London.

Watson, J., Fielding, A.H., Whitfield, D.P. *et al.* (2003). Golden eagle (*Aquila chrysaetos*) breeding performance in relation to climate in western Scotland during the period 1981-2000. *In Birds of Prey in a Changing Environment*, ed. by D.B.A. Thompson, S.M. Redpath, A.H. Fielding, M. Marquiss, and C.A. Galbraith. The Stationery Office, Edinburgh. pp 149-161.

Whitfield, D.P. (2002). Status of breeding dotterel *Charadrius morinellus* in Britain in 1999. *Bird Study*, **49**, 237-249.

Whitfield, D.P., McLeod, D.R.A., Fielding, A.H. *et al.* (2001). The effects of forestry on golden eagles on the island of Mull, western Scotland. *Journal of Applied Ecology*, **38**, 1208-1220.

Whitfield, D.P., Fielding, A.H., Gregory, M.J.P. *et al.* (2007). Complex effects of habitat loss on golden eagles *Aquila chrysaetos*. *Ibis*, **149**, 26-36.

Whitfield, D.P., Fielding, A.H., McLeod, D.R.A., and Haworth, P.F. (2004). The effects of persecution on age of breeding and territory occupation in Golden Eagles in Scotland. *Biological Conservation*, **118**, 249-259.

Wilson, J.D., Evans, A.D. and Grice, P.V. (2009). *Bird Conservation and Agriculture.* Cambridge University Press, Cambridge.

Wotton, S.R., Langston, R.H.W. and Gregory, R.D. (2002). The breeding status of the Ring Ouzel *Turdus torquatus* in the UK in 1999. *Bird Study*, **49**, 26-34.

Yalden, D.W. and Pearce-Higgins, J.W. (1997). Density-dependence and winter weather as factors affecting the size of a population of Golden Plovers *Pluvialis apricaria. Bird Study*, **44**, 227-234.

Zbinden, N. and Salvioni, M. (2003). Distribution, density and reproductive success of black grouse *Tetrao tetrix* in Ticino, southern Switzerland, 1981-2002. *Ornithologische Beobachter*, **100**, 211-226.

34 Prospects for the Future: the Uplands in Peril or Thriving?

Earl of Lindsay and Simon Thorp

Summary

1. We provide a stock-take on the state of the uplands in Scotland from the perspective of land managers. Much of our evidence base comes from our work within Scotland's Moorland Forum, which was formed in 2002 and comprises 29 member organisations.
2. We argue that Scotland's uplands are in a state of peril – ecologically, economically and socially. This is a particular concern given recognition of their importance as a provider of key ecosystem services.
3. The uplands are maintained largely by land managers, many of whom are privately funded, have specialist skills, are at the centre of the local communities and are responsible for the maintenance of the social and cultural infrastructure.
4. The uplands suffer from many disjointed policies and the lack of a coherent strategic purpose. There is an outstanding need for a moorland land use strategy to fill this gap, and the 2010 Scottish Government Rural Land Use Strategy is a welcome first step.
5. We propose that the management of the uplands is approached with consensus, coordination, collaboration, coherence and clarity. Traditional land uses, which contribute to a unique landscape, should be maintained, but adapted for the future. We should embrace the opportunities offered by the new enterprises and land uses. A balance between the different land uses should be developed, and we should seize opportunities for joint public and private funding. The interests of local communities need to be integrated into future proposals because in many areas these have been peripheral to management initiatives.

Lindsay, Earl of and Thorp, S. (2011). Prospects for the Future: the Uplands in Peril or Thriving? – *The Changing Nature of Scotland*, eds. S.J. Marrs, S. Foster, C. Hendrie, E.C. Mackey, D.B.A. Thompson. TSO Scotland, Edinburgh, pp 415-424.

34.1 Introduction

Virtually all of Scotland's uplands have been or are managed. Their landscapes and wildlife are a dynamic expression of the influence of management and comprise a unique assemblage of earth and biological resources – the epitome of a cultural landscape. Globally, heather moorland is virtually confined to Britain and Ireland, where large tracts are managed principally through muirburn (rotational burning to create a mosaic of moorland structures for the benefit of grouse), grazing for agriculture, field sports and/or conservation and amenity interests.

The uplands cover a range of habitats which typically occur above enclosed farmland. Beyond the climatic treeline the heaths and moorland becomes 'alpine' or 'montane'. Scotland's moorlands are open, semi-natural habitats, and at the extremities (north and west) they extend over terrain close to sea level, where they intermix with farmland. Moorland is a broad description of several habitats including dry and wet heaths, blanket bogs and rough grasslands. Some bird and animal groups occur in Scotland's uplands at higher densities or diversity than anywhere else (e.g. Ratcliffe and Thompson, 1988). As a whole, at least half of Scotland is upland, with moorlands representing some 38% (around 3 million hectares). Scotland's uplands are of international importance with more than twenty habitats listed under the EU Habitats Directive. In addition seven UK Habitat Action Plans exist to improve management for the uplands: Blanket bog; Inland Rock Outcrop and Scree Habitats; Mountain Heaths and Willow Scrub; Upland Calcareous Grassland; Upland Flushes; Fens and Swamps; Upland Heathland; and Limestone Pavements (BRIG, 2008).

Since its formation in 2002, Scotland's Moorlands Forum (see Box 34.1) has developed into a unique partnership that robustly engages with matters influencing the uplands of Scotland. The Forum provides the main opportunity for cross-cutting debates on the future of Scotland's uplands. It seeks consensus through its members on the key issues affecting the uplands, based on sound evidence and with the principal aim to achieve a sustainable future for Scotland's moorland.

The Forum currently consists of 29 member organisations. These are drawn from many sectors, and as a result of this diversity, it represents a broad and comprehensive range of opinion and expertise on Scotland's uplands. The Forum is not just about raising concerns; it is also about finding solutions that will bring sustainable and long-term benefits to Scotland's upland areas. In this paper we explore the contribution of the Moorland Forum to the management of Scotland's uplands, and discuss the effectiveness of current initiatives to look to what the future may have in store for Scotland's uplands.

Box 34.1 The Moorland Forum

Scotland's Moorland Forum strives to sustain and enhance the extent, diversity and range of habitats, species and enterprises encompassing moorland. The Forum wants to engender a greater awareness of these valuable habitats.

The Forum seeks to halt and reverse the loss of heather cover, and to find ways of enriching the overall interest of Scotland's moorland, not least its natural heritage. At least a quarter of Scotland's heather cover has been lost since the 1940s and it is estimated that this loss is continuing at a rate of about 0.5% each year. The retention, and restoration where possible, of moorland habitats and related species is a high priority for management action.

There is a long Scottish tradition of local stewardship of the land, based on both private and public funding sources. This needs to be built on to improve further the beauty, nature and social fabric of our moorlands.

The Forum continues to work with the Scottish Government to implement Natura 2000 legislation, the Nature Conservation (Scotland) Act 2004, and conservation management programmes to help to meet government and European targets, including the 2010 target to halt the loss of biodiversity.

We seek to eliminate all illegal practices, not least the persecution of birds of prey, and work, with the Scottish Government and land managers, towards adherence to all wildlife and countryside legislation.

As a key stakeholder, the Forum contributes to the passing of new legislation and the development and implementation of policies and initiatives in relation to moorland areas.

There are three meetings of the Forum each year and much of the output from the Forum is produced from Task Groups that are established to investigate particular issues or run a specific project.

Our **Partnership for Delivery 2008** was launched by Michael Russell, MSP, then Minister for Environment, in March 2008. It is available to download from the Documents page of the Forum's website: www.moorlandforum.org.uk . The website lists the details of the 29 members.

34.2 Concerns about the state of the uplands

Land managers are under increasing pressure in their efforts to generate a viable income to support their businesses, livelihoods and obligations. In many areas, traditional enterprises such as livestock productions, forestry, grouse shooting, stalking and fishing are struggling to produce sufficient income. Increasingly, land managers are scaling back their operations, reducing investment and future commitments, and seeking additional income from new enterprises such as renewable energy and access management. Many are pursuing as yet undeveloped sources of income from, for instance, the development of environmental markets to harness ecosystem service delivery opportunities, such as carbon storage.

The Countryside Survey (2007) reported on habitat changes across the UK (Carey *et al.*, 2008). As part of the same survey Norton *et al.* (2009) detailed the changes that had occurred in Scotland (Table 34.1). They showed no detectable significant changes, between 1998 and 2007, in the overall extent of six Broad Habitats which form the upland landscape mosaic across Scotland. However, they also noted that there had been a substantial decline of over 113,000ha in the extent of dwarf shrub heath, but this was not significant. Moorland is largely comprised of dwarf shrub heath, and a decline of 23% loss of heather moorland between 1948 and 1988 was reported by Mackey *et al.* (1998).

We are concerned about the apparent loss of heather cover. Historically, it has been replaced by forestry (broadleaved and coniferous woodlands), bracken (*Pteridium aquilinum*) and grasslands (acid and improved). Norton *et al.* (2009) report that there has been some changes in the conversion of dwarf shrub heath to other habitats, primarily coniferous woodland; calcareous grassland; acid grassland; bracken; fen, marsh and swamp; bog; and urban. This picture is not as straightforward as it seems as there have been changes in other habitats resulting in

Table 34.1 Extent of Upland Habitats 2007 compared with the extent in 1998 (from The Countryside Survey, 2007). Statistically significant change depicted by*.

Habitat Type	**2007**		**1998-2007**	
	000 ha	**% Scotland**	**change (00 ha)**	**% change**
Acid Grassland	983	12.3	72	7.9*
Bracken	132	1.6	10	8.4
Dwarf Shrub Heath	894	11.1	-18	-2
Fen Marsh Swamp	239	3	-22	-8.6
Bog	2044	25.6	5	0.2
Montane	38	0.5	1	1.9
Inland Rock	84	1	-7	-7.8
Total Upland Area	4414	55%		
Not Upland	3605.3	45%		
Scotland area	8019.3	100%		

conversion to dwarf shrub heath in coniferous woodland; acid grassland; and bog. Other studies have shown an increasing homogenisation of the uplands which may be a result of land management practices, climate or other factors (see Britton *et al.*, 2009; Rothero *et al.*, Chapter 37; Brooker, Chapter 32; Ross *et al.*, Chapter 36).

As a number of the upland habitats receive special protection (within Special Areas of Conservation and Sites of Special Scientific Interest). Results from the Site Condition Monitoring programme covering protected areas showed that 72% of upland habitats were in favourable condition, with a further 4% receiving remedial management (SNH, 2010).

As much as any part of Scotland, the uplands require strategic and sustainable management. Motivated, well-trained, capable people are needed to achieve this, and the need to be able to generate a standard of living that is comparable with other parts of Scotland. Without the ability to earn a fair reward there are concerns that it will become increasingly difficult to attract the right people into upland management. There is a real risk that a whole range of skills and experience will be lost.

There are considerable gaps in our knowledge about upland ecosystems, yet it is becoming more difficult to secure funding for the necessary research. Issues of concern to the broad membership of the Forum include sheep tick (*Ixodes ricinus*) impacts on birds, as well as their role in the spread of Lyme disease, and heather beetle (*Lochmaea suturalis*) impacts on heather extent, where more research is needed to updated guidance on best management practices.

The changing climate may well be influencing the condition of the uplands in ways that are not yet fully understood (see Brooker, Chapter 32; Pearce Higgins, Chapter 33; Thompson and Mackey, Chapter 42). Management needs to be adapted to take account of these changes and to ensure that the uplands are managed in a sustainable manner so that the vital ecosystem services are preserved and their iconic status maintained.

34.3 Ecosystem services

Ecosystem services can be viewed as providing a link between natural assets and human well-being (Millennium Ecosystem Assessment, 2005). These are a relatively new concept, but are increasingly important for our understanding of the uplands as a supplier of key services.

In Scotland, the value of ecosystem services and natural capital has been estimated at £17 billion with around 14% of Scotland's jobs being reliant on these services (Williams *et al.*, 2003).

Many of these ecosystem services are essential for the quality of life in urban and suburban areas, and the supply of clean drinking water is one of the most critical services. As demand for these services increases, the provisioning role of the uplands will become ever more important. Climate change is likely to increase the emphasis on the need for the maintenance of the supply of these services. For example, an estimated 70% of Scotland's drinking water is supplied from upland catchments, so any changes in climate could be critical to this provision.

Another increasingly important role for the uplands is the capture and storage of carbon and the key benefits that this will deliver in helping to tackle global warming. Within Scotland, there are 1.8 million ha of peat and this contains almost 25 times as much carbon as all plant life in the UK. Put another way, these peat soils hold almost a third (3 billion tonnes) of the carbon held by all of Europe's forests.

Food supply and security are predicted to become a major challenge in the future and the uplands may have an increasingly important role to play. At the FAO High Level conference in June 2008, Ban Ki-Moon, the Secretary-General of the United Nations, stated that to meet rising demand by the year 2030, world food production will need to rise by 50%. Others are predicting that global food production will have to double by 2050 (FAO, 2008). An additional factor of considerable importance is that climate change is likely to focus food production on the temperate zones. The demand for meat products from the emerging economies of India, China and other developing nations will increase as these countries are able to afford more of a western-style, protein-based diet. We need to consider the possible role of the uplands in response to these changes, whilst bearing in mind the limitations of such expansion into the uplands given the viability of the land for agricultural production (Hall, Chapter 25).

The economic value of the uplands is considerable. The income generated through farming, forestry, sporting enterprises was estimated at £240 million in Scotland in 2001 (PACEC, 2006) and tourism was estimated to contribute £4 billion in Scotland in 2008 (Visit Scotland, 2008). This underpins the livelihood of many fragile, rural communities. These communities are essential for maintaining the appropriate management of the uplands in order to safeguard the ecosystem services which include the social and cultural values associated with the uplands. Without people, and the management they are able to provide, these areas would become very different.

Increasingly, upland landscapes are important for recreation and access. They provide popular health and lifestyle opportunities and a 'safety valve' for an increasingly urban population. As transport infrastructure has improved, more people have been able to take advantage of the benefits offered by recreation in even the remote areas of the uplands. The cultural and historical importance of these areas should also not be ignored. The archaeology and heritage of the uplands comprise a valuable strand of Scotland's history and our increasing knowledge of it confirms that no part of Scotland has escaped the imprint of previous generations. An understanding of the development of these upland areas adds to the cultural interest that they offer, and therefore to our cultural heritage.

34.4 Discussion

The uplands are often thought of as a vast, self sustaining wilderness, but this is a mistaken view. The uplands have been shaped by the activities of people and livestock for millennia. They require management, particularly if we are to maximise the economic and biodiversity potential. Improved economic viability would in turn underpin new investment, improved management and better outcomes for people and nature.

Many may consider the environmental benefits as the most important feature offered by the upland areas of Scotland. A vision of wide-open spaces with mountains clad in purple heather in the late summer is an internationally revered image of Scotland. But it is not just heather moorlands that are important – well managed uplands will provide the ecosystem services on which we rely.

Protected areas serve to highlight the most valuable parts of the country in conservation terms and include Special Areas of Conservation, Special Protection Areas, National Parks, Sites of Special Scientific Interest, National Nature Reserves and National Scenic Areas amongst others. Such designations should enhance the management of key areas both for conservation and public benefit purposes. Scotland's three million hectares of moorland encapsulate a rich and important diversity of interests and sensitivities. It is therefore inevitable that this diversity can at times also lead to diverse opinions and conflicts.

Diverse voices and conflicting views have in turn led to advocacy that is often not based on evidence, incoherent policies and inadequate solutions with respect to the uplands. The uplands are in peril and cannot afford to suffer further from such neglect. Addressing this problem is a prerequisite to managing our upland areas better. Scotland can preserve its uplands and moorlands if it can harness the genuine diversity to work for a common purpose.

Since its formation in 2002, the Moorland Forum has provided a unique opportunity in the uplands for cross-cutting debate, consensus-building, and partnership working. The Forum has coordinated the skills, resources and commitment offered by its member organisations and it has encouraged collaboration across all agendas and sectors. In this way, the Forum is filling a vital gap and inspiring a more coherent approach to the future of the uplands. One of the key features offered by the Forum has been the opportunity to develop mutual trust and understanding between members. This has enabled collaboration across sensitive issues. The Forum provides an essential link between different agendas: science and research; government policy; economic interests; best practice management; people and communities; habitats and species; and public awareness. As this is a very wide agenda and the Forum has limited resources, a clear plan has been drawn up covering the Forum's activities where it considers it can make a difference.

34.4.1 The way forward: Forum Task Groups and the Upland Solutions Project

A large proportion of the Forum's delivery is through Task and Working Groups. In 2008, the work programme covered forestry, agriculture, carbon, access and awareness and muirburn. Papers were produced by the groups and circulated widely so as to be able to influence the formation of policy and provide guidance through the Forum's member organisations.

In 2009-2010, the Forum developed its *Upland Solutions*. In contrast to the Forum's previous work, this is a bottom-up project, engaging directly with landowners, land managers, local communities and other key interested parties. The project is operating in two target areas, Muirkirk and the Upper Findhorn catchment, and the issues are being addressed through three strands of enquiry: upland birds; upland economics; and carbon. Practical problems, and opportunities to address these where they exist, will be identified and solutions proposed. Barriers to what would otherwise be practical solutions are being identified, and how these might be overcome will be one of the most compelling outputs of this work.

This work provides an opportunity to harness the knowledge and experience available to the Forum through its members and to apply it to helping land managers achieve improvements on the ground. The lessons learned from this project will inform how such an approach could benefit other parts of the country in the future.

34.4.2 Challenges for upland management

The highest priority, as outlined above, is to identify what we want from the uplands and then to establish appropriate policy instruments to allow the managers of these areas to achieve objectives. As the uplands are slow to respond to change, we need to develop a long-term vision for them; short-term initiatives are not the answer.

The traditional land uses of agriculture, sporting activities and forestry have, with the notable exception of sporting activities, been dependent on public funding, and it is unlikely that this position will change in the foreseeable future. However, these land uses have produced the uplands as we know them today and will remain critical for their future management. The Forum will be playing a particularly active role in advising on the new Land Use Strategy for Scotland (Scottish Government, 2011).

There are a range of other challenges and opportunities, including the identification of potential sites for renewable energy generation, and increasing demands for access and recreation. The future role of the uplands in global food production and timber production should not be forgotten. There may be more scope within the new uses for the uplands both to increase the level of income and reduce reliance on public funding. There is particular interest in the development of Environmental Markets, which would provide a financial linkage between the users of ecosystem services and the upland land managers who provide them. Carbon storage and water supply offer the most immediate potential for this concept – but other ideas are in the pipeline.

The development of long-term viability is the key to delivering the outcomes we want for the uplands. Public sector support through direct funding and grant schemes is likely to be necessary, but income generation from other means to fund management costs should also be developed further. Private sector investment has been – and remains – significant but it invariably suffers from being poorly recognised and undervalued. There is scope to develop a much more collaborative public/private sector relationship, overcoming mutual suspicions, as a means of generating new opportunities and funds. We need these to finance and deliver long-term strategic and sustainable objectives.

Acknowledgements

The work of the Forum would not have been possible without the imagination of Scottish Natural Heritage (SNH) in forming it. Initially the Forum was run by SNH staff but, from 2007, SNH has provided a grant to cover the costs of the support work. Significant to what has been achieved is the support of the 24 founding member organisations and their continued commitment to the work of the Forum. Since November 2007, the Earl of Lindsay has been the Chairman of the Forum, and Simon Thorp its Secretary. The views expressed in this chapter are those of the authors, and should not be read as those of the Forum. The authors are grateful to an anonymous referee and Des Thompson for comments on the manuscript.

References

BRIG (ed. A. Maddock) (2008) (updated July 2010). *UK Biodiversity Action Plan; Priority Habitat Descriptions*. http://www.ukbap.org.uk/library/UKBAP PriorityHabitatDescriptionsRevised20100730.pdf

Britton, A.J., Beale, C.M., Towers, W. and Hewison, R.L. (2009). Biodiversity gains and losses: Evidence for homogenisation of Scottish alpine vegetation. *Biological Conservation*, **142**, 1728-1739.

Carey, P.D., Wallis, S., Chamberlain, P.M. *et al.* (2008). Countryside Survey: UK Results from 2007. NERC/Centre for Ecology & Hydrology. (CEH Project Number: C03259).

FAO (2008). *Report of the High-Level Conference on World Food Security: the Challenges of Climate Change and Bioenergy, 11-13.* Food and Agriculture Organisation, United Nations, Montreal.

Mackey, E.C., Shewry, M.C. and Tudor, G.J. (1998). *Land Cover Change: Scotland from the 1940s to the 1980s.* The Stationery Office, Edinburgh.

Millennium Ecosystem Assessment (2005). *Living Beyond our Means, Natural Assets and Human Well-Being, Statement from the Board.* Millennium Ecosystem Assessment Cambridge.

Norton, L.R., Murphy, J., Reynolds, B., Marks, S. and Mackey, E.C. (2009). *Countryside Survey: Scotland Results from 2007.* NERC/Centre for Ecology & Hydrology. The Scottish Government, Scottish Natural Heritage. (CEH Project Number: C03259).

PACEC (2006). *The Economic and Environmental Impact of Sporting Shooting.* BASC, CA, and CLA, in association with GCT.

SNH (2010). Notified habitats in favourable condition. Scottish Natural Heritage, Biodiversity Indicator S011.

Scottish Government (2011). *Land use Strategy.* http://www.scotland.gov.uk/Topics/Environment/Countryside/Landusestrategy.

Visit Scotland (2008). Research & Statistics, National Facts & Figures, Tourism in Scotland in 2008. http://www.visitscotland.org/research_and_statistics/national_facts_and_figures.htm, accessed on 6 December 2009.

Williams, E., Firn, J.R., Kind, V., Roberts, M. and McGlashan, D. (2003). The value of Scotland's Ecosystem Services and Natural Capital. *European Environment*, **13(2)**, 67-78.

35 Developing a Sustainability Assessment Tool for Upland Estates

Jayne H. Glass, Alister J. Scott and Martin F. Price

Summary

1. A novel approach, adapted from the Delphi method, develops a tool for monitoring sustainable upland estate management. This is based upon collaborative work between a range of land management professionals, researchers and policy-makers.
2. The work challenged participants to develop shared ideas and solutions for tackling sustainable management.
3. There is considerable scope for this method to be used in other situations where building consensus around sustainable resource management practices is problematic.

35.1 Sustainable upland estate management

Upland areas in the UK are currently experiencing many competing environmental, economic and socio-cultural pressures (see Reed *et al.*, 2009 for a more detailed discussion). In Scotland, the extent to which management practices seek a balance between the use of natural resources and the economic and social needs of communities is a key aspect of sustainability (Henton and Crofts, 2000). However, arguably relatively little academic or policy attention has been devoted to translating sustainability principles into practical upland estate management strategies because of the varied range of estate ownership types, estate management objectives and values and opinions of the numerous external stakeholders.

Within the contemporary literature on sustainability, participation is seen as a principal mechanism for improving communication and increasing consensus among stakeholders with contrasting management objectives (Irvine *et al.*, 2009).

Glass, J.H., Scott, A.J. and Price, M.F. (2011). Developing a Sustainability Assessment Tool for Upland Estates – *The Changing Nature of Scotland*, eds. S.J. Marrs, S. Foster, C. Hendrie, E.C. Mackey, D.B.A. Thompson. TSO Scotland, Edinburgh, pp 425-428.

For example, conventional face-to-face methods such as focus groups and workshops can assist deliberation on complicated issues where the opinions of many people must be understood and shared. However, problems arise when participants represent different backgrounds or expertise, or do not collectively have a history of good communication. Difficulties can also be encountered when a face-to-face exchange becomes dominated by the strength of conviction of key personalities. As a result, creative methods are needed to engage more effectively and equitably with stakeholders when tackling complicated situations surrounding the sustainable use of natural resources.

35.2 A novel way to find shared solutions

The sustainability assessment tool for upland estate management was developed using an anonymous, iterative process involving four developmental stages (see Figure 35.1 for an overview). This approach adapts the Delphi method, which is conventionally used to seek consensus among members of an expert 'panel'. Participants answer a series of questions and then repeatedly adjust their responses in light of feedback given about the responses of other participants (for more detail, see Linstone and Turoff, 2002). A 'policy Delphi' is a different approach which uses the repetitive nature of the process to explore both consensus and disagreement surrounding complex policy issues with an informed group (see Kenyon *et al.*, 2008). Both versions of Delphi have their problems; notably, high drop-out rates and an overly-prescriptive process that can stifle the creativity of the participants and the process facilitator.

We adapted the method further to make some improvements. The first round was carried out in interview format to establish rapport between the facilitator and the participants, increasing motivation and buy-in. This resulted in an 89% response rate over the whole process. The assessment tool was developed by the facilitator, using only the participants' opinions and ideas for the content; the format of the tool was not pre-determined. This allowed the participants to have ownership over the evolution of the process and recognised the creative role that the facilitator can play in collating and feeding back the responses for further reflection.

35.2.1 The process in more detail

The multi-disciplinary 'panel' of 19 stakeholders represented expertise in sustainability, rural/upland land use and/or estate management, incorporating land management professionals, researchers, policy-makers and members of representative bodies. This secured a range of interests that had not previously discussed sustainability in this context. Panellists did not know the identity of other participants during the process so that a safe environment for open dialogue was created.

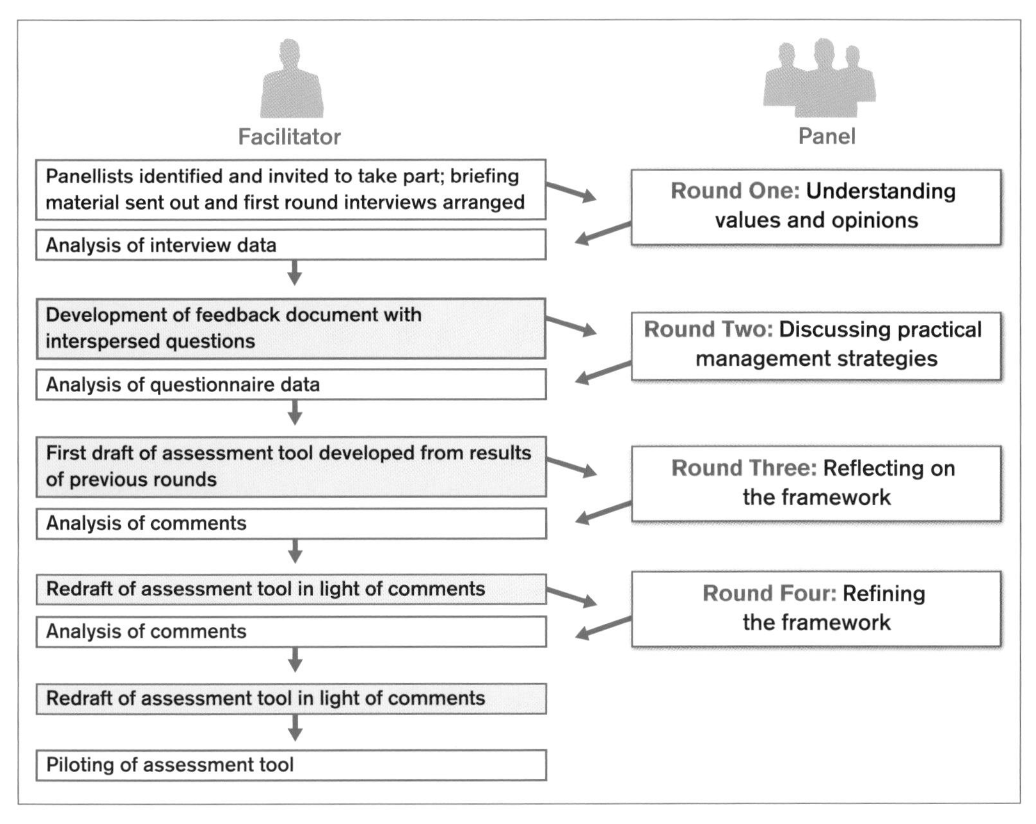

Figure 35.1 Overview of the process adapted from the Delphi method to seek consensus among members of an expert 'panel' (shaded boxes show when the facilitator took stock of the participants' ideas in order to promote the next stage of reflection and discussion).

A common definition of sustainability in the context of upland estate management was not presented to the panel at the outset. In the first round, interviews with each panellist aimed to explore and understand the participants' own perceptions of sustainability, based on their knowledge and experience. Practical objectives for sustainable management and potential constraining and enabling factors for putting these objectives into practice were also suggested by panellists. In the second round, interview findings were collated by the facilitator and returned to the panel in an unattributable combined feedback and questionnaire document, and each was invited to comment on points made by other panellists.

The results of the first two rounds were processed by the facilitator who actively reframed the panel's ideas into the first draft of a sustainability assessment tool. Using clear explanations and diagrams, the tool was returned to the panel for their comments; these comments were incorporated into a new version of the tool that was presented to the panel in round four (refining the framework) for further comment and subsequent amendment.

35.2.2 The tool in more detail

Spending time at the outset exploring different perceptions of sustainability allowed a working definition of sustainable upland estate management to be developed. Five 'sustainable estate principles' comprise this definition, around which the assessment tool is organised (Adapting Management; Broadening Options; Ecosystem Thinking; Linking into Social Fabric; Thinking beyond the Estate). 'Creativity', 'innovation' and 'proactive' attitudes were regularly cited by more than half of the panel as crucial for moving beyond traditional ideas to promote management that demonstrates a shift towards a more sustainable approach.

Over the course of the process, 16 'opportunities' for sustainable upland estates were identified, developed and endorsed by the panel. The extent to which an estate takes advantage of each opportunity can be assessed by the tool's user to judge whether an estate's management practices are deemed 'proactive' (more sustainable), 'active' or 'underactive' (less sustainable).

35.3 Conclusion

The approach we developed proved very effective for bringing together different stakeholders in order to find common solutions, going beyond what can be achieved using more traditional methods. The active role that the facilitator played in developing and feeding back material (based on the panel's input) created an excellent platform for continual deliberation, reflection and development of ideas. There is scope for this method to be applied to other situations where building consensus around how to achieve sustainable management of natural resources is problematic.

References

Henton, T. and Crofts, R. (2000). Key issues and objectives for sustainable development. In *Scotland's Environment: the future*, ed. by G. Holmes and R. Crofts. Tuckwell Press. East Linton. pp 75-91.

Irvine, R.J., Fiorini, S., Yearley, S. *et al.* (2009). Can managers inform models? Integrating local knowledge into models of red deer habitat use. *Journal of Applied Ecology*, **46**, 344-352.

Kenyon, W., Hill, G. and Shannon, P. (2008). Scoping the role of agriculture in sustainable flood management. *Land Use Policy*, **25**, 351-360.

Linstone, H.A. and Turoff, M. (2002). *The Delphi Method: Techniques and Applications.* Addison-Wesley, MA. Available from: http://www.is.njit.edu/pubs/delphibook/, accessed on 10 May 2010.

Reed, M.S., Bonn, A., Slee, W. *et al.* (2009). The future of the uplands. *Land Use Policy*, **26S**, S204-S216.

36 Is the Vegetation of the North-West Highlands Changing? Results from a 50 Year Re-visitation Study of Major Upland Vegetation Types

Louise C. Ross, Sarah J. Woodin, Alison J. Hester,
Des B.A. Thompson and H. John B. Birks

Summary

1. We re-surveyed vegetation plot data presented in '*Plant Communities of the Scottish Highlands*' to assess if there have been changes in plant species composition over the last 50 years. We worked on five major upland vegetation types in the north-west Highlands of Scotland.
2. Alpine heaths, grasslands and dwarf-shrub heaths have undergone more change than ombrogenous and soligenous mires, which have retained more of their original character.
3. Vegetational changes are characterised by an increased dominance of generalist upland graminoid species, decreases in the cover of dwarf-shrubs, forbs and lichens, and reduced distinction between vegetation types.
4. We discuss some of the potential drivers of these changes, which further research will explore in more detail.

36.1 Introduction

Throughout the twentieth century, the Scottish Uplands have been subjected to multiple and interacting drivers of change, including atmospheric nitrogen deposition, sheep and deer grazing, burning and climate change (Ratcliffe and Thompson, 1988). For plant species and communities, these drivers have often led to a loss of diversity (Britton *et al.*, 2009) and changes in the cover of plant

Ross, L.C., Woodin, S.J., Hester, A.J., Thompson, D.B.A. and Birks, H.J.B. (2011). Is the Vegetation of the North-West Highlands Changing? Results from a 50 Year Re-visitation Study of Major Upland Vegetation Types – *The Changing Nature of Scotland*, eds. S.J. Marrs, S. Foster, C. Hendrie, E.C. Mackey, D.B.A. Thompson. TSO Scotland, Edinburgh, pp 429-434.

functional groups (Milne and Hartley, 2001). Understanding how the magnitude of change varies between upland vegetation types is essential in developing appropriate conservation policies and management practices; yet such information is rarely available, especially over a longer time-scale. Re-visitation studies based on phytosociological survey data collected some decades ago can provide valuable insights into biodiversity change in a range of upland vegetation types, (for example, Klanderud and Birks, 2003; Britton *et al.*, 2009). In this paper we quantify and compare fine-scale changes in plant community composition in the north-west Highlands over the relatively long time-frame of 50 years. Original plot data were extracted from *Plant Communities of the Scottish Highlands* (McVean and Ratcliffe, 1962). Using a subset of these original data, we re-surveyed those plots 50 years later, to investigate changes in plant species composition and the relative abundance of plant functional groups in five major upland vegetation types.

36.2 Methods

Representative samples of natural and semi-natural vegetation were recorded from key mountain areas across the Scottish Highlands between 1956 and 1958 by Derek A. Ratcliffe and Donald N. McVean (McVean and Ratcliffe, 1962), in order to describe and classify upland vegetation types based on the presence and cover of

Plate 36.1 Drs Donald McVean (left) and the late Derek Ratcliffe, authors of *Plant Communities of the Scottish Highlands* (1962), in an Atlantic bryophyte-rich wood near Oban in 1990. © Des Thompson

the dominant species. These records provide a rare documentation of plant community composition five decades ago. The re-survey of 2007 and 2008 was restricted to selected vegetation types in the north-west Highlands, and was carried out as close as was practical to the time of year when each of the plots was originally surveyed. Dwarf-shrub heath (n=33), grassland (n=18), alpine heath (n=46), ombrogenous mire (n=22) and soligenous mire (n=7) plots were re-sampled.

The survey method described by McVean and Ratcliffe (1962) was followed as closely as possible in the re-survey. Sampling areas were re-located by the original six-figure national grid reference using a hand-held GPS unit, and the location of the $4m^2$ plot was selected using the information on slope, aspect and vegetation from the original survey. All plant species in the plots were recorded using percentage cover values. This method of re-placing plots when their precise original location is uncertain has been shown to be suitable for detecting temporal change with some degree of confidence (Ross *et al.*, 2010). Detrended Correspondence Analysis (DCA) was carried out on the 1956-58 and 2007-08 species composition data.

36.3 Results

The magnitude of change in plant species composition based on plot data from the five vegetation types was assessed by comparing the sample scores from axes 1-4 of the DCA of both surveys (see Table 36.1). Alpine heaths appear to have undergone the greatest shift in composition, with significant changes on all axes, while grassland and dwarf-shrub heath plots have undergone significant changes on three of the four axes. Soligenous mires have changed significantly on two axes, although ombrogenous mires have not undergone any significant changes. This ordination also

Table 36.1 Detrended Correspondence Analysis (DCA) axes where scores showed significant changes and plant functional groups with significant increased/decreased abundance in each vegetation type.

	DCA axes with significant changes in sample scores	**Functional groups with significantly increased abundance**	**Functional groups with significantly decreased abundance**
Dwarf-shrub heaths	1,2,4	Forbs Graminoids Pteridophytes	Dwarf-shrubs Lichens Shrubs
Grasslands	1,2,4	Graminoids	Forbs
Alpine heaths	1,2,3,4	Graminoids	Dwarf-shrubs Forbs Lichens
Ombrogenous mires	none	none	Bryophytes
Soligenous mires	2,4	Graminoids	none

shows that the re-survey plots are closer together than those of the original survey, particularly in dwarf-shrub heaths, grasslands and alpine heaths, suggesting a greater degree of compositional similarity today than 50 years ago. Generalist graminoid species such as purple moor-grass (*Molinia caerulea*) and deer grass (*Trichophorum cespitosum*) had greatly increased in cover, while declining species include crowberry (*Empetrum nigrum*) and alpine lady's-mantle (*Alchemilla alpina*).

Changes in species composition were also investigated by calculating changes in the mean percentage cover of plant functional groups, namely bryophytes, dwarf shrubs, forbs, graminoids, lichens, pteridophytes and shrubs (Table 36.1). Dwarf-shrub and alpine heaths had undergone the greatest changes in this respect, with significant declines in dwarf-shrub and lichen cover, and an increase in graminoid cover in both vegetation types, plus increased pteridophytes and decreased shrubs in the dwarf-shrub heaths. Forbs had increased in dwarf-shrub heaths and declined in alpine heaths. Grasslands, ombrogenous mires and soligenous mires have undergone significant changes in only one or two functional groups.

36.4 Discussion

The vegetation of the north-west Highlands has undergone marked changes over the last 50 years. Plots belonging to previously distinct vegetation types have become more similar in composition, suggesting some biotic homogenisation. An increase in widespread, generalist species at the expense of rarer, more specialised species supports this hypothesis. The magnitude of change in species composition varied between vegetation types, although there are similarities in the pattern of response. The marked change in alpine heaths is consistent with the presumed sensitivity of this vegetation type, due to a short growing season and low temperatures conferring low resistance and resilience (Milne and Hartley, 2001), and concurs with the findings of Britton *et al.* (2009) in other parts of Scotland. In grasslands, the results suggest a shift towards a denser more species-poor sward, where graminoids such as purple moor-grass have out-competed several open-ground forb species. In dwarf-shrub heaths, the apparent replacement of ericaceous dwarf-shrubs with graminoids detected in this study has also been described by, for example, Thompson *et al.* (1995).

Change in the two mire vegetation types has been less marked, although soligenous mires, which are usually of limited extent, appear to have been colonised by species such as purple moor-grass and deergrass from surrounding vegetation. Ombrogenous mires have changed least of all, suggesting that mires are more resistant to the impacts of environmental change drivers or have been exposed to them to a lesser degree. Overall, the results show increased similarity of plant species composition, which when characterised by the substantial increase in the cover of

Plate 36.2 Dr Louise Ross surveying a quadrat in Glen Tilt, Tayside. © Lorne Gill/SNH

generalist graminoids, suggests a loss of diversity both within and between vegetation types. The observed patterns of change are consistent with the effects of increased grazing pressure and nitrogen deposition, and possibly climatic warming (Milne and Hartley, 2001; Britton *et al.*, 2009), suggesting that these have been the key drivers of vegetation change in the north-west Highlands over the last 50 years.

Acknowledgements

This research is funded by a NERC-SNH CASE studentship with support from the Macaulay Institute.

References

Britton, A.J., Beale, C.M., Towers, W. and Hewison, R.L. (2009). Biodiversity gains and losses: evidence for homogenisation of Scottish alpine vegetation. *Biological Conservation*, **142**, 1728-1739.

Klanderud, K. and Birks, H.J.B. (2003). Recent increases in species richness and shifts in altitudinal distributions of Norwegian mountain plants. *The Holocene*, **13**, 1-6.

McVean, D.A. and Ratcliffe, D.N. (1962). *Plant Communities of the Scottish Highlands*. Monograph No. 1 of the Nature Conservancy. HMSO, London.

Milne, J.A. and Hartley, S.E. (2001). Upland plant communities – sensitivity to change. *Catena*, **42**, 333-343.

Ratcliffe, D.A. and Thompson, D.B.A. (1988). The British Uplands: their ecological character and international significance. In *Ecological Change in the Uplands*, ed. by M.B. Usher and D.B.A. Thompson, Blackwell, Oxford. pp 9-36.

Ross, L.C., Woodin, S.J., Hester, A.J., Thompson, D.B.A. and Birks, H.J.B. (2010). How important is plot relocation accuracy when interpreting re-visitation studies of vegetation change? *Plant Ecology and Diversity*, **3**, 1-8.

Thompson, D.B.A., MacDonald, A.J., Marsden, J.H. and Galbraith, C.A. (1995). Upland heather moorland in Great Britain: a review of international importance, vegetation change and some objectives for nature conservation. *Biological Conservation*, **71**, 163-178.

37 Climate Change and its Consequences on Bryophyte-dominated Snowbed Vegetation

Gordon Rothero, John Birks, Dave Genney, John-Arvid Grytnes and David Long

Summary

1. Scotland's snowbeds support unique communities of bryophytes (mosses and liverworts).
2. Resurveying snowbeds in the Cairngorms has shown that since 1989 there have been significant changes in the frequency of some species in core bryophyte-dominated snowbed vegetation.
3. During 2007 and 2008 a baseline network of monitoring transects was successfully set up across the main Scottish snowbed sites. This will allow for more accurate assessments of change in the frequency and extent of snowbed species in the future.

37.1 Introduction

Scotland's mountains are generally windy and the snow, both during and after snowfall, is very mobile, being blown by the wind onto lee slopes where large accumulations can occur. The depth and extent of these accumulations of wind-blown snow (snowbeds) depends on the extent of the catchment area, that is the area of plateau upwind of the snowbed off which the snow blows. In Scotland the prevailing wind is usually from the west or south-west and so snowbeds tend to form on slopes with an east or north-east aspect and these are also the slopes on which insolation (solar radiation) is very limited or absent during much of the year. Snow may lie well into the summer months and snowbeds support unique plant communities. In the UK, the Cairngorm plateau has the largest area of ground above 1,000m and provides an ideal catchment area for numerous snowbeds. However, other high mountains also have snow-gathering ground and there are

Rothero, G., Birks, J., Genney, D., Grytnes, J-A. and Long, D. (2011). Climate Change and its Consequences on Bryophyte-dominated Snowbed Vegetation – *The Changing Nature of Scotland*, eds. S.J. Marrs, S. Foster, C. Hendrie, E.C. Mackey, D.B.A. Thompson. TSO Scotland, Edinburgh, pp 435-440.

large and important snowbeds on the Ben Nevis-Aonach Mor range, on Ben Alder and on Creag Meagaidh, with smaller sites on the higher hills from Ben Lawers in Perthshire to Beinn Dearg in Ross-shire.

Bryophyte-dominated snowbed vegetation is rare in the UK, covering only a few hundred hectares and it contains a number of nationally rare and scarce species. As a result the habitat is of considerable conservation interest containing a number of species that have most, or all, of their Scottish records from within this habitat. About 50 species of bryophyte and lichen are either restricted to, or have their highest abundance in, snowbed vegetation in Scotland's Highlands. Climate change may alter the extent of this restricted habitat through changes in snowfall and the rate of summer melting.

We developed a research project which aims to:

- Determine the gross changes in the snowbed vegetation community by resurveying vegetation stands which were first surveyed in 1989; and
- Monitor any future changes in the extent and composition of bryophyte dominated snowbed vegetation by setting up permanent quadrats along fixed transects.

In this chapter we describe the initial results of the project.

37.2 Repeat of 1989-90 survey of snowbed vegetation on selected snowbed sites in the Cairngorms

The survey of bryophyte-dominated snowbed vegetation in 1989 and 1990 (Rothero, 1990, 1991a) was an extensive survey intended to determine the area covered by this type of vegetation and the distribution of its characteristic species and communities. Quadrat data were collected from homogeneous stands within the snowbeds for community analysis (Rothero, 1991b) but it was never intended that these samples would form the basis for future monitoring, so the quadrats were not marked in any way. The exercise in 2007-08 was essentially a repeat of that part of the survey.

Although it was not possible to re-locate the specific original quadrats, sampling was carried out so that the same numbers of quadrats were surveyed in stands of the same community on each of the sites and the same methodology was used. The sites visited are shown in Figure 37.1.

Improved experience in field identification by the surveyor means that rare species like the liverwort *Gymnomitrion apiculatum* may have been previously under-recorded and although this is not significant in the data analysis, it is of conservation interest.

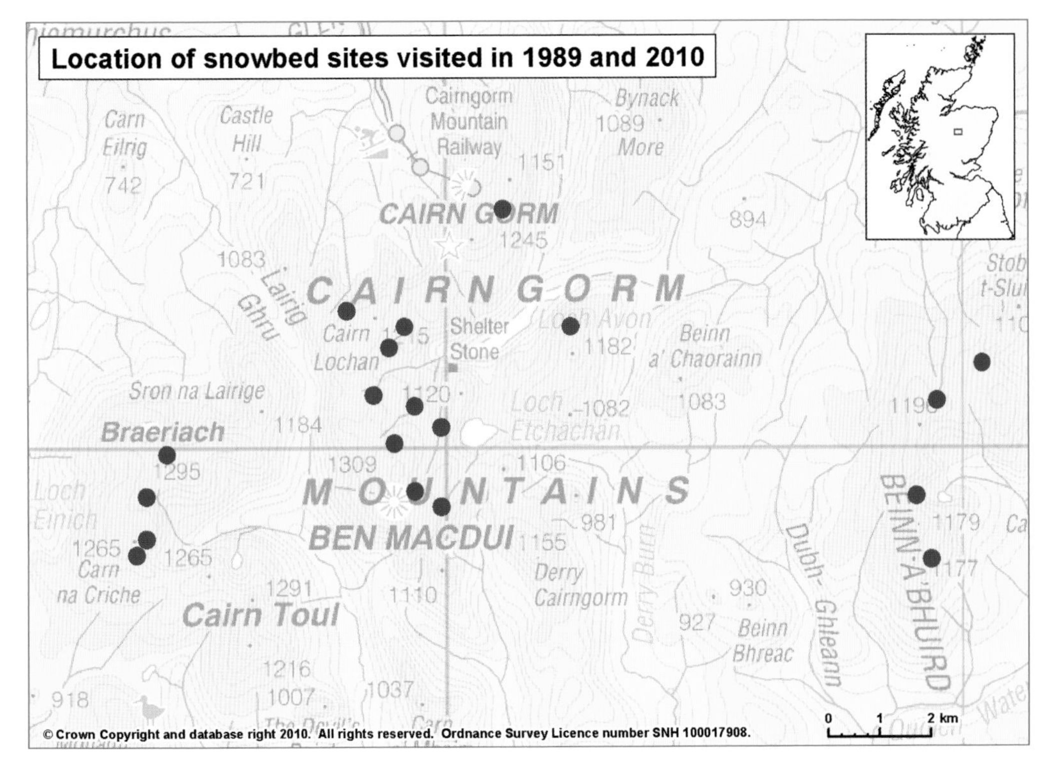

Figure 37.1 Snowbed sites (red dots) visited in the Cairngorms 1989-90 and 2007-08.

37.3 Analysis of frequency data

The resurveys have shown that since 1989 there have been significant changes in the frequency of some species in core bryophyte-dominated snowbed vegetation (Table 37.1). At the head of the list of increases since 1989 are the mosses *Oligotrichum hercynicum, Ditrichum zonatum, Pohlia nutans* and *Kiaeria falcata* and the vascular plants three-leaved rush (*Juncus trifidus*) and starry saxifrage (*Saxifraga stellaris*), the latter was not recorded on any survey site in 1989. The only significant decrease was the liverwort *Moerckia blyttii*.

The changes are difficult to interpret but may illustrate that the snowbed species are experiencing conditions more typical of exposed mountain summit habitats. Of particular concern is the increase in larger and more widespread montane vascular plants which may threaten important bryophyte species in the future. This finding is consistent with wider ranging studies which have shown a gradual homogenisation of Scottish vegetation types (Britton *et al.*, 2009; Brooker, Chapter 32; Ross *et al.*, Chapter 36).

Table 37.1 The number of plots in which species were present in 1989 and in 2007, their frequency in both years and the change in frequency. Typical snowbed species are in **bold**. The list excludes species recorded in less than five plots in both years. Codes are: VP – Vascular plant; M – Moss; LC – Lichen; LV – Liverwort.

Species	Plots 1989	Plots 2007	Frequency 1989	Frequency 2007	Difference in frequency
Oligotrichum hercynicum (M)	19	42	23%	51%	28% *
Saxifraga stellaris (VP)	0	17	0%	20%	20%
Ditrichum zonatum (M)	11	28	13%	34%	20% *
Pohlia nutans (M)	16	32	19%	39%	19% *
Juncus trifidus (VP)	10	25	12%	30%	18% *
***Kiaeria falcata* (M)**	**14**	**29**	17%	35%	18% *
Lophozia sudetica (LV)	42	55	51%	66%	16%
Racomitrium heterostichum (M)	38	49	46%	59%	13%
Racomitrium lanuginosum (M)	14	25	17%	30%	13%
Scapania uliginosa (LV)	2	12	2%	14%	12%
***Polytrichum sexangulare* (M)**	**58**	**67**	70%	81%	11%
Cladonia spp. (LC)	0	7	0%	8%	8%
Anthelia juratzkana (LV)	22	28	27%	34%	7%
Cephalozia bicuspidata (LV)	37	42	45%	51%	6%
Barbilophozia floerkii (LV)	36	40	43%	48%	5%
Anthelia julacea (LV)	7	10	8%	12%	4%
***Pleurocladula albescens* (LV)**	**29**	**32**	35%	39%	4%
Diplophyllum albicans (LV)	13	15	16%	18%	2%
***Marsupella brevissima* (LV)**	**35**	**36**	42%	43%	1%
Bare ground	32	32	39%	39%	0%
***Conostonum tetragonum* (M)**	**21**	**21**	25%	25%	0%
Deschampsia cespitosa (VP)	13	13	16%	16%	0%
Dicranum fuscescens (M)	8	7	10%	8%	-1%
Polytrichum alpinum (M)	11	10	13%	12%	-1%
Racomitrium fasciculare (M)	16	15	19%	18%	-1%
Carex bigelowii (VP)	25	23	30%	28%	-2%
***Kiaeria starkei* (M)**	**45**	**42**	54%	51%	-4%
Nardia scalaris (LV)	36	33	43%	40%	-4%
***Gnaphalium supinum* (VP)**	**12**	**8**	14%	10%	-5%
Huperzia selago (VP)	17	13	20%	16%	-5%
Marsupella condensata (LV)	14	10	17%	12%	-5%
Gymnomitrion concinnatum (LV)	9	5	11%	6%	-5%
Salix herbacea (VP)	25	21	30%	25%	-5%
Marsupella emarginata (LV)	6	1	7%	1%	-6%
***Pohlia ludwigii* (M)**	**20**	**15**	24%	18%	-6%
***Marsupella stableri* (LV)**	**12**	**6**	14%	7%	-7%
Marsupella sphacelata (LV)	18	11	22%	13%	-8%
Marsupella alpina (LV)	8	1	10%	1%	-8%
Deschampsia flexuosa (VP)	22	15	27%	18%	-8%
***Moerckia blyttii* (LV)**	**16**	**5**	19%	6%	-13%

* Indicates a significant difference between 1989 and 2007 ($p < 0.05$).

Plate 37.1 Snow may lie well into the summer months in east or north-east facing corries in the Cairngorms. These snowbeds eventually melt to reveal unique plant communities. © David Long/Royal Botanic Garden Edinburgh

37.4 Baseline monitoring of bryophyte-dominated snowbed vegetation in the Cairngorms

During 2007 and 2008 a baseline network of permanent quadrats along monitoring transects was set up across the main Scottish snowbed sites. This network will enable more accurate assessment of changes in the frequency and extent of snowbed species. Detailed site photographs were taken so that general change in the pattern of vegetation on sites could be assessed and permanent line transects were set up so that detailed changes in both the distribution and composition of the flora can be monitored. Suitable sites were selected from the Cairngorm snowbeds surveyed in 1989 (Rothero, 1990).

In setting up monitoring plots in fragile habitats like snowbed vegetation, it is important to minimise the damage caused by the monitoring process. Two monitoring methods were selected; permanent quadrats in an array over the site; and permanent transects in a line across the site. Both methods have advantages and disadvantages. Quadrats can be randomly located across a site and therefore can be used for statistical analysis. The main disadvantage is ensuring quadrat markers do not cause damage and can be relocated. Permanently marked transect lines have some clear advantages for use on snowbed vegetation. Snowbeds are usually relatively small and have steep environmental gradients so that a transect line of manageable length can cover a range of plant communities. The main disadvantages are that quadrats are not randomly distributed so statistical analysis is limited and the line concentrates trampling to a narrow zone.

37.5 Future monitoring

The purpose of this project was to provide a baseline for future monitoring of changes in snowbed vegetation. It is essential that subsequent monitoring visits are set up to ensure that they cover the same areas. In the future it may be possible to use satellite images to monitor extent and longevity of the important snowbeds and relate this to the species composition.

Predicted climate change may affect the upland habitats more than any other habitat in Scotland. This initial study and monitoring network provide an important insight into the impacts on one of our most vulnerable upland habitats.

Acknowledgements

This work was supported by Scottish Natural Heritage, Royal Botanic Garden Edinburgh and the Olaf Grolle Olsen Legat, University of Bergen. We are grateful to Simon Foster and an anonymous referee for improving the manuscript.

References

Britton, A.J., Beale, C.M., Towers, W. and Hewison, R.L. (2009). Biodiversity gains and losses: Evidence for homogenisation of Scottish alpine vegetation. *Biological Conservation*, **142**, 1728-1739.

Rothero, G.P. (1990). Survey of bryophyte-dominated snow-beds Part I. Cairngorms and Aonach Mor. *Scottish Field Unit Survey Report* No. 41.

Rothero, G.P. (1991a). Survey of bryophyte-dominated snow-beds Part II. The Highlands other than the main Cairngorms. *Scottish Field Unit Survey Report* No. 51.

Rothero, G.P. (1991b). *Bryophyte-dominated snow-beds in the Scottish Highlands.* MSc. University of Glasgow.

38 Results of a Volunteer-based Project to Map Upland Hill Tracks in the North East of Scotland

David Windle, Richard Gard and Kenny Freeman

Summary

1. Vehicle hill tracks were surveyed using volunteers' photographs.
2. Volunteers used digital cameras to photograph hill tracks within the Cairngorms National Park and hand held GPS devices to record the location of the tracks.
3. The data were used to build a database of information on the state of hill tracks in the Cairngorms National Park.

38.1 Introduction

This paper describes the volunteer hill tracks survey project run by the North East Mountain Trust, part funded by Scottish Natural Heritage (SNH) and the Cairngorms National Park Authority (CNPA). All parties recognised that, in recent years, there has been a rise in the number of planning issues relating to development of upland hill tracks. In many cases, the form of an appropriate response depends on the previous state of the track; rework to an existing track meriting a different response to the creation of a new track where there wasn't one previously. Thus, good historical records would be very useful.

The project was initiated to address gaps in existing records and to see if local people could be encouraged to become more involved with the state of the Cairngorms National Park. It started in 2007 and continues today with 1,391 geo-referenced photographs collected so far. Figure 38.1 shows the coverage achieved to date.

Windle, D., Gard, R. and Freeman, K. (2011). Results of a Volunteer-based Project to Map Upland Hill Tracks in the North East of Scotland – *The Changing Nature of Scotland*, eds. S.J. Marrs, S. Foster, C. Hendrie, E.C. Mackey, D.B.A. Thompson. TSO Scotland, Edinburgh, pp 441-446.

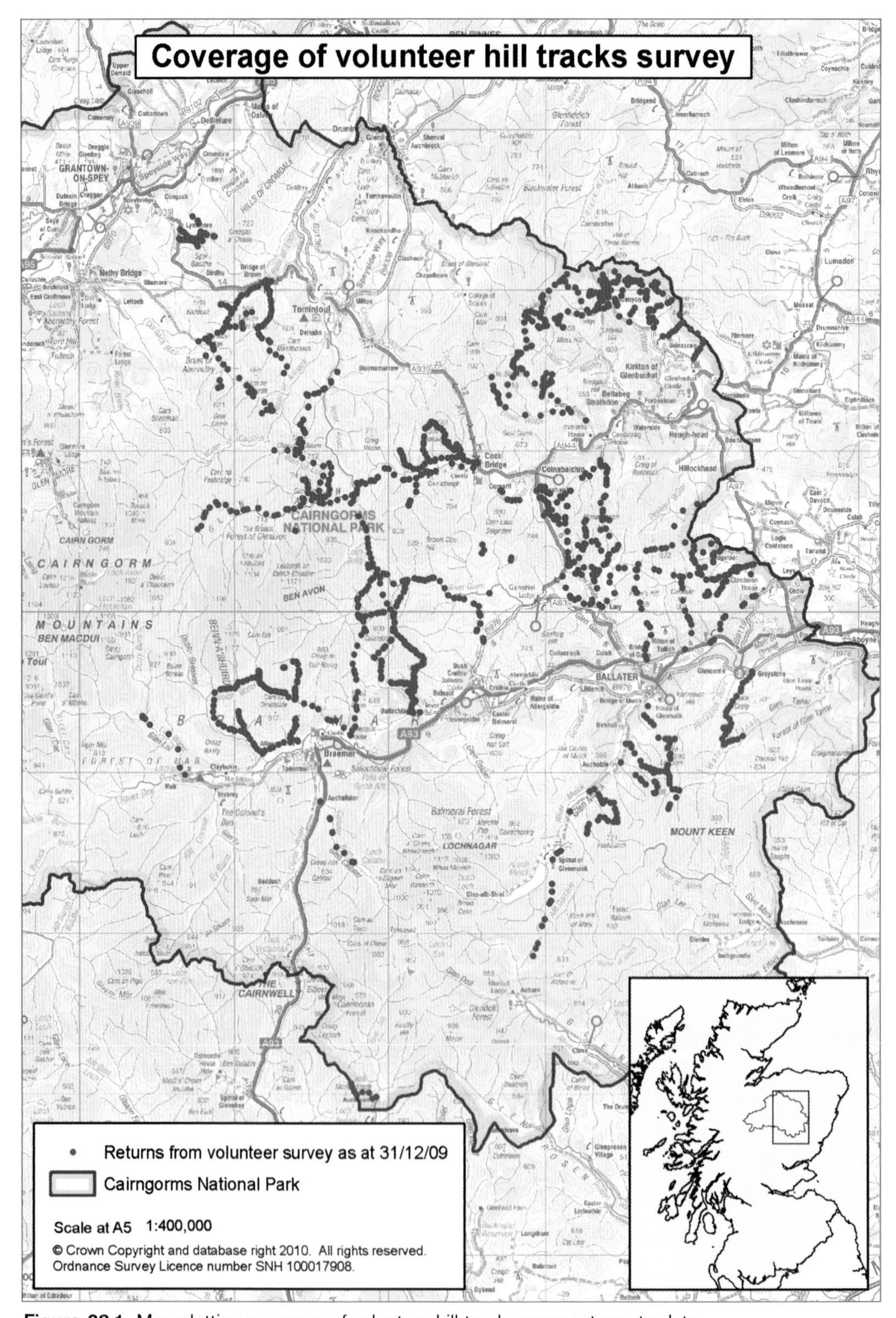

Figure 38.1 Map plotting coverage of volunteer hill track survey returns to date.

38.2 Methodology

The approach adopted was to take a series of digital photographs with each one identified by geographical coordinates, in this case, expressed as Ordnance Survey map references, taken from a hand held GPS device. Photographs were taken along the line of the track, preferably with some form of scaling device such as a walking stick set to one metre length in the foreground, as shown in Figure 38.2. Photographs were taken at intervals of 200-300m or where there was a notable change of feature such as track surface or width. The survey started with a pilot in the north east corner of the Cairngorms National Park and then expanded to cover a fuller eastern section as interest moved to tracks on the more eastern estates. A simple video was produced showing people what to do and training classes were run. Later, following demand, simplified ways of noting coordinates for each photograph were produced. Automatically transferring coordinate data directly from the GPS device obviously improves data quality and was used by some volunteers. However, some volunteers, although used to reading map references off a GPS screen, felt uncomfortable downloading GPS data and did the transfer manually. As the success of this project relied on the time and input from volunteers, it was not felt appropriate to force all volunteers to download the data in this way.

Figure 38.2 Example of photograph and record taking.

At the start of the project, consideration was given to using satellite photographs. This idea was rejected because the resolution was insufficiently reliable to distinguish important features such as adequacy of side drains, provision of silt traps, water bars and ability of the surface, both track and surrounding, to self drain. Also, the frequency of updating the satellite photographs would introduce delays when new tracks are built. In addition, an important aspect of the project was to encourage local participation in the state of the park. This would not have been addressed using satellite photography.

Initially, the coverage was random. Volunteers were encouraged to survey wherever they wanted within CNPA. As the database increased, people were directed to areas, and even specific tracks, to fill in gaps. However, as more and more hill tracks are built new 'gaps' appear all the time. For this reason, it's not possible to express the coverage achieved as a percentage of the total; the total length of track to be surveyed is continually increasing.

38.3 Encouraging volunteer participation

Encouraging volunteer participation was an important aspect of the project. The idea being that this would increase awareness of the mountain environment and hence increase the contribution of volunteers to the future of the park. Volunteer take up was variable, as was their output from year to year. As some volunteers have stopped, others have been recruited. A total of nine teams and individuals contributed to the project. The teams varied; some photographs were taken by people working alone, others were from teams of two to three people. Over time, a large database has been built up and although it is not currently available online it is hoped it will be in the future.

Publicity to recruit volunteers was generated by articles in the local newspapers, an interview on Radio Scotland and canvassing of the local hill walking clubs. A leaflet was also produced and circulated around member clubs and displayed in suitable shops.

38.4 Extraction of additional data

The original intention was to extract quantitative information on features such as track width and surface from each photograph and hence build up a track classification. The authors considered that, despite concerns over variations in scoring by individual contributors, a system of three indices; regeneration, erosion and drainage would be worth trialling. The work highlighted the fact that one of the most important features of an upland hill track is the adequacy of its drainage. A well-drained track will be stable over a long period of time whereas a poorly drained track will quickly erode, sometimes creating huge scars. Clearly this is very dependent on soil type and vegetation, factors that are not easy for non-experts to quantify. Hence, judging the adequacy of drainage is difficult and despite attempts to use local experts to build up this expertise, there was little success here. The indices for regeneration and erosion proved too difficult to apply with the volunteer survey workforce. Many of the volunteers felt that the indices were an additional, unnecessary burden and what few results were obtained were found to be highly variable and of no use.

38.5 Data specification

It was important to make the data simple in format and yet ensure that it meshed with work done by other agencies. Discussions were held with Scotways, National Trust for Scotland and Local Authorities as well as experts from the two funding agencies, SNH and CNPA. The information is held in a simple database or GIS layer as data points. Each has a unique photo identifier in the form DWW_123_456.jpg where DWW are the initials of the volunteer doing the survey, 123 is the track point number and 456 is the camera-generated digital photograph number. The database also holds any additional information, such as measured track width, running surface and drainage features provided by the contributor.

38.6 Use of data

Data from the project has already been used in support of the local planning process. In one example, photographs from the project were used to provide evidence that a newly constructed track was indeed a new track and not an old track repaired as claimed by the estate responsible for its construction. This resulted in an application for retrospective planning permission. In a second example, photographs were used to provide evidence that required remedial works had, in fact, not been carried out and that enforcement action was necessary.

38.7 Future direction

The project started in 2008 and during the first year, about 10% of the total photographs were collected. Despite the slow start, the authors have been encouraged by the eventual take-up. Work has started on talking to other Non-Governmental Organisations (NGOs) to see if they are interested in expanding the coverage and extending the work across the whole park.

The major source of reference material on upland hill tracks in the study area was a paper published by A. Watson (1984). It is planned to compare this data with the new data to gain a view on the rate of increase of hill tracks in the Cairngorms area.

The third area of focus is to start to fill in all the remaining gaps. As the surveyors are all volunteers, this needs to be approached sensitively. People might be less keen to volunteer if they feel that they are being overly directed.

Acknowledgements

We would like to thank all the volunteers without whom this project would not have been possible. The financial support of SNH and the Cairngorms National Park Authority is gratefully acknowledged. Particular thanks for their input are also due to Adam Watson, Sandy Walker, Ed Pilkington, Peter Holden and Judith Lewis.

Reference

Watson, A. (1984). A Survey of Vehicular Hill Tracks in North-East Scotland for Land Use Planning. *Journal of Environmental Management*, **18**, 345-353.

The Changing Nature of Scotland

Settlements and built development

Settlements and built development

When people think of Scotland they often conjure images of remote glens, snow-capped mountain tops and some of our rarest or most exciting birds and mammals. Whilst Scotland does indeed offer these, and much more, our towns or cities are also rich in habitats and species – something which is often forgotten. Eighty percent of the population live in towns and cities, and the wildlife contained therein is the only nature people see on a daily basis. The final part of this book looks at greenspaces, the creation of sustainable settlements and the ways in which we interact with nature in urban areas.

Some key events concerning nature in Scotland's urban environment since 1970

1972	Town and Country Planning (Scotland) Act 1972
1975	Town and Country Planning (Tree Preservation Order and Trees in Conservation Areas (Scotland) Regulations provides protection for trees in areas where they are considered to be of amenity value
1985	Central Scotland Countryside Trust (later Central Scotland Forest Trust) established to improve the environment of central Scotland
1989	Countryside Around Towns Forum and Steering Group established to review ways of improving the environment especially around towns
1991	Planning and Compensation Act 1991, recognising that consequences for the natural environment must be considered during the planning process
1992	Jupiter Urban Wildlife Centre opened in Grangemouth as a demonstration urban reserve developed from a derelict railway marshalling yard
1994	Review of Scotland's planning system
1995	*Framework for action for the natural heritage* in and around settlements published by SNH
1997	Town and Country Planning (Scotland) Act 1997
1997	Plant for Wildlife established (became Gardens for Life in 2001)
1991	Dundee City Council published Scotland's first 'open space strategy'

ew and old buildings, Edinburgh.
) Lorne Gill/SNH

2001	'*Rethinking Open Space*' published by the Scottish Executive makes key recommendations on the planning and management of open space in Scotland. SNH established the Greenspace for Communities Initiative to improve the quantity and quality of greenspace in and around Scotland's towns and cities
2002	greenspacescotland established to provide a national lead on local action to improve the environment in towns and cities
2004	National Planning Framework published
2005	Woodlands In and Around Towns initiative by Forestry Commission Scotland to improve the quality of life in towns and cities
2006	Planning etc. (Scotland) Act – central part of the most fundamental and comprehensive reform of Scotland's planning system in sixty years
2008	*Scottish Government Planning Advice Note 65*: *Planning and Open* Space, sets out advice on the role of the planning system in protecting and enhancing existing open spaces and providing high quality new spaces
2009	greenspacescotland published the first '*State of Scotland's Greenspace*' report
2009	Climate Change (Scotland) Act requires that all new buildings should utilise low and zero-carbon technologies
2010	*Scottish Planning Policy* published. A statement of the Scottish Government's policy on nationally important land use planning matters

Sources of information includes Collar (2010).

Greenspaces are described by greenspacescotland as places that 'bring the countryside into towns and cities'. Julie Procter and Eilidh Johnston (Chapter 39) discuss the *State of Scotland's Greenspace*, which in 2009 drew together baseline data from 20 local authorities on the quantity of greenspace as well as trends in public use and attitudes towards it. They show the surface area of available greenspace is equivalent to nine double beds per person. However, the difference in type of greenspace varies considerably between local authorities, with urban areas 'characterised by large formal parks'. They look at how greenspace is valued by people, and reveal that between 2004 and 2009 there was a 14% increase in the numbers of people using their local greenspace at least once a week for exercise. Tellingly, Procter and Johnston comment that '50% of those polled can walk to their local greenspace within five minutes, but this drops to 39% in the 15% of the most deprived areas of Scotland'.

Clive Mitchell (Chapter 40) of Scottish Natural Heritage stresses the importance of planning when designing new settlements, in particular to ensure that settlements are built at a 'human scale' – that is people can walk to the shops, park etc. within five minutes of where they live. Based on lessons learnt during six of SNH's Sharing Good Practice events, Mitchell illustrates how considerate planning can create a legacy of sustainable communities. Among his conclusions are that people and communities are at the centre of sustainable places. This sentiment was echoed by the talk given at the 2009 Conference by Jim Mackinnon (Scotland's Chief Planner) in which he remarked that 'a sustainable place is simply one where you want to be, where you want to live or want to gather.'

Two of SNH's indicators track changes in built development. The Natural Heritage Indicator (SNH, 2010) on built development shows that in 2009, one or more types of development were present within 56,496 kilometre squares (66% of squares in Scotland). The Scottish Biodiversity Indicator on the extent and composition of greenspace states that 'The amount and type of greenspace reflected within local plans is indicative of its value to both people and biodiversity and gives a measure of its protection'. The data show that in 2009, 25.2% of the total area of 171 settlements were covered by greenspace policies in local plans (SNH, 2009).

Biodiversity in Scotland's gardens was studied by Mike Toms, Liz Humphreys and Chris Wernham (Chapter 41). They noted that while private gardens (30% of Scotland's greenspace, Procter and Johnston, Chapter 39) are important for many species, these are difficult to monitor. Garden BirdWatch, introduced by The British Trust for Ornithology (BTO), involves garden-owners in a 'Citizen Science' approach to monitoring. The results have helped improve our understanding of annual and seasonal changes in garden use by birds and other wildlife. Interestingly the BTO study shows that goldfinch (*Carduelis carduelis*) numbers are increasing, and this is put down to a growing availability of bird feeders full of suitable seed mixes in private gardens.

If our settlements are to be sustainable we need to give them careful consideration in our planning system. This point was reinforced by Jim Mackinnon speaking at the Conference when he stated; 'For urban planning to be successful, it needs to be founded on an understanding of 'what was', 'what is', and 'what might be'. Some might say that this should include an acute awareness of the needs of nature within our settlements and built developments and how best to enjoy it.

References

Collar, N. (2010). *Planning.* 3rd Edition. Thomas Reuters (Legal) Limited, London.

SNH (2009). Extent and composition of greenspace. Scottish Natural Heritage, Biodiversity Engagement Indicator E02. www.snh.gov.uk

SNH (2010). Built development. Scottish Natural Heritage, Natural Heritage Indicator N2. www.snh.gov.uk

39 The State of Scotland's Greenspace

Julie Procter and Eilidh Johnston

Summary

1. Greenspaces can be described as any vegetated land or water within, or adjoining an urban area. They contribute to improving people's physical and mental health by providing places for informal recreation – walking, cycling, sitting, socialising and children's play – by bringing the countryside into towns and cities. Until recently there were little data about Scotland's urban greenspace resource. This paper reports on new and developing data on urban greenspace in Scotland and provides a baseline for analysing trends and examining the impacts of greenspace policy and investment.
2. Of Scotland's 32 local authorities, 20 have recorded almost 85,000 hectares of greenspace; this equates to 23 hectares per 1,000 people. Thirty percent of the greenspace is classified as private gardens, with natural and semi-natural greenspace making up a further 28%.
3. The quality of greenspace is often the most important factor in determining its use and benefit to local communities, however, it is not yet possible to report on this attribute. A number of local authorities are working on qualitative audits and it is expected that the second State of Scotland's Greenspace report (planned for 2011) will report on greenspace quantity and quality.
4. Public use of greenspace and attitudes towards it are important in realising the full range of social, economic and health benefits of these areas. Recent surveys show a trend of increasing use of greenspace, and very positive attitudes towards it, but also highlight the need to improve local greenspaces and tackle potential barriers to their wider use.
5. Greenspace data can be used in conjunction with a range of Geographic Information System (GIS) tools and socio-economic datasets to analyse the accessibility of spaces, inform decision making and support national research.

Procter, J. and Johnston, E. (2011). The State of Scotland's Greenspace – *The Changing Nature of Scotland*, eds. S.J. Marrs, S. Foster, C. Hendrie, E.C. Mackey, D.B.A. Thompson. TSO Scotland, Edinburgh, pp 453-464.

39.1 Introduction

An understanding of the extent and quality of our national greenspace resource is vital. It is becoming increasingly evident that good quality greenspaces contribute to increased physical activity levels and improved mental well-being (greenspace scotland, 2007), attract investment and create places where people want to live (greenspace scotland, 2008). Urban greenspace can also help to mitigate the impacts of flooding, air pollution and high temperatures, as well as supporting urban biodiversity and integrated habitat networks (greenspace scotland, 2008). Biodiversity conservation is a government priority and urban greenspace is fundamental to biodiversity conservation and in connecting people to nature. Data on greenspace can also provide a powerful tool for planning and delivering on local quality of life issues. While it is important that local authorities understand their greenspace resource and plan for its development and management strategically, a national picture can help to track progress and tackle large scale issues such as predicted climate change and health.

State of Scotland's Greenspace 2009 (greenspace scotland, 2009a) is a report based on information from 20 local authorities, covering 34% of Scotland's land area and 70% of its population. The data are for greenspace in urban areas – defined as settlements of 3,000 people or more and including a 500 metre buffer around the settlement for mapping purposes. Settlements of 3,000 people or more was adopted by greenspace scotland in 2003 as the definition of urban, in line with Scottish Government's Urban Rural Classification. The report details which types of greenspace are most prevalent in Scotland and the quantities of greenspace in different areas. This provides a benchmark for the future and will enable us to see the impacts of investment and policies to support greenspace.

39.2 Greenspace policy background

Greenspaces contribute to urban quality of life in many different ways and play an important role in developing a healthier, safer and stronger, wealthier and fairer, smarter and greener Scotland. The breadth of greenspace's contribution to a wide range of policies is described in *Making the Links: greenspace for a more successful and sustainable Scotland* (greenspace scotland, 2009b).

Recent planning policies (Scottish Government, 2007, 2008, 2010) recognise the importance of multi-functional, high quality greenspaces, and require local authorities to prepare a greenspace audit on a five-yearly basis and a greenspace strategy which will inform their Development Plan. Local authorities and this study use the typology of open spaces set out in Planning Advice Note (PAN) 65 on Open Space (Scottish Government, 2008) – summarised as follows:

- public parks and gardens;
- private gardens or grounds;
- amenity greenspace;
- play space for children and teenagers;
- sports areas;
- green corridors;
- natural/semi-natural greenspaces;
- allotments and community growing spaces;
- civic space;
- burial grounds; and
- other functional greenspace.

39.3 The greenspace data

As previously mentioned the data used in *State of Scotland's Greenspace 2009* (greenspace scotland, 2009a) were drawn from the open space audits of 20 local authority areas. These areas were selected for inclusion because they were able to provide information on greenspace quantity, sorted by a recognised planning typology. Table 39.1 lists the local authorities that provided data.

Table 39.1 Local authority areas who provided quantitative data for the State of Scotland's Greenspace 2009.

Aberdeen City	Fife
Aberdeenshire	Glasgow City
City of Edinburgh	Midlothian
Clackmannanshire	Moray
Dundee City	North Ayrshire
East Ayrshire	Perth & Kinross
East Dunbartonshire	Renfrewshire
East Lothian	Scottish Borders
East Renfrewshire	South Ayrshire
Falkirk	West Lothian

In 2007, with funding support from the then Scottish Executive, and continuing in 2008 with funding from Scottish Natural Heritage (SNH), greenspace scotland started a programme of greenspace mapping with Scottish local authorities. This greenspace characterisation mapping used GIS maps and aerial photography to produce a comprehensive map of all urban greenspaces, identifying their location and type, for 12 local authorities. The methodology used was originally developed and piloted in the eight Glasgow and Clyde Valley local authority areas by the Glasgow and Clyde Valley Structure Plan team, SNH and Forestry Commission Scotland (FCS). Experience gained from this pilot was applied to modify the methodology and the data from these first eight authorities are being updated. More detail about the greenspace mapping methodology is available in a series of guidance documents (greenspace scotland, 2010).

39.4 Findings on Scotland's greenspace

39.4.1 Overall national quantity

In total, the 20 reporting local authorities recorded 84,870 hectares of greenspace – equivalent in size to over 120,000 football pitches. This translates to over 23 hectares of greenspace per 1,000 people in the reporting authorities – equivalent in size to nine double beds per person! If private gardens are removed from the figures, this reduces the total to 16 hectares of greenspace per 1,000 people. Play spaces and sports areas together account for three hectares of greenspace per 1,000 people.

39.4.2 Types of greenspace

The data were also interrogated by PAN 65 typology. Two types account for more than half of the greenspace recorded by Scottish local authorities (see Table 39.2): private gardens or grounds (30%) and natural/semi-natural greenspace (28%).

Table 39.2 Proportions of different urban greenspace types in Scotland classified according to the Scottish Government's Planning Advice Notice 65 (Planning and open space) typology.

Open space typology	Percentage of Scotland's greenspace
private gardens or grounds	30%
natural/semi-natural greenspaces	28%
amenity greenspace	15%
sports areas	13%
public parks and gardens	9%
green corridors	3%
burial grounds	1%
other functional greenspace	1%
allotments and community growing spaces	<1%
civic space	<1%
play space for children and teenagers	<1%

Public parks and gardens, amenity greenspace and sports areas accounted for 9%, 15% and 13% of greenspace, respectively. Play spaces, allotments, burial grounds, green corridors and civic space tended to cover only small areas.

The quantity of different greenspace types varied widely between local authorities, with rural and suburban areas often having different types and distributions of greenspace when compared to inner cities. For example, rural and suburban settlements often have larger areas of amenity greenspace and are more likely to have large sports areas such as golf courses. However, certain urban areas are characterised by large formal parks and greater areas of green corridor and cemeteries. The proportions of greenspace types according to reporting authority are shown in Figure 39.1.

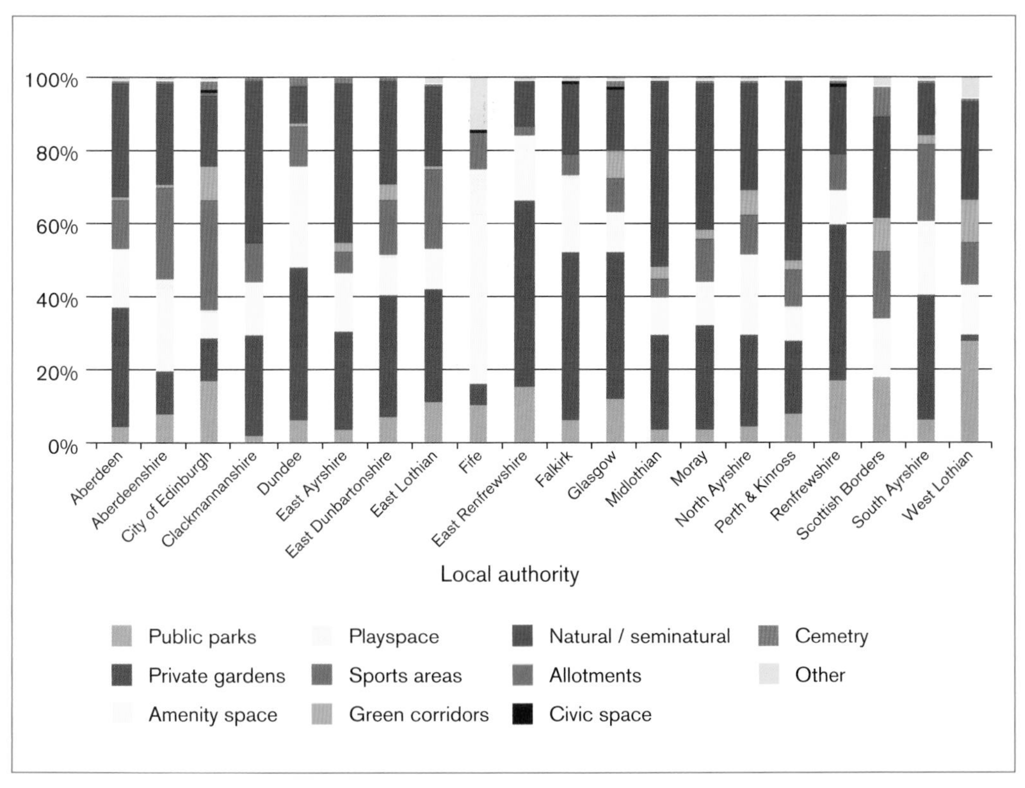

Figure 39.1 Proportion of different greenspace types in the reporting local authorities.

Even within one city there can be significant variation in the amount, type and distribution of greenspace. For example, in Edinburgh, the centre is dominated by public parks and gardens; however to the west of the city, there are higher levels of natural and semi-natural greenspace, as well as sports areas.

39.4.3 Accessibility of greenspace

The settlement pattern also has a significant impact on accessibility from a resident's perspective. The ease of accessing greenspace and whether the greenspaces can be easily connected to form convenient walking and cycling routes can be as important as how much greenspace there is in an area (see Section 39.5.1 for more information on accessibility analysis).

39.4.4 Quality of greenspace

While many people are concerned with the quantity of public greenspace and the perception that this may be reducing, the quality of greenspace is often the most critical factor in determining whether greenspace meets local needs and delivers a full range of benefits to local communities. In September 2009, 30 local authorities held some information on greenspace quantities and 20 of which had begun to audit the quality of their local spaces. However, very few quality audits have been completed or published. It is not, therefore, possible to provide any national picture of greenspace quality at this time.

In partnership with the Glasgow and Clyde Valley Green Network Partnership, greenspace scotland has produced guidance on auditing greenspace quality (greenspace scotland and Glasgow and Clyde Valley Green Network Partnership, 2008). *Greenspace quality – a guide to assessment, planning and strategic development* provides practical guidance on the assessment of greenspace quality and the ways in which quality standards can be developed and delivered. This guidance is being used by around half of the local authorities who are measuring, or have measured, greenspace quality.

A number of local authorities (including Aberdeenshire, East Lothian and Midlothian) have used the guide to design their open space audits and subsequent strategy development. In other areas, the suggested quality criteria and systems have been adapted to meet a more specific local need. For example, the City of Edinburgh Council's greenspace audit combines the greenspace scotland guidance and elements of the Green Flag Award Scheme. The Glasgow and Clyde Valley Green Network Partnership has adapted the criteria to look specifically at the quality of common areas and back courts in residential areas.

39.5 Using the greenspace dataset and maps

In addition to supporting local authority planning and management of greenspace, datasets and maps of greenspace offer potential for supporting decision making and research. Relatively simple analyses can be used to assess the accessibility of greenspace. The data can also be combined with information such as statistics on deprivation, health and economic status, to support more informed decision making on greenspace provision and investment. Combined with other spatial and biological datasets, it can for example, be used to identify green networks for walking and cycling and support the development of integrated habitat networks. The following examples highlight some ways in which greenspace data are used.

39.5.1 Accessibility analysis

Once the boundaries of greenspaces have been mapped in a GIS, accessibility analysis can be carried out, using either Euclidean (straight line) distances or network analysis (which involves modelling real world networks, such as roads and paths, and greenspace entry points). Network analysis gives a more accurate analysis of a greenspace's catchment area – enabling local planners to determine whether some neighbourhoods are under-provided in terms of access to greenspace.

This has been carried out in the Falkirk and Edinburgh greenspace audit work, allowing the Councils to identify deficiencies and over-provision in accessible greenspace. Accessibility maps can be complemented by statistics on the percentage of households with access to good quality greenspace within an acceptable travel distance.

39.5.2 Investment decision making

The Forestry Commission and partners have developed the Public Benefit Recording System (PBRS), a GIS tool which aims to bring together economic, social and environmental data so that woodland investment can be targeted where it can best deliver socio-economic growth. This system was used in the Newlands Strategic Investment Programme, where social, environmental and accessibility data were used to score derelict and underused sites in north-west England. The results showed where regeneration by forestry could bring maximum socio-economic benefits and enabled the Forestry Commission and North West Development Agency to prioritise their forestry investment work.

Since then, the PBRS has been used to plan Lancashire's green infrastructure strategy, by combining maps of the main green infrastructure priorities in relation to biodiversity, health, leisure, quality of place, inward investment and climate change mitigation. This analysis highlighted areas with the greatest need or opportunities for green infrastructure and informed the priorities for the strategy.

39.5.3 Research on health and greenspace

A study in England (Mitchell and Popham, 2008) used the greenspace category of a geographic dataset, the Generalised Land Use Database, to classify the pre-retirement age population into five 'greenspace exposure' groups based on the proportion of greenspace in their area. They then compared this with individual mortality records from the Office for National Statistics. The study found that populations exposed to the greenest environments also have the lowest levels of health inequality related to income deprivation. This suggests that physical environments which promote good health could be important in reducing socio-economic health inequalities. One of the study authors, Dr Richard Mitchell at the University of Glasgow, is currently carrying out a similar analysis for Scotland.

39.6 Trends in public perception and use of greenspace

While data on the quantity and quality of greenspace are a valuable resource, the full benefits of greenspace are contingent on how it is used and valued by people. Since 2004, greenspace scotland has commissioned three surveys (2004, 2007, 2009) of public opinion on urban greenspace. Each survey contacted over 1,000 adults living in urban Scottish settlements (defined as settlements with a population of 3,000 or over). The surveys have examined use of greenspace, public attitudes about greenspace and perceptions of local spaces. The most recent survey (Progressive Partnership, 2009) shows a steady rise in the use of greenspace since 2004, as well as a general increase in satisfaction with local spaces.

Key findings from the surveys are described below and the full results for the three surveys can be found on the greenspace scotland website.

39.6.1 Use of greenspaces

The surveys show a rise in use of local greenspaces since 2004, primarily for physical activity and relaxation. Key findings include:

- 63% of respondents now use their local greenspace once a week or more often, up from 49% in 2004;
- those in the 35-44 year age range are most likely to use local greenspaces;
- the most popular uses of greenspace are for walking, relaxation, play and exercise; and
- 50% of those polled can walk to their local greenspace within five minutes, but this drops to 39% in the 15% most deprived areas of Scotland.

39.6.2 Perceptions of greenspace

Since 2004, the surveys have revealed a consistent belief by respondents that greenspaces should be good places for play, physical activity, relaxation and seeing

Plate 39.1 Young people having fun at a skate park in Kelvingrove Park, Glasgow. © Lorne Gill/SNH

nature. People also believe that greenspaces should be attractive and make places 'a great place to live'. In 2009:

- around 90% of respondents agreed strongly that greenspaces should be good places for playing, physical activity and relaxation;
- 87% agreed strongly that greenspaces should be attractive, and made an area a great place to live; and
- over 80% agreed strongly that greenspace should provide opportunities to see nature, while just under 70% thought they should be good places to meet others from the local community.

Despite these positive expectations about greenspaces in general, most people report that their local greenspaces performed less well. The gap between expectations and local reality has remained relatively constant in all our surveys since 2004.

39.6.3 Future challenges

Whilst there is a high level of positive opinion surrounding local greenspaces, there is also a challenge to ensure that local spaces meet their potential in supporting well-being and creating sustainable places. Most people view their local greenspace positively, with 83% agreeing that it meets their needs (a 6% increase since 2007). Thirty nine percent of people are very satisfied with the quality of their local greenspace, and a further 44% are quite satisfied. Eighty six percent of people agree that it is important to have greenspaces in their local area. When asked about barriers to increasing their use of greenspace, respondents highlighted concerns about maintenance, lack of facilities and safety.

The positive views on greenspace show that people value their local spaces and recognise recent investment and efforts to improve greenspace. However, the barriers to use suggest that continued improvement work will be required to achieve the full range of social, economic and environmental benefits that greenspace can offer.

39.7 Conclusions

State of Scotland's Greenspace 2009 was produced in response to demand from government, local authorities and researchers for more information about greenspace quantity, quality and use. The findings of the report show that local authorities are making progress in recording and evaluating their greenspace. At this stage it is not possible to draw any conclusions on the quality of greenspace but some broad patterns in terms of amounts and distribution of greenspace can be drawn.

Overall, the data indicate that publicly accessible greenspace forms only part (typically 50-70%) of the greenspace within settlements. Public opinion data shows the strong importance that people place on accessible spaces for relaxation, exercise and socialising. It is not yet possible to state if the greenspace resource is diminishing, nor whether certain types of greenspace are being reduced in new developments, but this report offers a snapshot of quantity and typology of greenspace in urban Scotland and provides the basis for future work.

Good quality greenspace can deliver against a range of community needs, contributing to health improvement, local confidence and sense of community, social cohesion and wider environmental goals. This requires strategic planning for greenspace, which in turn relies on an accurate understanding of the current resource in settlements. This includes consideration of quantity, distribution, accessibility, facilities, condition and how well local needs are being met. Many local authorities are working on audits of greenspace, with more progress on the quantitative audit compared with the complex assessment of quality. Nonetheless, a number of innovative approaches to quality assessment are being used, often including strong elements of community engagement.

While the first report on Scotland's greenspace offers a progress report and an initial benchmark on greenspace quantities, future reports could identify trends in total amounts of greenspace and publicly accessible greenspace types, and may begin to provide evidence in relation to the widespread perception that greenspace resources are diminishing. In future, as quality data are gathered, it will be possible to set a benchmark for the overall quality of greenspace and key greenspace types. It will also be possible to analyse the greenspace data, nationally and locally, against data on health, deprivation, biodiversity, flooding and many other issues.

Feedback from local authorities who supplied data for the report suggest that data reporting could become part of a standardised approach, but that some core indicators could help to guide local authority greenspace audits, particularly in relation to quality. In 2010/11, greenspace scotland will work with local authorities to develop a framework for developing local greenspace standards for quality, quantity and accessibility. It is intended that the second State of Scotland's Greenspace report will be prepared in 2011.

References

greenspace scotland (2007). *The links between greenspace and health: a critical literature review.* greenspace scotland. Stirling.

greenspace scotland (2008). *Greenspace and quality of life: a critical literature review.* greenspace scotland. Stirling.

greenspace scotland (2009a). *State of Scotland's Greenspace 2009.* greenspace scotland. Stirling.

greenspace scotland (2009b). *Making the links: greenspace for a more successful and sustainable scotland.* greenspace scotland. Stirling.

greenspace scotland (2010). *Urban greenspace mapping and characterisation handbook.* greenspace scotland. Stirling.

greenspace scotland and GCV Green Network Partnership. (2008). *Greenspace quality – a guide to assessment, planning and strategic development.* greenspace scotland. Stirling.

Mitchell, R. and Popham, F. (2008). Effect of exposure to natural environment on health inequalities: an observational population study. *Lancet*, **372**, 1655-1660.

Progressive Partnership (2009). *Greenspace Scotland Omnibus Survey.* Progressive Partnership. Edinburgh.

Scottish Government (2007). *Scottish Planning Policy 11: Physical Activity and Open Space.* Scottish Government. Edinburgh.

Scottish Government (2008). *Planning Advice Note 65: Planning and Open Space.* Scottish Government. Edinburgh.

Scottish Government (2010). *Scottish Planning Policy.* Scottish Government. Edinburgh.

All greenspace scotland reports are available at http://www.greenspacescotland.org.uk

40 Making Sustainable Places (and Making Places Sustainable), Naturally

Clive Mitchell

Summary

1. Sustainable places are characterised as areas that: can be reached within a five minute walk; are part of strong communities; promote good health; offer rich functional biodiversity and contain buildings and places that are part of ecosystems.
2. This paper draws together the main conclusions from six events held on the theme of Making Sustainable Places. With a focus on the role of the natural heritage, the events looked at sustainable places from different perspectives (people and communities, participation, sustainable development, land use including local food and resource production, design and land use planning, and health).
3. I argue that sustainable places can help address some of the key challenges we face in relation to public health and climate change.

20.1 Introduction

During 2008-10 Scottish Natural Heritage (SNH) ran six Sharing Good Practice (SGP) events on *Making Sustainable Places.* These events differ from most training, seminars or conferences, in that they are participatory events for practitioners with varying levels of experience to share ideas and approaches on a topic relevant to their work and/or personal development. The events gave everyone the opportunity to focus – away from busy workloads – to explore, reflect, find inspiration and develop new relationships.

The idea for the *Making Sustainable Places* series was prompted by a research report commissioned by SNH (Entec UK Ltd, 2002). The purpose of the report was to provide advice on how peripheral housing developments can be planned (in

Mitchell, C. (2011). Making Sustainable Places (and Making Places Sustainable), Naturally – *The Changing Nature of Scotland*, eds. S.J. Marrs, S. Foster, C. Hendrie, E.C. Mackey, D.B.A. Thompson. TSO Scotland, Edinburgh, pp 465-478.

terms of their location) detailed siting, layout, and design to minimise any adverse impacts and maximise their benefits on the natural heritage. One of the main conclusions of the report was a difficulty in finding examples of good practice as it was unusual for housing developments to be designed explicitly to achieve natural heritage benefits. The recommendations encouraged the house-building industry to work with SNH and others to develop guidance on good practice.

The *Making Sustainable Places* events are a contribution to that process, and the content of this paper is drawn from them. The events attracted more than 250 people and gave the delegates opportunities to participate in and share ideas in workshops, as well as listen to over 40 presentations. These events provided an immensely rich resource, illustrating the main characteristics of sustainable places, based on practical experience throughout the UK and elsewhere in Europe.

The report outlined the role of the natural heritage in making both new and existing sustainable places. The report is structured around what makes a sustainable place, and how to make them happen. Sustainable places are all about people and places. Work involving leadership, thinking medium to long term, design and planning skills are required to develop the role of special places in society.

The paper concludes with some observations about the key physical characteristics, the importance of people, and some principles that appear to underpin sustainable places.

40.2 Sustainable places are all about...

40.2.1 ...people...

Sustainable places are valued by people: they are about people, places and neighbourhoods.

Know your audience. Most people connect with each other and with places at an emotional level (SGP, 2008a). Too often as professionals we mistakenly assume that everyone will respond to and engage with dispassionate rationalism.

Work with communities (SGP, 2008a, 2009a, b). In making sustainable places, it is important that organisations start working with people and communities early in the process and do things that matter to people, wherever the community might be starting from and wherever organisations from the public and private sectors might want them to be. Making sustainable places is a journey: it doesn't matter where the starting point is, just so long as there is one. Continuity matters.

Stick with it. The coming and going of individuals and organisations in community developments can be deeply unsettling (SGP, 2008a, 2009a, b). By contrast, the most successful projects typically take place over several years with a long term commitment from organisations and individuals and teams within them;

such as Fairfield in Perth and some estates have worked with communities over several hundred years.

Engage with organisations early on. This is likely to present a substantial challenge for public sector organisations. For example, if travel or energy is the primary driver it might be difficult for an organisation such as SNH to engage until the project moves directly onto the natural heritage. Communities seldom view places through the departmental fragments that make up the public sector – they see an integrated whole. Once the journey has started, it is likely to pick up on other aspects of sustainable places along the way. It is more likely that issues will be picked up in the way organisations would want the sooner the organisation engages in the process. But early engagement in projects that, on the face of it, do not connect with the role or remit of an organisation can be difficult to justify.

Break down professional barriers. Few individuals or organisations have all of the skills required to help communities make sustainable places (SGP, 2008a). Public and private organisations need to use skills and talent from a range of staff and work together to mix skills, break down professional barriers, and create stable, multi-disciplinary teams to work with communities and places (SGP, 2008a, 2009a, b). This presents a fundamental challenge to the way that resources are allocated to work with local communities. The outcome based approach of the National Performance Framework (Scottish Government, 2007) laid the foundations to overcome this but there is still a long way to go to align theory and practice.

Empower people. Communities should not feel that they are being subjected to something out with their control; they need to feel empowered to influence the changes around them (SGP, 2008a, 2009a, b). During the SGP events community representatives pointed out that development is often stalled by short term, fragmented funding from different bodies. Community empowerment requires communities to acquire assets and income so that they have the resources to do things themselves and do not have to rely on the patronage of others.

Be clear about what you are trying to achieve. Empowerment must combine idealism with hard-headed realism (SGP, 2009a, b). Asset transfer is a huge amount of work and responsibility (SGP, 2009a). Realism is essential to avoid sentimentality and to secure assets that will actually work (and avoid acquiring liabilities). It's important to recognise the value of commercial and non-commercial assets, and not to allow acquisition and management of the assets cloud the community goals: the assets are usually a means to an end, not necessarily an end in themselves (SGP, 2009b). This approach is the foundation of building social capital (SGP, 2009a).

Human capital is also important. This works at the individual level and includes supporting champions and early-adopters, helping them to connect with each other, so they do not feel that they are working in isolation (SGP, 2008a, 2009a). People often apply tried and tested approaches in their own area – there's no shortage of 'best practice' to mainstream (SGP, 2008a-d, 2009a, b). Allow people to take risks and make mistakes. This will encourage innovative thinking, new ideas or show different ways of doing things (SGP, 2009a). This requires political space to experiment and fail, free from the fear of blame – and presents another challenge for the public sector and scrutiny roles. This is not a call for reckless abandon.

If the journey towards a sustainable place is to progress and persist, then succession matters: who takes over from the current champion or early adopters, where is the new blood, how do you ensure continuity at the individual level (SGP, 2009a, b)?

Making sustainable places is a journey in which making the links between the *mechanics* of making things happen (inputs and outputs) must combine with the 'organic' *process* of building human and social capital (outcomes). This was summed up as *'it's the interstices – the glue – where good things happen'* (Gallagher, 2009 *pers. comm.*). The 'glue' that sticks the pieces together to make the whole greater than the sum of the parts.

This relationship between *product* and *process* was also captured in the call for '*no technology without sociology'* (SGP, 2008c). Technology is too easily perceived as a displacement activity for tackling real issues, such as changing behaviour and attitudes. Too often technology and behaviour changes are seen as opposites or alternatives. Making sustainable places requires both to work together, so that technology reinforces and facilitates behaviour change and vice versa.

40.2.2 ...and place...

Connectivity and connecting people matter. The order of *thinking* about making sustainable places is *people – space – buildings – transport* (Young, 2008 *pers. comm.*). The order of *doing* things might well be the opposite: it makes sense to start with a sustainable transport system and then work in the buildings that people live and work in and the spaces they will use. But if we don't start with people and keep thinking about fellow citizens throughout we are likely to make it difficult or impossible to work at the neighbourhood scale and foster an attachment between people and place. Too often places reflect development in reverse order from buildings to transport to spaces and people, making unsustainable places (SGP, 2008d).

Existing settlements should be the eco-towns of the future. Revitalising our existing settlements is as important as making new sustainable places (Power, 2008, *pers. comm.*). Nearly 90% of existing buildings will still be used in 2050. Buildings account for half of all carbon dioxide emissions – and these emissions need to be cut by at least 80% by 2050. There is potential to reduce energy consumption by 50%, even in buildings that meet recent building standards.

The spaces between buildings are crucial. The layout of our towns and cities is a major influence on our travel choices and transport has been a growing sector of the emissions inventory for the last 10-15 years (SGP, 2008a, d, 2009b). Use the spaces between buildings to connect people with each other and with place and offer alternative modes of transport (SGP, 2008d). Spaces should be redesigned to provide better surroundings and make infrastructure greener (SGP, 2009b). Avoid a tendency to focus on fragments of space here and there: look at the 'whole' to guide the creation of new spaces and management of existing ones. Avoid 'dead' spaces – these are the areas that are not frequented and are often overlooked – they can quickly become no-go areas or spaces in which anti-social behaviour can persist (SGP, 2008d).

For biodiversity the key is structure and form. In sustainable places, the function is more important than worrying unduly about composition (SGP 2008d). Examples include the role of biodiversity in sustainable urban drainage schemes, food production, local climate regulation, improving air quality, and links to physical and mental health. People are more likely to understand the relevance and importance of biodiversity if the function is clear. In many cases rich biodiversity and social function combine, but it is the knowledge of the social function that will help connect people and place.

Well designed spaces are the focus for social interaction, safe play, improved mental health and physical activity (SGP, 2008d). Infrastructure that is a social and environmental 'good' is the basis for a strong, healthy and just society. People cannot make healthy choices, such as walking and cycling, if the option is not there. Both urban design and planning should build for health benefits (SGP, 2008a, c). In contrast, by making cars rather than people the priority of our streets, we have created environments that are barriers to walking and cycling, so-called obesogenic environments (SGP, 2008c).

'When it comes to health – everything matters' (Jones, SGP 2008a). Health isn't just for the NHS: people, place, space, buildings and transport are all key determinants of health. The quality of the natural heritage in 'movement' networks (i.e. transport in the widest sense of the word), green networks and water networks matter too. Understanding the role of environmental factors in health problems and the action needed requires multi-disciplinary approaches (SGP, 2008a).

Sustainable places should be diverse and well integrated. Land uses and housing tenures are mixed, creating synergies between different policy areas (SGP, 2008b, d). For example, in Sheffield, re-development of the Manor Fields park using public funding became a catalyst for new private development which in turn funded a sustainable urban drainage scheme enriching local habitats (Stanyon, 2008). This revitalised place has transformed previously derelict land peppered with burnt-out cars into a common focus to bring people together.

As well as a positive vision of what a sustainable place looks like, contributors to the SGP events reminded us that it can be useful to remember some of the features that can make places discouraging and negative including:

- places designed for cars with visual cues that can be read at a glance including simplified, smooth, shallow buildings, sometimes large scale and monolithic that are often difficult for pedestrian access, with no consideration of human scale;
- poor signage, or signage with bigger letters and fewer words that is inappropriate to the human scale;
- seas of car parking;
- too little or poor quality greenspace;
- no peaceful spaces or rest areas;
- limited access to the outdoors; and
- sub-standard building design.

(Hoskins, 2008).

It's people *and* place that matter (not one or the other). Contributors to the SGP events saw huge potential in the new planning act, with local area development plans offering the opportunity to bring people together, including health practitioners to foster a much more holistic approach. To make sustainable places, the *ethos* of planning is crucial and must be characterised by a move away from piecemeal development to more deeply integrated organic growth.

40.3 Making this happen through...

40.3.1 ...leadership...

Support communities in developing and delivering their goal or vision. Whilst it is true that people make choices, the role of government, local services and businesses is to provide the opportunity to choose sustainable options – and to make those options the first choice or first-best solution (SGP, 2008b). Responsibilities here lie with government, business and individuals, but there is a clear requirement for government to establish clear leadership across all sectors.

Within government and the public sector generally, 'departmentalism' is an obstruction to what sustainable places are all about. It tends towards fragmented approaches that focus on specific components such as buildings, transport infrastructure or greenspace which result in bland, unsustainable design reflecting over-regulation (SGP, 2008b). In contrast, 'place-making' focuses on the way the components come together to shape a place, which is the way people experience them (SGP, 2008b). Organisations need to work in partnerships to make sustainable places. Aligning spend is important to exploit synergies between policy goals, such as a focus on active travel to align health and transport budgets and portfolios. The challenge raises similar issues to those discussed earlier (40.2.1 - *people*) in relation to allocating resources and building teams across different organisations around shared outcomes.

There was an overwhelming sense of frustration at the gap between an abundance of good practice and mainstreaming it, with a call to '*implement techniques and mainstream pilots*' (SGP, 2008b). In many cases we know what the problem is and we know what the solution is. *'We don't really need more guidance – just do it'* (SGP, 2008b). The Residential Landscape Checklist (Claydon, 2008) includes detailed guidance on sourcing materials and implementing artful rainwater management, planning for health outcomes, reusing materials, designing multifunctional spaces, minimising waste and maintenance, involving communities and designing for humans rather than cars, and more.

Simple solutions often deliver better outcomes. There was a plea to mainstream 'eco' based on eco minimalism or inexpensive, low-tech solutions. Some solutions are over-engineered, represented in the extreme by 'eco-bling' exemplified by poorly thought through applications of new 'showy' technologies (SGP, 2008b). An example of this might be a new micro wind turbine on a property that remains poorly insulated or is situated where turbulence means that the turbine hardly ever works. It might look great and send a positive message but delivers practically nothing in energy savings: worse, it might create a false sense of action and crowd out less visible measures that could make a bigger difference. Solutions should make the most of what is already in place. Examples included promoting existing transport alternatives through free accurate integrated public transport information before new engine technologies and reducing energy use in buildings by using passive solar gain and better insulated buildings that look familiar to most people (rather than futuristic 'eco-bling' designs). Solutions can and should work with the familiar – they don't have to be 'way-out' or weird. Applying approaches that change a place gradually is more likely to win over communities (SGP, 2008b).

Professional people from all the sectors required to make sustainable places have considerable energy and are often driven by a strong personal motivation to do better. Capitalise on this to improve performance and innovation – acknowledge successes and be critical friends (SGP, 2008a).

'Talk to the sceptics' (SGP, 2008a). Across the events a number of contributors observed that the SGP events invite a self-selecting audience, we are effectively preaching to the converted. We need to seek other perspectives, including housebuilders, engineers, drainage and transport managers, service providers and so on to build on these initial findings.

40.3.2 ...thinking medium-long term...

Engaging with communities is key to making sustainable, durable places (SGP, 2008a-d, 2009a, b). There is a sense of urgency – we do need to get on with making sustainable places and making existing places sustainable – but not at the expense of building in the time to ensure full, lasting engagement by communities. It would be a false economy to sidestep community engagement even if some projects might be delivered more quickly, because such projects are likely to be unwanted and fall rapidly into neglect and disrepair.

It seems self-evident, but as well as thinking long-term we should avoid short-term thinking. For example, it is too easy to underestimate the importance of landscape design in creating and maintaining sustainable places – the quality of local landscape is often one of the first considerations to be dropped in the urgency to get things done (SGP, 2008d). People want sustainable places and will pay for them as evidenced by the relationship between house prices and high quality local environments and communities: society and the environment need them (SGP, 2008b). That is not to say the high quality local environments need be the preserve of the more affluent – all of the events emphasised social inclusion and the cost effectiveness of sustainable places.

Allied to these themes is the importance of long-term continuity (SGP, 2008a, 2009a, b). This is demonstrated by some of the most successful projects where teams have been in place for several years – five for Manor Fields Park in Sheffield (Stanyon, 2008) and 20 for Fairfield in Perth (Young, 2008) – and were known to the community. This builds trust, reduces vandalism, creates sense of value and ownership, and allows developments to evolve – building both social and human capital, as discussed earlier (40.2.1 *people*).

Sustainability is a process, not a product (SGP, 2009a). Projects require on-going management and feedback to adapt to changing needs if they are going to succeed. For example in Darlington, one of three Sustainable Travel Demonstration Towns from 2004-2009 involved local communities to develop transport initiatives and then modified them based on feedback from users. Furthermore, a new school at Acharacle introduced a two year post-construction management clause into their architect's contract (Liddell, 2008, *pers. comm.*). Other examples include raising awareness of people living in houses with sustainable urban drainage schemes, that is, they need to adopt new behaviours (such as not pouring paint down the drains). Programmes should also be put inplace to care for parks and open spaces after implementation.

It is important to evaluate the success of actions taken, using both qualitative and quantitative measures that engage with all of the dimensions of sustainable places discussed in this paper (SGP, 2008a). But the mantra 'what gets measured gets managed' can lead to perverse outcomes, especially if we can't measure what matters or measure things that don't really matter. Indicators can be used to simplify complex systems and used intelligently can help to describe progress to outcomes. There will need to be some narrative to fill the gap between the simplified system of the indicator and the more complex system of the outcome. But too often indicators are turned into narrow measures of performance, become targets in their own right and reinforce the problems of departmentalism referred to earlier (40.2.1 *people*).

40.3.3 ...design...

People should be the starting point when designing sustainable places. We walk at 5km per hour, see small details and need a stimulating diverse environment to respond to – environment and cues created with this in mind are often referred to as being at a 'human scale' (Sim, 2008; Greaves, 2009). Martin Greaves (*op. cit.*) described this walkable scale as the 'five minute pint test', and David Sim (*op. cit.*) talked about 5km per hour architecture. If people want to be able to get a pint of milk or beer within five minutes of where they live, that is 400m walking at 5km per hour. This gives a 400m spatial envelope for design and planning. But in a car five minutes at 50km per hour gives a spatial scale of 4km, which is more typical for the design and planning of developments over the last 60 years. The five minute pint test is just a better way of saying 'access to goods and services, family and friends'.

David Sim (*op. cit.*) described part of Malmo in Sweden which has been re-developed around sociable public spaces, a compact (diverse and high density) building footprint with domestic 5km per hour scaled spaces (Figure 40.1). The irregular building layout creates shelter which is not possible in symmetrically arranged townscapes. Neilston in Glasgow and New Road in Brighton (Figure 40.2) are examples where existing spaces have been converted to 'people spaces'.

In a 5km per hour or 400m 'walkable environment' it is possible to make the connections between people and place and between buildings and ecosystems. It is also the community or neighbourhood scale. This is the basis of spatial planning for sustainable places. In contrast, designing communities around cars creates a '50km per hour environment' and architecture that has to be 'read' at glance, with large spaces and huge visual cues both in simplified building design and large signs with simple text in large letters, all of which dehumanise living spaces. At this larger scale it is not possible to make the connections between aspects of sustainable places.

Figure 40.1 5km/h architecture, an environment made for walking, Malmö, Sweden.

Figure 40.2 From 60km/h to 5km/h, New Road, Brighton. An example of how an existing space has been converted to a people space. © Gehl Architects

Creating places that have a clear purpose and include features that promote physical activity and encourage social interaction relies on high quality design. A plea from two of the events was for planners and decision-makers not to be afraid to say '*it's not good enough*' (SGP, 2008a, b). We should encourage people to expect better design and sustainable solutions.

Sustainable places exploit complementary goals in design (SGP, 2008b, d). This includes balancing private/semi-public and public spaces; balancing views from houses and streets with privacy; establishing shelter and passive solar gain for buildings; creating domestic scaled design and streetscapes which are overlooked and safe; creating greenspace – including green roofs – which enhance health, manage water and contribute to biodiversity. We could learn a lot from Scottish burghs such as Haddington, Cupar and Elgin, where the hearts of the towns are distinctive functional places that fit with the landscape, create shelter that suits the local weather and work at a human scale (Sim, 2008) – as well as looking to examples from continental Europe and elsewhere in the UK.

Spaces must be multifunctional (SGP, 2008b, d; 2009a, b). The space around our towns and between our buildings is where the most important functions for sustainable living are going to be located. These spaces have to work hard and were described as '*multi-tasking the landscape*' (SGP, 2009b). We need places to grow local food; recycle waste; manage water runoff and recycle water; provide drying greens; for access routes; as spaces for activity and restorative greenspace; shelter; solar gain; for urban cooling (including air flow and shade from trees) and renewable energy – and they have to look good and enhance biodiversity while reconnecting people with nature (SGP, 2008d, 2009b). That's a lot to ask – but that's what well designed, planned and managed spaces already do.

40.3.4 ...and planning...

Planning is a key tool in making sustainable places and more sustainable communities (SGP, 2008a-d; 2009a, b). The origins of planning lie in improving health and welfare conditions (e.g. Jones, SGP, 2008b), but a concern from a number of the events was that planners have come to be seen as regulators. There is a need for political backing and local and national support to re-energise the visionary nature of planning. New opportunities may arise from increased links between development planning and community development – especially through the Single Outcome Agreements for Community Planning Partners which set out the priorities for action, expressed as outcomes, and the visionary components of the new development plans.

Making sustainable places requires a focus on *'place-making'* (SGP, 2008b, d). Planning should be creative and enabling, not over-burdened with strategy and policy. Place-making requires strong development plans, built upon a better understanding of neighbourhoods and people's needs, and should focus on the way the components of a place come together rather than delivery of specific elements such as buildings, transport infrastructure or greenspace. Urban design needs to focus on people and the space between buildings, and the function of greenspace (SGP, 2008a, b, d). Planners may not always be the best people to deal with design, and training does not foster this (SGP, 2008b). Place-making requires multi-disciplinary teams to cover all of the different aspects discussed in this paper.

Avoid dogmatic policies (SGP, 2008b). We need to balance strong national legislation and guidance with common sense. Higher density mixed use building for housing, retail, services and business, more intimate spaces, car free areas, attractive, useable sustainable urban drainage schemes are all difficult to achieve with current regulations and over-engineering – they are possible but in spite of rather than because of regulations and the way that they are administered (SGP, 2008b). New initiatives sometimes miss the point – for example, why have 10 to 15% of energy created through expensive renewables in new development, rather than better passive design and insulation (SGP, 2008b)?

40.4 Conclusions

The most successful projects are those where the community has been involved, through consultation, management, co-ownership and active involvement (SGP, 2008a-d; 2009a, b). This is required to create landscapes which are valued, and greenspace that is used for health and reflects the needs of the community.

The series of SGP events were not based on a fixed definition or predetermined vision of a sustainable place. Agreeing one is likely to be contested, which at least in part reflects the fact that sustainable places do not, and should not follow a one-size-fits all mould. In spite of this, sustainable places do share some common characteristics, including:

- walkable environments;
- low resource use;
- strong communities;
- places that promote good health;
- connected – socially and physically;
- rich functional biodiversity; and
- buildings and places that are parts of ecosystems (especially through food, water and energy use).

They are also likely to be:

- *flexible* – responsive to change;
- *intimate* – in terms of relationships between people, and between people and place;

- *natural* – thriving within environmental limits; and
- *diverse* – the more diverse our social, economic and environmental systems, including enhanced biodiversity, the more resilient we are likely to be to future environmental and social change.

All aspects of sustainable places are interconnected and interdependent. This was captured by John Muir when he said '*when we try to pick out anything by itself, we find it hitched to everything in the universe*' (Muir, 1911).

Sustainable places are positive places. They hold the prospect of being much better than many of the existing places where people live and work in Scotland today. They are also central to addressing a number of key issues. For example, the requirements for places that promote good health are compatible with the requirements for low carbon places that are well positioned to adapt to the impacts of climate change.

Sustainable places mean doing things differently. They rely on collaboration and in recognising the potential in any development or intervention to make a place more, or less, sustainable. There is plenty of good practice to build on. To borrow a quote from Harry Burns (*pers. comm.*) speaking at the conference about the relationship between health and the environment '*If you do what you've always done, you'll get what you've always got.*'

Acknowledgements

The SGP events were scoped and planned in association with a core group comprising Steve Malone (Architecture and Design Scotland), Kristen Miller (Convention of Scottish Local Authorities), Russell Jones (Glasgow Centre for Population Health), Julie Proctor/Deryck Irving (Greenspace Scotland), Sheila Beck (NHS Health Scotland), Petra Bieberbach (Planning Aid for Scotland), Aedán Smith (RSPB), Veronica Burbridge (Royal Town Planning Institute), Jon Rathjen (Scottish Government), Paula Charleson (SEPA), Paul Sizeland/Julian Holbrook (Scottish & Northern Ireland Forum for Environmental Research), Phil Matthews/Maf Smith (Sustainable Development Commission), George Tarvit (Sustainable Scotland Network), Henry Collin (Transport Scotland).

I am indebted to all of the people who helped to plan, organise and contribute to all of the events, especially Tess Darwin and Karen Smith (SNH) and Alison Grant. Adept chairing of all of the events was provided by John Thomson (SNH) and Simon Pepper (for Productive Landscapes). I hope I have retained some of the intensity and excitement generated in each event, and captured the main messages. Any errors are entirely my own.

References

Claydon, A. (2008). *Residential Landscape Sustainability.* In: *Making Sustainable Places – Sustainable Landscapes: Inspiration and Implementation.* Sharing Good Practice event, 2 December 2008. SNH, Battleby.

Entec UK Ltd. (2002). *Review of Peripheral Housing Developments and their Impacts on the Natural Heritage.* Scottish Natural Heritage Commissioned Report F01AA504.

Greaves, M. (2009). *Enquiry by Design.* In: *Making Sustainable Places – The participant.* Sharing Good Practice event, 28 January 2009. SNH, Battleby.

Hoskins, G. (2008). *Cultural Healing; creating people places.* In: *Making Sustainable Places – Turning existing places into sustainable places.* Sharing Good Practice event, 9 October 2008. SNH, Battleby.

Muir, J. (1911). *My First Summer in the Sierra.* Penguin, Nature Classics.

Scottish Government. (2007). Scotland Performs, http://www.scotland.gov.uk /About/scotPerforms, accessed 19 July, 2010.

SGP (2008a). *Making Sustainable Places – Making it happen: sustainable places and sustainable development.* Sharing Good Practice event, 28 May 2008.

SGP (2008b). *Making Sustainable Places – Turning existing places into sustainable places.* Sharing Good Practice event, 9 October 2008. SNH, Battleby.

SGP (2008c). *Making Sustainable Places – A place for life.* Sharing Good Practice event, 27 November 2008. SNH, Battleby.

SGP (2008d). *Making Sustainable Places – Sustainable Landscapes: Inspiration and Implementation.* Sharing Good Practice event, 2 December 2008. SNH, Battleby.

SGP (2009a). *Making Sustainable Places – The participant.* Sharing Good Practice event, 28 January 2009. SNH, Battleby.

SGP (2009b). *Making Sustainable Places – Productive landscapes.* Sharing Good Practice event, 16 June 2009. SNH, Battleby.

Sim, D. (2008). *Sustainable Places are People Places.* In: *Making Sustainable Places - Sustainable Landscapes: Inspiration and Implementation.* Sharing Good Practice event, 2 December 2008. SNH, Battleby.

Stanyon, I. (2008). *People, Space and Place: integrating 'spongy' technology in the regeneration of despoiled land to valued green space.* In: *Making Sustainable Places – Turning existing places into sustainable places.* Sharing Good Practice event, 9 October 2008. SNH, Battleby.

41 Developing our Understanding of Biodiversity in Scotland's Gardens: the Role of the BTO's Garden BirdWatch

Mike Toms, Liz Humphreys and Chris Wernham

Summary

1. Gardens are an increasingly important habitat for biodiversity in the UK, but are difficult to monitor because they are in private ownership.
2. The British Trust for Ornithology (BTO) Garden BirdWatch scheme taps into the enthusiasm that many garden-owners have for garden wildlife and works with them to monitor this wildlife through a 'Citizen Science' approach.
3. Garden BirdWatch data have been analysed to understand the changes in annual and seasonal use of gardens by birds and other wildlife. The Garden BirdWatch scheme has established itself as a key source of information for the government's 'Indicator of breeding town and garden bird populations' in England, one of a number of habitat-based biodiversity indicators used in conservation science research.

41.1 Gardens as a habitat for wildlife

Gardens provide an important habitat for a number of bird species, including breeding song thrush (*Turdus philomelos*), house sparrow (*Passer domesticus*) and starling (*Sturnus vulgaris*) (Mason 2000; Newson *et al.*, 2009). Collectively, gardens occupy some 10% of the available land area within the UK (Gaston *et al.*, 2005), although this figure is significantly lower when Scotland is viewed on its own (less than 2.4%). Private gardens make a significant contribution to the amount of urban green space in Scotland (contributing some 30% by area, Anon. 2009) and

Toms, M., Humphreys, L. and Wernham, C. (2011). Developing our Understanding of Biodiversity in Scotland's Gardens: the Role of the BTO's Garden Birdwatch – *The Changing Nature of Scotland*, eds. S.J. Marrs, S. Foster, C. Hendrie, E.C. Mackey, D.B.A. Thompson. TSO Scotland, Edinburgh, pp 479-484.

are the main contributor to urban biodiversity (Cannon, 1999). Changes in the wider countryside, and in particular increasing pressures on land for housing and development, mean that it has become even more important for us to understand how gardens are used by birds and other wildlife.

Large scale studies of garden wildlife are difficult to implement because the vast majority of gardens are in private ownership. Consequently we may underestimate both the importance of gardens for wildlife and the size of the populations they may support (Bland *et al.*, 2004). For many people, gardens provide a daily opportunity to interact with wildlife. This interest can be utilised by adopting a 'Citizen Science' approach to involve garden owners in monitoring the wildlife in their garden. Records collected by these 'Citizen Scientists' can then be used for a range of purposes, including understanding the changes in annual and seasonal use of gardens by species (Cannon *et al.*, 2005). The British Trust for Ornithology (BTO) Garden BirdWatch data are used in the UK government's Town and Garden Bird Indicator, one of a suite of different biodiversity indicators currently used to chart the quality of the environment at different regional levels within England (BTO, 2009). It is hoped that similar indicators will be developed for Scotland.

41.2 Charting the changes in wildlife using gardens

Records for the BTO's Garden BirdWatch are collected on a weekly basis from approximately 1,000 Scottish gardens (see Figure 41.1). These records have shown the increasing use of gardens by goldfinch (*Carduelis carduelis*), great spotted woodpecker (*Dendrocopos major*) and nuthatch (*Sitta europaea*), the latter two species showing range expansions and the former responding to the growing availability of suitable seed mixes at garden feeding stations (Figure 41.2, Cannon *et al.*, 2005). Garden BirdWatch data have also revealed the changing seasonal patterns of garden use. Goldfinches, for instance, show a late winter peak in their use of gardens, followed by a smaller secondary peak, the latter matching the period over which these birds are producing eggs. The collection of Garden BirdWatch data over time allows for the detection of sudden changes in the pattern of garden use that may reflect changes in the wider countryside or the influence of other environmental factors. McKenzie *et al.* (2007), using Garden BirdWatch data, found that siskin (*Carduelis spinus*) and coal tit (*Periparus ater*) made greater use of gardens in years of poor sitka spruce (*Picea sitchensis*) cone crops. This specific type of change in garden use is the result of behavioural changes within individual bird populations, the siskins and coal tits turn to garden feeding stations in those winters when natural food resources were low. Other changes may be related to variation in population size, such as the rising occurrence of woodpigeons (*Columba palumbus*) in gardens, following a rapid population increase.

Figure 41.1 Distribution of sites with records in the BTO Garden BirdWatch, 1995-2009, across Scotland.

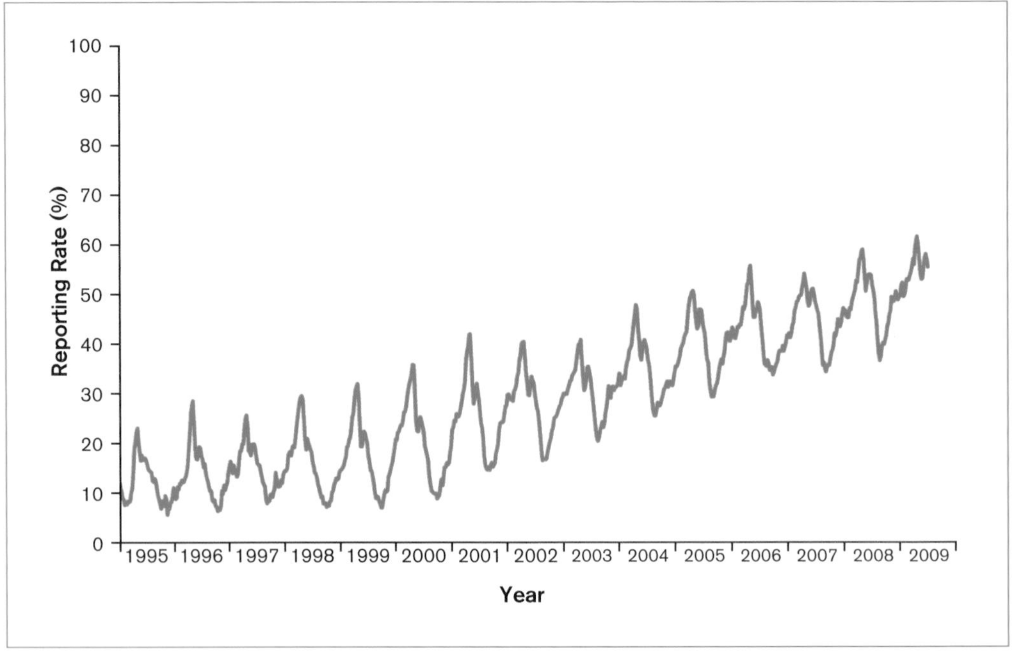

Figure 41.2 Change in the use of gardens by goldfinch, 1995-2009, as revealed by weekly records from the BTO Garden BirdWatch. Reporting rate is a measure of the proportion of sites at which the species was recorded in a given week.

The abrupt decline in the use of Scottish gardens by greenfinch (*Carduelis chloris*), evident in the late summer of 2007 (and repeated again in 2008), was due to a population decline of *c.*20% brought about by trichomonosis, an emerging infectious disease first identified in 2005 (Robinson *et al.*, 2010).

41.3 Beyond birds and gardens

The BTO Garden BirdWatch records of other taxa are also being used to monitor changes in the components of national populations that also use gardens. For species like hedgehog (*Erinaceus europaeus*) and grey squirrel (*Sciurus carolinensis*), it is possible to detect at least a 10% decline in occurrence at the national level over a 10-year period (Toms and Newson, 2006). In addition, weekly records of butterflies in gardens can be used to chart flight periods within a single season (Figure 41.3). Examination of such data over a run of years can reveal how the flight periods vary over time and in relation to climate change and periodic weather events.

Once enlisted, many Garden BirdWatch participants have gone on to carry out wildlife surveys beyond their gardens, supporting wider habitat studies, such as the BTO House Sparrow Survey, where participants visited randomly selected survey squares within the wider built environment (Chamberlain *et al.*, 2007). Data from this study were used to examine house sparrow habitat selection within urban

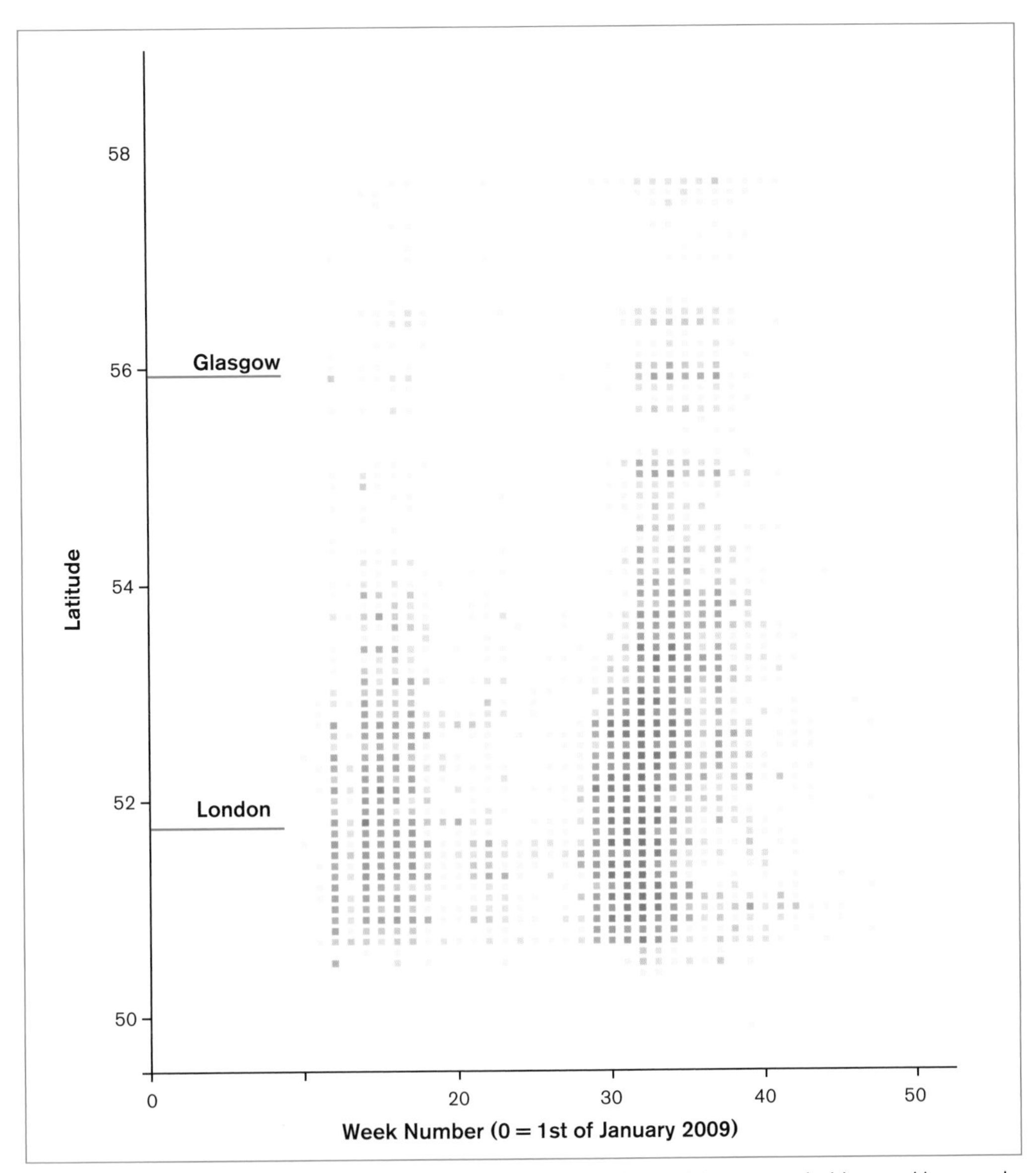

Figure 41.3 Phenology of peacock butterfly in gardens during 2009, as revealed by weekly records from BTO Garden BirdWatch. Increasing strength of colour shows an increasing number of reports of the butterfly at Garden BirdWatch sites. The horizontal red lines show the latitude of Glasgow and London.

areas. This survey highlighted the importance of urban allotments, city farms and houses with large and mature gardens for house sparrows (Chamberlain *et al.*, 2007). Through engaging with garden owners in 'Citizen Science' surveys, the BTO has been able to deliver a wider engagement with biodiversity within Scotland, while at the same time generating valuable information on how birds and other wildlife make use of the garden environment.

Acknowledgements

We are grateful for the support received from BTO Garden BirdWatch participants, who not only provide the all-important observations but also support the project financially.

References

Anon. (2009). *State of Scotland's Greenspace 2009.* Greenspace Scotland, Stirling.

Bland, R.L., Tully, J. and Greenwood, J.J.D. (2004). Birds breeding in British gardens: an underestimated population? *Bird Study*, **51**, 96-106.

BTO (1999). England Biodiversity Strategy Indicators. http://www.bto.org/research/indicators/england_indicators.htm, accessed on 11 May 2010.

Cannon, A. (1999). The significance of private gardens for bird conservation. *Bird Conservation International*, **9**, 287-298.

Cannon, A.R., Chamberlain, D.E., Toms, M.P., Hatchwell, B.J. and Gaston, K.J. (2005). Trends in the use of private gardens by wild birds in Great Britain 1995-2002. *Journal of Applied Ecology*, **42**, 659-671.

Chamberlain, D.E., Toms, M.P., Cleary-McHarg, R. and Banks, A.N. (2007). House Sparrow (*Passer domesticus*) habitat use in urbanised landscapes. *Journal of Ornithology*, **148**, 453-462.

Gaston, K.J., Warren, P.H., Thompson, K. and Smith, R.M. (2005). Urban domestic gardens (IV): the extent of the resource and its associated features. *Biodiversity and Conservation*, **14**, 3327-3349.

Mason, C.F. (2000). Thrushes now largely restricted to the built environment in eastern England. *Diversity and Distributions*, **6**, 189-194.

McKenzie, A.J., Petty, S.J., Toms, M.P. and Furness, R.W. (2007). Importance of Sitka Spruce *Picea sitchensis* seed and garden bird-feeders for Siskins *Carduelis spinus* and Coal Tits *Periparus ater*. *Bird Study*, **54**, 236-247.

Newson, S.E., Ockendon, N., Joys, A., Noble, D.G. and Baillie, S.R. (2009). Comparison of habitat-specific trends in the abundance of breeding birds in the UK. *Bird Study*, **56**, 233-243.

Robinson R.A., Lawson B., Toms M.P. *et al.* (2010). Emerging infectious disease leads to rapid population declines of common British birds. PLoS ONE 5(8): e12215. doi:10.1371/journal.pone.0012215.

Toms, M.P. and Newson, S.E. (2006). Volunteer surveys as a means of inferring trends in garden mammal populations. *Mammal Review*, **36**, 309-317.

The Changing Nature of Scotland

Conclusion

42 The Changing Nature of Scotland – Looking Ahead in a European Context

Des B.A. Thompson and Edward C. Mackey

Summary

1. We look ahead to some challenges for the conservation agencies and NGO sector striving to secure a better future for biodiversity in Scotland.
2. The Millennium Ecosystem Assessment and the ensuing UK National Ecosystem Assessment offer an important framework for taking work forward, but clarity on ecosystem services and the policy agenda for delivering these will be critical – something which will be no simple matter.
3. The 2010 State of the European Environment report and the actions arising from the 10th Conference of the Parties to the Convention on Biological Diversity (COP10) at Nagoya, Japan in October 2010, present a sobering overview of the state of nature in Europe and the action needed to improve its status.
4. In the face of climate change and a complex and dynamically changing land use environment, we need sound indicators of the health of the environment and the drivers of change. We need to harness the beneficial drivers and tackle the inimical ones; important progress has been made in this area, and Scotland may be able to provide leadership.
5. Whilst grassroots interest in nature is increasing, and numbers of people volunteering for environmental work is apparently growing, we remain concerned about the paucity and dwindling number of individuals with specialist knowledge in many fungal, plant and animal taxa. Given that some of these, such as lichens, mosses and fungi, can be robustly reliable indicators, we need to take a fresh look at how we can develop and maintain a broader base of expertise – which also contributes to making the word 'biodiversity' resonate with excitement and enjoyment, rather than a welter of bureaucracy.

Thompson, D.B.A. and Mackey, E.C. (2010). The Changing Nature of Scotland – Looking Ahead in a European Context – *The Changing Nature of Scotland*, eds. S.J. Marrs, S. Foster, C. Hendrie, E.C. Mackey, D.B.A. Thompson. TSO Scotland, Edinburgh, pp 487-498.

Mountain bearberry and juniper below Meall a' Ghiubhais, Beinn Eighe. © SNH Images

42.1 Introduction

Our understanding of how Scotland is changing, and the reasons for this, has moved on at pace over the past ten years. The chapters in this book attest to this progress, but also point to much still needing to be done. In his personal reflections on the state of biodiversity in Scotland almost 15 years ago, Aubrey Manning (1997) remarked during the closing session of a conference on biodiversity: 'Sustainability' sits alongside 'biodiversity' as a currently fashionable term, much paraded by politicians when talking about plans for development.' At the end of his provocative essay, Manning commented: 'I know that we are all totally convinced that conservation is not a luxury, an optional extra we can afford when the economy picks up, but a vital necessity if our species is to have a long-term future.' These words continue to have resonance today, as the UK again faces difficult economic times, and many developments are still pitched as being sustainable and for biodiversity. In the finale to a more recent SNH conference on the state of Scotland's environment, Crofts and Henton (2002) reviewed five components needed to sustain Scotland's environment (data, understanding, interpretation, policy development, and new mechanisms), and identified some key policies which needed to be integrated much better to secure greater environmental benefits, such as fundamental reform of agriculture support mechanisms. Reflecting on both of these accounts, a hard-headed analysis suggests that much has not changed. Our evidence base is now much stronger in terms of being able to say more about what is happening on protected areas, and more widely. We have a better understanding of the reasons for change, and what needs to be done to improve matters.

Looking ahead we, consider some key areas for further work over the next ten years which, we hope, will remove or at least lessen the adverse changes, and bring about richer benefits for nature. We have deliberately provided detail on some of the UN and EU reports published recently to help reach a wider audience.

42.2 Ecosystem services – a new mantra

If 'Biodiversity' came of age in common parlance in the 1990s, then 'Ecosystem Services' did so ten years later following the publication of the Millennium Ecosystem Assessment (United Nations Environment Programme, UNEP, 2005a). An 'ecosystem service' is obtained by us from the environment. These services are the transformation of natural assets (soil, plants, animals, air and water) into entities which we can value (see UNEP, 2005b). The services can be 'provisioning' such as food and water; 'regulating' for flood and disease control; 'cultural' in offering spiritual, recreational or other such benefits; or 'supporting' in relation to soil formation and retention, nutrient or water cycling, or in producing atmospheric oxygen. The ecosystem 'goods' include food, building materials such as wood and stone, medicinal plants, recreation, and a host of others many of us take for granted.

Since publication of the Millennium Ecosystem Assessment, UNEP has hosted a programme of work on 'The Economics of Ecosystems and Biodiversity' (TEEB) which explores valuation of ecosystem services and the economic justification for investment in conservation, restoration and protection. Overall the programme is trying to demonstrate how we can take into account the economic value of ecosystems and biodiversity in policy decisions – at national and international levels – to promote environmental protection (see TEEB, 2009, 2010; Brink, 2011).

As we outlined in the Preface to this book, ecosystems have been altered more rapidly and more extensively over the past 50 years than in any comparable time period in human history – and changes to biodiversity across the globe have been massive and largely negative (UNEP, 2005a). Several chapters in the book look at values we can attach to Scotland's environment in terms of money (Blaney and Rowse, Chapter 3; Hesketh-Laird, Chapter 22), health (Burns, Chapter 13; Crawford *et al.*, Chapter 12), recreation – with much of that supporting our physical and mental health (Mitchell and Bushby, Chapter 14), and special and distinctive landscapes (Fenton *et al.*, Chapter 9).

In terms of valuing our environment (SNH, 2009), Scotland's environmental assets underpin economic growth. Outputs from activities which depend on the natural environment are estimated at £17.2 billion a year – 11% of Scotland's total output. This supports 242,000 jobs – 14% of all full time jobs in Scotland. Even specific ecosystems are having values apportioned to them. For instance, across woodlands, health benefits (e.g. from avoiding illness due to physical exercise) – up to £19 million a year; and carbon sequestration – estimated to be worth up to £2.6 billion. These figures point to key work to be taken forward – to broaden the valuation of the vital importance of ecosystems and their services, and therefore nature, to people as well as the environment in its own right (see TEEB, 2010).

The publication of the first National Ecosystem Assessment for the UK on 2 June 2011 (see NEA, 2011) will stimulate substantial work in Scotland and the other countries to develop a new framework for sustaining the environment. The overview chapters here have already identified some of the critical ecosystem services we need to undertake work on, covering the seas and coast (Scott *et al.*, Chapter 16; Turrell, Chapter 17), rivers and their catchments (Spray, Chapter 21; Gilvear, Chapter 22; McNeill and Sutherland, Chapter 24), towns and cities (Procter and Johnston, Chapter 39; Mitchell, Chapter 40), lowland farmland (Wilson, Chapter 26; McCracken and Midgley, Chapter 27), woodlands (McIntosh, Chapter 29; Quine and Edwards, Chapter 30) and up into the uplands (Brooker, Chapter 32; Lindsay and Thorp, Chapter 34). Here, we have an important opportunity to contribute to, indeed lead, the thinking on some key strategic policies. Notable is the Land Use Strategy (the first strategy was laid before the Scottish Parliament on 17 March 2011, Scottish Government, 2011; and see Hall, Chapter 25; Lindsay and Thorp, Chapter 34). This strategy is a key commitment under Section 57 of the Climate Change (Scotland) Act 2009, and of course points to even wider matters which have to be addressed in the face of adapting to climate change (e.g. Parmesan and Yohe, 2003; Thomas, 2011; Brooker, Chapter 32; Pearce-Higgins, 2011 and Chapter 33 for the uplands; Angus *et al.*, Chapter 18 for the coast; and Lambert *et al.*, Chapter 19 for cetacean watching – a growing recreational pursuit, which contributes to some local economies). At sea, a major national marine plan is being developed (Baxter *et al.*, 2011), and again an ecosystems approach is needed to quantify the habitat and species resources we have, and their condition.

42.3 Biodiversity – looking ahead globally

We have moved a long way in the last ten years, at the beginning of which fundamentally important and globally collaborative research was being done to identify hotspots for biodiversity (see Myers *et al.*, 2000). The European 2010 biodiversity assessment (of Europe, Caucasus, Central Asia and Russia) confirmed that Europe would not achieve its target of halting biodiversity loss by 2010 (EEA, 2010a). There were several sobering conclusions in the assessment. Freshwater ecosystems are under pressure, with the quantity and quality of habitats and abundance of many species declining. Mountain ecosystems are especially vulnerable to impacts from agriculture, tourism, infrastructural development and climate change. Forest ecosystems have endured historical declines, but in the last 20 years deforestation has been largely reversed. Coastal and marine ecosystems' biodiversity has declined in recent decades, mainly due to erosion of coastal and estuarine wetlands and dune systems, overexploitation of marine fisheries, and pollution. Agricultural ecosystems' biodiversity has fallen, and grassland ecosystems' biodiversity has declined through habitat loss and degradation due to intensified farming or abandonment of agricultural land. Urban ecosystems are seldom well integrated into wider biodiversity considerations.

42.4 Beyond 2010 - trying to move forward with biodiversity at the heart of policies

Among the 47 Decisions made at the 10th Conference of the Parties to the Convention on Biological Diversity (COP10) at Nagoya, Japan in October 2010 there was Decision X/2 – dealing with the preparation of a new Strategic Plan for the period 2011-2020 (COP, 2010a). While recognising that the 2010 biodiversity target had inspired action at many levels, the underlying drivers of biodiversity loss had not been sufficiently reduced. Action had neither been on the scale required nor integrated sufficiently into broad policies, strategies and programmes. On the basis that biological diversity underpins ecosystem functioning and the provision of ecosystem services essential for human well-being, five strategic goals have been devised in the Strategic Plan 2011-2020. These seek to: a) address the underlying causes of biodiversity loss; b) reduce pressures on biodiversity; c) safeguard and, where necessary, restore biodiversity and ecosystem services; d) ensure the continued provision of ecosystem services and equitable access to them; and e) support capacity-building, including the generation, use and sharing of knowledge, and securing access to necessary resources.

Under these goals there are 20 headline targets for 2015 to 2020 (the 'Aichi Biodiversity Targets'). Building on work undertaken to develop the 2010 biodiversity indicators, we now need to deliver outcome-based indicators for the post-2010 period (COP, 2010b). While there is a direct read-across to the 2010 indicators, for example for 'trends in extent of selected biomes, ecosystems and habitats', others need to be developed. Indicators which address the need for stronger institutional arrangements, such as the extent to which biodiversity is incorporated into national accounts and physical planning, will call for new metrics (COP, 2010c).

The European Union baseline for biodiversity in 2010 has been established to assess progress (EEA, 2010b). While species extinction has evidently not been as rapid as in other regions, a substantial proportion of European species are threatened: marine mammals – 25% threatened; amphibians – 22%; reptiles – 21%; dragonflies – 16%; terrestrial mammals – 15%; birds – 12%; and butterflies – 7%. Indeed, only 17% of habitats and species covered by the EC Habitats Directive are in 'favourable' condition. Concerns include the expansion of invasive non-native species, the low capacity of degraded ecosystems to respond to climate change, environmental pressures arising from agriculture, and over-exploitation of the seas (e.g. 88% of marine targeted fish species being overfished).

Initiatives to address the 2020 headline target include: the preparation of an EU framework on invasive alien species; a soils framework directive; reform of the Common Agriculture and Common Fisheries policies; full implementation of the nature directives; continued implementation of the Water Framework Directive (with its ecosystem-wide approach to water catchment management to achieve good ecological status); and the Marine Strategy Framework Directive with its target of 'good environmental status' in all EU marine regions by 2020. The post-2010 biodiversity targets for Europe, reflecting the Nagoya decisions, are expressed in terms of a medium-term headline target and a longer-term vision (EEA, 2010c). The headline target is 'Halting the loss of biodiversity and the degradation of ecosystem services in the EU by 2020, and restoring them in so far as feasible, while stepping up the EU contribution to averting global biodiversity loss'. The vision guiding this states: 'By 2050 European Union biodiversity and the ecosystem services it provides – its natural capital – are protected, valued and appropriately restored for biodiversity's intrinsic value and for their essential contribution to human wellbeing and economic prosperity, and so that catastrophic changes caused by the loss of biodiversity are avoided.'

On 3 May 2011 the European Commission adopted the EU Biodiversity Strategy (European Commission, 2011) commenting that 'there are six main targets, and 20 actions to help Europe reach its goal. Biodiversity loss is an enormous challenge in the EU, with around one in four species currently threatened with extinction and 88% of fish stocks over-exploited or significantly depleted.' We have to hope that this will lead to concerted work to improve the state of nature. The Strategy's six targets are clear, covering: the full implementation of EU nature legislation to protect biodiversity; better protection for ecosystems, and more use of green infrastructure; more sustainable agriculture and forestry; better management of fish stocks; tighter controls on invasive alien species; and a bigger EU contribution to averting global biodiversity loss.

42.5 Scotland – looking to the future

By 2020 we need to halt biodiversity loss and the degradation of ecosystem services, and be able to demonstrate this. As with the global and European biodiversity assessments, Scotland's 2010 contribution concluded that considerable progress had been made by many people and organisations which care about Scotland's wildlife (Mackey and Mudge, 2010). While biodiversity loss had undoubtedly been slowed – and in some cases arrested – halting it fully requires renewed and sustained efforts over a longer period (see Mackey and Mudge, 2010).

A major problem for the future is that pressures on biodiversity at the global level will increase. Population growth and increasing affluence throughout large parts of the world are already pushing-up demand for food and natural resources, and the vagaries of climate change and other factors are adding to uncertainties of supply. The drive for food security and its consequences for land use and biodiversity has recently been helpfully explored in detail by Pollock (2011) and colleagues. This work sets out the challenge and uncertainties over how best to safeguard natural capital against a background of increasing pressure on land in the UK. The depressed state of the economy throughout much of the developed world makes it all the more difficult for us all to work in ways whereby we can secure a healthier future for biodiversity.

In Scotland, there are growing requirements for housing and infrastructure developments, renewable energy generation and carbon conservation, woodland expansion, and food production. Improving air and water quality, reducing waste generation and conserving ecosystem functions and biodiversity will all help meet these. We have established indicators for measuring these changes, and these remain relevant for the 2020 assessment and will be updated as needed. Several of the preceding chapters demonstrate the significant progress being made in developing metrics on biodiversity and change (Foster *et al.*, Chapter 2; Newcombe, Chapter 5; Gillings *et al.*, Chapter 7; Dobson *et al.*, Chapter 20; Spray Chapter 21; Wilson, Chapter 26; Pearce-Higgins, Chapter 33; Glass *et al.*, Chapter 35; Rothero *et al.*, Chapter 37; Procter and Johnston, Chapter 39), as well as wider issues, such as health benefits (Marrs and Foster, Chapter 11; Crawford *et al.*, Chapter 12) and measuring sustainability (Mitchell, Chapter 40). Additionally, reducing Scotland's ecological footprint is a National Indicator (Scottish Government, 2010a). Scotland's planning policy makes explicit reference to biodiversity, conservation and sustainable development (Scottish Government, 2010b). Progress is underway in Scotland and the rest of the UK to improve electronic access to information, one of the latest examples being implementation of the INSPIRE Directive to create a European Union (EU) spatial data infrastructure (European Union, 2007).

Scotland's Biodiversity Strategy (SBS, which is to be reviewed and updated in 2011) takes a 25-year perspective on work needed to care for nature (Scottish Executive, 2004). With the development of action plans for species, habitats and regions (Local Biodiversity Action Plans, LBAPs), a range of biodiversity duties have fallen to government and local authorities as well as agencies and business. This has given rise to a growth in the bureaucracy of biodiversity – groups, processes and indeed a new jargon have emerged out of all this.

Looking ahead, we have to find new and more effective ways of communicating our concerns as well as our aspirations – and the success stories. This has to have resonance with what people see happening around them as well as with what the evidence base is pointing to. The revised SBS will have new targets and actions which must be easily measured – and understood. Work is also underway to develop a monitoring strategy for Scotland; and as part of this SNH is developing a biodiversity surveillance strategy. In the future, more systematic information gathering, analyses and reporting should contribute to a better public and organisational awareness of wildlife and ecosystems in Scotland, and to more informed decision taking.

Taking this forward, we need to be creative in thinking about how we adapt to change. Thomas (2011), for instance, provokes some new thinking regarding the priorities for translocation of plant and animal species in the face of climate change. He suggests, for example, that rather than thinking about the reintroduction of Eurasian lynx (*Lynx lynx*) to Scotland, we should think about the introduction of the most endangered cat in the world – the Iberian lynx (*Lynx pardinus*) – to suitable habitat in Britain. Whilst there are guidelines on reintroductions and introductions counselling against this sort of proposal currently, we may need to think more critically and laterally in the face of species extinctions – or accept that some of these will occur without any human intervention, though due to human pressures. Pearce-Higgins (2011) develops an interesting model for one of our most widespread upland birds – the Eurasian golden plover (*Pluvialis apricaria*) – in the face of climate change. He suggests that some site based adaptation management, such as predator control, could reduce the adverse impacts of climate change (in this case, lower numbers of tipulid (cranefly) prey emerging from peatlands following warmer summers in the preceding year, with ensuing reductions in golden plover brood survival). Related work shows the value of wetting peatland habitats, through blocking long-standing grips, to increase tipulid abundance (Carroll *et al.*, 2011). Studies such as these importantly delve into the detailed nature of climate change and the sorts of compensatory and counteracting management measures which could be deployed to address some of the adverse impacts.

42.6 People working with nature

In all of this work we need knowledge and information about nature to inform the many choices we have to make. We need accessible evidence, effective communication and leadership in showing how to tackle emerging problems. SNH has a key role here in demonstrating adaptive management in the face of change. This will involve a degree of risk taking, and an active deployment of an evidence base derived from protected areas, study sites and research programmes. Crucially, we will need to develop better alliances with other agencies, businesses, the voluntary bodies and people more widely – without this, there is a risk of being unheard. Toms *et al.* (Chapter 41) provide a telling example of involving people in recording what is happening to nature – in gardens. Philip Ashmole (Chapter 31) demonstrates how bold leadership and tenacity amongst a small number of enthusiasts and dedicated individuals can reap great rewards for nature – and he cautions against a bureaucracy that can dissipate the energy needed to make exciting projects happen. Ross *et al.* (Chapter 36) show how two pioneer botanists (Donald McVean and the late Derek Ratcliffe) provided a framework for describing upland and woodland habitats, and a baseline against which we can understand changes in environmental quality; Rothero *et al.* (Chapter 37); Windle *et al.* (Chapter 38); Moore (Chapter 10) and Lilly *et al.* (Chapter 4) give other examples of important historical changes documented because of the industry of a few individuals many years ago.

One area which concerns us is the still low numbers of field naturalists, especially those working on the more obscure or specialist groups of fungi, plants and animals. Some excellent field guides have been produced recently (e.g. Poland and Clement, 2009; Atherton *et al.*, 2010), and some of these have contributed to national surveys with huge public/volunteer participation (see for birds: Gillings *et al.*, Chapter 7; Cook *et al.*, Chapter 15; Toms *et al.*, Chapter 41; and for butterflies: Brereton *et al.*, Chapter 6). We are seeing evidence of many more people getting involved in some surveys, and a growth in the numbers of people volunteering for environmental work (see Marrs and Foster, Chapter 11), but we now need build on this. The Open University iSpot project (Open University, 2011) is an excellent means of broadening the public's active interest in the diversity of nature. We have to find ways of maintaining and broadening the skills base. By way of example, the Highland Biological Recording Group (HBRG, 2011) is 25 years old this year, and by February 2011 more than 150,000 records had been submitted to the National Biodiversity Network (NBN). Such is the interest within this group that 'The Recorders' Year' was established to spotlight some of the less well known taxa. Some recently published books popularise some of these – such as fungi (Boddy and Coleman, 2010) and bugs (Marren and Mabey, 2010). Clearly, a lot of work is being done to raise the awareness of the rich diversity of nature; but we need more people on the ground participating in fieldwork, and indeed mentors for this. After all, commenting on the silver anniversary meeting of the HBRG, Collier (2011) made the salutary comment: 'How sad that once again no youngsters were present'.

We have to connect with many more people to raise the appeal of nature, and that has to include being part of the workforce studying and raising awareness of what is happening. The word 'biodiversity' should resonate with excitement and enjoyment, rather than an unwieldy bureaucracy. For SNH, perhaps, that is one of its own special challenges – finding ways of kindling interest in nature amongst sectors and in areas until now disinterested or even dismissive. The evidence base on environmental change is developing well, and the strategic steer for better care and wider recognition of the value of nature is clear internationally. The real challenge now is to do things on the ground and in our everyday lives to benefit the nature and standing of Scotland.

Acknowledgements

We thank Sue Marrs, Simon Foster, Catriona Hendrie and Roddy Fairley for providing ideas and comments on this chapter.

References

Atherton, I., Bosanquet, S. and Lawley, M. (2010). *Mosses and Liverworts of Britain and Ireland: a Field Guide.* British Bryological Society, Stafford.

Baxter, J., Boyd, I.L., Cox, M. *et al.* (eds.). (2010). *Scotland's Marine Atlas – Information for The National Marine Plan.* Marine Scotland, Edinburgh. http://www.scotland.gov.uk/Topics/marine/education/atlashttp://www.scotland.gov.uk/Publications/2011/03/16182005/0, accessed 30 March 2011.

Brink, P. ten (ed.) (2011). *The Economics of Ecosystems and Biodiversity in National and International Policy Making.* Earthscan, London.

Boddy, L. and Coleman, M. (eds.) (2010). *From Another Kingdom: the amazing world of fungi.* Royal Botanic Garden, Edinburgh.

Carroll, M.J., Dennis, P., Pearce-Higgins, J.W. and Thomas, C.D. (2011). Maintaining northern peatland ecosystems in a changing climate: effects of soil moisture, drainage and drain blocking on craneflies. *Global Change Biology, 2011*; DOI: 10.1111/j.1365-2486.2011.02416.x

Collier, R. (2011). Country Diary: Highlands. *The Guardian.* 24 March 2011. http://www.guardian.co.uk/environment/2011/mar/24/country-diary-highlands-naturalists

COP (Conference of the Parties to the Convention on Biological Diversity) (2010a). *Decision X/2: Strategic Plan for Biodiversity 2011 – 2020.* Tenth meeting, Nagoya, Japan, 18-29 October 2010 (http://www.cbd.int/decision/cop/?id=12268).

COP (2010b). *Decision X/7: Examination of the outcome-oriented goals and targets (and associated indicators) and consideration of their possible adjustment for the period beyond 2010.* Tenth meeting, Nagoya, Japan, 18-29 October 2010 (http://www.cbd.int/decision/cop/?id=12273).

COP (2010c). *Revised and Updated Strategic Plan: Technical Rationale and Suggested Milestones and Indicators.* UNEP/CBD/COP/10/9 Tenth meeting, Nagoya, Japan, 18-29 October 2010 (http://www.cbd.int/doc/meetings/cop/cop-10/official/cop-10-09-en.pdf).

Crofts, R. and Henton, T. (2002). Sustaining Scotland's environment. In *the State of Scotland's Environment and Natural Heritage*, ed. by M.B. Usher, E.C. Mackey and J.C. Curran, TSO, Edinburgh, pp 321-332.

European Commission (2011). *Our life insurance, our natural capital: an EU biodiversity strategy to 2020.* European Commission, Brussels.

EEA (European Environment Agency) (2010a). *Assessing biodiversity in Europe – the 2010 report.* EEA Report 5/2010. EEA, Copenhagen.

EEA (2010b). *The European Environment State and Outlook 2010: Synthesis.* EEA, Copenhagen.

EEA (2010c). *EU 2010 Biodiversity Baseline; Post-2010 EU biodiversity policy.* EEA, Copenhagen

European Union (2007). Official Journal of the European Union: Directive 2007/2/EC of the European Parliament and of the Council of 14 March 2007 establishing an Infrastructure for Spatial Information in the European Community (INSPIRE).

Highland Biological Recording Group (2011). http://www.hbrg.org.uk/, accessed on 30 March 2011.

Mackey, E.C. and Mudge, G.P. (2010). *Scotland's Wildlife: An assessment of biodiversity in 2010.* Scottish Natural Heritage, Inverness.

Manning, A. (1997). Biodiversity conservation in Scotland: personal reflections. In *Biodiversity in Scotland: status, trends and initiatives*, ed. by L.V. Fleming, A.C. Newton, J.A. Vickery and M.B.Usher. TSO, Edinburgh. pp 286-294.

Marren, P. and Mabey, R. (2010). *Bugs Britannica.* Chatto & Windus, London.

Myers, N., Mittermeier, R.A., Mittermeier, C.G., da Fonseca, G.A.B. and Kent, J. (2000). Biodiversity hotspots for conservation priorities. *Nature*, **403**, 853-858.

NEA (2011). *The UK National Ecosystem Assessment.* http://uknea.unep-wcmc.org/, accessed 30 March 2011.

Open University (2011). The iSpot project website: http://www.ispot.org.uk/, accessed 4 May 2011.

Parmesan, C. and Yohe, G. (2003). A globally coherent fingerprint of climate change impacts across natural systems. *Nature*, **421**, 37-42.

Pearce-Higgins, J.W. (2011). Modeling conservation management options for a southern range-margin population of golden plover *Pluvialis apricaria* vulnerable to climate change. *Ibis*, **153**, 345-356.

Poland, J. and Clement, E. (2009). *The Vegetative Key to the British Flora.* BSBI, London.

Pollock, C. (2011). *Regional case study: R1. The UK in the context of North-west Europe – Food for thought: Options for sustainable increases in agricultural production.* Foresight Project on Global Food and Farming Futures, The Government Office for Science, London.

Scottish Executive (2004). *Scotland's Biodiversity – It's In Your Hands: A strategy for the conservation and enhancement of biodiversity in Scotland.* Scottish Executive, Edinburgh.

Scottish Government (2010a). *National Indicators.* http://www.scotland.gov.uk/About/scotPerforms/indicators/ecologicalFootprint, accessed December 2010.

Scottish Government (2010b). *Scottish Planning Policy.* Scottish Government, Edinburgh.

Scottish Government (2011). *Land Use Strategy.* Scottish Government, Edinburgh.

Scottish Natural Heritage (2009). *Valuing our Environment: The Economic Impact of Scotland's Natural Environment.* SNH, Battleby.

TEEB (2009). *The Economics of Ecosystems and Biodiversity for National and International Policy Makers – Summary: Responding to the Value of Nature* 2009. United Nations Environment Programme, Bonn.

TEEB (2010). *The Economics of Ecosystems and Biodiversity: Mainstreaming the Economics of Nature: A synthesis of the approach, conclusions and recommendations of TEEB.* United Nations Environment Programme, Bonn.

Thomas, C.D. (2011). Translocation of species, climate change, and the end of trying to recreate past ecological communities. *Trends in Ecology and Evolution*, **26**, 1-6.

UNEP (United Nations Environment Programme) (2005a). *Millennium Ecosystem Assessment. Ecosystems and Human Well-Being: Synthesis.* Island Press, Washington DC.

UNEP (2005b). *Millennium Ecosystem Assessment: Current Status and Trends.* Island Press, Washington, DC.

Index

Notes

1. Most entries refer to **Scotland**, except where otherwise indicated
2. **Bold** page numbers **indicate chapter extents** and **illustrations**.
3. *Italicised* page numbers indicate *boxes*, *chronologies*, *figures*, *maps*, *tables*, and *Latin* names of species. There are often textual references on the same pages.
4. Numbers followed by n indicate footnotes.
5. Front cover images are identified on page iv.